INTERNATIONAL ENERGY AGE

C000311489

THE IEA NATURAL GAS SECURITY STUDY

OECD
OCDE
PARIS 1995

INTERNATIONAL ENERGY AGENCY 2, rue André-Pascal, 75775 Paris Cedex 16, France

The International Energy Agency (IEA) is an autonomous body which was established in November 1974 within the framework of the Organisation for Economic Co-operation and Development (OECD) to implement an international energy programme.

It carries out a comprehensive programme of energy co-operation among twenty-three* of the OECD's twenty-five Member countries. The basic aims of the IEA include:

i) co-operation among IEA participating countries to reduce excessive dependence on oil through energy conservation, development of alternative energy sources and energy research and development;

ii) an information system on the international oil market as well as consultation with oil companies;

iii) co-operation with oil producing and other oil consuming countries with a view to developing a stable international energy trade as well as the rational management and use of world energy resources in the interest of all countries;

iv) a plan to prepare participating countries against the risk of a major disruption of oil supplies and to share available oil in the event of an emergency.

* IEA participating countries are: Australia, Austria, Belgium, Canada, Denmark, Finland, France, Germany, Greece, Ireland, Italy, Japan, Luxembourg, the Netherlands, New Zealand, Norway (by special agreement), Portugal, Spain, Sweden, Switzerland, Turkey, the United Kingdom, the United States. The Commission of the European Communities takes part in the work of the IEA.

ORGANISATION FOR ECONOMIC CO-OPERATION AND DEVELOPMENT

Pursuant to Article 1 of the Convention signed in Paris on 14th December 1960, and which came into force on 30th September 1961, the Organisation for Economic Co-operation and Development (OECD) shall promote policies designed:

— to achieve the highest sustainable economic growth and employment and a rising standard of living in Member countries, while maintaining financial stability, and thus to contribute to the development of the world economy;
— to contribute to sound economic expansion in Member as well as non-Member countries in the process of economic development; and
— to contribute to the expansion of world trade on a multilateral, non-discriminatory basis in accordance with international obligations.

The original Member countries of the OECD are Austria, Belgium, Canada, Denmark, France, Germany, Greece, Iceland, Ireland, Italy, Luxembourg, the Netherlands, Norway, Portugal, Spain, Sweden, Switzerland, Turkey, the United Kingdom and the United States. The following countries became Members subsequently through accession at the dates indicated hereafter: Japan (28th April 1964), Finland (28th January 1969), Australia (7th June 1971) New Zealand (29th May 1973) and Mexico (18th May 1994). The Commission of the European Communities takes part in the work of the OECD (Article 13 of the OECD Convention).

FOREWORD

The central objective of the International Energy Agency (IEA) has always been to promote the energy security of its member countries. When it was set up a little more than twenty years ago, the main threat was seen in terms of a disruption to oil supplies and this was the focus of security planning. In recent years, however, the IEA has increasingly seen energy security from a much broader perspective. This study of natural gas security is one example of that development.

The study was called for by IEA Ministers at their biennial meeting in 1993. They drew attention to the special characteristics of natural gas and its increasing importance to the IEA's overall energy security. Demand for natural gas is growing across the IEA, particularly in power generation. Dependence on outside suppliers is also growing and in many regions sources of supply are becoming more remote and the transportation routes more complex and potentially risky. Natural gas infrastructure is inherently less flexible than that for oil; there is no world market and each region has a limited number of suppliers.

The IEA therefore embarked on a comprehensive review of gas security, which examines all aspects of the issue, both long term and short term, across all regions of the OECD. The study looks at projected supply and demand; at the possible impact of a gas supply disruption and the implications for other fuels and for individual countries; at the growing use of gas in power generation; and at changing market structures and the introduction of competition, analysing their possible impact on gas security. The executive summary and conclusions of the study, included as Chapter 1 of this book, were endorsed by IEA Ministers in 1995. As the study demonstrates, IEA countries are in general well placed to withstand potential disruptions in their natural gas supplies.

The book is published on my authority as Executive Director of the IEA.

Robert Priddle
Executive Director

INTRODUCTION

The purpose of this study is twofold: to discuss and clarify the concept of security of supply in relation to natural gas and to provide factual information on various aspects of gas security and on the present and future security situation of individual IEA countries.

The book is divided into two distinct parts: the main text and the country annexes. Chapter 1 gives an executive summary of the study. Chapter 2 gives an introductory overview and clarification of the notion of security of supply. Chapter 3 establishes a demand backdrop against which supply issues are discussed, to bring out the long term security issues. Demand and supply balances for each of the three OECD regions are established. It should be stressed, however, that these balances are not forecasts as such but scenarios used to throw light on the issues involved. Country specific considerations pertaining to security of supply are analysed in more detail in the country annexes.

Chapter 4 gives a brief overview of past structural and regulatory changes in the gas markets of the three OECD regions and their implications for security of supply. It then sets out to discuss possible future structural and regulatory changes and what they could mean for security of supply.

Chapter 5 deals with gas in power generation and the implications for security of supply: gas demand for power generation will in all probability show higher growth than any other component of demand.

Chapter 6 describes how the OECD regions could cope with gas supply disruptions. The issues in the three regions are different, and this is reflected in the approach taken. OECD Europe faces the most complex security issues and more text is devoted to this region than to others.

Chapter 7 deals with the effects of gas supply disruptions on markets for other fuels, in particular those for petroleum products.

The country annexes in the second part of the book give information on the specific situation in IEA member countries as well as in those non-member countries which are significant gas producers or transit countries. The general approach has been to shed light on security issues by describing government policy, gas demand, supply and infrastructure and the ability to cope with gas disruptions.

The project has benefited significantly from information and advice provided by gas companies and governments. It goes without saying, however, that the final responsibility for the study lies with the IEA. This book was conceived and produced by the Long Term Office of the IEA but reflects an Agency-wide co-operation. The core project team consisted of the following persons:

Jonathan Angel

Anne Bolle

Malcolm Keay

Gudrun Lammers

Trevor Morgan

Bjorn P. Saga (project co-ordinator)

Robert Skinner.

In addition the following IEA staff contributed significantly:

Teresa Malyshev

Bruce McMullen

Stephen Perkins

Jeffrey Pierson

Ottar Skagen

John Soderbaum

Philip Starling

Jennifer Vacciannia

Michael Williams.

The project has also benefited from co-operation with external institutions. Oystein Noreng of the Norwegian School of Management provided ideas on the future structure of the European gas market. A summary of his ideas are found in Annex 1 to the study. L'Observatoire Mediterraneen de l'Energie undertook a study on gas supply and gas transit issues on which the project has drawn. A summary of the study, whose main authors were Michel Grenon, Manfred Hafner, Amor Khelif and Naji Abi-Aad, is given in Annex 2. Douglas Pacquin of the U.S. Department of Energy made a major contribution to the U.S. country annex and the sections dealing with the U.S. in Chapter 6.

TABLE OF CONTENTS

I. EXECUTIVE SUMMARY   17

DEFINING GAS SECURITY   17

LONG TERM SUPPLY AND DEMAND   18

DEREGULATION   19

GAS IN POWER GENERATION   20

EFFECTS OF GAS SUPPLY DISRUPTIONS   20

II. THE NATURE OF GAS SECURITY   23

THE GENERAL CONCEPT   23

DIFFERENCES BETWEEN OIL AND GAS SECURITY   24

GAS SECURITY - GUARDING AGAINST RISKS   25

MEASURES TO PROMOTE SECURITY   27

ACCEPTABLE RISK   30

CONCLUSIONS   31

III. LONG TERM GAS DEMAND AND SUPPLY   33

CURRENT GAS DEMAND AND TRADE   33

FUTURE DEMAND FOR GAS   36

GAS SUPPLY ISSUES   39

Global Gas Reserves   40

The Elements in Cost of Supply   41

    Costs of Production   41

    Pipeline Transportation Cost   46

    LNG Costs   47

Comparison of Existing Cost Estimates - Methodological Problems   49

Present and Future Gas Pricing 51
    North America 52
    Asia/Pacific 53
    OECD Europe 54

Supply Costs 55
    Gas Supply Costs for Europe 55
    Gas Supply Costs for Asia/Pacific 69
    Gas Supply Costs for North America 70

Concluding Remarks on Supply Costs 70

REGIONAL GAS BALANCES 73

North America 73

OECD Europe 74

OECD Pacific 78

IV. STRUCTURAL AND REGULATORY CHANGES IN THE GAS INDUSTRY 81

INTRODUCTION 81

STRUCTURAL AND REGULATORY CHANGES IN NORTH AMERICA 81

Market Development and Sectoral Composition 81

Sourcing of Gas 82

Wellhead Price Deregulation and Supply 82

Open Access and Unbundling of Transportation Services 83

Changes in Contract Structures 84

Duration of Contracts 86

Pricing 86

Development in Pipeline Construction 87

Emergence of Market Hubs 87

Development in Storage Capacity and Use of Storage 88
    Transition to Daily Balancing on Pipelines 89
    Partial Loss of the "Aggregation" Effect 90
    Increased Value of Storage 90
    The General Tightening of Supply and Demand after 1991 90
    Changes in the Electricity Generation Industry 90

Unbundling and Rebundling 90

Security of Supply Aspects of End-user Market Competition 91

STRUCTURAL CHANGES IN EUROPEAN GAS MARKETS 93

Market Development and Sectoral Composition 94

Sourcing of Gas 95

Developments in Gas Contracting   96

Developments in Transportation Infrastructure   97

Construction of Storage   98

RECENT REGULATORY CHANGES IN OECD EUROPE   100

Regulatory Changes on a National Level   101

Recent Developments in the United Kingdom   101

Recent Developments in Germany   103

Regulation Concerning TPA on a National Level   103

Gas Industry Tendency toward Horizontal and Vertical Integration   104

Conclusion   106

FUTURE DEVELOPMENTS IN EUROPEAN GAS MARKETS   106

More Competition, but Driven by Regulation or by Market Forces?   107

STRUCTURAL AND REGULATORY CHANGES IN THE OECD PACIFIC REGION   113

Japan   114

Australia and New Zealand   115

V.   GAS IN POWER GENERATION AND IMPLICATIONS FOR SECURITY OF SUPPLY   119

HISTORICAL DEVELOPMENTS   119

FACTORS INFLUENCING NATURAL GAS USE IN POWER GENERATION   120

Economic Factors   120

Fuel Efficiency and Environmental Impacts   123

The Influence of Regulation, Liberalisation and Privatisation   124

Load Management   125

THE PROSPECTS OF GAS USE FOR POWER GENERATION   127

SECURITY IMPLICATIONS OF GAS USE IN POWER GENERATION   130

Short-term Flexibility of the Power Supply System   130

Future Flexibility of the Power Supply System   134

CONCLUSIONS   138

VI.   COPING WITH DISRUPTIONS   141

INTRODUCTION   141

OECD EUROPE   141

Introduction   141

Diversity and Flexibility   142
    Supply   142
    Swing   143
    Storage   143
    Fuel-Switching   144

Reactions to a Supply Disruption   144

Supply Disruption Risks   146
    Political   146
    Technical   147

Supply Disruption Analysis   148
    The Scenarios   148
    Methodology   149
    Results   150
    Data and Assumptions   154

Prospects for Future Security from Disruptions   163
    Supply Diversification   163
    Supply Flexibility   171
    Storage   172
    Demand Structure   175
    Other Factors   176

Conclusions   177

NORTH AMERICA   177

CANADIAN EXPERIENCE DURING THE WINTER OF 1992/93   178

Supply Difficulties   178

Options Used to Maintain Gas Flows to End-Users   181

US EXPERIENCE DURING THE COLD SNAP OF JANUARY 1994   182

Background   183

Effects on the Gas Industry   183

General Natural Gas Industry Operations during Peak Demand Periods   184

Industry Actions during January 1994   185
    Production   185
    Imports   186
    Storage   187

Problems Encountered at the Transmission and Distribution Level   187

Government Actions during the Cold Spell   188

Lessons Learned   189

Conclusions   189

MAINTAINING RELIABILITY IN THE NATURAL GAS
DELIVERY SYSTEM IN THE FUTURE   190

FUTURE LOAD PROFILES AND CAPACITY REQUIREMENTS   192

FUTURE DELIVERY CAPACITY REQUIREMENTS
AND INDUSTRY CONSTRUCTION PLANS   194

VII. EFFECTS OF GAS SUPPLY DISRUPTIONS ON MARKETS FOR OTHER FUELS   197

SUBSTITUTABILITY OF GAS OUTSIDE THE POWER SECTOR   197

Overview   197

Fuel-Switching in Industry   199

Potential for Switching from Natural Gas in Industry in OECD Countries   200

   North America   200

   OECD Europe   204

   OECD Pacific   206

Prospects for Multi-firing in Industry   207

EFFECTS OF GAS SUPPLY DISRUPTIONS ON MARKETS FOR OTHER FUELS   208

Introduction   208

OECD Europe   208

   Potential Impact of Gas Supply Disruption on Demand for Other Fuels   208

   Potential Impact of Gas Supply Disruption on International Oil Markets   213

North America   216

OECD Pacific   217

SUMMARY AND CONCLUSIONS   218

ABBREVIATIONS AND CONVERSION FACTORS   219

ANNEX 1: STRUCTURAL CHANGE IN THE EUROPEAN GAS MARKET   221

**ANNEX 2: FUTURE NATURAL GAS SUPPLY FOR EUROPE,
THE ROLE OF TRANSIT COUNTRIES AND SECURITY OF SUPPLY**   237

COUNTRY ANNEXES 245

Australia 247

Austria 255

Belgium 259

Canada 263

Denmark 273

Finland 277

France 281

Germany 285

Greece 289

Ireland 291

Italy 293

Japan 297

Netherlands 305

New Zealand 311

Norway 315

Portugal 321

Spain 323

Sweden 327

Switzerland 329

Turkey 333

United Kingdom 337

United States 345

Belarus 355

Bulgaria 365

Czech Republic 371

Hungary 381

Kazakhstan 389

Poland 397

Romania 407

Russia 415

Slovakia 435

Turkmenistan 441

Ukraine 449

Mexico 455

Trinidad and Tobago 463

Venezuela   469

Brunei-Darussalam   475

Indonesia   483

Malaysia   495

Algeria   509

Libya   523

Nigeria   527

Iran   531

Iraq   537

Kuwait   541

Oman   543

Qatar   545

Saudi Arabia   553

United Arab Emirates   555

REFERENCES   561

LIST OF TABLES

Chapter 3

3.1 OECD Gas Production, Trade and Consumption, 1993   33

3.2 Estimated International Gas Trade by Pipeline and LNG Tanker, 1994 (bcm)   34

3.3 OECD Gas Consumption by Main Sector in 1992   35

3.4 Gas Share in TPES in OECD Countries   35

3.5a Gas Demand Forecast: OECD Europe   37

3.5b Gas Demand Forecast: North America   37

3.5c Gas Demand Forecast: OECD Pacific   38

3.6 Gas Demand in the Three OECD Regions —
Comparison of Country Submissions and the WEO Projections   38

3.7 Comparison of Reserve Estimates for Natural Gas   42

3.8 Costs of Transportation for Various Annual Capacities and Different Distances   47

3.9 Total Costs for LNG Plants of Various Capacities and Transportation Distances   49

3.10 Full Cost of Gas: Delivered to European Union Border   56

3.11 Competitiveness of Natural Gas with Gasoil   60

3.12 Competitiveness of Natural Gas with Heavy Fuel Oil (1% sulphur) in Industry   62

3.13 Natural Gas Competitiveness in a Combined Gas-steam Cycle Plant (55% efficiency) ompared with Coal (43% efficiency) for Electricity Generation   63

3.14 Value of Natural Gas at the EU Frontier Compared with Gasoil, LSFO* and Coal as Electricity Generation Fuels   64

3.15 Average Gas Price to EU frontier   65

3.16 Full Costs of Supply for Gas Delivered at the Nearest European Border at 10 and 15 per cent Discount Rates for Transportation Costs   67

3.17 Gas Balance for North America   73

3.18 Gas Balance for OECD Europe   75

3.19 OECD Europe's Dependence on Various Suppliers   78

3.20 Gas Balance for Japan   79

Chapter 4

4.1 Sectoral Shares in OECD Europe Gas Consumption   94

4.2 Gas Share in TPES in OECD Europe   95

4.3 European Gas Network Interconnections, 1992-1993   99

4.4 Possible Effects of Political Intervention in the Gas Market   109

Chapter 5

5.1 Percentage Share of Natural Gas in Electric Power Generation   120

5.2 Gas Input to Power Generation, OECD Europe   129

5.3 Reserve Margins in Electricity Supply in OECD Countries   132

5.4 Single-fired and Multi-fired Gas Capacity in OECD Countries   133

5.5 Price Differentials between Firm and Interruptible Gas Contracts   137

Chapter 6

6.1 Supply to OECD Europe in 1992   143

6.2 Interruptible Sales Contracts in 1992   145

6.3 Current Key European Gas Installations   148

6.4 Security Indicators for Countries Supplied by Russia or Algeria   151

6.5 Response during First Year to a Total Disruption in Russian Supplies Starting on October 1st   152

6.6 Response during First Year to a Total Disruption in Algerian Supplies Starting on October 1st   153

6.7 Assumptions Behind Political Disruption Scenarios for France   156

6.8 Existing Supply Contracts and Production Forecasts   164

6.9 Future Supply Requirements   166

6.10 Possible New Supplies for OECD Europe   167

6.11 Forecast Supply Diversification   169

6.12 Assumed Load Factors in 2010 for Supplies to OECD Europe   171

6.13 Spare Supply Capacity: Possible Response to a Russian Disruption   173

6.14 Spare Supply Capacity: Possible Response to an Algerian Disruption   174

6.15 Storage Development Plans - OECD Europe   175

6.16 Gas Demand Forecast - OECD Europe   176

6.17 Natural Gas Imports as a Percentage of Total Gas Deliveries by State, January, 1994   186

6.18 Sources of Natural Gas Supply, January, 1994   187

Chapter 7

7.1 Possible Alternatives to Natural Gas in Primary Industrial Uses   199

7.2 Energy Prices for Industry, 1992   200

7.3 Natural Gas Consumption, United States   201

7.4 Capability to Switch from Natural Gas to Alternative Fuels, United States   202

7.5 Fuel-switching Capability in Industry, OECD Europe   205

7.6 Alternative Fuels to Natural Gas in Industry, OECD Europe   205

7.7 Effect of Gas Supply Disruptions on Demand for Other Fuels, OECD Europe   210

7.8 Effect of Gas Supply Disruptions on Demand for Heavy Fuel Oil
and Gasoil/Diesel, OECD Europe   211

7.9 Incremental Increases in Demand for Heavy Fuel Oil as Proportion of Total Sales   212

LIST OF FIGURES

Chapter 3

3.1 EU Supplies to 2010   65

3.2 Natural Gas Export Potential   68

3.3 New Supplies to Mainland Europe   69

3.4 Gas Costs in North America   71

Chapter 5

5.1 Multi-fired Gas Capacity, OECD   135

Chapter 6

6.1 Seasonal Storage Use   144

6.2 Supplies to Continental Europe in 1992   147

6.3 Effects of a Russian Supply Disruption Starting October 1st, Austria   154

6.4 Effects of an Algerian Supply Disruption Starting October 1st, Belgium   156

6.5   Effects of a Russian Supply Disruption Starting October 1st, France   157

6.6   Effects of an Algerian Supply Disruption Starting October 1st, France   157

6.7   Effects of a Russian Supply Disruption Starting October 1st, Germany   158

6.8   Effects of a Russian Supply Disruption Starting October 1st, Italy   159

6.9   Effects of an Algerian Supply Disruption Starting October 1st, Italy   160

6.10a Effects of an Algerian Disruption Starting October 1st, Worst Case, Spain   161

6.10b Effects of an Algerian Disruption Starting October 1st, Best Case, Spain   162

6.11 Demand and Available Supply in the Event of a Russian Supply
         Disruption, Switzerland   163

6.12 Typical Flow of Natural Gas   179

6.13 Natural Gas Flows during Peak Periods   185

6.14 Growth in Seasonal Gas Demand from 1989 to 2010   191

6.15 Profile of Gas Loads and Delivery Capacity for 2010   192

6.16 Requirements for New Delivery Capacity by 2010   193

6.17 Future Requirements and Industry Construction Plans
         for New Underground Storage   195

Chapter 7

7.1   Industrial Gas Use, United States, 1992   201

7.2   Fuel Switching from Natural Gas in Industry, United States   203

7.3   Methodology for Calculating Effect of Gas Supply Disruption
         Scenarios on Demand for Other Fuels   209

7.4   Impact of Increased Heavy Fuel Demand Caused by Gas Supply Disruption   214

I. EXECUTIVE SUMMARY

IEA countries rely on a mix of measures, appropriate to their circumstances, to promote gas security. In general, they are well placed to withstand potential disruptions in supply, whatever the origin. However, careful monitoring will be needed to ensure that the appropriate level of security protection is maintained as gas demand grows. In addition, some countries which rely mainly on single sources of supply or are still developing their gas infrastructure need to consider further measures to improve their security.

The projected growth in gas demand does not of itself constitute a security problem, provided security measures are maintained and strengthened as recommended. Supplies are potentially available to meet forecast demand; indeed in many regions already contracted supplies will be available to cover demand through to early next century. However, international cooperation and a stable framework for investment and trade are needed to encourage the long term commitments necessary to develop the supplies needed for the period beyond.

DEFINING GAS SECURITY

There are major differences between gas and other energy markets, particularly oil. These differences, such as the rigid nature of transportation infrastructure, the relative difficulty of storage and the regional nature of markets, need to be taken into account in any consideration of gas security.

Security risks fall into two broad categories:

long term risk that new supplies cannot be brought onstream to meet growing demand for either economic or political reasons;

risk of disruptions to existing supplies such as political disruptions, accidents or extreme weather conditions.

No gas system is entirely risk-free. Gas security is best seen in terms of risk management, that is reducing to an acceptable level the risks and consequences of disruptions.

Management of risk is a central activity for the gas industry and its customers. Where possible market mechanisms should be the basis of security decisions. Nevertheless there is a role for Governments to play:

■ in setting a framework in which risks can be managed and costs reduced, in particular through securing a framework internationally for investment and trade and facilitating interconnection and exchanges among neighbouring countries;

■ in determining acceptable security levels, especially where small customers and safety are concerned;

■ in providing a legal basis for dealing with emergency situations.

LONG TERM SUPPLY AND DEMAND

Most forecasters see gas demand rising substantially over the next 15 years. The IEA's own survey of member countries indicates that they expect gas demand growth between 1992 and 2010 of 29% in North America, 46% in OECD Pacific and 70% in OECD Europe. The single most important factor driving this growth is demand for gas in power generation.

World gas reserves are abundant and none of the OECD regions faces a physical constraint to making the required quantities of gas available. However, supplies will increasingly have to be sourced more distantly from consumption areas. Transportation costs, which already make up a high share of total costs, are therefore set to become increasingly important.

Whether the required volumes can be brought onstream in time to meet the growing demand for gas may depend on the movement in energy prices.

Under a scenario of rising oil prices[1], to which gas prices in many regions remain coupled, there would seem to be no problem in economic or commercial terms in bringing new supplies to markets given current cost estimates.

Under a scenario of constant oil prices the conclusion is less clear. For example, at an oil price of US$18 per barrel, an analysis prepared for the IEA of the costs of possible new supply projects for Europe shows that only a small proportion of the forecast demand growth to 2010 could be met under current cost and pricing conditions.

Without increased oil prices, the challenge for the industry will be to reduce costs and to concentrate its marketing on those sectors prepared to pay a premium for gas. Significant cost reductions may be possible through the introduction of new technology, particularly in offshore production, while new pricing concepts can help reduce the exposure of new projects to oil price fluctuations.

There is also a political dimension to the development of new supply sources. New arrangements for international cooperation such as the Energy Charter Treaty, particularly in the areas of transportation and transit, could reduce the risk of politically generated disruptions which might otherwise prevent new supplies from being brought to market. An economic benefit of reduced risk is lower cost associated with the reduced rate of return required for new projects.

Analysis of the three OECD regions suggests the following conclusions:

North America has an adequate potential reserve base, an efficient gas industry and well-functioning, price responsive markets that should ensure a balanced demand and supply over the forecast period.

---

1. For example, in the IEA's 1995 *World Energy Outlook*, the *Capacity Constraints* case assumes the oil price rises to US$28 per barrel by 2005.

OECD Europe has already contracted for the vast majority, if not all, of its needs up to 2000. Based on the IEA survey of member country demand forecasts, considerable new volumes of imported gas (around 50 Mtoe, excluding possible contract extensions) will be required by 2010. An important share of these supplies will probably have to come from areas where political stability and transit issues are currently of some concern. In the demand cases studied, however, Europe's dependence on any single supplier would not increase greatly.

Japan is the only country in the OECD Pacific region dependent on long-distance gas imports. It has already contracted for supplies beyond its forecast needs in 2000, and the difference between supplies and forecast demand in 2010 is small. Several projects are under consideration which could cover the additional demand. Some are expansions of existing projects and these are generally cheaper than completely new developments.

DEREGULATION

Liberalisation and competition are increasingly affecting gas markets throughout the IEA. The implications for security depend both on the form of liberalisation and the characteristics of the gas market into which it is introduced, although it is difficult to find instances where liberalisation and competition have jeopardized security of supply.

In particular it is necessary to distinguish different aspects of liberalisation, such as third party access, unbundling of transmission and supply, and competition in the residential market and their impacts on different elements of security, such as contract structures, storage and use of interruptible contracts. Even in individual markets the implications of liberalisation for security can be complex.

Nonetheless the evidence from particular markets where competition has been introduced does not suggest that competition need be incompatible with secure gas supplies. In general there is evidence of positive impacts on some elements of security such as development of production, transmission and storage capacity.

There is also evidence, in North America, that flexible and market-responsive pricing and the information and control systems developed to respond to a deregulated market help in moving gas rapidly in an emergency to where it is most needed. In other circumstances, different approaches may be equally effective. In Europe, for instance, a well-developed system of cooperation between gas companies facilitates the transfer of gas in emergencies.

The impact on contract structures will also depend on market circumstances. In markets where competition has been introduced there is less emphasis on long term contracts and a variety of different contract structures and terms exist, providing additional flexibility. There is no reason to believe, in the circumstances of these markets, either that competition and long term contracts are fundamentally incompatible, or that long term contracts are a necessary condition of supply security. Views are divided as to whether this conclusion can be extended to markets such as those in Continental Europe and Japan.

GAS IN POWER GENERATION

Gas is generally viewed as a favourable fuel for electricity generation for several reasons:

■ recent technological improvements have dramatically raised conversion efficiencies;

■ low capital cost, short lead times and the ability to add capacity in relatively small increments have decreased overall costs of new gas plants which are thus particularly favoured in competitive and deregulated electricity markets;

■ relatively low emissions of CO_2 and pollutants such as SO_2 enable generators to meet increasingly stringent environmental regulations at moderate cost.

Peak demand for gas and for electricity often coincide. In order to realise gas' potential in electricity generation the gas and electricity supply industries must address their load management requirements. They must develop appropriate arrangements to minimise cost and guarantee adequate flexibility to cover demand.

Gas use in power generation does not create security of supply problems at current levels. The power supply system has considerable flexibility through spare capacity and fuel switching capability. However the growth of gas use for power generation and its effect on gas security must be monitored.

EFFECTS OF GAS SUPPLY DISRUPTIONS

The short-term security risks perceived in each of the three OECD regions differ markedly.

North America has a diversified supply structure with around 9,000 gas producers. Although reserves are concentrated in a small number of regions, there are a large number of deposits and the transportation infrastructure is highly developed. Political disruptions are less relevant in North America than, for example in Europe. Of greater interest is the ability of the North American system to endure stress, for instance, as the result of extreme weather conditions. Both the US and Canadian gas supply systems have recently been tested by severe weather conditions and both systems performed well.

OECD Europe is dependent for a significant share of its supplies on deliveries transported over large distances from outside the region. The major non-OECD suppliers are Russia and Algeria. A political disruption represents the risk with the greatest consequences.

Japan's gas market is different from those in the other IEA regions. Japan is almost completely dependent on imported LNG, most of which is used for power generation. Reliance is placed on long-term contracts with several stable suppliers, modular supply and delivery systems which limit dependence on any single installation, and the possibilities for fuel substitution and sharing via the electricity generation system. The arrangements have served Japan well and no short-term security problems have been encountered.

Analysis of political disruptions in **OECD Europe** reveals that most countries could continue to supply their core customers for many months, and in some cases indefinitely, in the event of a total disruption in deliveries from their single largest non-OECD suppliers. European gas companies have in place supply flexibility in the form of spare import capacity from other suppliers, reserve production capacity and seasonal storage. Demand can also be reduced by cutting supplies to those customers who can easily switch to alternative fuels (mainly heavy fuel oil). Nevertheless, some countries with comparatively new and small gas markets are more heavily dependent on individual suppliers than others and would fare badly in the event of a sustained disruption. These countries should continue their efforts to diversify their supply sources, to develop underground storage capacity and to maintain demand flexibility through the use of interruptible contracts.

One effect of a substantial disruption to **OECD Europe** gas supplies would be a large increase in demand for heavy fuel oil. Under a scenario of a total interruption in Russian supplies, European demand for fuel oil could rise by 30%. The result would be a surge in the price of fuel oil and a consequent increase in crude runs. The price of lighter products might even *go down*. The incremental demand, however, represents only around 3% of global demand for fuel oil. In the event of a prolonged gas supply disruption the effect of a reduced price differential between fuel oil and other products would diminish as increased supplies of fuel oil and low sulphur crude were made available in Europe.

None of the OECD regions is excessively dependent on individual facilities and all are relatively well prepared for short-term incidents of a technical nature. Some countries, however, are less well equipped to deal with political disruptions and the development of this security risk should be monitored closely.

II. THE NATURE OF GAS SECURITY

Energy security is central to the purpose of the IEA, primary among its "Shared Goals", and a (or the) major energy policy objective for all IEA countries. This chapter discusses the concept of gas security as it will be applied in this study; identifies the special characteristics of gas, as opposed to other fuels and especially oil, which must underlie any discussion of gas security; distinguishes the main elements of security and describes the main measures taken to promote security. It identifies the main purpose of gas security measures as to minimise the risks of disruptions in supply or, more fully, to reduce to an acceptable level the risks and potential consequences of a disruption in, or non-availability of, the supply of natural gas.

THE GENERAL CONCEPT

Energy security has been defined in various ways. In the IEA's 1985 publication *Energy Technology Policy*, energy security was defined as "an adequate supply of energy at reasonable cost". The European Commission (1990) provided a somewhat fuller definition: "security of supply means the ability to ensure that future essential energy needs can be met, both by means of adequate domestic resources worked under economically acceptable conditions or maintained as strategic reserves, and by calling upon accessible and stable external sources supplemented, where appropriate, by strategic stocks". Yet these definitions are difficult to apply in practice, especially to a fuel like gas. What is an "adequate" supply? What are "essential needs"? There are in practice in most IEA countries significant economic limits on the extension of the gas network: some people who might like gas (at least if it were provided at "reasonable cost") do not in practice have access to the system. On the other hand, since natural gas is, in almost all of its uses, substitutable by other fuels, it could be argued that it is not an essential component of energy security - indeed it forms no part of the energy supply of some countries, like Norway, without creating a security problem. So the concept of adequate supply is inappropriate as an operational basis for gas security.

Similarly the criterion of "reasonable cost" begs many questions. Who is to determine what is "reasonable"? It could be argued that in the last analysis a reasonable cost is the price the free operation of market forces would produce and "adequate supplies" are the supplies that would be available at that price. Energy security is then simply another way of saying avoiding market distortions. Yet for most countries the concept of "energy security" involves more than just the free operation of market forces - important though that is. The IEA's "Shared Goals"[1] specifically recognise this additional Government function. But what exactly does it imply as applied to a particular fuel like gas?

---

1.   The "Shared Goals" were adopted by the IEA Ministers at their June 4, 1993 meeting in Paris.

DIFFERENCES BETWEEN OIL AND GAS SECURITY

At the outset, it is important to take account of the differences between fuels. The energy security debate has primarily been conducted in terms of oil security. In considering the potential applicability of this debate to gas, some significant differences between the oil and gas markets should be highlighted:

■ oil has a much larger share of TPES - twice as high as that of natural gas for the OECD as a whole (42.5% vs. 20% in 1992);

■ much oil use is non-substitutable. About 60% of oil consumption is in transport, where economic alternative fuels are currently lacking. This sector is also politically sensitive;

■ oil supplies have been disrupted on at least seven occasions since 1950 (Iranian boycott 1951-53; Suez crisis 1956; Six-Day War 1967; Yom Kippur War 1973; Iranian revolution 1979; Iran/Iraq War 1980; Gulf crisis 1990-91). All these disruptions were essentially political in origin rather than market driven. In some cases there were strong market price responses of varying durations; in others there was spare capacity available to substitute for the disrupted production and only limited price effects. However the two major oil "crises" of 1973 and 1979, with their fundamental price impact, have had a major impact on public opinion and policy-making;

■ there is a world oil market. Oil is by far the world's most traded commodity. OECD oil imports are more than 8 times as high as OECD gas imports. A disruption to oil supply tends to affect the whole world oil market. Individual countries or regions are not isolated from market developments in other regions.

By contrast:

■ there has never been a major disruption in external gas supplies to the OECD (though there have been a number of supply "hiccups" in deliveries from external suppliers, while internal supplies have suffered short-term disruptions: e.g., because of industrial action);

■ gas markets are still essentially regional. While there is some linkage between regions (e.g., LNG trade across the Atlantic; Australian LNG sales to Spain; the Middle East as potential supplier to both Europe and Asia-Pacific), it is for the moment very limited. Price formation, and actual prices, in the different regions (indeed between independent parts of the same region, such as between the UK and Continental Europe) can be very different. There is no reason why a shortage of supply in one region should affect another directly (though there will be an indirect impact through the effect on the world oil price of any switch to oil);

■ the reason for this regional structure, as the IEA's 1994 study on gas transportation discusses in some detail, is the high cost of gas transportation, which is a very capital intensive business. This also means, among other things, that delivery systems are relatively inflexible. Most OECD natural gas supply is by pipeline. It requires a fixed physical link all the way from producer to consumer; the number of alternative routes to that particular consumer, if one producer's output is interrupted, is limited. As gas infrastructure matures, the flexibility of the network increases. Nonetheless major rigidities remain. To take a simple example, switching the destination of a cargo of oil from mainland Europe to the UK is an everyday occurrence; for gas, although the UK has LNG import facilities, it does not happen;

■ as the example indicates, the limitations are economic and contractual as well as physical. Although LNG offers greater flexibility than pipeline supply in physical terms, the contractual structures for both LNG and pipeline gas (outside North America) are generally based on long-term exclusive contracts to reduce the risks involved in the large upfront investments. The scope for additional or switched supplies tends therefore to be limited;

■ outside North America this long term contract structure limits the scope for an endogenous price shock (though a lagged and indirect price effect, stemming from a jump in the price of oil, against which the gas price is usually escalated, remains a possibility). The long-term interdependence of producers and consumers (represented not only in the high levels of capital investment but also in the high levels of income from gas sales - the largest source of hard currency earnings for more than one supplying country) means that continuity of supply is in the interests of both parties. Just as consumers have few or no alternative suppliers in an emergency, so suppliers have few or no alternative customers. In North America the market situation is quite different but also limits the scope for disruption: there are many (some 9000) suppliers and many purchasers. The price mechanism allocates supplies effectively; new supplies can be brought on stream quickly and in modest increments. Finally, the markets are largely self-sufficient. The three countries trading with each other in North America are linked via the NAFTA trading system and the prospect of political disruption (i.e., a Government-imposed interruption to supply designed to achieve a political objective) is negligible;

■ on the other hand, supply of gas to the final consumer is regulated by Governments in most countries, as are the transmission and distribution of gas, because of the natural monopoly characteristics of these latter functions. Gas companies are therefore generally subject to controls on prices, at least to residential customers; they sometimes need regulatory or Government approval for investments; and they often need Government approval for imports and exports. Such controls are rare (and decreasing) in OECD oil markets;

■ finally, all gas companies are very conscious of the need both to preserve a reputation for security of supply (since oil is nearly always an alternative) and to maintain high levels of security and safety (a supply shortage which led to a drop in pipeline pressure could lead to a major safety hazard). Security of supply is central to their ability to sell and companies work individually and collectively to avoid security risks.

The nature of the security issues that arise with gas, and of potential Government involvement, is therefore very different from those arising with oil. In particular, the focus is very much on avoiding physical shortages rather than on price shocks, and the global dimension is much less prominent. This does not mean that there are no international aspects; in fact there are many, discussed further below. Nonetheless, the differences from oil are great enough to suggest that we need to start from first principles in considering gas security issues, rather than seeing oil as a precedent.

GAS SECURITY - GUARDING AGAINST RISKS

The basic dictionary definition of security is the state of being "safe against adverse contingencies", and it is suggested that this is the concept we need to apply to gas. In relation to natural gas supply, the "adverse contingencies" to be guarded against are primarily those of a disruption to, or non-availability of, supply (the distinction is explained below). There are other "adverse contingencies" - e.g., supply falling below the required standard - but they are more technical matters falling outside the scope of this study.

Three broad classes of risk can be identified:

i) technical risk, e.g., that, as a result of an accident, terrorist incident or natural catastrophe, a major supply facility is put out of action. For some countries this could be a significant short term problem. As noted in Chapter 6 of this study, which looks at ways of coping with short term supply disruptions, some countries are significantly dependent on single facilities. In most cases, however, such a problem could be resolved relatively quickly: estimates, even in the most serious cases, are in months rather than years.

ii) failure to mobilise long-term supply or ensure deliverability. This describes the situation of "non-availability" of supply where gas demand or economic gas-consuming investment outpaces gas supply or gas-producing investment and deliverability. One of the starting points of this study is the growth in gas demand forecast over the next twenty years. Given the long lead times (outside North America) for the construction of production capacity and (in North America and other areas with deregulated markets) the separation of responsibility for supply and for transportation capacity, there is, at least in theory, a risk either that the new supplies needed will not be mobilised, or that there will be insufficient delivery capacity so that supplies cannot be made available to what would otherwise have been a willing customer.

Long-term security of this sort is by its nature difficult to define and over-simplified analysis can be misleading. Two common approaches are to look at projected demand and contracted supply and estimate the "gap" between them, with the size of the gap being an indication of the size of the potential security problem; or to look at reserve/production ratios, with the implication that the smaller the ratio, the sooner gas may run out, and the more real is the security problem. Both approaches are conceptually flawed if the intention is to provide an absolute measure of security though both have their uses in particular circumstances. What both approaches tend to ignore is the market and economic factors which — more than any real or putative supply/demand mismatch — underlie the ratios. Broadly speaking, companies want to reduce the risks they see as most relevant to their profitability. This will generally mean developing gas as late as possible (since this defers expenditure and reduces the uncertainties about the future) but also reducing market risk (i.e., the risk that it will not be possible to sell the gas profitably) as far as possible. The extent to which expected demand is covered will depend significantly on the lead time within which, in particular gas markets, new supplies can be brought on stream, or purchased on the open market. Thus, in the US, contracts to cover expected demand may not always be seen as necessary: a liquid spot market is available to match supply and demand. Some purchasers will nonetheless wish to trade off price and supply risks via long-term contracts. In the UK, where new supplies can be brought on stream within a few years and a short-term gas market is developing, a mixture of short and long term contracts is also becoming the norm. Such structures can provide more flexibility than a market within which only long-term contracts are possible. However the supply position for some countries may necessitate long-term commitments to mobilise gas supplies, and the lead time for mobilising them may be long. In these circumstances plans looking forward a number of years are an important determinant of purchasing behaviour.

Similarly with reserve/production ratios, typical North American ratios of under 10 years reflect essentially the economics of gas supply there - it is not worth going to the expense of proving up reserves over a longer period. This does not in any sense set a limit to the ultimately available resource. For example, US proven reserves in the lower 48 states are some 160 tcf, but the resource base has been estimated at some 1,295 to 1,600 tcf (6 to 10 times higher) (Natural Petroleum Council, 1993). Even in countries with a less commercial approach to reserve evaluation, the ranges are huge. For instance Russia's proved reserves are some 1,600 tcf; estimates of its resource base go as high as 7,500 tcf or more (5 times higher).

World proved gas reserves equal about 60 years' production. The true resource base is certainly many times that. The relevant question in a security context is not whether the resource exists but whether the conditions are right for the resource to be mobilised.

In the end, of course, there is no such thing as a long-term supply/demand gap. In the long term — indeed in the short term too if the market allows it — supply and demand always meet at a price, even if not at the level originally expected. Nonetheless, there would be a welfare loss if a gas source, which could have been brought to market economically, is not developed because of market barriers such as failure to create a framework within which adequate incentives are available to compensate for risk, or if the risks are unnecessarily high.

iii) the third category of risks is of political events, which can be both short and long-term in their impacts: that is, the risks include both the possibility of a disruption to an existing supply, for a shorter or longer period, for political reasons and the possibility that gas supplies which are economically available from a particular source will not be mobilised because the political risks are too high. In principle industrial action, within or outside IEA member states, could be considered under this heading as a form of deliberate disruption to supply designed to achieve a specific collective objective.

Gas security as discussed in this study involves protection against all these risks. Absolute security, in the sense that all risks are reduced to zero for all consumers, is likely to be impossible, certainly very expensive. Many consumers will be prepared to accept some diminution in the security of their supply in exchange for lower prices. Different classes of consumer may well make different trade-offs in this respect. Nonetheless they will all have a strong interest in seeing that their chosen level of security is actually achieved. A number of measures can be taken which will either reduce the chances of an adverse contingency occurring, or reduce its impact if it does occur.

MEASURES TO PROMOTE SECURITY

Starting again from first principles, the IEA's "Shared Goals" identify a number of measures to promote security, most of which seem relevant to gas. The Goals include the following statements specifically relating to security:

Goal 1 Diversity, efficiency and flexibility within the energy sector are basic conditions for longer-term energy security: the fuels used within and across sectors and the sources of those fuels should be as diverse as practicable.

Goal 2 Energy systems should have the ability to respond promptly and flexibly to energy emergencies. In some cases this requires collective mechanisms and action - IEA countries co-operate through the Agency in responding jointly to oil supply emergencies.

Goal 5 Improved energy efficiency can promote both environmental protection and energy security in a cost-effective manner.

Goal 6 Continued research, development and market deployment of new and improved energy technologies make a critical contribution to achieving the objectives outlined above [which include energy security].

Goal 8 Free and open trade and a secure framework for investment contribute to efficient energy markets and energy security.

Goal 9 Co-operation among all energy market participants helps to improve information and understanding, and encourage the development of efficient, environmentally acceptable and flexible energy systems and markets worldwide. These are needed to help promote the investment, trade and confidence necessary to achieve global energy security and environmental objectives.

Taking the concepts in turn:

Diversity is clearly recognised as contributing to gas security by all IEA countries. No single definition of diversity is, however, universally relevant. In some cases diversity refers to the number of producers and the transport options (e.g., North America); in others it refers mainly to the number of supplying countries (Europe); elsewhere to the number of independent supply trains (Japan). The key underlying concept is whether it is conceivable that supply from different sources could be interrupted by a single event or related events. The more diverse the supply base the smaller the proportion of supply that could conceivably be interrupted in this way.

Flexibility is essentially a matter of substitutability, which in turn has a number of components:

- substitution of one source of gas by another (which requires the necessary production and transportation capacity to be in place). In some cases (e.g., Japan) the alternative gas source may be technically distinct from the primary source — substitution of manufactured gas from naphtha for LNG;

- substitution of gas by another fuel, either directly (through use of alternate firing facilities in a single plant) or indirectly (e.g., in the case of electricity, by use of alternative plant);

- substitution of less energy intensive activity - changes in behaviour or production processes.

These forms of flexibility, and their implications, are discussed in Chapters 5 - 7. Underlying them all is the flexibility provided by freely operating markets, the absence of trade barriers, and effective price signals. As discussed in Chapter 4, this element of security can therefore be influenced by market structures and regulation.

Emergency Response Measures. These are discussed in more detail in Chapter 6 and a full listing will not be attempted here. The main measures are:

- storage
- interruptible contracts and other forms of demand restraint

■ surge production

■ supply sharing

■ contingency planning

Particular mixes are appropriate to the circumstances of particular countries and emergency response plans vary. Shared Goal 2 refers to IEA cooperation, specifically in relation to oil. This is less directly relevant to gas though — see below — international cooperation has a role.

Energy Efficiency. The relevance is primarily through the flexibility in the short term to switch to more efficient processes, as noted above. Some would argue that since longer term energy efficiency reduces dependence on energy, including imported energy, it also reduces vulnerability to a disruption.

Research and Development clearly contribute, as the Shared Goals note, to a number of objectives, including efficiency, flexibility and security.

Free markets underlie both short term flexibility of response and long-term mobilisation of investment. They are the most important single contributor to energy security.

Cooperation among Market Participants is also vital. There are a number of aspects to this. Between producers and consumers they include stable frameworks for investment and trade, long-term trust and the ability to make long-term commitments. Among consumers, free trade and sharing agreements are also relevant. Other international dimensions include the following:

■ in Europe, especially, a disruption in supplies from one of the main external suppliers would affect more than one country;

■ as noted above, a disruption in gas supplies would have major oil market effects - discussed in Chapter 7 of this study;

■ the risk of disruption can be mitigated by clear international rules on the transit of gas during a dispute (such as those in the Energy Charter Treaty);

■ further international interconnections would help increase flexibility in responding to an emergency as would freer international gas exchanges.

Certain other forms of security measures, which do not appear in the "Shared Goals", are not pursued here. Specifically:

Military Action is not a matter for the IEA.

Domestic self-reliance is not now regarded by the IEA as of itself a security measure. In some cases (e.g., US gas) domestic production does fulfil many of the criteria set out above - e.g., diversity, efficiency and flexibility. But there have been cases in the energy sector - e.g., UK coal - where domestic production has not satisfied these criteria and has therefore increased rather than decreased security risks. It is true that underlying much of the debate on gas security there has been a concern about growing dependence on imports. But the level of imports should not of itself be taken as an indication of a security problem: it is more a question of the market structures within which these imports take place, the inflexibility of the delivery systems, the lack of diversity etc, as discussed above. Indigenous supplies may equally be subject to disruption, e.g., by industrial action, if the necessary flexibility, diversity etc. are not present.

Industrial Relations While industrial disputes can be a cause of disruption, and while there are measures which can reduce the risk of such disruptions (e.g., conciliation and arbitration machinery) these are not matters which this study seeks to address.

In short, there are a large number of possible measures relevant to improving security as it has been defined here (reduction of risk). However, it certainly does not follow that all these are measures for Government. At its heart the gas business is very much about mutual risky interdependencies and ways of managing that risk are primarily, as in any other market, for the companies and individuals involved. The Government's role is twofold:

■ to provide a clear framework which reduces non-commercial risks and encourages investment and trade;

■ given the monopoly characteristics of the gas industry, in some cases the Government, acting either directly or through a regulatory body, will define what is the acceptable level of risk or security to be achieved by the utility.

ACCEPTABLE RISK

In principle, in a free market individual consumers can decide for themselves what is an acceptable level of gas supply risk, for instance choosing interruptible contracts with varying degrees of permitted interruption; or choosing suppliers on the basis of a trade off between price and security guarantees offered. In such cases Governments have no role in defining what is an acceptable level of individual risk.

However, gas markets tend to be imperfect: they are characterised by a high degree of monopoly (in the transmission and distribution systems which, as noted above, tend to be natural monopolies). There are also significant externalities (gas systems, unlike other energy systems, do not "fail safe", and an individual supply failure may have implications for the whole supply system, e.g., if it causes pressures to drop across the whole network. There are also information gaps. Residential customers may lack the knowledge to make informed judgements about supply security; they also lack the means, for instance future gas contracts, individual gas storage and access to the spot market (if it exists) are all impractical for most such customers. There are also practical problems. It is often difficult to implement fine degrees of interruptibility - remote disconnection of gas is not practical in most countries so interruptible consumers generally have to disconnect themselves; it would not at present be feasible for the industry to rely on this process for very large numbers of separate customers as compliance would be impossible to monitor (though the necessary technology might be developed if the market required it). It can in short be difficult or impossible to apply the concept of security at individual, rather than system level.

Decisions on security of supply are therefore often taken at industry, regulatory or Government level. Generally these decisions are not based on a full cost-benefit analysis or on strictly economic criteria, but on technical criteria - e.g., the ability to withstand a 1 in 20 or 50 winter, that is a winter with low temperatures (degree days) at the level that would be expected only 1 year in 20 or 50; or the ability to maintain supplies without interruption until the temperature falls below a certain point, say -10°C. Some examples are given in the country annexes. As is apparent, these criteria are essentially judgemental.

It might be possible to produce more sophisticated economic calculations but the problems would be formidable. First, when it comes to valuing the cost of a disruption, information is lacking. The premium for firm over interruptible gas in Europe for instance gives only a partial indication, since in practice interruptible contracts are much less risky than they appear - in fact, they are rarely interrupted in most countries, and are often effectively a form of price discrimination between those customers whose alternative energy source is fuel oil and those whose alternative is more expensive gas oil. Customer attitude surveys, of the sort that have been undertaken with electricity, appear not to have been widely undertaken for gas. Part of the problem lies in the system risk externality noted above, which makes it difficult for individual consumers to put a value on security of supply — while interruptions to electricity supply, though short-lived, occur with some frequency and with limited (though still expensive) results, most gas companies aim not to have **any** generalised interruptions because of the practical and safety problems involved in restoring supply. They tend therefore not to evaluate security directly in terms of the costs and benefits for individual customers.

The supply side of the equation can also be difficult to evaluate. The cost of storage or of extra pipeline capacity is relatively straightforward, but the costs and benefits of, for example, diversity of supply sources are much more difficult to quantify (though, in principle, this calculation is possible). It is somewhat easier to define a minimum cost solution (i.e., not to compare costs with benefits but to look at the lowest cost means of providing a defined level of security) but again a number of specific assumptions have to be made.

Starting from first principles may help throw light on the issues involved but does not provide a practical methodology. On this basis the value of security of gas supply cannot ultimately be higher than the cost of the alternatives, since gas is nearly always substitutable by another fuel. But the cost of the alternative, in the short term, can be very high indeed. That is, for those without dual-firing there may simply be no short term alternative except to do without and perhaps face a system safety risk. Even for those with dual-firing there is a price to pay in the cost of the alternative facilities and the possible impact on oil prices. In the long term, alternative fuelling facilities could be provided for all customers: the cost would be more difficult to evaluate. Apart from the cost of the equipment itself there is the possible longer term impact on the prices of the alternatives, oil in particular, and a security and diversification cost through the loss of one major fuel option.

CONCLUSIONS

The main conclusions from this analysis are that:

- traditional definitions of energy security are not useful starting points for the present study;

- in particular, there are major differences between gas and other energy markets, particularly oil, and these need to be taken into account in any consideration of gas security;

- gas security is best seen in terms of risk management: reducing to an acceptable level the possible risks or consequences of a disruption in gas supply or non-availability of supply;

- risks fall into three broad categories: technical, long-term and political;

- risk management is central to the gas business and is primarily a matter for companies and their customers, especially with regard to technical risks;

- nonetheless there is a role for Governments in setting a framework within which risks can be effectively managed and sometimes in determining the acceptable level of system risk;

- a number of specific measures for promoting security can be identified, consistently with the IEA's Shared Goals;

- market mechanisms should where possible be the basis of security decisions. However for smaller, particularly residential, customers it may not always be practicable for individual users to determine the level of risk acceptable to them. Companies, regulators and Governments may need to be involved in setting security criteria;

- no generalised cost-benefit ratio, balancing the cost of these measures against their benefits, seems to be practical within the scope of this study. It will be for individual countries, operating through the mechanisms appropriate to them, to decide what is the acceptable level of security and the best mix of measures to achieve it;

- nonetheless there are significant international dimensions to the issue, including the need for a secure framework for investment and trade, facilitating interconnection and supply sharing, and possible impacts on world oil markets.

These and other aspects of gas security are explored in more detail in Chapters 3 through 7.

III. LONG TERM GAS DEMAND AND SUPPLY

CURRENT GAS DEMAND AND TRADE

The OECD accounts for about 43% of total world marketed production of natural gas and for 49% of total world consumption. Thus, as a whole, it is a net importer. The degree of self-sufficiency, however, varies significantly over the three regions:

Table 3.1 provides an overview of gas production, trade and demand in the three OECD regions in 1993:

Table 3.1   OECD Gas Production, Trade and Consumption, 1993 (bcm)

	OECD	**North America**	**Pacific**	**OECD Europe**
Production	931	666	32	233
Imports	291	65	55	171
Exports	147	67	7	73
Total Consumption	**1059**	**650**	**81**	**328**

Source: Oil and Gas Information.

■ North America[1] is basically self-sufficient in gas. A gas deficit in the United States is to a large extent covered by imports from Canada. In addition, the United States has some gas trade with Mexico and imports small volumes of LNG from Algeria;

■ the OECD Pacific region consists of two countries that are self-sufficient (Australia, also a net exporter, and New Zealand) and Japan which imports 96% of her gas needs;

■ the OECD Europe region is a net importer of gas. In addition to a considerable intra-regional gas trade, OECD Europe is to a certain extent also dependent on imports from sources outside the OECD area. In 1993, such imports (mainly from Russia and Algeria) supplied 30% of total gas consumption.

Only about 16% of total world marketed production of natural gas is traded internationally. In 1994, OECD countries received 83.4% of the total volume traded. Table 3.2 gives a complete overview of international movements of gas in 1994 by pipeline and by LNG tanker. A salient feature in this context is the high dependence of OECD Europe and Japan on imports, a large portion of which have to transit through several countries before reaching the country of destination.

---

1. Throughout this chapter, North America refers to the United States and Canada.

Table 3.2 Estimated International Gas Trade by Pipeline and LNG Tanker, 1994 (bcm)*

Importing Countries	North America			Latin America			Western Europe						Eastern Europe	Africa			Middle East			Asia/Oceania					World Total Imports by Pipeline + LNG
	CAN	USA	Total	BOL	MEX	Total	DEN	NETH	NOR	UK	GER	Total	CIS	ALG	LIB	Total	ABU	SHR	Total	AUS	BRU	IND	MAL	Total	
North America	**71.40**	**1.04**	**72.44**		**0.20**	**0.20**								**1.42**		**1.42**									**74.06**
Canada		1.04	1.04																						1.04
United States	71.40		71.40		0.20	0.20								1.42		1.42									73.02
Latin America		**1.05**	**1.05**	**1.98**		**1.98**																			**3.03**
Argentina				1.98		1.98																			1.98
Mexico		1.05	1.05																						1.05
Western Europe							**1.75**	**40.80**	**26.83**	**0.87**	**3.66**	**73.91**	**67.10**	**28.35**	**1.48**	**29.83**				**0.45**				**0.45**	**171.29**
Austria									0.32		0.25	0.57	5.05												5.62
Belgium								5.26	2.63			7.89		3.98		3.98									11.87
Finland													3.4												3.4
France								5.11	6.95			12.06	11.5	7.65		7.65									31.21
Germany (eastern)											1.95	1.95	7.2												9.15
Germany (western)							0.91	24.58	9.98	0.40		35.87	23												58.87
Italy								4.47				4.47	13.39	11.78	0.05	11.83									29.69
Luxembourg								0.68				0.68													0.68
Netherlands									2.82	0.47		3.29													3.29
Spain									1.1			1.1		4.55	1.43	5.78				0.45				0.45	7.53
Sweden							0.84					0.84													0.84
Switzerland								0.70			1.46	2.16	0.38												2.54
United Kingdom									3.03			3.03													3.03
Former Yugoslavia													3.18	0.39		0.39									3.57
Eastern Europe													**33.73**												**33.73**
Bulgaria													5												5
CSFR													13												13
Ex-USSR																									0.50
Hungary													5.53												5.53
Poland													5.8												5.8
Romania													4.4												4.4
Africa														**1.49**		**1.49**									**1.49**
Tunisia														1.49		1.49									1.49
Middle East													**4.97**	**0.38**		**0.38**		**4.60**	**4.60**						**9.95**
Dubai																		3.60	3.60						3.60
North Emirates																		1.00	1.00						1
Turkey													4.97	0.38		0.38									5.35
Asia/Oceania		**1.57**	**1.57**														**4.25**		**4.25**	**8.08**	**7.72**	**35.09**	**12.49**	**63.38**	**69.2**
Japan		1.57	1.57														4.25		4.25	8.08	7.36	24.94	10.6	50.98	56.8
Singapore																							1.50	1.50	1.50
South Korea																					0.36	7.15	0.39	7.90	7.9
Taiwan																						3		3	3
TOTAL EXPORTS	**71.40**	**3.66**	**75.06**	**1.98**	**0.20**	**2.18**	**1.75**	**40.80**	**26.83**	**0.87**	**3.66**	**73.91**	**105.8**	**31.64**	**1.48**	**33.12**	**4.25**	**4.6**	**8.85**	**8.53**	**7.72**	**35.09**	**12.49**	**63.83**	**362.75**

Source: Cedigaz (1995).

* Abbreviations used in this table are defined in the list of Abbreviations on page 219.

Table 3.3 shows the breakdown of total consumption by main sectors in the OECD:

Table 3.3   OECD Gas Consumption by Main Sector in 1992 (per cent)

	OECD	**North America**	**OECD Pacific**	**OECD Europe**
Electricity	17.2	12.9	57.9	16.0
Other Transformation*	10.9	13.4	1.1	5.5
Industry	32.4	34.8	19.4	32.5
Other**	39.5	38.9	21.6	46.0

*   Including pipeline fuel and consumption in transport
** Mainly consists of residential/commercial demand

As evident from Table 3.3, the structure of the gas markets in the three regions exhibits considerable differences:

■ In North America, the transformation, industry and the residential sectors each constitute roughly a third of total gas use;

■ Gas use in OECD Europe is more tilted toward the residential/commercial sector than in the rest of the OECD;

■ In the OECD Pacific region (in particular, Japan) a very high share of gas supply goes into power generation.

Table 3.4   Gas Share in TPES in OECD Countries (per cent)

Country	1992	2005
Canada	28.0	28.4
Unites States	23.6	23.5
Australia	16.1	15.8
Japan	10.5	10.4
New Zealand	30.7	33.1
Austria	20.8	23.7
Belgium	17.4	27.1
Denmark	11.0	20.6
Finland	8.8	12.3
France	12.1	12.3
Germany	16.7	20.0
Greece	0.6	10.5
Iceland	—	—
Ireland	18.6	17.4
Italy	25.8	34.8
Luxembourg	12.2	16.3
Netherlands	48.5	50.9
Norway	14.2	13.1
Portugal	—	8.2
Spain	6.2	12.2
Sweden	1.3	2.3
Switzerland	7.6	10.6
Turkey	6.9	20.2
United Kingdom	23.2	26.1

Source: Member country submissions.

In 1992, the share of gas in total OECD TPES was 20%. The shares were 24.1% in North America, 11.9% in the Pacific and 17.1% in OECD Europe. These shares are expected to stay relatively stable in North America and the Pacific, but the share is expected to increase in Europe. Table 3.4 shows the shares of gas in TPES for all OECD countries in 1992 and 2005, based on country submissions to the IEA.

The share of gas in TPES varies across countries from zero to almost 50% and reflects availability of gas and the maturity of each country's gas market. Most of the countries in which the gas share is expected to increase significantly over the next few years are dependent upon external supplies, and, thus security of supply issues may be relevant.

The fact that the three OECD regions are in different situations in terms of self-sufficiency and demand structure explains both the attitude taken to security issues and the differing approaches used in this study. As explained in Chapter 6, different approaches to the analysis of short term security issues have been used in the three regions. The approach to long term issues in this chapter also reflects the varied situation in the three regions.

FUTURE DEMAND FOR GAS

This study does not focus to a large extent on gas demand issues.[2] Nonetheless, gas demand forecasts from all the IEA member countries have been collected for two reasons:

- The forecasts made in the context of the IEA's 1995 *World Energy Outlook* (WEO) provide only regional figures, not national ones.
- It was seen as desirable to have member countries' views on the future development of gas demand in order both to compare them with the *WEO* projections and to be able to discuss supplies based on a demand backdrop for each country.

One of the methodological problems involved in elaborating a total gas demand forecast for all member countries is to ensure consistency in the assumptions used. Although the forecasts presented below are based on submissions from member countries, there is reason to believe, however, that the assumptions used do not deviate substantially from the assumptions used in the *WEO* projections.

Tables 3.5a, 3.5b and 3.5c show total gas demand for the period to 2010 for all the countries in the three OECD regions.

Table 3.6 shows a comparison between the forecasts submitted by governments and those of the IEA's 1995 *World Energy Outlook.* Detailed assumptions and a description of the two cases can be found in the *WEO.* This study refers to the *Capacity Constraints* case which has assumptions based on an average oil import price of US$17 (in 1993 US dollars) in 1995 increasing to US$28 in 2005 and flattening out thereafter. Economic growth rates of between 2.3% and 2.7% are assumed for the three OECD regions, with highest growth in the OECD Pacific. No major policy changes are assumed.

---

2. The IEA projections for total energy demand including gas demand projections over the period to 2010 are put forth in the 1995 *World Energy Outlook.*

Table 3.5a   Gas Demand Forecast: OECD Europe

	Demand (Mtoe)			Growth Rate (% p.a.)	
	1992	**2000**	**2010**	**1992-2000**	**2000-2010**
Austria	5.2	6.4	8.3	2.6	2.6
Belgium	9.0	12.8	14.0	4.5	0.9
Denmark	1.7	3.5	3.9	9.2	0.1
Finland	2.4	3.6	4.3	5.2	1.8
France	27.9	34.0	39.5	2.5	1.5
Germany	56.8	71.5	79.5	2.9	1.1
Greece	0.1	2.6	3.2	50.3	2.1
Ireland	2.0	1.5	2.0	-3.5	2.9
Italy	41.0	56.5	69.6	4.1	2.1
Luxembourg	0.5	0.6	0.7	2.3	1.6
Netherlands	32.8	35.9	37.0	1.1	0.3
Norway	-	0.5	1.0	-	7.2
Portugal	-	1.6	3.0	-	6.5
Spain	5.2	12.8	14.7	11.9	1.4
Sweden	0.6	1.0	1.8	6.6	6.1
Switzerland	1.9	2.5	3.2	3.5	2.5
Turkey	3.8	16.4	25.1	20.1	4.3
UK	50.2	61.0	85.5	2.5	3.4
Total	**241.1**	**324.7**	**395.9**	**3.8**	**2.0**
of which:					
Industry	*85.2*	*113.2*	*128.4*	*3.6*	*1.3*
Electricity	*34.7*	*73.6*	*113.3*	*9.9*	*4.4*
Residential/Commercial	*115.0*	*127.2*	*141.1*	*1.3*	*1.1*
Unattributed	*6.2*	*10.7*	*12.8*		

Source: Member country submissions.

Table 3.5b   Gas Demand Forecast: North America

	Demand (Mtoe)			Growth Rate (% p.a.)	
	1992	**2000**	**2010**	**1992-2000**	**2000-2010**
USA	457	517	574	1.6	1.1
of which:					
Industry+	*173*	*203*	*222*	*2.0*	*0.9*
Electricity	*69*	*78*	*110*	*1.5*	*3.5*
Residential/Commercial	*174*	*186*	*183*	*0.8*	*-0.2*
Unattributed	*41*	*50*	*59*		
Canada	55.2	69.6	91.2	2.9	2.7
Total	**512.2**	**586.6**	**665.2**	**1.7**	**1.3**

Source: Member country submissions.
+ includes cogenerators.

Table 3.5c   Gas Demand Forecast: OECD Pacific

	Demand (Mtoe)			Growth Rate (% p.a.)	
	1992	**2000**	**2010**	**1992-2000**	**2000-2010**
Japan	47.3	62.4	67.9	3.5	0.8
Australia	14.6	17.2	25.3*	2.1	3.9
New Zealand	4.52	5.14	2.09	1.6	-8.6
Total	**66.3**	**84.7**	**95.2**	**3.1**	**1.2**
of which:					
Industry	13.4	16.1	19.5	2.3	1.9
Electricity	40.5	51.6	53.3	3.1	0.3
Residential/Commercial	11.4	15.4	18.3	3.1	0.3
Unattributed	1.0	1.5	4.1		

* IEA Secretariat estimate.
Source: Administration and Gas Companies.

Table 3.6   Gas Demand in the Three OECD Regions — Comparison of Country Submissions and the WEO Projections (Mtoe)

	1992*	2000	2010
North America	**512**	**587**	**665**
WEO Projection	512	597	697
Pacific	**66**	**85**	**95**
WEO Projection	66	82	122
OECD Europe	**242**	**325**	**396**
WEO Projection	242	314	412

* Based on member country submissions.

Based on Tables 3.5 and 3.6 the following observations can be made:

■ For the year 2000, the forecasts based on member country submissions are somewhat higher than the *WEO* forecast for Europe and the Pacific, but lower for North America. In 2010, however, the submitted forecasts for all regions are substantially lower than the WEO.

■ In OECD Europe and North America, the strongest growth in demand is expected to take place in the power generation sector. In the OECD Pacific, demand growth is very strong in this sector over the first half of the projection period. For the whole OECD, the increase in gas for power generation accounts for roughly half of the total increase in demand. Chapter 5 provides detailed analysis of this phenomenon.

■ In North America, regulatory policies that increase competition in natural gas markets, advances in gas-fired technology and a growing emphasis on a cleaner environment contribute to the general increase in gas demand. Demand in the residential/commercial sector is expected to grow modestly over the period to 2010. Although gas will continue to be the primary fuel for new housing and conversions, improved efficiency of replacement and new furnaces will have a moderating effect on growth in this sector. The industrial sector will grow more briskly. Rising gas use resulting from increased competitiveness in industrial markets will be partially offset by technological advances in industrial processes and the use of more efficient equipment. The continued shifting of the industrial base away from energy intensive industries to less energy intensive ones such as electronics and pharmaceuticals will have a further dampening effect on future demand. Another possible impediment to North American natural gas demand growth is the advancement of technology for use of coal or fuel oil. Coal resources are more abundant than natural gas and a breakthrough in clean coal technology could displace some future gas consumption. Also, deregulation of the electrical industry in the US could lead to "Retail Wheeling" of electricity across state lines. Areas with excess generating capacity could supply other market areas and thus reduce the demand for new gas-fired facilities.

■ In the Pacific region, growth in gas demand in the residential/commercial and the industrial sectors is roughly equivalent in absolute terms. The gas penetration rate in the residential/commercial sector in this region is still relatively low.

■ In OECD Europe, gas demand in the industry sector is expected to grow more strongly during the first half of the period compared with the post 2000 period. Gas penetration in the residential sector of some of the biggest gas consuming countries is approaching saturation. The penetration rate is low or nonexistent in some of the less mature or new gas consuming countries, and it seems that most of this potential will only be realised after 2000. The gas markets in the countries constituting OECD Europe are very diverse, and the major forces driving demand in the two traditional sectors vary substantially across countries.

GAS SUPPLY ISSUES

This section provides a general introduction and a discussion of gas reserves, methodological problems involved in estimating supply costs, present and future gas pricing, costs of supply, analysis of gas balances for each region as well as some conclusions as to whether demand and supply can be matched.[3]

The increase in demand described above gives rise to questions of whether, from where and at what costs this demand can be met. Although the global gas resource base is immense and reserves are abundant, gas is not necessarily easily available in any market or at any time. In contrast to the oil market, there is no global market for natural gas. This is mostly due to the fact that the transportation of gas is difficult and costly. Natural gas has, in relation to its volume, a relatively low energy content. One cubic metre of gas under normal pressure contains about one-thousandth the energy of the same volume of crude oil. For the cost of shipping one unit of energy in the form of gas from the North Sea to the European continent, for example, an equivalent energy unit in the form of oil could be shipped twice around the globe. Transportation is thus a limiting factor to the development of a flexible and global market for gas. The fact that only 16 per cent of global gas production is internationally traded demonstrates the role of transportation in the gas chain as well as its limiting effect on the development of gas markets.

---

3. Further discussion can be found in the recent IEA publication *Oil, Gas and Coal Supply Outlook* (IEA, 1995a), companion volume to the IEA's 1995 *World Energy Outlook*.

There are today three world regions which could be described as individual gas markets. Mexico, Canada and the United States form the North American gas market, which is characterised by a high degree of transparency and competition among various suppliers and consumers of gas. The second market is Europe, where indigenous production is considerable. Nevertheless, trade within the region is extensive and imports from outside the region are becoming increasingly crucial. The European market is still dominated by a relatively small number of participants and is less transparent and competitive than the North American market. The Asian market encompasses most of the world trade in LNG. Although some short term sales agreements recently have been concluded, this market is still dominated by long term contracts.

The discussion below takes account of the regionalisation of gas markets as well as other commercial and technical characteristics and draws heavily on the recent IEA publication, *Natural Gas Transportation: Organisation and Regulation* (IEA, 1994).

Global Gas Reserves

In general, natural gas reserves are classified into three groups, proved, probable and possible reserves. Cedigaz (1994), for example, defines **proved reserves** to be those located in thoroughly explored reservoirs which already are in production or under development. They correspond to discoveries of which production is feasible under current economic and technical conditions. **Probable reserves** are discovered reserves exhibiting a good probability of being produced under economic and technical conditions similar to those of proved reserves. Probable reserves are measured more roughly and the reservoirs are not yet equipped to produce. **Possible reserves** correspond to identified reservoirs in undrilled zones adjacent to proved or probable geological volumes. The identification of such reserves is dubious and their assessment relies on assumptions of geometry and impregnation of these reservoirs. There is, in addition, a more hypothetical class of potential resources, corresponding to unidentified reservoirs. Other sources publishing reserve estimates on a regular basis and government bodies estimating reserves for individual countries apply the same type of definitions with minor modifications or probabilities of economic recoverability attached to the three groups of reserves.

Reserve reporting has been one of the greatest impediments to a thorough understanding of world resources. Reserves cannot be directly measured and quantifications are always estimates, depending not only on the definitions applied but also on the estimator's judgement in the analysis and interpretation of available geological, engineering and economic data. To recognise what is actually being reported in principal areas of hydrocarbon occurrence is only one of the problems; others are to understand whether field growth and changes in reserve estimates might be due to new discoveries, new recovery methods or to the reclassification of reserves. Further, it is not always clear whether associated gas is included in the reserve estimates, nor whether conventional resources only have been reported or whether unconventional resources are included. The classification of gas resources into the various categories can change over time and as a result of changes in economic and technological conditions or the perception thereof. Formulations like "production is reasonably feasible in current economic and technical conditions" or "quantities which geological and engineering information indicate with reasonable certainty can be recovered in the future from known reservoirs under existing economic and operating conditions" are obviously relatively vague and open to interpretation. Economic and technical conditions depend to a large degree on the market price of natural gas, which again depends on the price of alternative fuels and expectations related to the future development of those prices. Petroleum prices can fluctuate rapidly and heavily and attempts to predict the future path of prices can be difficult. Therefore, almost by definition, estimates of reserves and their classification will differ, depending on by whom and when they are assessed.

In the subsequent analysis of the various gas producing countries' potential for gas production and exports, estimates for their reserve base are presented. These are reproduced in Table 3.7 in aggregated form. The estimate for proved reserves is from Cedigaz (1994) and the Oil and Gas Journal, both of which annually publish reserve estimates on a country by country basis and explain their main reassessments. The mode ultimate resources estimated by Charles D. Masters (1994) are included in the table to indicate their order of magnitude. Masters arrives at estimates for ultimate resources by adjusting the quantities of ultimately producible gas in the US and Canada by field growth factors derived from the historical field growth pattern of US fields. For other countries a field growth rate ranging from one-third to two-thirds that of the United States was applied.

Two observations are relevant to Table 3.7:

■ The estimates vary substantially according to the method used and thus illustrate the difficulty in identifying and measuring gas reserves.

■ World gas reserves are abundant but are, to a large extent, located far from the main consumption centres. For instance, both Europe and North America account for a much smaller share of total world reserves than their share of world gas consumption. In general, however, the reserve situation is not expected to be a limiting factor for the further development of OECD gas markets.

The Elements in Cost of Supply

It is evident from the above discussion of reserve definitions that the size of reserves depends on economic conditions for the production and consumption of natural gas. These are influenced by total costs of production on the one hand and by the prices of natural gas and alternative fuels in the market and the expectation for their future development on the other hand.

Costs of Production

Production costs should reflect the costs of exploring and developing a gas field and bringing the gas to the wellhead. They depend on several factors. Whether the gas is produced from a pure gas reservoir or in association with oil can have a considerable impact on the cost of production. Sometimes there is a choice whether to produce associated gas with the oil or to leave it in the ground; sometimes the production of gas at the same time is inevitable. As associated gas is perceived as a byproduct of oil production, it tends to be cheaper than nonassociated gas because the costs of production are covered by oil revenues. If the associated gas is reinjected without increasing the oil recovery or without being producible at a later date, the alternative value of this gas is negative. If the gas is flared at the wellhead, its alternative value is zero. The gas has a positive alternative value when it is used as energy in the production process, either when it increases the oil production by maintaining reservoir pressure or when it is marketed. Yet, the costs of production of this gas are likely to be low. The share of total production costs attributed to the gas might be roughly reflected in its alternative value.

Table 3.7   Comparison of Reserve Estimates for Natural Gas

COUNTRY	OIL & GAS JOURNAL (1.1.94)			CEDIGAZ (1.1.94)			C.D.MASTERS IDENTIFIED			C.D.MASTERS ULTIMATE		
	TCF	BCM	% OF TOTAL	BCM	% OF TOTAL	TCF	BCM	% OF TOTAL	TCF	BCM	% OF TOTAL	
OECD												
WESTERN EUROPE												
Austria	0.7	18.9327		21	0.01							
Denmark	4.3	120.9259	0.09	215	0.15							
France	1.2	35.092	0.02	30	0.02							
Germany	12.1	342.7979	0.24	198	0.13							
Greece	0.3	8.49	0.01	9	0.01							
Ireland	0.6	17.3479	0.01	31	0.02							
Italy	10.7	301.8195	0.21	360	0.24	13.2	373.56	0.26	47.7	1349.91	0.42	
Netherlands	68.1	1928.8431	1.36	1875	1.27	71.1	2012.13	1.39	141.2	3995.96	1.25	
Norway	70.5	1994.8104	1.41	2805	1.89	106.7	3019.61	2.08	226.8	6418.44	2.00	
Spain	0.7	19.81	0.01	18	0.01							
Turkey	0.4	10.4993	0.01	25	0.02							
United Kingdom	21.5	609.6386	0.43	630	0.43	72.5	2051.75	1.41	120.2	3401.66	1.06	
Other						26.5	749.95	0.52	109.4	3096.02	0.97	
Total Western Europe	191.1	5409.0073	3.81	6217	4.20	290	8207	5.66	645.3	18261.99	5.70	
for domestic use	52.5	1485.3538	1.05	1537	1.04	112.2	3175.26	2.19	277.3	7847.59	2.45	
for exports (Norway and Netherlands)	138.6	3923.6535	2.76	4680	3.16	177.8		3.47	368	10414.4	3.25	
NORTH AMERICA												
US	165.0	4669.9245	3.29	4675	3.16	339	9593.7	6.61	1427.1	40386.93	12.61	
Canada	94.8	2683.4909	1.89	2640	1.78	128.7	3642.21	2.51	485.2	13731.16	4.29	
Total North America	259.8	7353.4154	5.18	7315	4.94	467.7	13235.91	9.12	1912.3	54118.09	16.90	
ASIA PACIFIC												
Australia	19.6	554.8781	0.39	2986	2.02	77.3	2187.59	1.51	104.8	2965.84	0.93	
New Zealand	3.2	89.2865	0.06	132	0.09	5.7	161.31	0.11	8.4	237.72	0.07	
Japan	1.0	29.6018	0.02	30	0.02							
Total Asia Pacific	23.8	673.7664	0.47	3148	2.13	83	2348.9	1.62	113.2	3203.56	1.00	
TOTAL OECD	474.8	13436.189	9.46	16680	11.26	840.7	23791.81	16.40	2670.8	75583.64	23.60	

Table 3.7   Comparison of Reserve Estimates for Natural Gas (continued)

COUNTRY	OIL & GAS JOURNAL (1.1.94)			CEDIGAZ (1.1.94)		C.D.MASTERS IDENTIFIED			C.D.MASTERS ULTIMATE		
	TCF	BCM	% OF TOTAL	BCM	% OF TOTAL	TCF	BCM	% OF TOTAL	TCF	BCM	% OF TOTAL
NON OECD											
EASTERN EUROPE AND FSU											
Albania	0.4	9.905	0.01	2	0.00						
Bulgaria	0.3	7.075	0.00	7	0.00						
Croatia	1.3	35.4316	0.02								
Czechoslovakia	0.5	13.018	0.01	11	0.01						
Hungary	3.4	96.5596	0.07	88	0.06						
Poland	5.5	154.9991	0.11	155	0.10						
Romania	8.0	226.4	0.16	445	0.30	16.5	466.95	0.32	61.1	1729.13	0.54
Serbia	1.6	44.714	0.03		0.00						
FSU	1997.0	56515.1	39.81	57500	38.82	1552.2	43927.26	30.28	3785.5	107129.65	33.45
Other						10.3	291.49	0.20	39.3	1112.19	0.35
Total East. Europe & FSU	2017.8	57103.202	40.23	58208	39.29	1579	44685.7	30.80	3885.9	109970.97	34.33
MIDDLE EAST											
Abu Dhabi	188.4	5331.72	3.76	5324	3.59						
Bahrain	5.9	166.97	0.12	159	0.11	9.6	271.68	0.19	12.5	353.75	0.11
Dubai	4.4	124.52	0.09	121	0.08						
Iran	730.0	20659	14.55	21000	14.18	864.7	24471.01	16.87	1248.6	35335.38	11.03
Iraq	109.5	3098.85	2.18	3100	2.09	76.6	2167.78	1.49	178.4	5048.72	1.58
Israel	0.0	0.3962	0.00	1	0.00						
Jordan	0.2	5.66	0.00	28	0.02						
Kuwait	52.4	1482.92	1.04	1498	1.01	56.9	1610.27	1.11	66.1	1870.63	0.58
Neutral Zone	1.0	28.3	0.02			11.7	331.11	0.23	13.7	387.71	0.12
Oman	20.0	566	0.40	600	0.41	15.5	438.65	0.30	22.6	639.58	0.20
Qatar	250.0	7075	4.98	7070	4.77	250	7075	4.88	253.4	7171.22	2.24
Ras al Khaimah	1.1	31.13	0.02	31	0.02						
Saudi Arabia	185.4	5245.688	3.70	5134	3.47	176.5	4994.95	3.44	484.6	13714.18	4.28
Sharjah	10.7	302.81	0.21	303	0.20						
Syria	7.0	198.1	0.14	227	0.15	5.1	144.33	0.10	5.7	161.31	0.05
Yemen	15.0	424.5	0.30	481	0.32						
Total UAE						200.1	5662.83	3.90	257.3	7281.59	2.27
Other						16.5	466.95	0.32	16.7	472.61	0.15
Total Middle East	1580.9	44741.564	31.52	45077	30.43	1683.2	47634.56	32.84	2559.6	72436.68	22.61

Table 3.7 Comparison of Reserve Estimates for Natural Gas (continued)

COUNTRY	OIL & GAS JOURNAL (1.1.94)			CEDIGAZ (1.1.94)		C.D.MASTERS IDENTIFIED			C.D.MASTERS ULTIMATE		
	TCF	BCM	% OF TOTAL	BCM	% OF TOTAL	TCF	BCM	% OF TOTAL	TCF	BCM	% OF TOTAL
AFRICA											
Algeria	128.0	3622.4	2.55	3700	2.50	176.5	4994.95	3.44	214.1	6059.03	1.89
Angola	1.8	50.94	0.04	48	0.03	5.8	164.14	0.11	9.6	271.68	0.08
Cameroon	3.9	110.37	0.08	110	0.07						
Congo	2.7	76.41	0.05	77	0.05	2.7	76.41	0.05	5.3	149.99	0.05
Egypt	15.4	435.82	0.31	595	0.40	19.3	546.19	0.38	39.4	1115.02	0.35
Equatorial Guinea	1.3	36.79	0.03	37	0.02						
Ethiopia	0.8	22.64	0.02	25	0.02						
Gabon	0.5	14.15	0.01	14	0.01	0.7	19.81	0.01	1.7	48.11	0.02
Ghana	0.8	22.64	0.02	24	0.02						
Ivory Coast	0.5	14.15	0.01	15	0.01						
Libya	45.8	1296.14	0.91	1289	0.87	45.9	1298.97	0.90	67	1896.1	0.59
Madagascar	0.0	1.981	0.00	2	0.00						
Morocco	0.0	0.9056	0.00	3	0.00						
Mozambique	2.3	65.09	0.05	45	0.03						
Namibia	5.2	147.16	0.10	147	0.10						
Nigeria	120.0	3396	2.39	3451	2.33	121.9	3449.77	2.38	254.1	7191.03	2.24
Rwanda	2.0	56.6	0.04	57	0.04						
Somalia	0.2	5.66	0.00	6	0.00	2.1	59.43	0.04	15	424.5	0.13
South Africa	0.9	26.6869	0.02	27	0.02						
Sudan	3.0	84.9	0.06	86	0.06	0.9	25.47	0.02	27.1	766.93	0.24
Tanzania	4.1	116.03	0.08	118	0.08						
Tunisia	3.2	90.56	0.06	91	0.06	3.1	87.73	0.06	14.8	418.84	0.13
Zaire	1.0	28.3	0.02	1	0.00						
Other						22.9	648.07	0.45	83.8	2371.54	0.74
Total Africa	343.5	9722.3235	6.85	9968	6.73	401.8	11370.94	7.84	731.9	20712.77	6.47
ASIA											
Afghanistan	3.5	99.05	0.07	100	0.07	3.1	87.73	0.06	19.8	560.34	0.17
Bangladesh	25.2	713.16	0.50	708	0.48	10.8	305.64	0.21	26.2	741.46	0.23
Brunei	14.0	396.2	0.28	400	0.27	12.2	345.26	0.24	22.5	636.75	0.20
China	59.0	1669.7	1.18	2000	1.35	38.9	1100.87	0.76	227	6424.1	2.01
Taiwan	2.4	67.92	0.05	68	0.05						

Table 3.7 Comparison of Reserve Estimates for Natural Gas (continued)

COUNTRY	OIL & GAS JOURNAL (1.1.94)			CEDIGAZ (1.1.94)			C.D.MASTERS IDENTIFIED			C.D.MASTERS ULTIMATE		
	TCF	BCM	% OF TOTAL	TCF	BCM	% OF TOTAL	TCF	BCM	% OF TOTAL	TCF	BCM	% OF TOTAL
India	25.4	717.5182	0.51	23.9	718	0.48	23.9	676.37	0.47	42.1	1191.43	0.37
Indonesia	64.4	1822.1804	1.28	105.9	2662	1.80	105.9	2996.97	2.07	188.9	5345.87	1.67
Malaysia	76.7	2170.61	1.53	64.4	2148	1.45	64.4	1822.52	1.26	110.5	3127.15	0.98
Myanmar	9.8	277.34	0.20	9.2	278	0.19	9.2	260.36	0.18	15.5	438.65	0.14
Pakistan	22.9	649.202	0.46	23.9	651	0.44	23.9	676.37	0.47	59.8	1692.34	0.53
Papua New Guinea	15.0	424.5	0.30	12.2	548	0.37	12.2	345.26	0.24	29.5	834.85	0.26
Philippines	3.0	84.334	0.06		71	0.05						
Thailand	5.7	162.442	0.11	10.8	181	0.12	10.8	305.64	0.21	33.7	953.71	0.30
Vietnam	3.7	104.71	0.07	3	106	0.07	3	84.9	0.06	11.6	328.28	0.10
Other												
Total Asia	330.7	9358.8666	6.59	318.3	10639	7.18	318.3	9007.89	6.21	787.1	22274.93	6.95
LATIN AMERICA												
Argentina	26.5	749.95	0.53	33.1	522	0.35	33.1	936.73	0.65	59.7	1689.51	0.53
Barbados	0.0	0.1981	0.00		0	0.00						
Bolivia	3.9	111.2473	0.08	5.8	118	0.08	5.8	164.14	0.11	14.9	421.67	0.13
Brazil	4.8	136.6324	0.10	19	137	0.09	19	537.7	0.37	50.4	1426.32	0.45
Chile	3.9	110.37	0.08	7.1	109	0.07	7.1	200.93	0.14	10.3	291.49	0.09
Columbia	10.0	283	0.20	11.3	283	0.19	11.3	319.79	0.22	22	622.6	0.19
Cuba	0.1	2.83	0.00		0	0.00						
Ecuador	3.8	107.54	0.08	1.1	108	0.07	1.1	31.13	0.02	7.3	206.59	0.06
Guatemala	0.0	0.283	0.00									
Mexico	70.9	2007.9982	1.41	70.1	1973	1.33	70.1	1983.83	1.37	208.9	5911.87	1.85
Peru	7.0	199.2037	0.14	13.6	325	0.22	13.6	384.88	0.27	32.5	919.75	0.29
Trinidad & Tobago	8.5	239.5595	0.17	15.4	240	0.16	15.4	435.82	0.30	25.2	713.16	0.22
Venezuela	128.9	3647.87	2.57	126.5	3750	2.53	126.5	3579.95	2.47	252	7131.6	2.23
Other												
Total Latin America	268.4	7596.6822	5.35	303	7565	5.11	303	8574.9	5.91	683.2	19334.56	6.04
TOTAL WORLD	5016.2	141958.83	100.00	5126	148137	100.00	5126	145065.8	100.00	11318.5	320313.55	100.00
Total OPEC	2019.4	57150.378	40.26	2202.2	58447	39.45	2202.2	62322.26	42.96	3466.2	98093.46	30.62
Total OECD	474.8	13436.189	9.46	840.7	16056	10.84	840.7	23791.81	16.40	2670.8	75583.64	23.60
Total OECD Europe	191.1	5409.0073	3.81	290	6238	4.21	290	8207	5.66	645.3	18261.99	5.70

Note: 1 Mtoe is equivalent to 1.27 bcm; 1 bcm = 0.0353147 tcf.

The costs of producing nonassociated gas are largely affected by the type of reservoir, the difficulty in developing and producing it and the available and applicable production technologies. Production technologies have been developed and improved vastly in recent years. Starting at the wellhead, recent development seems to indicate that there is still a huge untapped potential for lowering production costs.

In general, total costs of production tend to be higher for offshore than for onshore production and higher the harsher the production environment is. This can partly be offset by the size of the field, as large amounts of producible gas lower the unit cost of production through economies of scale. Presently, around 21% of world marketed production is produced offshore.

Pipeline Transportation Cost[4]

Contrary to the costs of production, it is easier to establish some rules of thumb for pipeline transportation costs. Pipeline systems are built to assure an uninterrupted flow of gas from a production point to a delivery point and range in complexity from a direct link between a supplier and a consumer to an interconnected network with multiple supply and demand nodes. Pipelines can be laid offshore and onshore, above ground and under ground, and as a combination of the four, even crossing several countries. Pipelines differ in size (diameter) and pressure. The larger a pipeline's diameter, the higher is its capacity, however, with a large diameter, pressure in the pipe will drop more quickly. Over long distances, therefore, it is necessary to boost the pressure with compressors at regular intervals. The physical lifetime of a pipeline can be around 50 years. However, its economic life can be much shorter and will determine over which period initial investment should be depreciated. Whether a pipeline is a direct link between producer and consumer or forms part of a network, the same factors are principal in the determination of construction costs:

- the length of the pipeline
- the maximum flow required for a day of peak demand
- the trade off between pipeline diameter and the number of compressor stations
- terrain, rights of way, etc.

The length of a pipeline is determined by the origin of the gas to be transported, the point of delivery and the possibility of using already existing infrastructure. The capacity requirements of a pipeline depend more on maximum than annual flow. Usually, transmission costs are barely affected by increasing annual transmission volumes for a given peak capacity, while new investment is needed for increasing peak capacity adding significantly to transmission costs. The same maximum capacity can be yielded by different combinations of compressor spacing and pipeline diameter. While laying pipelines requires high capital costs, compressors have higher operating costs and lower capital costs. Generally, it is therefore more economic to build pipelines with smaller diameter and more compressors, if peak capacity is only to be used for a short period each year or if the necessity for increases in peak capacity seems less probable. As long distance pipelines require extremely high capital costs, operation at high load factors is usually crucial to maintain viability.

---

4. The discussion in this section is based on analysis carried out by the IEA and published in *Natural Gas Transportation: Organisation and Regulation*, 1994.

A generic formula for costing pipelines can be established, based on diameter, pressure and distance. Other factors, that are more difficult to quantify, such as the specifications of the terrain or waters to be crossed, climatic conditions, population density, safety regulations and market specific factors as labour costs and the competition situation in pipeline construction, usually cannot be accounted for in such formulae. Possible transit fees are also not included.

Based on data from onshore pipeline projects submitted to the US Federal Energy Regulatory Commission (FERC) in 1990/1991, material costs accounted for 38% of pipeline construction costs, and labour for 36%. Miscellaneous costs, including surveying, interest during construction, administration, overhead, contingencies and FERC fees, accounted for 22%, while rights of way accounted for 4% of total construction costs (IEA, 1994, p.47). Costs for offshore pipeline construction depend on the maximum rated capacity and the depth of water. Less information is available in this area; however, recent construction plans for the North Sea suggest costs in the range of US$ 2.4 to 4 million per mile for diameters of 30 to 40 inches and operating pressures of up to 190 bar (IEA, 1994).

Fixed costs for pipelines consist of operation and maintenance costs which are estimated to correspond to an annual proportion of construction costs of 2% onshore and 1% offshore. Maintenance costs for compressors are partially related to use and run at around 3 to 6% of investment costs for operation at a relatively high load factor. Fuel costs, which represent the principal variable cost, correspond to 0.3% of total throughput.

Increasing distance of transportation has the largest impact on costs per Mbtu of gas piped offshore, whereas the cost of LNG transportation is less affected by distance. As can be seen from Table 3.8, differences in unit costs for transportation in onshore and offshore pipelines are less distinct the larger the annual volumes are. Also, pipeline transportation becomes relatively more competitive to LNG transportation with increasing annual capacities.

Table 3.8   Costs of Transportation for Various Annual Capacities and Different Distances (1993 US$ per Mbtu)

Capacity (bcm/year)	Onshore pipeline				Offshore pipeline			
	5	10	15	20	5	10	15	20
1000 km	0.7	0.4	0.3	0.3	0.9	0.6	0.5	0.5
3000 km	1.9	1.2	1.0	0.9	2.7	1.9	1.5	1.3
5000 km	3.3	2.1	1.7	1.5	4.5	3.1	2.5	2.2
7000 km	4.5	3.0	2.5	2.2	6.2	4.4	3.4	3.1

Source: (Pauwels, 1994), p.118, 119.

LNG Costs

Gas is less costly to transport over very long distances in liquefied form as LNG compared with pipeline transportation. However, while gas can be piped in its gaseous state, it needs to be compressed in order to be transported by ship. A full LNG chain, thus, consists of a liquefaction plant, generally with at least two trains, ships to transport the LNG and a regasification terminal including storage at the point of arrival. Since gas was first transported as LNG around 1965, economies of scale have improved considerably, both through the size of liquefaction trains and the size of vessels. For example, the capacity of a train has increased from around 0.5 million tonnes of LNG per year in the 1960s to some 2.5 million tonnes in the 1990s. For future plants, a further increase in capacity of a single train to close to 3, in the longer term possibly even 4, million tonnes per year may be possible. If gas prices remain relatively stable, costs of production continue to grow and distances between production sites and markets widen, increases in capacity would not only result in significant economies of scale, but might even be necessary in order to bring LNG to markets.

For a LNG chain of around 6 bcm per year and transportation distance of 3,500 and 5,500 kilometres, liquefaction accounts for 50 to 60%, transport for 25 to 35%, and regasification for some 15% of the full costs (excluding the costs of the gas to be liquefied) (Hafner, 1993).

For the liquefaction facilities, the cost of adding trains is considerably lower than that of the first train, since the required infrastructure must be built along with the first train. Thus, for example, the average cost per train of the Indonesian six train LNG plant at Arun was reduced by 16% with the construction of the last three trains. The construction cost of LNG facilities can vary geographically depending on the cost of land, environmental and safety regulations, labour costs and other local conditions. Various estimates indicate construction costs for a plant with a capacity of liquefying 5 bcm per year of US$1.4 to 2 billion and US$2 to 3 billion for a 10 bcm plant (Hafner, 1993). Liquefaction is energy intensive and about 12% of the gas intake in a plant is used as fuel for liquefaction. Annual operating and maintenance costs amount to around 4% of capital investment (IEA, 1994).

The distance between producer and market and the volume to be transported are important in the determination of the cost of shipping. A greater number of smaller carriers translates into more frequent port calls and reduced storage requirements, but offers little scope for economies of scale. There are three typical sizes for LNG carriers; ships with a volume of 25,000 to 50,000 cubic metres are employed in cross-Mediterranean trade, while larger ships of 70,000 to 100,000 cubic metres and the new generation ship of 125,000 to 136,000 cubic metres are used more in long distance supplies to Japan. Most of the recently built LNG tankers have been in the third range. A new ship of this category is estimated to cost around US$250 billion. According to ship constructors, it would be possible to build vessels with a capacity of around 200,000 cubic metres. Although capacity would be increased by more than 50%, investment costs would only be around 30% higher than for the current size ships. Overall delivery costs could thus be reduced. However, the size of current port and terminal infrastructure restricts the use of larger tankers. LNG carriers are more costly to operate and maintain than oil tankers of similar size, and annual fixed costs are between US$5 to 8 million. In addition to fuel oil, 0.1 to 0.25% of the cargo tank capacity per voyage day is used as fuel.

Regasification costs, which account for around 15% of total costs in the LNG chain, depend mostly on costs for port development, required storage volume and safety regulations. The potential for improvement in economies of scale has partly been and can further be realised by larger storage tanks, where capacity has grown from 80,000 cubic metres in the 1980s to 100,000 to 120,000 cubic metres in current projects and envisaged capacities of more than 150,000 cubic metres towards the turn of the century. Various estimates indicate construction costs of US$500 million for regasification terminals with an annual capacity of around 5 bcm.

Based on the assumption of a rate of return of 10%, and representing costs for a "normal" projects, i.e., a project conducted in an average environment and without unforeseen major difficulties which would boost costs, the various estimates presented above can be summarised and transferred to unit costs. These are shown in Table 3.9.

Table 3.9   Total Costs for LNG Plants of Various Capacities and Transportation Distances (1990 US$ per Mbtu)

Capacity	6 bcm/year	12 bcm/year	18 bcm/year
Liquefaction	1.2-1.6	0.9-1.2	0.8-1.1
Regasification	0.4	0.4	0.4
Transportation: 1000 km	0.2	0.2	0.2
8000 km	1.6	1.6	1.6
Total (1000 km)	1.8-2.2	1.5-1.8	1.4-1.7
Total (8000 km)	3.2-3.6	2.9-3.2	2.8-3.1

Source: Hafner (1994).

While liquefaction costs are reduced with increasing capacity, regasification and transportation costs appear to be unaffected by volumes. Shipping costs are shown here for only two distances. They grow by around US$0.20 per Mbtu per 1,000 kilometres. It should also be noted that liquefaction costs may vary significantly as a function of construction market conditions. On the other hand, if LNG were produced from an existing plant where capacity would be increased by addition of one or several new trains, liquefaction costs would be lower. Also, if second hand ships could be used for transportation, shipping costs would fall. Therefore, as conditions in reality will most probably differ from assumptions on which the calculations for the above table are based, these numbers should be interpreted as giving orders of magnitude for LNG costs, rather than as an accurate "price list".

Comparing the cost estimates from Tables 3.8 and 3.9, allows some indicative conclusions on the break even points between pipeline transportation and transportation of liquified gas. For annual volumes less than 10 bcm, the break-even between LNG and offshore transportation is at around US$2 per Mbtu for a distance of around 3,000 km. For larger distances, transportation in offshore pipelines becomes more costly per Mbtu than transportation in the form of LNG. The relationship between LNG and onshore pipeline costs for small volumes is different, with a break even point at around 4 000 km and US$2.50 per Mbtu. For larger annual volumes of gas to be transported, the break even point moves in favour of pipeline gas. Thus, for annual volumes between 10 and 15 bcm, the break even cost is around US$2.50 to $3 for distances between 4,000 and 6,000 km. Volumes around 20 bcm per year are less costly to ship as LNG for distances of more than 7,000 km, at which it costs about US$2.80 per Mbtu.

Comparison of Existing Cost Estimates — Methodological Problems

Total natural gas supply cost should reflect the following four elements: exploration and development; operation or production; transport to the market; and local distribution. It is often difficult to find and compare the costs of gas supply from current fields, and it is even more problematic to arrive at reliable and comparable estimates for the costs of future supplies. Even when such estimates are available, their interpretation is fraught with a number of problems.

Dahl and Gjelsvik (1993) undertook a survey of 18 cost studies for the European gas market which looks at cost estimates for fields already in production and discusses theoretical reasons for differences in those estimates. It also gives a survey of the available estimates and quantifies the differences between them. Although this work focuses on cost estimates for current gas supplies, it is of relevance for cost estimates for natural gas in general.

Theoretically, costs should be presented as a specified aggregation of the categories they are composed of. While exploration, development and production costs should be the same from a given field for all recipients of that gas, transportation costs will clearly depend on the distance to be bridged, as well as on the means of transportation and thus will differ from country to country. Further, local distribution costs will differ even within a given country from residential to industrial consumers due to economies of scale. Knowing which categories have been included in costs of gas supply is thus crucial, especially for the purpose of comparing different estimates. However, cost estimates often fail to specify the cost categories accounted for, thus leading to variations in estimates which are difficult to explain.

Another source of uncertainty around the interpretation of cost estimates is the lack of transparency within each category and also in the aggregated cost estimate. There are several reasons for this type of uncertainty (Dahl and Gjelsvik, 1993):

■ The European gas market, for example, is dominated by relatively few and big companies. In such markets, price data are not necessarily a good indicator of costs. That is one of the reasons for initiatives towards more transparency and open access in the gas markets, supported, for instance, by the European Commission.

■ Gas is often a joint product with oil or other liquids. In these cases, costs need to be allocated to the various products. Cost allocation can be based on the various products' energy content. For fields that contain mainly gas, the value of other hydrocarbons can be subtracted from the total costs of production leaving the remaining costs to be distributed over gas production only.

■ Cost usually differ widely from field to field, but tend to be aggregated when they are reported.

■ *Ex ante* and *ex post* project costs can differ substantially. For example, for 23 North Sea projects from 1970 to 1980, 20 had overruns with an average overrun for all projects of 95%.[5] One possible reason for cost overruns can be the scarcity of equipment during times of high oil and gas prices and, therefore, high activity that might have led to higher costs.

■ Petroleum or gas projects are characterised by large investments and relatively high up front capital costs. Assumptions about capital life, capacity, capacity utilisation, production profiles and discount rates affect above ground unit costs. Discount rates can or cannot account for risk premiums and differ widely. Depending on the discount rate chosen the cost of gas supply from a given field can differ by 20%.

■ Further, reserves in a field are often revised during a field's life time, most often in an upward direction, and can change unit costs.

In order to compare costs, the data usually have to be converted several times in order to bring them to a comparable basis. Given that conversions might be necessary to account for energy content, volume and weight, exchange rates or purchasing power parities, and inflation, there may be significant variation in estimates.

---

5. *Petroleum Times*, October 1985, p. 358.

The uncertainties in cost comparisons of gas from fields already in production are also, and maybe even more, correct for the costs of future supplies. In addition, for future supplies there are uncertainties regarding capacity in current fields and infrastructure. New developments of fields or even of new production regions require heavy investments, while increasing production from existing facilities is normally less costly. The capacity utilisation and availability of existing infrastructure and the potential need for construction of new infrastructure present additional uncertainty for the costs of new supplies.

Cost estimates involve different methods. Some apply a "top-down" approach by starting with a given oil price, transforming it into a gas price, subtracting estimated costs for distribution, transport, storage, possibly liquefaction and thus arriving at a price which would "remain" to cover costs of production (this method shows some parallel to netback pricing principles but does not result in "true" costs of supply). Others apply a "bottom-up" approach by trying to estimate how much potential future gas supply would cost to be produced, adding costs for transportation, storage, distribution, etc. and deriving a gas price which may or may not be competitive. Although both methods contain the same cost elements, the estimation of those elements and the results might differ.

Present and Future Gas Pricing

Before discussing available material on gas supply costs and discussing the matching of future demand and supply, it is useful to consider gas pricing and to understand the mechanisms through which costs are translated into prices and how they influence each other. A brief overview of price mechanisms and issues in the three OECD regions is therefore presented along with some consideration as to how gas pricing mechanisms could develop in the future.

Historically, two ways of gas pricing have been dominant: netback pricing and cost of service pricing.[6] Netback pricing assumes as a starting point that gas faces competition in end uses, which is true most of the time. The price of gas in each end use is set so that it is competitive with the alternative fuel in question, taking into account not only the fuel cost but also operating and capital costs. The price of gas in the various end use segments is then netted back to the border of the country in question by deducting distribution and transmission costs. The netback prices are then weighted by the volumes going into the various segments to arrive at an average border price for gas. That price could then be the basis for negotiations between buyers and sellers.

Cost of service prices conceptually start at the other end of the gas chain. It is a bottom up approach in the sense that it starts by specifying production costs, gathering costs and transmission costs, adds a profit element and arrives at a cost based price including a profit at the delivery point, which typically could be a border. The seller would of course not necessarily reveal his true costs in each part of the chain, and the rate of return to be earned will of course be the main point in the negotiations between sellers and buyers. It should be stressed that no matter what the conceptual approach to pricing is, the fixing of the price is rarely the result of a mechanical approach. In the end, the negotiating skill and strategic position of the parties will have a considerable influence on the final result. It is likely that the two pricing concepts only identify the price ranges within which negotiations take place.

Unlike for oil, there is no world market price for gas. The major reason for this is that gas markets are regionalised, usually because of the geographical distances between markets

---

6. In recent years, however, pricing of gas based on gas to gas competition has become widespread in North America.

and the ensuing high transportation costs. With future growth in the world LNG trade, however, there may be more price correlation between the major gas markets in the world.

For the purpose of this study, a distinction is made between the North American gas market, the Asian/Pacific market and the European gas market. If wholesale prices of gas in these three markets are compared, significant differences in level are found. In the second quarter of 1994, the average spot price at Henry Hub in the United States was US$1.95 per Mbtu. During the same period the average LNG import price into Japan was around US$3.30 per Mbtu whereas the average European border price could be estimated to be around US$2.30 per Mbtu. These prices are not necessarily representative of each region, however, and thus may not be indicative of the relative price levels. Nevertheless, the discussion below focuses on why these differences do exist and what will influence the future gas price in each region.

North America

Over the past few years the gas market in North America has developed towards a commodity market. Gas prices are primarily fixed as a function of gas to gas competition, and short term changes in supply and demand are more or less immediately reflected in spot gas prices. Short term contracts are the rule rather than the exception. The long term contracts that exist often contain references to some type of spot gas price indicator. The North American gas market offers such a variety of gas contracts that it is very difficult to give a complete overview. In spite of the fact that gas to gas competition is important for price formation, there is no doubt that the prices of alternative fuels like coal and oil products still influence the gas price in some cases. Ignoring regional differences, the price of coal in certain bulk applications constitutes a kind of floor price for natural gas. On the other hand, the price of oil products constitutes a ceiling for gas prices in some applications. In North America there is still a sizeable potential for short term switching between oil products and gas. In the market segments where this is the case, oil product prices will curb an upward trend in gas prices. This means that in periods of low oil prices, gas prices will be constrained, whereas in period of high oil prices, gas prices will not necessarily track oil prices.

There is no single explanation for the fact that the price level of gas in North America tends to be lower than in the two other OECD regions, though relevant factors include relatively low production costs (the greater part of production takes place onshore), the long history of the gas industry, which implies a high share of amortised facilities, a competitive, private industry with strong incentives for cost reductions and a regulatory framework encouraging efficient operation of the industry.

In a security of supply context it might be argued that the level of the future gas price in North America is less pertinent than elsewhere in the OECD for at least two reasons: both supply and demand are more responsive to price changes in the short term than elsewhere, which means that prices will take care of the allocation of physical quantities in cases where there are shortages; and the lead times for development of new gas reserves are shorter. However, the fact that the gas price will have a strong influence on the position of gas in the energy balance makes future gas prices very significant.

A fairly widespread opinion in North America is that the gas market will tighten up within the time horizon of this study. Over the past few years, technological innovations and environmental constraints have reduced the size of the market that can switch readily between gas and oil. There is now more headroom for gas prices to increase relative to oil, because the remaining switchable market increasingly features tradeoffs between gas and higher-cost distillate oil or low-sulphur fuel oil. The result could be a new price relationship between gas and oil and a more diffuse spectrum of interfuel competition. Within a fairly broad band, however, the gas price will basically be driven by the demand for and supply of gas.

Asia/Pacific

The Asian gas market is still dominated by LNG. Historically, Japan was the dominant buyer, while Indonesia was the dominant seller. The market is now much more diversified, since both the number of sellers and buyers has increased, but the pricing principles have not changed significantly.

Originally, LNG prices to Japan were cost based. At a relatively early era of the LNG business, however, it turned out that LNG had to be priced in relation to the alternative fuel in power generation, which at the time was oil. From the very beginning, however, LNG has been sold at a premium compared with crude oil on a heat equivalent basis. This is due to the fact that costs of producing, transporting and regasifying LNG are very high, and have to be reflected in the price. In most contracts the LNG prices reflect (with a time lag) the price development of one or more crude oils exported by the LNG producing country in question. The link to the crude oil price is very direct in the sense that the LNG price fluctuates in the same way as the crude oil price. As a result of oil price fluctuations, for instance, the price of Indonesian LNG delivered to Japan fell from US$3.70 per Mbtu in April 1993 to US$3.37 per Mbtu in July 1994, only slightly above the all-time low of US$3.04 per Mbtu reached in January 1994.

Most of the LNG contracts existing today were entered into at a time when future crude oil prices were expected to become higher than they are today. In fact, LNG buyers had been paying prices around US$5 per Mbtu before the collapse of the crude price in 1986. Since lead times for LNG projects are very long and the sales contracts normally are concluded before any construction begins, even LNG projects that have come on stream recently have been negotiated with price expectations different from those prevalent today. This is demonstrated in the case of the Australian Northwest Shelf project which came on stream in 1989 based on an assumed oil price of US$2 per barrel. Because of low oil prices, the partners in the project claim that revenues are barely sufficient to cover operating costs.

LNG buyers are presently in a dilemma: they realise that to encourage new grassroots LNG projects, higher prices are required, but they are reluctant to admit this for fear that higher prices for new LNG would also spur a demand for higher prices in existing contracts. This, however, now seems unavoidable since a price adjustment already has taken place in the case of Australian LNG to Japan. An "S-curve" concept has been introduced in the price formula which provides for an almost linear evolution of the LNG price relative to the basket of crude oils imported by Japan as long as the basket price remains within an agreed range. But when that price reaches either a floor (of around US$17 per barrel, cif Japan) or ceiling (about US$25 per barrel), the evolution in the LNG price slope is slowed to protect either the seller's interest (in the first case) or that of the buyer (in the second case). The absolute increase in the LNG price when oil prices are between the floor and the ceiling is relatively modest (around US$0.10 per Mbtu). The "S-curve" concept could also be used in contracts for new LNG projects. A higher price could also be achieved through other mechanisms:

- a premium over the oil price formula by deeming a higher crude price;
- price based on alternative fuels, such as coal;
- price based on gas to gas competition or LNG spot prices.

The last option does not appear to be viable in the foreseeable future. The second option is similar to a type of contract used for gas to power generation in Europe: the "indifference principle." In this contract, the operating and capital costs of a gas fired power plant and a coal fired power plant are compared and the gas price set equal to the difference between total costs for the coal plant (including fuel costs) and the operating and capital costs of the gas fired plant, so that the buyer is indifferent between the two alternatives. The gas price is escalated with coal prices and inflation. The advantage of the indifference principle seen from the seller's point of view is that it gives a higher initial base price (around US$5 per Mbtu) and thus makes it easier to embark upon a project. The concept, however, gives a lower upside potential if one believes that coal prices will increase less over time than the oil price.

Recent agreements indicate that a combination of a deemed crude price and application of the "S-curve" concept combined with concessions on financing, etc. might become the preferred solution in the future. LNG prices in the Asian Pacific market will in this case keep their close link to oil prices but the link will be less direct than before.

OECD Europe

Like the Asian LNG market, the European gas market is characterised by long term take-or -pay contracts. Put simply, the European wholesale price level is higher than the North American level and lower than the Asian level largely because of the mix of pipeline gas and LNG, which on average has to be transported over long distances. The price formulas in European contracts are primarily based on netback pricing rules with crude oil or oil products as main escalators, since oil products historically have been the main competitors to gas. All the main suppliers into Europe have crude prices and/or petroleum product prices as price escalators in their contracts. Other escalators like inflation and electricity prices are used, but the predominant escalator is oil. Gas prices are normally recalculated quarterly with a 6 to 9 month lag to oil price changes.

Although the overwhelming portion of long-term European gas supply contracts are characterised by netback pricing, two new features have recently emerged:

- In a few contracts for gas sales into power generation, a new pricing formula based on the indifference principle has been used. The gas price in these contracts is completely decoupled from the oil price. The initial base price in such contracts could typically be 30% higher than in an oil based contract, and thus represents a reduction in risk from the seller's point of view. This type of contract is a response to a need for diversification in the sales contract portfolio away from complete dependence on oil.
- In the UK, liberalisation of the gas market has led to changes in contract structures. One effect has been to diversify the type of escalators found in gas supply contracts. In addition to oil, escalation against coal, electricity, general inflation and a range of other price indices can now be found. A spot market for gas has arisen, and it is probably only a question of time before reference to spot market prices for gas will be found in long-term contracts.

Thus, although the gas price in Europe is still intimately linked to the oil price, this could change over the next few years, especially under a scenario of low oil prices. The crucial issue is very much the same as for the Asian LNG market, i.e., whether the current gas price level is sufficient to bring the needed new supplies to the market. In the case of Europe, however, it is even more difficult to tell exactly how much gas could be brought to market at the current price level. Although perhaps premature in the context of a discussion of current gas prices, a couple of comments concerning the relationship between oil and gas prices in the future are presented:

■ In the *Capacity Constraints* case in the IEA's 1995 *WEO*, in which the oil price rises to US$28 per barrel by 2005, the need for a decoupling of the gas price from the oil price will not be acute.

■ Under a low oil price path, for example, in the IEA's *Energy Savings* case in which the oil price remains flat at US$18 per barrel over the projection period, the amount of new gas that could profitably be brought to market is more limited than in the *Capacity Constraints* case. Unsatisfied demand at current prices could then spur a rise in gas prices either by raising the gas price in relation to oil on a heat equivalent basis or by introducing new pricing concepts that would raise the base price, as for instance the indifference principle. Based on this principle, electricity producers would be able to pay a higher price for gas than the present price (under the condition that escalation is no longer based on oil). In a situation where gas producers are reluctant to commit themselves because of low prices, demand from electricity producers could therefore break the deadlock. This could probably happen more easily in a situation where electricity producers were able to buy gas directly from producers. A precondition for this would be easier access to transmission

Supply Costs

As indicated above, attempting to establish a supply curve for gas is fraught with a number of methodological and data problems. The supply curve concept may also be criticised for being too static. Given that discussions within the gas industry often focus on the interplay between costs and prices, an attempt is made to provide an overview of some of the studies in this area.

Gas Supply Costs for Europe

The most thorough and comprehensive study concerning gas supply costs in Europe was undertaken by Pauwels (1994). This study defines a number of demand scenarios for the countries in the European Union (as the Union looked before 1 January 1995) and pairs them with existing supply options, taking the cost of such supplies into account. The cost of gas, based on a cost plus approach, is compared with gas netback values based on calculation of what gas can be sold for in the different market segments. Based on this comparison, the sufficiency of gas supplies is discussed.

For his demand scenarios, Pauwels uses the following price assumptions:

	HIGH	LOW
Crude oil price (cif)	US$ 29 (1993) per barrel	US$ 18 (1993) per barrel
Coal import price (cif)	US$ 57 (1993) per tonne	US$ 45 (1993) per tonne
Gas border price	US$ 4.10 (1993) per Mbtu	US$ 2.60 (1993) per Mbtu

The assumed gas border prices are based on netback calculations. The oil price assumptions are similar to the assumptions made in the IEA's 1994 *World Energy Outlook*.

Table 3.10 summarises Pauwel's cost estimates for gas delivered to European Union border.

Table 3.10   Full Cost of Gas: Delivered to European Union Border (1993 $ per Mbtu)

Country of Origin	Total cost at E.U-12 Border ($/Mbtu)	Transport costs IRR=10% (internal rate of return)	Transit costs ($/Mbtu)	Production costs ($/Mbtu)	Deposit size	Production type	Transport type
Netherlands: Groningen*	0.25	0.15	0,00	0.10	giant	onshore	onshore pipeline
Netherlands: onshore	0.75	0.15	0.00	0.60	small	onshore	onshore pipeline
Algeria: Transmed - Italy	1.06	0.45	0.11	0.50	giant	onshore	onshore and offshore pipeline (via Sicily)
Norway: Ekofisk - Emden	1.34	0.34	0.00	1.00	large	offshore (70 m)	offshore pipeline
Algeria: Maghreb - Spain	1.39	0.75	0.14	0.50	giant	onshore	onshore and offshore pipeline (via Gibraltar)
Norway: East Sleipner - Emden	1.56	0.46	0.00	1.10	medium	offshore	offshore pipeline
Netherlands: North Sea	1.60	0.60	0.00	1.00	small	offshore	offshore pipeline
Norway: Frigg - St. Fergus	1.77	0.27	0.00	1.50	medium	offshore	offshore pipeline
Norway: Heimdal - Emden	1.82	0.57	0.00	1.25	medium	offshore	offshore pipeline
Norway: East Sleipner - Zeebrugge	1.89	0.79	0.00	1.10	medium	offshore	offshore pipeline
Norway: Troll - Emden	1.96	0.76	0.00	1.20	large	deep offshore (300 m)	offshore pipeline
Algeria: LNG Montoir	1.99	1.49	0.00	0.50	giant	onshore	LNG
UK: Interconnector - Zeebrugge	2.10	0.60	0.00	1.50	small & medium	offshore	offshore pipeline
Norway: Statfjord - Emden	2.14	0.89	0.00	1.25	small & medium	offshore	offshore pipeline
Norway: Tordis - Emden	2.19	0.89	0.00	1.30	small	offshore	offshore pipeline
Norway: Troll - Zeebrugge	2.29	1.09	0.00	1.20	large	deep offshore	offshore pipeline
Norway: Oseberg - Emden	2.31	0.81	0.00	1.50	small	offshore	offshore pipeline
Libya: LNG (10Gm3) - Italy	2.43	1.93	0.00	0.50	medium	onshore	onshore pipeline + LNG
Norway: West Sleipner - Emden	2.66	0.46	0.00	2.20	medium	offshore	offshore pipeline
Libya: LNG (4Gm3) - Italy	2.71	2.21	0.00	0.50	medium	onshore	onshore pipeline + LNG

Table 3.10   Full Cost of Gas: Delivered to European Union Border (1993 $ per Mbtu) (continued)

Country of Origin	Total cost at E.U-12 Border ($/Mbtu)	Transport costs IRR=10% (internal rate of return)	Transit costs ($/Mbtu)	Production costs ($/Mbtu)	Deposit size	Production type	Transport type
Egypt: LNG (5Gm3) - Italy	2.81	2.11	0.00	0.70	small & medium	onshore and offshore	onshore pipeline + LNG
Norway: Haltenbanken - Emden	2.92	1.50	0.00	1.42 (average cost)	small & medium	offshore	offshore pipeline
Nigeria: LNG - Italy **	2.97	2.27	0.00	0.70	small	onshore and offshore	LNG
Norway: West Sleipner - Zeebrugge	2.99	0.79	0.00	2.20	medium	offshore	offshore pipeline
Russia: Western Siberia - EU-12	3.22	1.88	0.84	0.50	super giant	onshore (permafrost)	onshore pipeline
Norway: Haltenbanken - Zeebrugge	3.25	1.83	0.00	1.42	small & medium	offshore	offshore pipeline
Qatar: pipeline Ashkelon - LNG Italy	3.28	2.78	0.00	0.50	super giant	offshore (low depth)	offshore + onshore pipeline + LNG
Qatar: pipeline Sidi Kerir - LNG - Italy	3.32	2.82	0.00	0.50	super giant	offshore (low depth)	offshore + onshore pipeline + LNG
Russia: Yamal - EU 12	3.37	1.98	0.64	0.75	super giant	onshore (permafrost)	pipeline onshore + offshore Yamal - continent
Nigeria: LNG - Italy	3.40	2.70	0.00	0.70	medium	offshore	LNG
Qatar: LNG - Italy	3.51	3.01	0.00	0.50	super giant	offshore (low depth)	offshore pipeline + LNG
Oman: LNG - Italy	3.57	3.07	0.00	0.50	medium	onshore	offshore pipeline + LNG
Iran: pipeline Turkey - LNG Italy	3.75	2.82	0.43	0.50	giant	onshore + offshore	offshore pipeline + LNG
Venezuela: LNG - EU 12	3.83	2.73	0.00	1.10	medium	offshore	LNG
Iran: pipeline Turkey - Italy	4.09	2.04	1.55	0.50	giant/large	onshore + offshore	onshore pipeline

Table 3.10 Full Cost of Gas: Delivered to European Union Border (1993 $ per Mbtu) (continued)

Country of Origin	Total cost at E.U-12 Border ($/Mbtu)	Transport costs IRR=10% (internal rate of return)	Transit costs ($/Mbtu)	Production costs ($/Mbtu)	Deposit size	Production type	Transport type
Norway: Barents Sea - LNG Wilhelmshafen	4.17	2.27	0.00	1.90	small & medium	offshore	LNG
Norway: Barents Sea - LNG Zeebrugge	4.20	2.30	0.00	1.90	small & medium	offshore	LNG
Turkmenistan: pipeline Turkey - LNG Italy	4.25	2.85	0.90	0.50	large	onshore	onshore pipeline + LNG
Turkmenistan: pipeline Turkey - Italy	4.38	1.88	2.00	0.50	large	onshore	onshore pipeline
Turkmenistan: pipeline FSU - Germany	4.49	1.99	2.00	0.50	large	onshore	onshore pipeline
Russia: new gas Barents Sea - EU 12	4.65	3.15	0.00	1.50	giant	offshore	LNG
Qatar: pipeline Turkey - Italy	4.70	1.85	2.35	0.50	super giant	offshore (low depth)	offshore + onshore pipeline

EU 12 is European Union as of 1994, i.e., before expansion.
* Delivered at neighbour country border.
** If second hand tankers are used, the total cost at the EU border is 2.97 $/Mbtu.
Source: Pauwels (1994).

Total cost comprises production cost, transportation cost and transit fees. Production cost estimates are based on estimates from producers and from the specialised trade press. Transportation cost has been calculated with an internal rate of return of 10%. Relatively simple rules of thumb have been used for the calculation of transportation costs in each case, taking into account the size of the annual gas flow, distance and the difficulty of the terrain, etc.[7] In the cases where transit fees are relevant, the figures in Table 3.10 are assumed to be those presently paid. With new projects, the transit fees are necessarily more subjective, given that these would have to be negotiated in each case.

Table 3.10 describes costs for both existing and new projects. Total supply costs vary considerably from US$ 0.25 per Mbtu in the case of gas from Groningen to US$ 4.70 per Mbtu in the case of pipeline gas from Qatar. Except for gas coming from the North Sea basin, transportation and transit costs largely exceed production costs. This underlines the importance of optimising the organisation of and reducing the costs of transportation in the future.

In most uses, gas is competing with other fuels, thus limiting the price which could be charged. Pauwels has made some relatively simple calculations to analyse the competitiveness of gas from various sources in three segments of the gas market: the public distribution sector, the industrial sector and the electricity generation sector. Since an understanding of gas' competitiveness relative to other fuels is fundamental to a discussion of gas sourcing, these calculations will be explained in detail.

The Public Distribution Sector

For a number of possible gas supply sources, Table 3.11 shows which crude oil price each project can support before gas becomes uncompetitive compared with its main competitor, in this sector, gasoil.

The calculations in Table 3.11 are based on a number of assumptions:

■ The cost of gas is compared with that of gasoil at the burner tip. Since the table initially presents the cost of gas at the EU border (column 1), transportation cost from the border to the burner tip has to be included. This cost consists of two elements: transmission cost and distribution cost.

■ Transmission is assumed to take place at 650 kilometres (considered as an average transportation distance within the EU) and also includes storage. The public distribution sector is assumed to account for two thirds of total storage costs (column 2).

■ Average distribution cost is assumed to amount to around US$ 2.16 per Mbtu (column 3).

■ Gas enjoys a 15% premium over gasoil, i.e., gas may cost 15% more than gasoil without losing its competitiveness. This in turn means that the gasoil price at the burner tip should be 15% lower than the gas price (column 5).

■ After having deducted gasoil transportation costs from burner tip to refinery, the burner tip gas price can be translated into a gasoil price per barrel at the refinery (column 7). The unit cost of gasoil is assumed to be 1.25 times that of crude oil, and column 8 translates the gasoil price into a corresponding crude price.

7. See the IEA's study on gas transportation for additional information. (IEA, 1994)

Table 3.11 Competitiveness of natural gas with gasoil. Gas supplied to burner tip via public distribution

Cost of gas in Europe "at consumer's gate" ($/Mbtu)	1	2	3	4=1+2+3	5=4/1.15	6	7=(5-6) x 5.74*	8=(7/1.25) x 1.049*
	Cost CIF EU12 border	Cost of long distance transport (650 km & storage)	Distribution cost	Total cost at burner tip	Total cost at burner tip	Cost of transport (insurance inc.)	Cost of gasoil ex-refinery	Cost CIF frontier crude oil equivalent
Discount rate 10%	gas	gas	gas	gas	gasoil	gasoil	gasoil	($/b crude)
Netherlands: Groningen	0.25	0.705	2.155	3.110	2.705	0.073	15.103	12.687
Algeria: Transmed - Italy	1.06	0.705	2.155	3.920	3.409	0.077	19.112	16.062
Norway: Ekofisk - Emden	1.34	0.705	2.155	4.200	3.653	0.079	20.511	17.229
Algeria: Maghreb - Spain	1.39	0.705	2.155	4.250	3.696	0.079	20.759	17.437
Norway: Troll - Emden	1.96	0.705	2.155	4.820	4.192	0.082	23.587	19.813
Algeria: LNG - France Montoir	1.99	0.705	2.155	4.850	4.218	0.082	23.736	19.938
U.K.: gas pipeline Interconnector - Zeebrugge	2.10	0.705	2.155	4.960	4.313	0.083	24.281	20.396
Norway: Troll - Zeebrugge	2.29	0.705	2.155	5.150	4.479	0.084	25.224	21.188
Norway: Haltenbanken - Emden	2.92	0.705	2.155	5.780	5.026	0.087	28.349	23.813
Russia: ex Siberia gas - EU12	3.22	0.705	2.155	6.080	5.287	0.089	29.838	25.064
Qatar: Ashkelon pipeline - LNG Italy	3.28	0.705	2.155	6.140	5.339	0.089	30.135	25.314
Russia: new gas Yamal - EU12	3.37	0.705	2.155	6.230	5.418	0.089	30.582	25.689
Nigeria: LNG - Italy	3.40	0.705	2.155	6.260	5.444	0.090	30.731	25.814
Qatar: LNG - Italy	3.51	0.705	2.155	6.370	5.539	0.090	32.276	26.272
Iran: Turkey pipeline - LNG Italy	3.75	0.705	2.155	6.610	5.748	0.091	31.276	27.272
Venezuela: LNG	3.83	0.705	2.155	6.690	5.818	0.092	32.864	27.606
Norway: Barents - Zeebrugge	4.20	0.705	2.155	7.060	6.139	0.094	34.700	29.148
Turkmenistan: Turkey pipeline - LNG Italy	4.25	0.705	2.155	7.110	6.183	0.094	34.948	29.356

* Conversion factors used in converting cost of gas from $/Mbtu to cost per barrel and then into crude oil equivalent.
Source: Pauwels (1994).

Analysis of Table 3.11 indicates that the number of projects that would yield a rent in the sense that total cost would be lower than the oil price required for the project to be competitive with gasoil is very limited. Only four projects would earn a rent at an oil price of US$ 18 per barrel. These calculations are based on full costs in transmission and distribution. Consequently, if transmission and distribution facilities are assumed on average to be amortized by 50%, which according to Pauwels is a realistic hypothesis, the picture will improve but not dramatically.

The Industrial Sector

Table 3.12 shows the same calculations for the industrial sector where gas' main competitor is Low Sulphur Fuel Oil (LSFO, 1% sulphur).

Column 7 of Table 3.12 presents for each of the same gas projects the oil price that would allow gas to be competitive with Low Sulphur Fuel Oil at the burner tip. It has been assumed that the premium of gas over LSFO is 5% and that the price of LSFO ex-refinery is equal to 0.75 times the price of crude oil. The same average transportation distance as in Table 3.11 has been assumed, but there are no distribution costs. It has been assumed that the industrial sector accounts for one third of storage costs incurred since industrial customers are assumed to take their supplies primarily from the medium and high pressure pipelines. Again, the number of gas projects that are competitive at an oil price of, for example US$ 18, is very limited even in a case where the transportation facilities are amortised by 50%.

The Power Generation Sector

Most of the time, coal is gas' main competitor in the power generation sector. In Table 3.13, calculations have been made as to the competitiveness of the same gas projects as used in Tables 3.11 and 3.12 in relation to coal.

Column 8 of Table 3.13 shows at what coal prices gas from the various projects would still be competitive. The calculations are based on the following assumptions:

■ A combined cycle gas plant with an efficiency of 55% is compared with a coal fired power station with FGD equipment having an efficiency of 43%.

The competitive equilibrium between the two plants is expressed by the following equation: $P_g = 1.28 \, P_c + 2.20$ where P_g is the price of gas and P_c the price of coal, 1.28 is the coefficient resulting from the yields of the two types of plants, and 2.20 is the coefficient resulting from the relationship between unit investment costs for the two types of plants. This equations allows the determination, for a given gas price, of the coal price where there is a competitive equilibrium between the two fuels at the burner tip.

■ Average transportation distance for gas within the EU is again assumed to be 650 kilometres. Since the power plants are linked to the high pressure transmission grid, no storage or distribution costs are incurred.

■ The comparison takes into account the average cost of transportation from port to power station and the cost of conditioning the fuel before combustion.

Table 3.12 Competitiveness of natural gas with heavy fuel oil (1% sulphur) in industry

Cost of gas in Europe "at consumer's gate" ($/Mbtu)	1 Cost CIF EU12 border	2 Cost of long distance transport (650 km & storage)	3=1+2 Total cost at burner tip	4=3/1.05 Total cost at burner tip	5 Cost of transport (insurance incl)	6=(4-5) x 6.10* Cost of fuel ex-refinery	7=(6/0.75) x 1.049* Cost CIF frontier crude oil equivalent
Discount rate 10%	gas	gas	gas	fuel oil	fuel oil	($/b fuel oil)	($/b crude)
Netherlands: Groningen	0.25	0.53	0.781	0.743	0.111	3.857	5.399
Algeria: Transmed - Italy	1.06	0.53	1.591	1.515	0.114	8.549	11.968
Norway: Ekofisk - Emden	1.34	0.53	1.871	1.782	0.114	10.170	14.238
Algeria: Maghreb - Spain	1.39	0.53	1.921	1.829	0.114	10.460	14.644
Norway: Troll - Emden	1.96	0.53	2.491	2.372	0.116	13.762	19.266
Algeria: LNG - France Montoir	1.99	0.53	2.521	2.401	0.116	13.935	19.510
U.K.: gas pipeline Interconnector - Zeebrugge	2.10	0.53	2.631	2.505	0.117	14.573	20.402
Norway: Troll - Zeebrugge	2.29	0.53	2.821	2.688	0.117	15.673	21.942
Norway: Haltenbanken - Emden	2.92	0.53	3.451	3.286	0.119	19.322	27.051
Russia: "old" Siberian gas - EU12	3.22	0.53	3.751	3.572	0.120	21.060	29.484
Qatar: Ashkelon pipeline - LNG Italy	3.28	0.53	3.811	3.629	0.120	21.408	29.971
Russia: new gas Yamal - EU12	3.37	0.53	3.901	3.715	0.120	21.929	30.700
Nigeria: LNG - Italy	3.40	0.53	3.931	3.743	0.120	22.103	30.944
Qatar: LNG - Italy	3.51	0.53	4.041	3.848	0.121	22.740	31.836
Iran: Turkey pipeline - LNG Italy	3.75	0.53	4.281	4.077	0.121	24.130	33.782
Venezuela: LNG	3.83	0.53	4.361	4.153	0.121	24.594	34.431
Norway: Barents - Zeebrugge	4.20	0.53	4.731	4.505	0.122	26.737	37.431
Turkmenistan: Turkey pipeline - LNG Italy	4.25	0.53	4.781	4.553	0.123	27.026	37.837

* Conversion factor used in coverting cost of HFO from $/Mbtu to cost per barrel and then into crude oil equivalent.
Source: Pauwels (1994).

Table 3.13 Natural gas competitiveness in a combined gas-steam cycle plant (55% efficiency) compared with coal (43% efficiency) for electricity generation

Equilibrium price CIF of coal Pc for a given gas price Pg	1	2	3=1+2	4=conv 3(GJ)	5=relation*	6=conversion of 5 into tonnes	7	8=6-7
	Pg border	Cost of transport to burner tip (650 km)	Pg to burner tip	Pg to burner tip	Total cost at burner tip	Pc at burner tip	Cost of transport & preparation of coal	Pc CIF frontier EU12
Discount rate 10%	$/Mbtu PCS	$/Mbtu PCS	$/Mbtu PCS	$/GJ PCS	$/GJ PCI	$/t	$/t	$/t
Netherlands: Groningen	0.25	0.36	0.61	0.57	(1.22)	(30.54)	12.0	(42.54)
Algeria: Transmed - Italy	1.06	0.36	1.42	1.34	(0.56)	(13.92)	12.0	(25.92)
Norway: Ekofisk - Emden	1.34	0.36	1.70	1.61	(0.33)	(8.18)	12.0	(20.18)
Algeria: Maghreb - Spain	1.39	0.36	1.75	1.65	(0.29)	(7.15)	12.0	(19.15)
Norway: Troll - Emden	1.96	0.36	2.32	2.20	0.18	4.54	12.0	(7.46)
Algeria: LNG - France Montoir	1.99	0.36	2.35	2.22	0.21	5.16	12.0	(6.84)
U.K.: gas pipeline Interconnector - Zeebrugge	2.10	0.36	2.46	2.33	0.30	7.41	12.0	(4.59)
Norway: Troll - Zeebrugge	2.29	0.36	2.65	2.51	0.45	11.31	12.0	(0.69)
Norway: Haltenbanken - Emden	2.92	0.36	3.28	3.11	0.97	24.23	12.0	12.23
Russia: ex Siberia gas - EU12	3.22	0.36	3.58	3.39	1.22	30.39	12.0	18.39
Qatar: Ashkelon pipeline - LNG Italy	3.28	0.36	3.64	3.45	1.26	31.62	12.0	19.62
Russia: new gas Yamal - EU12	3.37	0.36	3.73	3.53	1.34	33.46	12.0	21.46
Nigeria: LNG - Italy	3.40	0.36	3.76	3.56	1.36	34.08	12.0	22.08
Qatar: LNG - Italy	3.51	0.36	3.87	3.66	1.45	36.34	12.0	24.34
Iran: Turkey pipeline - LNG Italy	3.75	0.36	4.11	3.89	1.65	41.26	12.0	29.26
Venezuela: LNG	3.83	0.36	4.19	3.97	1.72	42.90	12.0	30.90
Norway: Barents - Zeebrugge	4.20	0.36	4.56	4.32	2.02	50.49	12.0	38.49
Turkmenistan: Turkey pipeline - LNG Italy	4.25	0.36	4.61	4.37	2.06	51.52	12.0	39.52

* Equilibrium relationship between gas price and coal price at burner tip (PCI): Pg = 1.28 Pc + 2.20.
Note: PCS is pouvoir calorific superieur (gross calorific value) and PCI is pouvoir calorific inférieur (net calorific value).
Source: Pauwels (1994).

Table 3.13 indicates that, at coal prices below US$ 40 per tonne, gas from all the projects under these assumptions is competitive with coal. This means that gas is competitive under the assumptions made for the coal price in Pauwel's study, similar to the ones made by the IEA in its 1995 *World Energy Outlook.*

In Table 3.14 the equilibrium prices for gas have been summarised. Under differing price assumptions for oil and coal, this table shows the prices that could be charged for gas at the EU border and still allow gas to remain competitive. In Table 3.15, the same figures are used to calculate an average competitive equilibrium price for gas by weighting the various segments of the gas market together. (In addition to the three sectors discussed above, a new sector, "other", is included. The other sector has the same equilibrium price as the industrial sector. This sector presumably comprises all gas use that is not included in the original three sectors). The weights used reflect the sectoral distribution expected to prevail in 2010. As indicated in Table 3.15, the market should be willing to pay US$2.60 per Mbtu at an oil price of US$18 per barrel and a coal price of US$45 per tonne, whereas the market should be willing to pay US$4.10 per Mbtu at an oil price of US$29 per barrel and a coal price of US$57 per tonne. These figures are based on full costs. In a case where the transportation and distribution facilities are assumed to be amortized by 50%, the equilibrium prices change somewhat. In the US$18 per barrel/ US$45 per tonne case, the gas price that could be paid in competition with gasoil is 29% higher, the gas price paid in competition with LSFO is 7% higher and the gas price in competition with coal is 2.7% higher.

Table 3.14   Value of Natural Gas at the EU Frontier Compared with Gasoil, LSFO* and Coal as Electricity Generation Fuels

	Oil price ($1993 per barrel CIF)	Coal price ($1993 per tonne CIF)	Competitive equilibrium price of gas to EU frontier ($1993/Mbtu)	
			Full cost	Cost (transport network & distribution) amortized by 50%
Gasoil	30	-	4.40	4.83
	28	-	3.92	4.35
	18	-	1.52	1.96
Heavy fuel	30	-	3.28	3.41
	28	-	3.04	3.16
	18	-	1.80	1.93
Coal for electricity	-	57	5.10	5.23
generation	-	45	4.52	4.64

* Low sulphur fuel oil
Source: Pauwels (1994).

Comparing the prices that the market should be willing to pay with the costs of gas supplies in the first column of Table 3.10, yields a positive rent (i.e., a positive difference between price and cost) for most cases when the gas price in 2010 is US$4.10 per Mbtu, corresponding to an oil price of US$29 per barrel. Since most of the projects in Table 3.10 yield a positive rent, there should, according to Pauwels, be no problem in finding suppliers willing to deliver the gas that Europe will need. Under a scenario where the oil price stays around US$18 per barrel, however, corresponding to a gas price of US$2.60 per Mbtu, very few projects show a positive rent, and there could be difficulties in meeting supply.

Table 3.15   Average Gas Price to EU frontier ($1993 per Mbtu)

Sector	Sectoral demand breakdown assumed in 2010	Crude oil price: $18 (1993/barrel) Coal price CIF Europe: $45 (1993/tonne)		Crude oil price: 29$ (1993/barrel) Coal Price CIF Europe: $57 (1993/tonne)	
		CIF gas price to EU frontier ($/Mbtu)	CIF weighted gas price ($/Mbtu)	CIF gas price to EU frontier ($/Mbtu)	CIF weighted gas price ($/Mbtu)
Residential and commercial	34.5%	1.52	0.52	4.16	1.44
Industry	23.6%	1.8	0.42	3.16	0.75
Other sectors (excl. electricity)	9.9%	1.8	0.18	3.16	0.31
Electricity production	32.0%	4.52	1.45	5.1	1.63
			$2.60/Mbtu		$4.10/Mbtu

Source: Pauwels (1994).

Figure 3.1 illustrates how a EU 12 gas demand of some 450 bcm in 2010 could be covered. It indicates that unless a higher price is paid for the gas than either current prices or the prices assumed to prevail under an oil price regime of around US$ 18 per barrel, sufficient volumes of gas may not come forward.[8]

Figure 3.1   EU Supplies to 2010

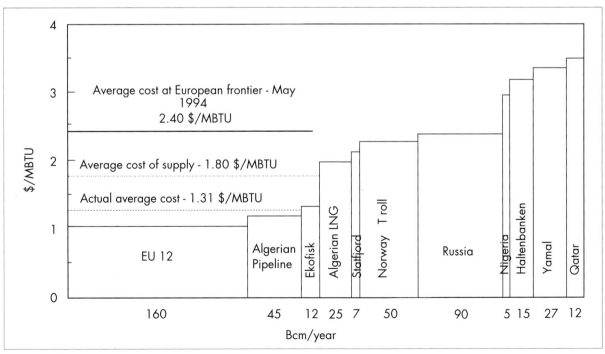

Source: Pauwels (1994).

---

8.   Pauwels also describes a scenario with lesser demand as a consequence of higher gas prices and discusses supplies under that scenario.

Given that calculations like the ones reproduced here tend to be subjective in nature, another set of figures resulting from a slightly different approach are presented. At the initiative of the IEA, l'Observatoire Mediterranéen de l'Energie (OME) examined a number of possible supply sources for gas to Europe with a special emphasis on transit issues. In this context, an attempt was made to calculate the supply cost for these gas supply possibilities. Table 3.16 shows the result of these calculations.[9]

The figures in Table 3.16 are the result of the following assumptions and procedures:

■ Production cost is based on evaluations made in each producer country. It is difficult to compare the OME figures with Pauwels' results because production costs vary from one field to another, and neither of the studies indicate consistently and precisely which field the gas would come from. The estimates from OME, however, seem to be slightly lower.

■ For the calculation of the transportation cost the following assumptions have been applied: with a 10% discount rate, the cost of pipeline transportation is US$ 0.40 per Mbtu per 1000 kilometres; with 15% it is US$ 0.50 per Mbtu per 1000 kilometres. For LNG, the liquefaction and regasification cost is US$ 1.60 per Mbtu at a 10% discount rate and US$ 2.10 per Mbtu at a 15% discount rate. Shipping costs have been calculated according to the following formula: 0.1727 + 0.2042 *(1/1000)* nautical miles.

■ Transit fees for each supply source depend on the number of transit countries crossed and the situation of each country. OME has systematically evaluated a number of variables that could influence on the transit fees that have to be paid, as for instance the transit country's need for gas, its foreign exchange needs, its economic and local political power and its negotiating power. As a function of the values of these variables, the countries have been characterised and attributed a high, low or a medium transit fee. The low transit fee amounts to from US$ 0.14 to US$ 0.17 per Mbtu per 100 kilometres, the medium from US$ 0.18 to US$ 0.24 per Mbtu per 1000 kilometres and the high from US$ 0.18 to US$ 0.24 per Mbtu per 1000 kilometres. The determination of these fees are to a certain extent based on subjective evaluation, but at least a systematic attempt has been made at analysing the issues.[10]

Figure 3.2 shows the result when the potential supplies from the sources indicated in Table 3.16 are ranked according to costs.

The studies by Pauwels and the OME may be characterised as 'academic' in the sense that they have been compiled by institutions outside the gas industry. It is interesting to note, however, that they both represent views that are largely in line with those of the industry. An example of this is given in Figure 3.3 which illustrates the view of one of the major oil and gas companies as to the cost of supply. It estimates the cost of producing gas and delivering it to Europe from five main potential supply sources. In each case, the estimate is based on production from a new greenfield development with delivery using existing infrastructure - where there is spare capacity - or newly constructed pipelines or LNG facilities. The estimate accounts for both capital and operating costs; all costs have been discounted to 1994.

---

9. Since Table 3.16 only includes new projects, the country list differs from that of Table 3.10.

10. See the gas transportation study (IEA, 1994) for a further discussion of transit issues.

Table 3.16   Full Costs of Gas Supply Delivered at the Nearest European Border at 10 and 15 per cent Discount Rates for Transportation Costs (1995 US$ per Mbtu)

Supply country	Transport route	Production cost	Transportation cost 10% 15%	Transit fees	Total costs* 10% 15%
Russia	Belarus	0.4 - 0.8	2.1.- 2.6	0.3 - 0.4	3.0 - 3.6
	Ukraina		2.3 - 2.8	0.4 - 0.5	3.5 - 3.9
Turkmenistan	Iran, Turkey		2.5 - 3.1	0.7 - 0.9	3.6 - 4.2
	Caspian Sea, Turkey	0.3	2.6 - 3.1	0.6 - 0.8	3.6 - 4.1
	Russia, Ukraine		2.6 - 3.2	0.7 -0.9	3.7 - 4.3
Iran	Turkey		2.5 - 3.1	0.5 -0.6	3.4-4.0
	Caucasus/Ukraina	0.3	2.5 - 3.0	0.7 -0.9	3.6 - 4.1
	LNG		2.4 - 2.9	0.25	3.0 - 3.5
Iraq	Turkey	0.4 - 0.6	2.0 - 2.5	0.5 -0.6	3.0 - 3.6
	Syria + LNG		2.5 - 3.1	0.1-0.15	3.1 - 3.7
Qatar	North Africa		2.5 - 3.1	0.8 -1.1	3.8 - 4.4
	Turkey	0.3	2.5 - 3.1	0.7 -1.0	3.7 - 4.2
	Egypt + LNG		2.9 - 3.0	0.3 -0.4	3.6 - 4.3
	LNG		2.4 - 2.9	0.25	3.0 - 3.5
Saudi Arabia	North Africa		2.4 - 3.0	0.5 -0.8	3.4 - 4.1
	Turkey	0.3	2.5 - 3.1	0.6 -0.9	3.6 - 4.2
	Egypt + LNG		2.8 - 3.5	0.1	3.2 - 3.9
UAE	LNG	0.4 - 0.6	2.5 - 3.0	0.25	3.2-3.8
Oman	LNG	0.5 - 0.7	2.4 - 3.1	0.25	3.2 - 3.8
Nigeria	LNG	0.5 - 0.7	2.5 - 3.0	0	3.1 - 3.6
Algeria	Tunisia		0.8 - 1.1	0.1 -0.2	1.5 - 1.8
	Morocco	0.4 - 0.6	0.8 - 1.1	0.1 -0.2	1.5 - 1.8
	LNG		1.7 - 2.3	0	2.3 - 2.8
Libya	Tunisia		0.9 - 1.1	0.1 -0.2	1.5 - 1.7
	Pipe subsea	0.4 - 0.6	0.9 - 1.2	0	1.5 - 1.7
	LNG		1.8 - 2.3	0	2.3 - 2.8
Norway	Pipe subsea	1.2 - 1.5	1.0 - 1.5	0	2.3 - 2.9
Venezuela and Trinidad & Tobago	LNG	0.6 - 1.0	2.5 - 3.0	0	3.3 - 3.8

* Average production costs (excluding royalties) and average transit fees are based on estimated 1995 values. Transportation costs are discounted at 10% and 15% rates.
Source: OME (1995).

Figure 3.2   Natural Gas Export Potential

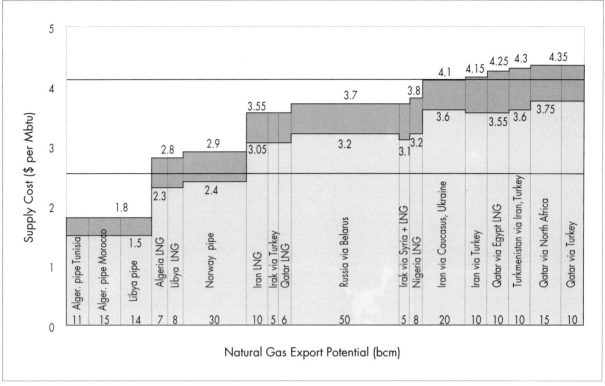

Source: OME (1995).

Figure 3.3 also shows the border prices of gas in Europe at an oil price of US$ 16 to 18 per barrel and the estimated value of gas in a new power plant. According to this source, the gas price corresponding to a North Sea (Brent) oil price of US$ 16 to 18 per barrel is around US$ 2.40 to 2.70 per Mbtu. In fact, there has been pressure to increase border prices in recent negotiations between producers and buyers. Usually negotiations take place on a three year cycle, with the latest round resulting in a reported 15 to 20% increase in the border price. This increase has been taken into account in the level of current prices in Figure 3.3.

According to the same source, the potential value of gas in a newly constructed gas-fired power station is US$ 3.50 to 4.00 per Mbtu versus a new coal fired station. This is significantly higher than current border prices and probably represents the maximum price that could be realised for gas in the European market.

Figure 3.3 shows that the lowest cost new gas supplies for mainland Europe are from the North Sea, where a well developed infrastructure and proximity to markets result in costs in the range US$ 2.50 to 3.25 per Mbtu. Algeria similarly has a well developed infrastructure, which will be enhanced by the completion of the GME pipeline giving it access to new markets. The cost of supply for Algerian gas into Europe by pipeline is estimated to be in the range US$ 2.50 to 3.50 per Mbtu. Some Russian gas can probably be delivered through new pipelines at around US$ 3.25 per Mbtu but as the distance from market increases the potential costs rise to over US$ 3.50. LNG and Middle Eastern supplies are also estimated to cost at least US$ 3.50 per Mbtu delivered to Europe.

Qualitatively, Figure 3.3 conveys the same message as the supply cost curve based on Pauwel's figures, i.e., that, apparently, the volumes of new gas available at a low oil price are not sufficient to cover future demand. This is, however, a too static approach to the issues involved, and more gas can probably be brought profitably to market even at current prices.

Figure 3.3   New Supplies to Mainland Europe

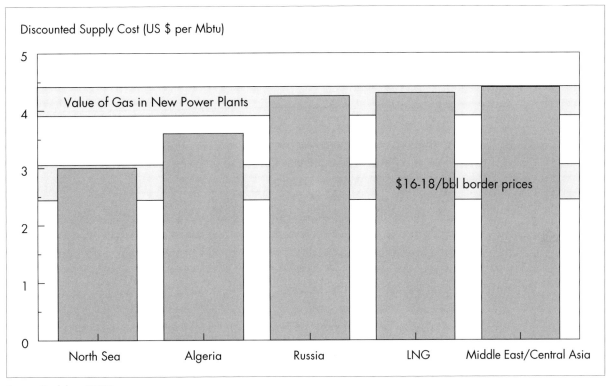

Source: Hawkshaw (1994).

Gas Supply Costs for Asia/Pacific

The only country in the OECD Asia/Pacific region which is dependent on gas imports is Japan. Along with a number of other LNG importing countries, Japan is in a similar position as the importing countries in Europe, i.e., at current LNG prices, it may not be possible to get new projects off the ground. The cost of taking LNG to Japan from the Middle East is even higher than for Europe, and new pricing concepts may in some cases be needed for new projects to materialise. Given that LNG does not compete with cheaper pipeline gas in Japan, it should be easier to bridge the gap between present prices and prices needed for new projects than in Europe.

A number of schemes are under consideration for long distance pipelines to transport gas from the large gas reserves in Siberian Russia and central Asia. These plans, which are very much at the formative stage, include pipelines from Yakutsk to Korea and Turkmenistan to China and Japan. An ASEAN scheme linking Malaysia, Indonesia and even northern Australia to markets in Japan, Korea and Taiwan has also been suggested. The cost of these schemes is estimated to be considerable, and there are many potential technical difficulties including the politics of pipelines crossing several international borders. It is therefore likely that, over the time horizon of this study, Japan will have to rely on new LNG supplies to satisfy its growing gas demand.

Gas Supply Costs for North America

North America does not share the European and Japanese preoccupation with future gas supply costs. The is largely the case because the region is self-sufficient in gas and reserves are considered to be plentiful, in spite of a relatively low R/P ratio. Investigations have also shown that reserves can be exploited at reasonable costs, causing no immediate concern about the long-term supply situation.

In its 1994 *Supply and Demand Technical Report*, Canada's National Energy Board (NEB) summarised cost curves for gas from five principal supply regions in both the United States and Canada. In order to develop a better understanding of the undiscovered gas resource, the NEB estimated pool size distributions for major supply regions in Canada and the United States. These resource distributions were then matched with the appropriate estimates of the costs to find, develop and produce the incremental resource. Input variables for the cost calculation are pool size, production profile, by-product volume, capital costs, operating costs and exploration and development drilling risk. The resulting costs were compared with those of other sources, and there was good correlation between them.

Figure 3.4 shows the comparative supply costs. For the generation of these supply cost curves, the supply costs of individual pools for a given region or basin were sorted in ascending order, based on the assumption that lower cost pools (which are typically larger pools) will be discovered and produced first. The relatively flat and low part of the individual curves typically represents the half cycle cost of developing the remaining established reserves in the area. Operating costs account for around 75 per cent of these costs, with capital costs a relatively modest component (25 per cent). As full cycle costs are incurred, pool sizes diminish and less resource is added per dollar of expenditure, the costs become higher and increase more rapidly. In the market, competitiveness of the supplies shown here can change slightly after transportation costs for bringing the gas from the producing region to the market have been added. As a general observation the curves shifts to the right over time as a result of technological improvements.

Concluding Remarks on Supply Costs

Although the shape of the two supply curves for gas to Europe described above differ in some aspects, as they represent slightly different approaches, the general conclusion is clear. First, European gas demand, as a result of one possible future development of the gas price, can be met from various sources. Second, both analysts seem to agree that the least costly gas is that piped to continental Europe from the North Sea Basin, followed by Algerian gas, then by gas from Russia. LNG is a relatively high cost source of supply, only exceeded by gas from very distant sources, such as the Middle East or Central Asia. These conclusions are also in line with views presented by the gas industry.[11]

According to the figures quoted above, an oil price of US$ 18 per barrel corresponds to a gas price of around US$2.60 per Mbtu quoted at the EU border. The netback calculation referred to above implies a number of assumptions about efficiencies and costs. Starting at the burner tip,

---

11. See presentation by BP's John Hawkshaw: "Where Will Europe's Future Supplies Come from?", given at the GASTECH conference in Kuala Lumpur, October 1994.

Figure 3.4   Gas Costs in North America

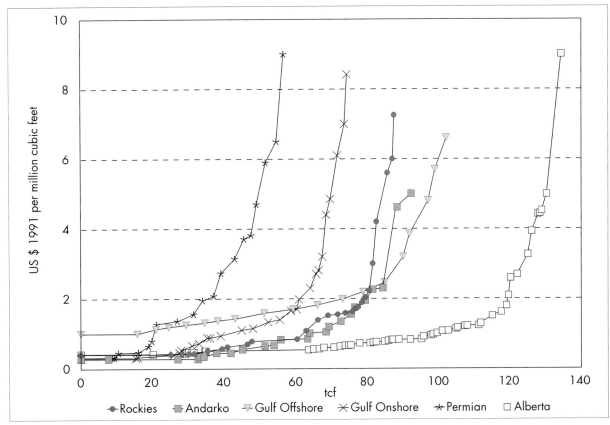

Source: NEB (1994b).

it may be possible to increase the efficiency of gas using equipment installed at the end user's. Gas distribution and transmission in the consumer country account for a high share of the price to end consumers (IEA, 1994). Experience from countries where competition in gas markets has been introduced shows that there is potential for lowering transmission and distribution costs. Efficiency improvements and cost savings could increase the value of gas to the buyer at the import point and thereby enable him to pay a higher price. The discussion so far has demonstrated that there is nothing static about costs in the parts of the gas chain located upstream of the import point.

Starting at the wellhead, recent developments indicate that there is still a huge untapped potential for lowering production costs. Studies recently done in the United Kingdom and in Norway indicate that it is possible to cut total production costs by 30 to 50% over the next few years. Ways of cutting costs include horizontal drilling, technology for producing in deeper water, developing smaller gas accumulations through remote tiebacks and the optimal use of existing infrastructure. Partnerships within and between organisations are also critical to the realisation of these improvements. Within organisations the integration of functions and skills into teams with a common goal and the development of ways of sharing learning through linked teams have enabled producers to develop a new approach to projects. This has been paralleled by producers working together to avoid duplication and to recognise mutual interests. Producers have worked with contractors to ensure shared incentives in achieving the most effective implementation of projects. In some cases it is also clear that changes in tax regimes can provide incentives to reduce costs and encourage investments by making developments more attractive.

Experience from the United States shows that over the last few years it has been possible to add more reserves for a given level of exploration. While in the mid-1980s there were roughly 9 bcf of reserve additions per exploratory well completed, in recent years this has increased to nearly 20 bcf. Over the past few years finding costs in the United States have also declined considerably due in part to technological advances. Looking at the list of countries that are potential supply sources for gas deliveries to Europe there is nothing to indicate that the potential for production cost savings in these countries is less than in the OECD countries.

As appears from Table 3.16, transportation and transit costs constitute a high share of the delivered gas price at the importing country's border. In relative terms, therefore, the biggest potential for cost savings are found in this part of the chain. Figure 3.2 has a shaded area that indicates the difference between a 15% and 10% internal rate of return on investments in transportation. The figure indicates that a lower rate of return might have a sizeable impact on the total cost level. There is generally a trade-off between risk and return. If risk reducing devices could be found, this could make a lower rate of return acceptable to the owners of the transportation facilities and thereby lead to lower project costs. One such risk reducing device could be loans at favourable interest rates from international lending institutions.

Quite a few of the gas supply projects listed above are LNG projects. Generally, transportation costs account for an even higher share of the total delivered price of gas in the case of LNG than for pipeline gas. This means that it is even more important to find ways of reducing the total cost of such projects. Considerable efforts in this direction have been made by French companies involved in various parts of the LNG chain. The conclusion over the past few years is that economies of 20% are achievable and that 30% are possible in the future.

In addition to cost saving measures, there are also other mechanisms that could be applied to overcome or mitigate the apparent supply cost problem:

■ Some segments of the gas market can pay a higher price than the market as a whole. As pointed out above, this is the case in the electricity sector when the alternative to a new gas fired power plant is a coal fired power plant. The use of the so-called "indifference" principle is one way of assuring a higher gas price and at the same time decoupling from the oil price. The beauty of the concept is that it reduces risk for both parties but makes the buyer pay a relatively high price for the gas at the outset, facilitating the seller's decision to embark upon a new project. A widespread use of this concept probably requires better possibilities for direct deals between electricity producers and producers of gas, which again hinges on easier access to transportation capacity. In the present European market, the fact that in most countries there is one dominating gas company which monopolises the transportation network and does not consider market segmentation and discrimination to be in their interest, is probably an obstacle to this kind of development. If over time the cost level turns out to become a serious obstacle to bringing new gas volumes to the market, a large scale breakthrough for this kind of contracts could alleviate the situation, but possibly to the detriment of some unsatisfied demand in other market segments. The same type of concept could possibly also be applied in cases where LNG is involved, in which cases high costs may be an even more difficult problem to solve.

■ Some producers/sellers may have a perception of and a way of calculating costs that are different from those underlying the figures above. Russia may be a case in point here. The fact that Gazprom inherited the Russian infrastructure at virtually no cost, implies a basis for cost calculations which is different from than the one used in Western Europe (see the Annex on Russia for further discussion of these issues). Therefore the cost levels indicated for Russian supplies may be overstated.

■ Some gas projects receive substantial revenues from sales of NGLs or condensates. This is the case for a number of fields in the North Sea and in Algeria. These revenues will of course strengthen the economics of these fields.

■ Quite frequently the nameplate capacity of new gas supply facilities is exceeded by real production figures. LNG trains often produce 20% more than nameplate capacity. The unit costs indicated above may therefore in some cases be somewhat overstated.

■ In the past, oil price expectations have played an important role in gas project development decisions. The Troll project and most of the present LNG projects were developed with an expectation of a higher oil price than its current level. For projects like these with very long lead times it is very risky to base a development decision on a specific oil price path. If one believes that over time there will be shifts in the oil price level, contractual mechanisms safeguarding against adverse development in the oil price should be sought. A potential producer/transporter is normally ready to accept a lower rate of return if its profits are less exposed to fluctuations. Increased use of such safeguarding mechanisms could therefore be one way of getting more projects off the ground.

REGIONAL GAS BALANCES

In this section the demand figures described above will be matched with supply possibilities with reference to the considerations mentioned in earlier sections. The intention is not to propose concrete ways of covering future demand but to illustrate possible balances as well as the issues involved. Unless otherwise indicated, the demand forecasts used are the ones obtained from member countries. Most of the material underlying the supply considerations will be found in the country annexes.

North America

Based on submissions from the United States and Canada, Table 3.17 has been established for OECD North America (excluding Mexico):

Table 3.17   Gas Balance for North America (tcf)*

	1992	**2000**	**2010**
Demand	23.21	25.17	28.53
Indigenous production:			
US	18.48	20.06	20.96
Canada	4.48	5.31	5.8
Total	22.96	25.37	26.76
Supply Yet-to-be Secured	—	-0.2	1.77
Possible imports (bcm)*:			
Venezuela		8	8
Trinidad		1.2	1.2
Nigeria			1

* As a rule of thumb, 1 bcm = 0.0353147 tcf.

From a security of supply point of view the figures in Table 3.17 appear reassuring. Over most of the period there could potentially be a supply surplus. Around 2010 there is an apparent shortfall.[12] Given the responsiveness and the efficiency of the gas markets in North America it should be possible to supply the additional volumes if needed. In the table no trade with Mexico has been assumed. This is clearly not correct; there is already some gas trade with Mexico. The US currently exports minor volumes to Mexico, but in the second half of the outlook period Mexico could become a net exporter. At present, however, it is very difficult to determine Mexico's trade status, as financially necessary investments could become a limiting factor.

The possibility of LNG imports into North America has been indicated. Import of LNG from Algeria already takes place on a limited scale and will continue, and small volumes from the Nigerian LNG project have been contracted. In addition, there could be LNG deliveries from Venezuela and from Trinidad and Tobago before the end of the outlook period. It is expected, however, that LNG supplies will only play a very limited role in total North American gas supplies within the time horizon studied here. But it should be stressed that LNG supplies play a significant role in gas supplies in some regions of the US.

OECD Europe

The European gas market consists of OECD Europe and the countries of Central and Eastern Europe. OECD Europe is estimated to contain 4.3 per cent of global proven reserves of gas (Cedigaz, 1994), most of which are situated in Norway, the Netherlands and the United Kingdom. These three countries are or will be exporting significant volumes of gas to the rest of Europe. Central and Eastern Europe contain only 0.6 per cent of global gas reserves and are even more dependent on gas imports than the Western European economies. These countries have also expressed a desire to diversify away from Russian supplies and are, therefore, likely to compete with OECD Europe for gas from other sources; they also function as transit countries for gas being transported in an east-west direction and can consequently not be regarded separately from OECD Europe. Finally, there are signs that the European market is becoming more integrated which makes a separate discussion inappropriate. For statistical reasons, however, the demand/supply balance will focus on OECD Europe.

Europe has, in the past, been able to satisfy a relatively high share of gas consumption with indigenous production. It is, however, becoming more dependent on external supplies. The region is heterogenous in the sense that it consists of both net importers and net exporters of gas as well as countries meeting their demand or parts of it through domestic production (indigenous production for local use).

Gas is currently imported into OECD Europe via pipelines and in the form of LNG. In 1994, according to Cedigaz (1995), LNG imports amounted to about 11 per cent (18.6 bcm) of a total 173.1 bcm of gas imports into OECD Europe, while 89 per cent was imported through pipeline.[13]

Table 3.18 represents one example of how gas demand in OECD Europe could be covered during the period up to 2010. The table uses the demand forecast compiled from the country submissions to the IEA.

---

12. In the IEA's 1995 *WEO* the demand figures are even higher in 2010 (around 31 tcf).

13. For an overview of pipelines and LNG terminals, reference is made to the IEA gas transportation study (IEA, 1994).

Table 3.18   Gas Balance for OECD Europe (Mtoe)

	1992	**2000**	**2010**
Demand	**241.4**	**324.7**	**395.9**
Production for own use	112.3	123.9	138.2
Contracted Imports from:			
Norway	23.3	47.8	54.5
Denmark	1.8	3.0	3.0
France	0.3	0.5	
Germany	1.0	1.8	1.6
Italy		0.1	0.1
Netherlands	30.9	15.2	10.4
UK (Markham volumes)		0.5	0.5
Russia	49.6	57.5	12.1
Algeria	27.9	46.4	38.0
Nigeria		0.4	4.2
Libya	1.7	1.3	
Secured Supply	**248.8**	**298.4**	**262.6**
Regional Supply Yet-to-be Secured	**-7.4***	**26.3**	**133.3**
Assumed contract extensions:			
Norway		5.4	12.4
France			0.5
Germany			0.2
Netherlands		13.6	14.3
Russia		1.4	47.7
Libya			1.3
Algeria			8.1
Subtotal extensions		**20.4**	**84.5**
Production for own use			0.9
Norway		0.4	2.1
UK Interconnector		3.0	11.0
Algeria		0.9	7.5
Russia		7.7	15.8
Qatar		2.3	2.3
Denmark		0.1	0.9
Turkmenistan			8.7
Subtotal possible new supply		**14.4**	**49.2**
Total new supplies		**34.8**	**133.7**

*   Contracts include flexibility conditions and thus contracted volumes may exceed actual deliveries.

Notes: 1. As a rule of thumb, 1 Mtoe is equivalent to 1.27 bcm, although this can vary among supplies.

2. The regional supply yet-to-be secured for 2000 does not include contracted supply beyond forecast demand in some countries. This is because oversupply in one country in the region cannot be used to fill undersupply in another. When contracted supplies exceed forecast demand, this may be due to uncertainty regarding precise contract data. Thus the total new supplies for the region as a whole may seem to more than satisfy regional yet-to-be secured supply.

3. It should be stressed that the assumed contract extensions and new supplies in Table 3.18 are not forecasts but illustrations of what might occur over the period to 2010.

The assumptions underlying the table are as follows:

■ Production for own use is defined as OECD gas production that is not exported. For instance the share of Dutch production going to the domestic market is included here. The production figures are based on forecasts submitted by member countries.

■ The figures for contracted volumes are based on Cedigaz (1993) and IEA efforts to produce a complete overview of existing gas contracts. Given that most contracts are not in the public domain, the figures may not be exhaustive or completely accurate.

■ Production for own use and contracted volumes are considered to be secured supplies. Supplies yet-to-be secured can come from either extensions to existing contracts or new contracts.

■ Assumed contract extensions represent the IEA's estimate of those contracts that might be renewed.

In the previous section, a number of gas supply projects are described and ranked according to costs. When choosing between projects to cover unsecured supply, one possible criterion on which to base this choice is estimated costs. In practice, however, the procedure would be much more complicated. Factors such as established relationships, perceived political stability in the producing country and transit countries and diversification considerations would also be taken into account. The figures in the table do not reflect any specific set of criteria, but rather suggest one among several ways of covering apparent deficits. Having said that, it is also clear that countries with established client relationships and existing infrastructure have a competitive edge.

Concerning the figures in the table the following observations can be made.

■ Production for own use in member countries is expected to increase somewhat over the forecast period, but less than demand, thus increasing the need for imports.

■ Contracted import volumes from some of the major suppliers, in particular Russia, will level off and decline before the end of the forecast periods. Contract extensions are therefore necessary for these countries. Reserve/production capacity considerations should not be obstacles in any of the countries, with the possible exception of the Netherlands where a restrictive export policy might influence this issue.

■ The unsecured supply in 2000 is only around 26 Mtoe. This volume can probably be covered without problem, but it is difficult to say precisely from where. Because of this uncertainty and the existence of spare capacity in new and existing infrastructure in the short term, the total new supplies in 2000 more than cover the difference between secured supply and forecast demand. The sources of supply indicated in Table 3.18 should not be viewed as a forecast.

■ The unsecured supply in 2010 amounts to around 133 Mtoe. Judging from the information gathered and reproduced in the annexes to this study, traditional suppliers of gas into Europe are in a good position to fill most of this need. According to the cost figures given above, supplies from these countries should be competitive under a regime where the oil price is allowed to increase according to the assumptions underlying the *WEO* forecast (i.e., US$ 28 per barrel in 2005). The figures for each of the sources merit some comment:

• The figure for supplies from Norway would imply an increase beyond what is presently considered likely (total annual exports of 59 Mtoe (75 bcm) in 2010 versus a total export of 69 Mtoe (around 88 bcm) according to the table). Judging by the reserve potential, however, the higher level is possible.

- The UK Interconnector to the continent is planned to have a capacity of around 16 Mtoe (20 bcm) and there will be a strong economic incentive to fill this capacity. A strong demand for gas in Continental Europe could maintain the flow from the UK in spite of the fact that this pipeline will be equipped to take flows in both directions.

- An additional 15.6 Mtoe (20 bcm) from Algeria would bring total export volumes to around 53.6 Mtoe (68 bcm), lower than the stated goal (i.e., 59 Mtoe or 75 bcm) of representatives of Sonatrach and the government. As indicated below the potential is probably higher.

- According to evaluations put forward in the annex on Russia, supplies from Russia could most likely be increased substantially. Although the reserve potential is no obstacle, an increase of the order of magnitude indicated would require some investment in transportation infrastructure. The planned pipeline through Belarus and Poland will have an initial capacity of 25 Mtoe (32 bcm). Possibilities for relatively cheap expansion of the capacity through the Ukraine also exist.

- Under the demand scenario on which Table 3.18 is based, the scope for more LNG into Europe is limited. While Algeria will continue to export gas also in the form of LNG, new LNG has been contracted from Nigeria and Qatar and could arrive around the turn of the century. New projects could replace some of the volumes allocated to the above mentioned countries, motivated for instance by a wish to diversify supplies.

■ To the extent that the countries mentioned above were not able or willing to supply the necessary volumes, there are other potential projects that could do so.

The demand figures in Table 3.18 for 2010 are somewhat lower than the figures in the IEA's 1995 *WEO*. Under the IEA *Capacity Constraints* price scenario, there should be no major problems in supplying the necessary extra volumes given that gas prices are allowed to increase in line with the oil price.

The 1994 version of the IEA's *WEO* contained a demand case which, assuming a constant oil price of US$ 18 per barrel, was considerably higher than the 1995 *WEO* figures referred to above. From a reserve point of view there should be no difficulty in covering such additional demand. If the message indicated by the supply cost curves reproduced above is correct, it would, however, be economically difficult to bring such volumes to the market under low prices. But as already indicated, a cost curve approach is probably too static. Cost reductions and new ways of contracting gas could considerably improve the prospects of bringing sufficient volumes to the market. In a high demand case, further supplies could come from both old and new suppliers:

■ Russia could probably supply substantial new volumes, even at prices corresponding to an oil price of US$ 18 per barrel.

■ Algeria could potentially increase its exports beyond the stated goal of 59 Mtoe (75 bcm) a year. Volumes of around 79 Mtoe (100 bcm) have been suggested.

■ Apart from Libya, most of the other projects that could supply additional gas volumes require transit through one or more countries. Both Iran and Turkmenistan have huge gas reserves that could be marketed in Europe.

Although the focus in this section has been on OECD Europe, the continent of Europe should be regarded as one gas market. The countries in central and eastern Europe will also see future growth in demand for gas and will potentially compete for volumes from some of the same sources that will supply OECD Europe countries. Historically, these countries have taken all their supplies from Russia. In some of them, there is indigenous production, but these volumes have recently declined and are not expected to increase substantially in the future. A special feature of these countries is that most of them have only short-term contracts with Russia. Over the next few years these contracts will have to be renewed or renegotiated, creating an opportunity for the countries to diversify their supply sources. Efforts in this direction have already been apparent for some time, so far with little success, primarily because of the lack of ability to pay the prices required to take gas from the North Sea for instance. Both for economic and geographical reasons it is likely that Russia will remain the main supplier to these countries.

According to the *Capacity Constraints* case of the IEA's 1995 *WEO*, gas demand in Central and Eastern European countries could increase by around 31 Mtoe (39 bcm) over the projection period with most of the growth taking place after 2000. Given the supply situation that has been described for Russia, it is difficult to see this additional demand creating major problems for the all-European gas balance.

One consequence of this supply picture is increased reliance on supplies from outside of the OECD Europe region. The relative decline in indigenous production for local use will have to be compensated for by increased imports from within the region or by increased imports. Table 3.19 illustrates how the various suppliers' shares might change over the outlook period if the above supply picture is realised.

Table 3.19   OECD Europe's Dependence on Various Suppliers (per cent)

	1992	**2000**	**2010**
Indigenous production not for exports	45.1	37.2	35.1
Russia	19.9	20	19.1
Algeria	11.2	14.2	13.5
Norway	9.3	16.1	17.4
Netherlands	12.4	8.7	6.2
Others	2.1	3.8	8.7

Under the assumptions chosen, the share of imports from external sources would increase but not dramatically. The major source of new supplies is Norway. The increase in volumes from other sources, whether LNG or pipeline gas, represent greater diversification.

Another implication of increased external sourcing is the growing importance of transit. Some of the new projects that are candidates for deliveries into Europe rely on transit through several countries. The problems and issues arising from this are dealt with in Annex 2.

OECD Pacific   As Australia and New Zealand are expected to remain self-sufficient in gas over the forecast period, Japan is the only country for which a gas balance is established in this region. Apart from a very small level of indigenous production, Japan is entirely dependent on LNG imports. Prospects for pipeline deliveries of gas within the time horizon for this study are probably slight. Table 3.20 shows one possible gas balance for Japan.

Table 3.20   Gas Balance for Japan (million tonnes of LNG)

	1992	2000	2010
Demand	**40**	**53**	**58**
Indigenous production	1.4	1.0	0.5
Contracted volumes			
Australia	5.8	7	0
United States	1	1.1	0
Brunei	5.5	5.5	5.5
Indonesia	16.5	21	2.2
Malaysia	7.5	10.6	4.6
Abu Dhabi	2	4.4	4.4
Qatar	-	6	6
Secured Supplies	**39.7**	**56.3**	**23.2**
Supply Yet-to-be Secured	**0**	**0 (- 3)**	**35**
Extension of contracts on high level/use of spare capacity:			
Australia	0	0	7
United States	0	0	1.1
Indonesia	0	0	18.8
Malaysia	0	0	6
Subtotal extensions	**0**	**0**	**32.9**
New contracts needed for incremental volumes, which could be taken from:			**2**
Malaysia (MLNG 3)	0	0	5
Australia (Burrup, 2 trains)	0	0	2.5
Indonesia (Badak, train 3)	0	0	1.5
Qatar	0	0	8

Based on the submitted demand forecast, demand in 2000 is already more than covered. An apparent demand/supply gap opens up between 2000 and 2010, but this could be covered almost entirely by extending existing contracts. There are also several possibilities for new supplies.

The addition of two trains at the Australian LNG plant at Burrup would bring an additional 5 million tonnes on the market, which are assumed to be split between Japan and the East Asian market. A third train at Badak in Indonesia and the realisation of a third LNG plant in Malaysia would provide a total of 10.3 million tonnes of LNG, some of which could be contracted to Japan. Additional volumes could be provided by Qatar, where an expansion of production is not threatened by supply availability. Gas from Sakhalin, where costs of production might be relatively high due to climatic conditions, but which is in proximity to the Japanese market, or LNG from the Natuna field in Indonesia as well as supplies from Oman, Papua New Guinea,

Vietnam or Yemen could also be used to meet incremental demand. Alternatively, if OECD deliveries were preferred, the timely development of the Gorgon fields in Australia, and possibly supplies from Alaska, could provide the required volumes.

In the context of the *Oil, Gas and Coal Supply Outlook* (IEA, 1995a), the balance for Japan has been established simultaneously with a balance for the rest of East Asia. The East Asian market is also relatively well supplied at least to the turn of the century. Strong growth up to 2010 is expected to require supplies from new projects, but satisfaction of this demand does not seem to be incompatible with sufficient volumes for Japan. The real issue for the Asian LNG market is that of finding arrangements whereby the price of LNG would justify new developments.

IV. STRUCTURAL AND REGULATORY CHANGES IN THE GAS INDUSTRY

INTRODUCTION

Although the three OECD regions are structurally different, have different regulatory histories and are at different stages in relation to the introduction of competition in gas markets, they have all managed to ensure security of supply in physical terms. In fact, none of the three regions has experienced major gas supply disruptions in recent years. The cost of security of supply in economic terms is beyond the scope of this study. The objective of this chapter is more modest: it is to look at the impact of structural and regulatory changes in the gas industry in recent years on security of supply.

Since the concept of security of supply has a number of aspects, it will be necessary to specify which aspects apply in the various contexts. It should also be kept in mind that there is no simple causal relationship between structural and regulatory change and security of supply. The interrelationships between the various factors are complex. Structural changes in the gas industry may take place as a result of regulatory developments, but may also have other causes, including security considerations (for instance, an increase in the number of import sources for gas). In recent years regulation aimed at introducing more competition into gas markets has often led to important structural changes that in time have had effects on security of supply, although the primary objective of these regulations (or deregulation) was to increase efficiency and benefit final consumers. Given that it is impossible to make controlled experiments to evaluate the causality between the factors involved, this chapter attempts to observe regulatory and structural changes in the three OECD regions over the past few years and to point to their apparent effects on security of supply.

This chapter will therefore focus on security of supply and will deal with organisational and regulatory issues only to the extent necessary as background for the discussion of security. A more extensive treatment of many of the regulatory issues can be found in the recent publication Natural Gas Transportation: Organisation and Regulation (IEA, 1994). Chapter 6 and some of the country annexes also contain elements relevant to the discussion in this chapter.

STRUCTURAL AND REGULATORY CHANGES IN NORTH AMERICA

Market Development and Sectoral Composition

The gas industry in North America is in many ways mature. Gas production and consumption in the United States peaked in 1972, but fell substantially until 1986. In that year, gas delivered to consumers was only three-quarters of its 1972 level. However, since 1986 there has been a consistent growth in gas consumption both in the United States and Canada. This growth has coincided with the decontrol of wellhead prices and a restructuring of the natural gas transportation system. Recently, total consumption has again approached the level it reached around 1972.

Since 1972 the sectoral composition of gas consumption in the United States has also changed quite dramatically. Whereas residential and commercial gas consumption accounted for 43.4% of total gas utility industry sales in 1972, their shares had increased to 72.4% by 1993, basically to the detriment of industry's share. This development is reflected in the number of customers which increased from 42.9 million in 1972 to 57.8 million in 1993. The change in market composition has made the provision of secure and reliable gas supplies even more challenging since residential/commercial consumers are more vulnerable to supply disruptions than industrial customers and are also more demanding as far as load balancing is concerned. All sales to the residential sector are firm, whereas in 1993, 10.8% of US utilities' sales to the commercial sector and 52.5% of total sales to the industrial sector were interruptible.[1] Judging over recent years, the share of interruptible sales appears to have increased in the commercial sector but declined in the industrial sector: overall, interruptible volumes have increased since 1991. In security of supply terms, this is an important development, since use of interruptible contracts is one of the most important ways of meeting supply disruptions.

Sourcing of Gas

North America is largely self-sufficient in gas, but the United States has traditionally been a net importer. In 1972 it imported 4.7% of its needs. The share stayed constant until the gas market started growing again around the mid 1980s. In 1993, imports had reached about 10% of total gas needs, with imports from Canada accounting for 96.3% of total imports. Minor volumes were imported from Mexico and Algeria. Although small in a total context, imports from these two countries are nonetheless significant in terms of security of supply for the utilities that are dependent on them. The fact that LNG imports are much lower than originally planned (mainly for economic reasons) has left the United States with considerable spare LNG import capacity. Some of this capacity could potentially be reactivated for imports or used as storage facilities.

United States gas supply is well diversified, 32 states produce gas, although production is concentrated in Texas, Louisiana and Oklahoma. The growth in imports from Canada since 1986 (almost a tripling between 1986 and 1993) has contributed significantly to diversification. Currently there are 16 pipeline interconnections for gas exports from Canada to the US, spread out along the joint border. There are also some imports of gas into Canada from the US, although of much smaller volumes than in the opposite direction.

Wellhead Price Deregulation and Supply

Gas production in the United States is only now regaining the peak level of 1972. After a considerable decline between 1972 and 1985, production in the United States and Canada started growing in 1986 and has grown consistently since then. In both countries gas price deregulation is an important factor. Price deregulation started in 1978 in the United States and in 1985 in Canada. By 1993, wellhead gas prices had been completely deregulated in both countries. The initial effect of deregulation was a surplus of gas since exploration and development were

---

1. *Gas Facts 1994*, The American Gas Association, Washington 1994.

encouraged whereas demand for gas weakened during the first years after deregulation. When demand started to rise in Canada in 1986, only about 60% of the productive capacity was in use. Recently this percentage has risen to some 85%. In 1989, annual capacity utilisation in the United States was 83.1%, but this had risen to 92.6% by 1993 (Natural Gas Supply Association, 1994). For short-term security of supply, a gas surplus may appear desirable, but this does not take into account the inefficient use of up-stream capital. One problem that arose when production was shut in as a consequence of the gas bubble was that nobody really knew what share of that capacity could be mobilised in a shortage situation, because of insufficient maintenance, etc. The surplus gave weak incentives for exploration and production and thus could potentially have had a negative impact on future gas deliverability.

For North America as a whole the ratio between reserves and production has gone down since 1983 (from around 15 years to about 11 years). This is partly an indirect effect of price deregulation and partly an effect of regulatory changes, like the revision of the export surplus determination procedures of the National Energy Board (NEB) in Canada in 1987. Expressed differently, it may be said that a "tin on the shelf" concept has been replaced by a "just in time" concept.

It is difficult to get precise estimates of the number of gas producers in North America, but the number seems to be somewhere between 8,000 and 10,000. Precise figures for the number of producing gas wells in the United States do exist: the number increased from 243,244 in 1985 to 286,168 in 1993. An increase should in principle mean a greater diversification of supplies and more reliability.

Wellhead price deregulation was a necessary first step towards a truly competitive gas market in North America. Introduction of mandatory third party access (TPA) to pipelines and unbundling of the various functions in the gas chain have also been necessary building blocks. The IEA's Gas Transportation study describes the impact of FERC Orders 436 and 636 in the US, and similar legislation in Canada. In the following sections the effects of these measures on gas market structures and on security of supply will be discussed. Although some of the regulatory measures have a specific North American background, there is no doubt that some of the experience obtained during the transition to more competitive markets is of a general nature and therefore of interest to the other OECD regions.

Open Access and Unbundling of Transportation Services

Very broadly speaking, what has taken place over the last ten years or so in North America is that natural gas customers have been allowed to purchase supplies directly from gas producers. The opening up of the transmission pipeline system has enabled gas buyers to negotiate sales contracts directly with producers without an intermediary. Historically, the big interstate natural gas pipeline companies provided a "bundled" sales service including both sales and transportation services, including load balancing and storage. The relationship between a merchant pipeline company and a gas customer, typically a local distribution company (LDC), was characterised by long-term contracts under which the pipeline company arranged for gas acquisition and transportation and the LDC received the gas at the city gate and was responsible for distribution of the gas. Responsibilities for security of supply were clear: the pipeline company undertook to supply gas according to the contract at the city gate and was responsible for procurement, transportation and load balancing. The LDC was responsible for delivering gas to its end consumers. It did not have to worry about supply problems as long as its forecasts and gas purchase contracts were prudent and the pipeline company met its obligations. The company was in a good position to do so since it would typically have a number of suppliers and customers and well developed transportation and storage facilities. With open access to pipelines facilities and direct deals between gas customers and gas producers, this situation changed: the gas customer now has to take responsibility for supply and see to it that he gets a contract with a gas producer which is satisfactory in security terms. After the introduction of unbundling under Order 636, the LDC now has to enter into a series of contracts along the gas chain to get the gas needed, whereas under the old system one contract with a merchant pipeline company would generally suffice.

The system described does not, however, allow retail consumers (apart from big industrial users and electricity producers) to buy their gas directly from producers, since LDCs still largely retain their monopoly position in the franchise area beyond the city gate. This situation has changed in some provinces in Canada and is now changing in some states in the US. In these cases end consumers, even individual residential consumers, are free to choose among several gas suppliers. In practice, of course, few private apartment owners would contract directly with a gas producer. Between the end consumers and gas producers there are normally gas aggregators and gas marketers who take care of gas procurement and arrange for transportation on transmission and distribution pipelines.

According to the Energy Information Administration in the US, the restructuring of the North American gas industry toward more competition has achieved its fundamental objective of reducing the cost of supplies and the cost of getting those supplies to the burnertip (DOE/EIA, 1995). The restructuring has also meant a shift in responsibility for security of supply and has led to structural changes that might have implications for security of supply.

Changes in Contract Structures

TPA to the pipeline systems coupled with ample availability of gas in North America has encouraged a competitive market with a large number of sellers and buyers and created a basis for a shorter term market with market based pricing. The contracts between the merchant pipeline companies and the LDCs had traditionally been long term. From 1983 the share of total gas volumes traded in the spot market in the United States increased dramatically. From 5% of total consumption in 1983, the spot market volume increased to 51% in 1986 and to 74% in 1988, but then started to decline, reaching 60% in 1989 and 50-60% in 1990 (De Vany and Walls, 1994). Current estimates indicate that nearly half of gas sales are under contracts lasting more than one year, 35% are on a 30-day basis and the balance under medium term contracts (one year or less). As the gas bubble in North America has diminished over the last few years the tendency has been towards contracts of a somewhat longer term, but with pricing increasingly linked to spot or futures prices.

In the United States most gas sales contracts are treated confidentially. This makes it difficult to get precise information on contract structures. Such information is more easily available in Canada, where the National Energy Board (NEB) has undertaken a survey of the development in gas contracting after deregulation. This material has been dealt with in detail in the IEA's gas transportation study (IEA, 1994) and only the main conclusions will be summarised here:

- The volumes of gas sold under long-term contracts (duration of five years or more) have declined significantly since 1985, both absolutely and relatively.

- The average size of long-term contracts has declined since deregulation, but their number has increased dramatically.

- The number of contracts containing take-or-pay (TOP) provisions has declined and the TOP thresholds have been reduced.

- The reduced use of TOP provisions has to a large extent been compensated by other risk-reducing contractual devices.

- Contract prices are typically based on market value and indexed to the buyer's alternatives — usually the price of US supplies of gas, or in a smaller number of cases, oil products.

In short, two types of changes have taken place: on the one hand, a development towards shorter term contracts, on the other hand, changes in the structure of long-term contracts.

Gas contracts normally contain a number of mechanisms whose function is to ensure security of offtake seen from the seller's point of view and security of supply seen from the buyer's point of view. After the introduction of competition the variety and number of such mechanisms have increased, partly to compensate for the reduced use of inflexible TOP provisions, for instance:

- Dedicated reserves or reserve-based contracts: These require the seller to set aside specific physical reserves to fulfil the commitments of a contract. Reserve-based contracts normally prevent the seller from selling this gas to others without the permission of the buyer.

- Corporate warranties: For example, a contractual commitment by the seller to maintain adequate reserves and deliverability to meet its obligation, or a commitment to maintain a specified level of total reserves relative to the seller's total commitments (a reserves/production ratio equal to or greater than ten years is common).

- Buyer's right to reduce contract quantities: The buyer can reduce contract quantities if the seller fails to deliver nominated volumes for reasons other than force majeure. This kind of provision has become widespread in gas contracts and reflects the importance buyers attach to reliability of supply when entering into a long term contract.

- Seller indemnities: The seller has an obligation to explicitly indemnify the buyer against specific costs that may arise as a result of failures by the seller to deliver nominated volumes.

- Daily obligation to deliver: Under most firm contracts, the buyer may nominate up to the Daily Contract Quantity (DCQ) each day and the seller is committed to meet the nomination. A number of contracts executed since deregulation give the buyer the right to nominate above DCQ on any given day. Buyers may use this right to purchase limited quantities of peaking gas in order to meet unexpected demand or to give the buyer a source of backup gas supply in case one of its suppliers encounters deliverability difficulties.

The above mechanisms are primarily used to ensure security of supply from the buyer's point of view. Similar mechanisms have also been introduced to give the buyer incentives to offer the seller a regular and reliable offtake of gas.

Duration of Contracts

Some gas buyers would claim that short-term contracts are intrinsically less secure than long-term contacts. In the autumn of 1991, a group of electricity executives met officials from the US Department of Energy and argued that an inability to obtain long-term gas contracts meant that supplies were unreliable and that the construction of gas fuelled generating stations was being discouraged. The contact between the DOE and the electricity industry resulted in research of which the main conclusion was that efficiency in gas markets would be obtained by allowing each participant in the gas industry to enter into the contract that was most appropriate for his or her individual need (Sutherland, 1993). Seen from a security point of view, the pricing mechanism of the contract is much more important than the duration of the contract. Traditional long-term take or pay contracts, which in the United States often had fixed or very inflexible pricing mechanisms, could in fact be seen as a threat to security of supply because they could introduce inefficiencies and the risk of contract breach in markets where prices do not reflect current market conditions. Natural gas supplies can be secured over a long term on a reliable basis either by successive spot purchases or by contracts of various durations.

Even if the duration of a gas contract is not the most important parameter for security of supply, it is important that gas sellers and buyers have the possibility of making a free choice in this respect. This has not always been the case. Before deregulation, the NEB in Canada imposed maximum requirements on the length of gas export contracts. For some buyers it is important to have the possibility of obtaining a long-term contract — for instance, a power producer dependent on a single supplier. To be willing to make the investment, the producer might consider a long term contract to be a prerequisite. If a gas sales contract involves substantial new investments, for instance in field development, financing institutions may also have some influence on the duration of the contract, although this is probably more widespread when pipeline construction is involved.

Pricing

Prices in gas contracts in North America are increasingly indexed to escalators that reflect current market conditions. Escalation with spot or futures prices for gas is most frequent, but references to other fuels, in particular oil products, are still widespread. Spot markets in gas quickly came into being as TPA was introduced. Just a few years after the open access orders, spot prices at more than 50 markets were reported. None of these markets had been active before open access: there had been only scattered spot transactions accompanying the limited transport programs that preceded open access. The volume of gas transported on behalf of customers — gas not owned by the pipeline — rose rapidly, reaching 80% in just a few years. As more gas trades began to take place in the spot market, prices declined and began to converge over the network. A series of studies has shown that spot prices became highly integrated within just two years of open access; within four years field prices at scattered locations across the network were so tightly linked that they approached informational efficiency. De Vany and Walls (1994) note that the present price at each location, adjusted for transport cost, reflects the marginal value of gas at every point across the entire network; this is the economist's hallmark of efficient allocation.

Market responsive prices are important for security of supply in that they ensure an efficient allocation of available gas in a shortage. Those who need the gas most will be able to get it by bidding the required price. In other gas markets such as Europe, allocation in a shortage situation would have to rely mainly on other criteria because gas prices are not sensitive to short-term market developments.

Development in Pipeline Construction

If the length and degree of integration of the pipeline system in a region is one indicator of the level of security or reliability of supply, the level of pipeline construction in North America after deregulation indicates that security of supply has increased. Some feared that after the restructuring of the interstate natural gas pipeline industry there might be less interest in pipeline construction, as a consequence of unbundling of the transportation function from the merchant function. This has not been the case: in the United States the total length of the entire pipeline system, including field and gathering pipelines, transmission pipelines and distribution pipelines increased by 11.4% between 1986 and 1993 (American Gas Association, 1994). The corresponding figure for Canada between 1988 and 1992 was 16.6% (Canadian Gas Association, 1994). From 1992 to 1993 interregional pipeline capacity in the United States increased by 2.8%. Further additions to capacity up to 1996 are expected to give a total increase of 7% relative to 1992 capacity. One possible explanation for this may be the rate of return regulation on pipelines in North America which limits the risk of such projects. During the first years after restructuring, interstate transmission pipelines in the United States had problems in obtaining the rate of return allowed under FERC regulation, but the rate of return has increased in recent years.

In view of where the new pipeline projects and the expansion of existing systems have taken place, there is no doubt that the North American interstate natural gas pipeline system has become more integrated and flexible, contributing to a higher deliverability of gas. The number of connections between Canada and the United States has increased and new interregional pipelines in the US have been built.

Since the pipeline systems serve a variety of customers buying and selling gas based on different types of contracts, there are also many types of transportation contracts. For the construction of new pipelines, however, there are requirements both from regulatory bodies like FERC and NEB and from financing institutions that influence the contract structure. In many cases banks prefer ship or pay contracts for 10 to 12 years to be willing to finance a new project. On the other hand, so-called "at risk" pipelines have also emerged in recent years. This means that permission to build a pipeline is granted in spite of the fact that firm contracts do not exist for the whole capacity; the pipeline is at risk for the costs of the uncommitted capacity.

Emergence of Market Hubs

Increasing flexibility in buying and selling gas has been an important development since restructuring. This flexibility has to a large extent been achieved through the development of market centres or hubs. The interstate pipeline grid includes areas where several pipelines can do business. These are natural market centres where many gas buyers and sellers can do business. In 1993, three new market hubs were created in the US, bringing the total number to over 20. The hubs are geographically dispersed throughout the US, mainly near supply basins, storage sites, and downstream pipeline interconnections. Hubs provide both physical and transactional services. Physical services include gas wheeling (a service whereby gas is transferred between pipelines at a common market hub: this service is helpful in the event of emergency shutdowns on one or more pipelines) and parking (i.e., short-term storage of natural gas, techniques such as linepack are used to create extra gas deliverability at the hub itself rather than transferring the gas to an underground storage facility) as well as transportation, storage, compression and processing. Transactional services offered consist of title transfer, buyer-seller matching, balancing, and electronic bulletin board information. According to the EIA (1994), market hubs are an integral part of restructuring gas services because they:

- promote greater competition by bringing more buyers and sellers together;
- improve the efficiency of the pipeline system by linking supply, storage, pipeline interconnect, and distribution areas more completely;
- improve reliability by giving end users access to more supply options than they had in the past.

The creation of market hubs has facilitated the following developments which presently characterise the North American gas industry, all more or less direct results of provisions in Order 636:

Implementation of Pipeline Capacity Release Programs

A secondary market for pipeline capacity has developed which gives more flexibility to holders of capacity rights to release firm capacity they do not need to other shippers. This makes it more attractive to enter long-term capacity contracts. This secondary market probably also contributes to increased utilisation of pipeline capacity.

New Services

An array of new services are now on offer to help end users take advantage of the restructured industry. A broad mix of new transportation, storage, balancing, risk management, supply and rebundling is now available. End users are now able to pick and choose only the services they need from an expanded menu of options. The new service selections enable end users to more easily make tradeoffs between the quality of service they want and the price they are willing to pay. The actors in the market are able to let their need for security of supply or reliability be reflected in the prices they pay for the various relevant services.

Flexible Receipt and Delivery Points

Pipeline customers with firm capacity rights now have more flexibility in choosing where to inject or withdraw gas along pipeline trunklines. These changes were instituted to promote the secondary market for capacity. Purchasers of released capacity may specify, at no extra cost, different receipt and delivery points than those belonging to the releasing shipper, as long as the gas moves along the same transportation path within the same zone.

Development in Storage Capacity and Use of Storage

In the US, the number of storage facilities remained quite stable over the period between 1986 and 1993. The total working gas volume has shown an upward, though fluctuating, trend. Recently there has been a dramatic increase in developed and planned storage. Most of this new storage is salt cavern or other high-deliverability storage where gas can be injected and withdrawn on a continuing basis throughout the year. Planned storage expansions will increase peak-day deliverability from underground storage facilities by 27% by the end of the decade (EIA, 1994).

In Canada there has been a significant increase in storage capacity since deregulation. Between 1988 and 1992 there was a 43% increase in total storage reservoir capacity; the number of pools increased from 27 to 36 and total working gas increased by 37% (Canadian Gas Association, 1994). Current Canadian storage projects will increase daily deliverability from storage by more than 30% over the next few years.

The two main forces driving the recent development in storage in the United States are implementation of Order 636 and the reduction in excess North American wellhead deliverability (the gas bubble). Historically, most of the storage capacity in the United States has been held by the interstate pipelines. Under Order 636, the pipelines unbundled sales gas service and priced its components (gas supply, storage, and transportation) separately, and on a comparable basis to sales service. Many pipelines opted not to continue to offer sales service. Responsibility for obtaining seasonal and peak-day supplies was thus transferred to LDCs and end-users, and the need for storage was also transferred from pipelines to LDCs and end-users. As a result, interstate pipeline storage capacity which formerly supported the pipeline's sales service was released to the market. This involved assignment of storage capacity to former sales customers first, with any remaining capacity offered to the rest of the market. In general, LDCs had been the largest sales customers of the pipelines, and the state regulator usually favoured the LDCs holding storage to balance core markets. Thus, LDCs assumed most of the released storage capacity.

Some interstate pipelines continue to offer a variation of peak-day supply via "no-notice service". This is theoretically a transportation service, but can also be considered a delivered peak-day supply service, where the gas supply is not purchased from the pipeline, but rather is borrowed. The borrowed gas must be paid back by the user within a few days or weeks. Pipelines retain some storage in order to be able to provide this service. The EIA (1994) estimates that interstate pipelines will retain control of only 10 to 20% of their storage capacity after Order 636. The remaining 80-90% will be held by LDCs and end-users.

The Canadian market structure and use of storage before deregulation were dramatically different from those of the US. In the US, storage control shifted to LDCs as a result of deregulation. In Canada, LDCs dominated storage ownership and use before deregulation. Previous to 1989, the main interprovincial Canadian pipeline, TransCanada PipeLines (TCPL) held delivered service gas supply contracts with LDCs in eastern Canada. This delivered service was similar to US sales service, including gas acquisition and pipeline transportation, but did not include balancing. LDCs did their own load balancing using market area storage. In 1989, TCPL became solely a transporter and its delivered service contracts were terminated. LDCs and end-users began to purchase gas directly from producers and marketers and to use TCPL transportation to move gas to markets. Storage ownership was not affected by this, but changed as a result of other developments in the Canadian gas market which are described below.

The increased use of storage over the last few years is primarily due to the following factors:

Transition to Daily Balancing on Pipelines

Under FERC Order 636, shippers are required to be in daily balance on US pipelines. Most long-haul pipelines in Canada already had strict balancing limits on shippers and in 1992 daily balancing was implemented on the NOVA pipeline system in Alberta, where balancing previously took place on a monthly basis.

Partial Loss of the "Aggregation" Effect

In the past, pipelines transported gas on behalf of a large number of shippers, many of whom had daily imbalances. However, because some shippers had positive and others negative imbalances, to some extent imbalances cancelled out. The pipeline acted as a market centre, clearing offsetting imbalances. The pipeline then used storage to manage any remaining imbalances. With Order 636, each individual shipper was required to be in balance, creating increased demand for short-term storage. It is expected, however, that, as better market mechanisms for clearing offsetting imbalances develop, the demand for short-term storage may abate somewhat.

Increased Value of Storage

The changing market structure and changing gas contracting practices have created possibilities for earning money on storage by exploiting price fluctuations.

The General Tightening of Supply and Demand after 1991

The increased demand for gas in relation to deliverability creates the possibility for better use of wellhead deliverability by using storage to level the demand on an annual basis.

Changes in the Electricity Generation Industry

In recent years, many gas-fired non-utility electricity generation facilities have been constructed in the US. There is now a general surplus of generating capacity, and many of these plants, which were anticipating baseload generation, may sit idle for 10 to 30 days per year. These projects generally have long-term gas supply arrangements, and the change from baseload generation to dispatched generation alter gas supply requirements. When the plants are not operating, project sponsors often opt to inject gas into storage.

Many utility electric generators' peaking plants use natural gas. These plants have extremely low load factors so gas supply using short-term storage is very attractive. This need is driving some of the US development of short-term storage, particularly salt cavern storage.

Unbundling and Rebundling

The requirement in Order 636 that pipelines "unbundle" their services has already led to important changes in the North American gas industry. The industry's structure has probably not completely adjusted to these changes. One crucial question is whether the future will be characterised by a large number of firms offering a menu of unbundled services to, for instance, LDCs or whether there will be incentives to rebundle the components involved in serving LDCs' need for gas supplies. Warwick (1994) argues that the underlying economic fundamentals of so-called on-demand gas service to LDCs suggest that significant economic efficiencies can be created by rebundling the components of that service and marketing over wide geographic regions. Economies of scope and scale will favour larger firms over smaller ones, which could lead to the consolidation of marketing companies and an ultimate industry structure closer to oligopoly than to the competitive model. Firms serving multi-regional markets will experience lower costs in providing delivery flexibility than will marketers serving smaller market areas, because the pooling of markets reduces the peaks and valleys in demand. As there are real economies of geographic diversification, firms large enough to market to several regions will have a cost advantage over less geographically diversified competitors. Even more important in this context is that large marketers are likely to be more efficient providers of supply reliability than smaller ones. With a larger supply portfolio, a large marketer will be less vulnerable to an individual producer's failure to deliver. By accessing more geographically diversified supply basins, large marketers can also better pool interruption risk, such as may be caused by hurricanes or freezing weather. In addition, large marketers will be in a better position to offer LDCs financial guarantees of performance.

Efforts to introduce competition in the US gas market have so far focused on the part of the gas chain located upstream of the city gate. The issues raised for security of supply are also relevant when competition is introduced at end user level. Canada is, however, much more advanced than the United States in this respect, and the Canadian experience will be used to illustrate the issues involved.

Security of Supply Aspects of End-user Market Competition

Since 1987 end consumers in Ontario, Canada have been able to buy their gas directly from producers, bypassing the LDCs that had traditionally supplied them. From a share of almost 100% in 1986, the share of LDCs in total Ontario supplies fell to around 40% in 1992/93 but then increased to around 50% in 1994.

Direct purchases of gas have taken place using two main methods:

a) T-service under which the end consumer buys his gas and arranges for transportation to the city gate. From there, the LDC, without taking title to the gas, undertakes to transport the gas to the point of use.

b) Buy/Sell arrangements under which the LDC buys the customer's gas at a receipt point on the upstream pipeline at a price equal to its Weighted Average Cost Of Gas (WACOG). The LDC resells the gas to the customer at a regulated rate including a tariff for transportation at the point of use. The customer's saving is the difference between the LDC's WACOG and the customer's acquisition cost.

An important point to note in this context is that, because of the way they are regulated, the LDCs in Canada make no direct profit on the merchant function as such. They make their regulated rate of return on their (pipeline) asset base. Thus, in terms of profitability, distributors are indifferent as to whether end consumers obtain a better deal on gas prices.

T-service turned out to suit relatively few large industrial customers, while the Buy/Sell arrangement was appropriate for smaller customers. What typically took place was that aggregators, brokers or marketers (ABMs) aggregated demand from small consumers under direct purchase agreements. In this way it was possible even for individual residential customers to choose their own gas supplier, thereby reducing their gas bill. Over a few years, several hundred thousand customers turned to direct purchases of gas. The LDCs did not necessarily regret this as they still earned their regulated return on transmission and distribution: furthermore, since in some cases the customers could buy more gas at lower prices, the LDC could in fact benefit from the development.

During periods of market tightness, for instance during the cold spell of the winter 1992/93, it turned out that the system had some weaknesses in relation to security of supply. Some of the marketers did not have sufficiently strong and enforceable contractual arrangements with producers, and had to turn to the LDCs for assistance when they were faced with physical shortages and financial problems as a consequence of having to buy expensive gas in the spot market. Thanks to the LDCs, no consumers were cut off during the cold spell of 1992/93, but the problems of some of the marketing companies spurred initiatives to improve security of supply. A result was the establishment of a Minimum Conditions of Supply (MCS) code of practice between the LDCs and their marketers for supplies to the "core market", that is residential and commercial customers taking less than 50,000 cubic metres a year. The essential elements of the MCS are as follows:

a) core market supplies will be based on a three-year rolling supply arrangement;

b) the utility requires the supplier to demonstrate a three-year firm supply contract, firm transportation contracts, and the necessary removal permits (permission to take gas out of the producing province);

c) the marketer is required to give the utility notice of intent to continue to supply the customers from the end of the contract (two years hence);

d) before the end of the contract year, the marketer is required to add another year of supply to maintain the three-year rolling supply arrangement;

e) if the marketer fails to provide notice under c) the utility will acquire replacement supply and the direct purchase arrangement will expire at the end of year three.

An important security of supply aspect of the MCS is "MCS 10". This is a provision required by the distributor whereby those supplying the core market must have at least 10% of their average daily volumes to this market "back-stopped", i.e., when required by the distributor they can call up an additional 10% of these market volumes from producers. The distributor can use this provision -i.e., call up MCS 10 gas- if the supply to industrial buy/sell consumers fails. The MCS also require the marketers to provide a Corporate Warranty of Supply of which the most important elements are as follows:

■ suppliers warrant that over the term of the direct purchase arrangement they have the required removal permits, all processing and firm transportation to the specific delivery points and sufficient gas to fulfil contractual obligations;

■ suppliers agree joint and several liability for all costs arising from non-performance. The utility can recover costs arising from non-performance from the supplier, marketer or customer, at its discretion;

■ 90 days prior to the end of each year, the supplier must inform the utility of desire to renew the warranty and provide additional warranty if required.

From a legal point of view it is still unclear whether the LDCs are required to play the role of supplier of last resort (Stern, 1994). In practice, however, they do play this role and it seems that they do not object to doing so since in effect it does give them a number of business opportunities. Experience from Canada thus suggests that some kind of framework for ensuring continuity of supply is very important. It has to be stressed, however, that no customer was ever cut off as a consequence of introduction of competition on end user level.

Under the old regulatory regime in North America there were some instances where demand for gas could not be satisfied. No such events have been recorded for the period after deregulation. The deliverability of the North American gas supply system has been severely tested on some occasions in recent years (see Chapter 6), and the system has stood these tests very well. Pipeline and storage construction has increased, markets have become more flexible, integrated and price responsive. Where competition in end user markets has been created, adequate mechanisms to ensure security of supply have been created. It could therefore be concluded that there is no evidence that deregulation and introduction of competition have jeopardised security of supply. There is, on the contrary, reason to believe that security of supply has been enhanced after deregulation.

STRUCTURAL CHANGES IN EUROPEAN GAS MARKETS

In spite of strong demand and import growth, developments in European gas markets since the IEA's previous study on security of supply (which was completed in the spring of 1983) have been less dramatic than in North America; in particular, in most countries the changes in structure and regulation have been much less radical than in North America. This does not mean that the level of security of supply has not been affected over the period between 1980 and today. Some countries have adopted measures to introduce competition in their gas markets that are similar to those taken in North America, and a general development in the direction of a more competitive gas market in Europe can probably be expected, though the pace may be slow. This necessitates a discussion of possible future developments in gas market structures and their impact on security of supply.

The European and North American gas markets are different. For instance, the European gas market has a much shorter history and is much less mature but more import dependent. The basis and scope for competition in such a market are of course different from those in North America. The main differences between the markets and the implications for the introduction of competition are discussed in detail below, but the distinctions need to be borne in mind. Although some North American experience has relevance for the discussion of Europe, it is most relevant to situations like that of the United Kingdom, where the parallels are closest.

From 1980 to the present, there have been no major disturbances in European gas supplies, and only in very few cases have end consumers suffered as a consequence of deficient gas supplies. It is still relevant, however, to look at how past changes have influenced security of supply and the possible impact of future changes.

Market Development and Sectoral Composition

With three exceptions, gas demand in OECD Europe increased every year from 1980 to 1993. In total, gas demand increased by some 36% over the period. As the Table 4.1 indicates, however, the sectoral composition of aggregate demand has not changed significantly.

Table 4.1   Sectoral Shares in OECD Europe Gas Consumption (per cent)

	1980	**1992**
Electricity	15.0	16.0
Other transformation*	5.2	5.5
Industry	36.5	32.5
Other**	43.3	46.0

* Including pipeline fuel and consumption in transport.
** Mainly consists of residential/commercial demand.
Source: IEA Energy Balances.

The major change in sectoral composition of gas demand over the period has been a limited shift from industrial to residential/commercial demand, a normal development for a gas market which is still reaching maturity. The total number of gas customers in OECD Europe is now around 70 million. The development in the number of household customers in Germany, which increased by 43% from 1980 to 1993 (from 7.6 million to 10.9 million) is a good indication of what has taken place in the major gas consuming countries. Secure supplies to the growing number of residential/commercial customers has been the major challenge faced by gas companies in this area over the period.

Demand for gas for power generation was constrained over much of the period as a result of a European Community prohibition. Following the repeal of this prohibition in 1989, gas consumption in power generation has been increasing vigorously in some countries. As discussed in Chapter 3, increasing demand in this sector is expected by IEA member countries to be the most important single factor driving future gas consumption growth.

Demand for gas in OECD Europe is heavily concentrated in a small number of countries. In 1980, the United Kingdom, the Netherlands, Italy, Germany (including the former East Germany), France and Belgium accounted for 99.4% of total gas demand. In 1993, this share had diminished somewhat to 91%.

Gas security of supply becomes more important as the share of gas in total energy supply increases. Table 4.2 indicates the development in the share of gas in TPES for the countries in OECD Europe since 1980.

In general, OECD Europe's dependence on gas has increased over the period, increasing the importance of reliable supplies. The only country that has reduced its dependence on gas over the period is Belgium. Since around 1980, gas has been introduced in Denmark, Greece, Sweden and Turkey. A decision to do so has been taken in Portugal. More recent gas importers, including countries like Finland and Spain, in most cases located on the periphery of Europe, are often the most vulnerable to gas supply disruptions since at the outset they are normally dependent on a single or limited number of suppliers.[2]

---

2. In this context see also the security study by Eurogas: *Security of Supply of Natural Gas in Western Europe*. Brussels, November 1994.

Table 4.2   Gas Share in TPES in OECD Europe (per cent)

Country	1980	1992
Austria	16.7	20.8
Belgium	19.3	17.4
Denmark	-	11.0
Finland	3.2	8.8
France	11.4	12.1
Germany	16.1	16.7
Greece	-	0.6
Ireland	8.7	18.6
Italy	16.3	25.8
Luxembourg	11.5	12.2
Netherlands	46.4	48.5
Norway	4.6	14.2
Portugal	-	-
Spain	2.1	6.2
Sweden	-	1.3
Switzerland	4.7	7.7
Turkey	-	6.9
United Kingdom	20	23.2

Sourcing of Gas

In 1980 the share of gas supplies in OECD Europe coming from indigenous sources was 88%. By 1992 the share had declined to a little less than 70%. For the region as a whole this has obviously meant increased dependence on external supplies, though in practice there has been little diversification. Except for occasional cargoes of LNG from overseas, OECD Europe has continued to import gas from exactly the same sources as in 1980, i.e., Russia, Algeria and Libya. Since 1980, only two countries, Austria and Switzerland, have joined the group of countries having more than one supplier. Sweden, Denmark, Ireland, Finland and Turkey still have only one supplier, although Ireland and Turkey will shortly have a second.

During the 1980s, Belgium started to receive gas supplies in the form of LNG, joining Spain, France and Italy as LNG importers. Such supplies accounted for only 11.7% of total gas imports (including intra-European trade) into OECD Europe in 1993.

In spite of the fact that the number of extra-European gas suppliers has stayed the same over the last 15 years, the extent to which gas imported into Europe crosses more than one border has increased, which means that transit has become a more important issue. The break-up of the former Soviet Union and the split of the former CSFR increased the number of transit countries for gas to Europe. In fact, nearly all Russian gas coming into OECD Europe is now transited through a third country. The issues raised in terms of security of supply have been clearly demonstrated by the transit of Russian gas through the Ukraine. The controversies on transit between Russia and the Ukraine have given rise to the only real shortfall problem in any IEA country in recent years; on some occasions disturbances in supplies from Russia have led to shortages for industrial consumers in Turkey.

All gas imports through pipeline from Algeria are transited through a third country. Some of the exports from the Netherlands and Norway also pass through third countries within the OECD. In 1992, the share of gas imports in OECD Europe passing through third countries was 69%. Of this, some 75% came through non-member countries. (LNG ships may pass through the waters of third countries, but LNG trade is here regarded as involving only two countries.)

Developments in Gas Contracting

One obvious problem encountered in discussing gas contracts in Europe is that such contracts are not normally in the public domain and therefore not open to scrutiny. It is therefore difficult to say anything precise about developments in this area over the last 10 to 15 years. Nonetheless, disregarding recent developments in the United Kingdom, it is probably fair to say that international contracting for gas supplies in Europe has not changed dramatically over the last 15 years. The basis for gas imports in Europe has always been long-term take or pay contracts. Sellers are companies like Gasunie in the Netherlands, Gazprom in Russia (earlier Sojuzgazexport), Sonatrach in Algeria and the companies of the Troll group and the GFU in Norway. Buyers are typically state owned monopolies like GDF in France and SNAM in Italy or private companies like Ruhrgas in Germany. There is no doubt that the type of contract concluded in the past has provided a good basis for secure gas supplies in Europe in general and in particular that it has been instrumental in providing the basis for developing new gas supply projects where gas is being introduced into new countries or has seen rapid expansion in existing markets.

The basic concept of the contracts has not changed: they still have a duration of 20-25 years and a pricing mechanism which links the gas price to the development in crude oil prices or petroleum product prices (gasoil and heavy fuel oil) with a lag. At the beginning of the 1980s the link to oil prices was stronger than today; over time the basket of escalators has become a little more diversified in that other fuel prices are also used as references to some extent. Contracts now also provide for more frequent price revisions than before, i.e., opportunities for sellers and buyers to renegotiate the base price of the contract.

An interesting feature of the European gas contracting culture is that adverse price developments have not led to disturbances or changes in supplies outside what the volume conditions in contracts allow, with the possible exception of Algeria in the first half of the 1980s. What the North Americans call price majeure, i.e., a situation where the seller decides to reduce his supplies to an existing customer because he can get a better price for his gas elsewhere, seems to be non-existent in Europe.

Over the past 15 years there has been a move away from field specific depletion contracts towards supply contracts. This means that the seller, instead of committing to deliver gas from a specific field, undertakes to deliver gas from a specific group of fields or to deliver gas without specifying where the gas will come from. In security of supply terms this is potentially positive since it decreases reliance on specific fields. This development has been seen in Norwegian gas sales contracts, and appears to be present in the contracts of other gas exporters.

Although the overwhelming bulk of imports into Europe is delivered under the type of contracts outlined above, it is interesting to note the recent emergence of a new type of gas contract for sales into power generation, exemplified by the contract concluded between the GFU in Norway and SEP, the major electricity network in the Netherlands. The main principles of this type of contract, which is based on the indifference principle, have been described in Chapter 3. Suffice it to say that this type of contract can contribute to long-term security of supply in that it makes it economically feasible to embark upon new projects even in a situation where oil prices are low.

Over the past few years LNG spot deals have emerged as a new feature in the European gas supply picture. Such transactions, formerly extremely rare, seem to be on the increase: in 1994 there were ten such spot transactions worldwide, up from nine in 1993 and five in 1992.[3] The total volume of these deals was around 2 bcm in 1994, of which 60% ended up in Europe. Under such spot deals European countries have received LNG cargoes from Algeria, Libya, Australia and Abu Dhabi. Such transactions add more flexibility to the market. This flexibility was illustrated by Spain's purchase of LNG from Australia where it was possible for large tankers (too large for the Spanish terminals) to deliver their cargoes to Belgium in exchange for Algerian cargoes redirected from Belgium to Spain. The Spanish terminal at Huelva is now being expanded to handle 125,000 cubic metre tankers.

Concerning contracts further downstream in the gas market, it seems that there has been an increase in the volume sold under interruptible contract over most of the period considered, though the number has stagnated recently. The extent to which the potential for cut off under such contracts is used varies a lot from country to country though most interruptible customers experience very much less than the maximum interruption allowable under their contracts. Interruption takes place rarely in the United Kingdom, and interruptible customers are almost never cut off in France. As analysis in Chapter 6 shows, interruptible supplies play a potentially important role in shortage situations. Multi-fired capacity in the electricity sector plays a similar role. The share of gas fired electricity generating capacity which is multi-fired has increased absolutely and relatively in OECD Europe over the time period considered here.

Developments in Transportation Infrastructure

The length of the pipeline network (excluding distribution pipelines) in OECD Europe increased from 123,300 km to 171,900 km between 1980 and 1990 (Chabrelie, 1994), i.e., an increase of 39% which is slightly higher than the increase in gas consumption over the same period. In security of supply terms these figures do not of themselves demonstrate an improvement. Some of the pipeline construction took place because new countries decided to introduce gas. In some countries with more mature markets, however, for instance Germany, extension and integration of the pipeline system also has contributed to security of supply. In recent years, a number of new international gas interconnections have been built. Table 4.3 gives an indication of the number of such interconnections that exist and are planned. The table includes a number of countries outside OECD Europe either because they are suppliers to OECD Europe or transit countries for gas to this region. Seen from a security of supply point of view, this sort of static picture has obvious limitations:

---

3. *Petrostrategies*, Volume 9, No. 424, February 6, 1995.

■ It does not show the direction of gas flows.

■ It does not show the possibilities for reversal of gas flows in a crisis. For instance in a shortfall in Danish production gas can be imported from Germany, whereas normally gas flows from Denmark to Germany.

■ It does not show the possibility for backhaul flows and gas swaps in the system.

Table 4.3 also indicates a number of planned pipeline interconnections. Since 1993, the year for which the table was compiled, some of the planned pipelines have become operational, for instance the pipeline between France and Spain constructed to bring Norwegian gas to Spain. Other planned pipelines, like the Interconnector between the United Kingdom and the Continent and the new pipeline between Algeria and Spain, will contribute to more diversified supplies and a more integrated pipeline system.[4]

As far as construction of LNG facilities in OECD Europe is concerned, the only major development that has taken place since 1980 is the construction of the LNG reception and regasification facilities at Zeebrugge in Belgium. Over the period, three terminals, one in France, one in the United Kingdom and one in Spain have been closed.

Construction of Storage

Construction of gas storage has increased significantly over the period considered: underground storage capacity in OECD Europe increased from 12.9 bcm (working gas volume) in 1980 to 28.85 bcm in 1989 (Cornot, 1994). By the end of 1992 it had increased to 43.5 bcm. Available gas volumes from storage increased from 5.4% of annual demand in 1980 (corresponding to around 20 days of average consumption) to 14% of total consumption in 1992 (corresponding to around 51 days of average consumption). Use of gas storage is one of the most important instruments to counter gas disruptions in the main gas consuming countries in OECD Europe. On this basis it can be concluded that security of supply in those countries has probably been enhanced over the past 15 years. There are also indications that storage capacity will increase rapidly in the future. Submissions from IEA member countries indicate that the total storage volume in OECD Europe can be expected to increase to around 60 bcm by the year 2000. Using the same countries' demand forecasts, however, this means that storage capacity as a percentage of demand would increase only slightly to 14.6% or 53 days of average demand.

Thus, the major gas consuming countries seem to be well equipped with storage capacity and will become increasingly so in the future. For some of the smaller gas consumers, often newcomers in the market and dependent on a single or limited number of suppliers, the situation is less reassuring. Countries like Finland, Sweden, Switzerland and Ireland have no storage capacity. Spain has little storage capacity compared with its consumption, but has plans for significant additions by 2010. Turkey has only recently inaugurated a new LNG storage facility. One major reason for this insufficiency of storage is the lack of sites that are suitable from a physical point of view. In some cases international co-operation may alleviate the situation: for instance, Switzerland has an agreement for storage capacity in France (in addition to having a very well diversified supply portfolio), and Sweden until recently had a similar agreement for storage in Denmark.

---

4. For more systematic information on new pipeline projects and gas infrastructure in general, reference is made to the IEA gas transportation study (IEA, 1994).

Table 4.3   European Gas Network Interconnections, 1992–1993

	Algeria	Austria	Belgium	Bulgaria	CIS	Czecho-slovakia	Denmark	Finland	France	Germany	Greece	Hungary	Italy	Ireland	Luxem-bourg	Morocco	Nether-lands	Norway	Poland	Romania	Spain	Sweden	Switzer-land	Tunisia	United Kingdom	Yugo-slavia
Algeria													✓			■					■			✓		
Austria					✓	✓				✓		■	✓													✓
Belgium									✓	■			✓		✓		✓	■							■	
Bulgaria					✓						✓									✓						
CIS						✓		✓	✓	✓	■	✓	✓						✓	✓			✓			✓
Czechoslovakia										✓																
Denmark										✓												✓			■	
Finland																										
France										✓							✓	✓			■		✓			
Germany															✓		✓	✓	✓				✓			
Greece																				✓						
Hungary																				✓						✓
Ireland																									■	
Luxembourg																										
Morocco																					■					
Netherlands													✓					✓					✓			
Norway																					■				✓	
Poland																										
Romania																										
Spain																										
Sweden																										
Switzerland													✓													
Tunisia													✓													
United Kingdom																										
Yugoslavia													✓													

✓ Existing connection   ■ Planned connection

Source: Marie-Françoise Chabrelie: *European Natural Gas Trade by Pipeline*, Cedigaz, 1993

Costs are also relevant to the discussion of adequate storage. Some countries would argue that there is a limit to the costs which can be borne by consumers to provide for storage as long as gas is to remain competitive with other fuels.

RECENT REGULATORY CHANGES IN OECD EUROPE

Since organisation and regulation of the gas industry in Europe are dealt with at some length in the IEA's 1994 gas transportation study, this chapter will review only recent international and national regulation having implications for security of supply.

Within the European Union, two directives have been passed in recent years that could indirectly have implications for security of supply:

■ the directive repealing the prohibition on burning natural gas in power stations. Since this was a precondition for the expansion of gas consumption in power stations, it may be said to have had a profound impact on the whole European supply situation and also on security of supply issues in the electricity industry itself.

■ the transit directive, which was adopted to facilitate the transit of natural gas between high pressure transmission grids. This directive has been implemented, but has so far had little practical significance. Its most important aspect is perhaps the fact that it has to some extent served as a model for the transit provisions in the Energy Charter Treaty.

The Energy Charter Treaty, signed in December 1994, contains a number of provisions, in particular transit issues, that in one way or another could influence future security of supply. The Treaty states (Article 7) that transit states shall not, in the event of a dispute over any matter arising from the transit in question, interrupt or reduce the existing flow of energy goods. The Treaty has been signed by most of the countries on which OECD Europe is dependent for its gas supplies, though not Algeria, Tunisia, Morocco and Libya.

Over the past few years, much of the discussion on the future of the European gas industry has taken as its point of departure the proposals from the European Commission on the internal market for energy, put forward in 1992. The original version, which proposed mandatory third party access to networks for both electricity and gas, was rejected by a majority of EU member countries. New versions were put forward in December 1993. For gas, the new directive proposal introduced the concept of "negotiated third party access". As the term implies, access to pipelines under the directive would not be mandatory but subject to negotiation. At the present time (June 1995), the destiny of the proposal is still not clear.

Recently the Commission of EU has submitted to the Council and to the European Parliament a proposal relating to trans-European networks in the energy sector. The proposal includes:

(i) guidelines which will identify the objectives, priorities and projects of common interest in this sector. These guidelines constitute a set of criteria for the identification of the most appropriate projects with a Community-wide dimension in the development of energy networks;

(ii) a decision for measures that create a favourable climate for energy network projects and cover the administrative, technical and financial aspects of such projects;

(iii) a financial Regulation which specifies the methods of financial contributions for projects of common interest identified in the guidelines.

The proposal accommodates the view of the gas industry, expressed in the context of the recent discussion of EU energy policy, that in the outlying regions of the Community, public subsidies for setting up new networks can be justified on the basis that although possibly unprofitable in the short term such projects will contribute to long-term security of supply, as well as to economic and social cohesion.

In the Green Paper called "For a European Energy Policy", the European Commission states that it believes "that security of supply shall be ensured through an open market functioning under competitive conditions at all stages from production to transportation, in conformity with the Treaty (of Rome)". It is difficult to see how competitive conditions in the gas market can be arrived at without some form of effective access to transportation. Third party access to pipelines therefore remains a key question, and the implications for security of supply are discussed below. First, however, current market developments and structural changes affecting security of supply will be reviewed.

Regulatory Changes on a National Level

As far as responsibility for security of supply is concerned, the general picture in OECD Europe is relatively simple: in cases where there is a monopoly, often a state owned gas company taking care of all gas activity including imports, transmission and distribution, the responsibility is with that monopoly. In countries like France and Italy, where the dominating gas company is not responsible for all distribution, it is still generally responsible for security of supply except in the part of the gas chain closest to the end consumer where the local distribution company is responsible. The situation in Germany is similar, except that there is more than one transmission company which is responsible in their respective areas. In most countries the gas company responsible for security of supply operates according to defined security of supply criteria or standards, defined by itself or in co-operation with the Government in question.

In the EU, competition authorities have put pressure on some countries to abolish import monopolies in the energy industry, and Denmark and Finland have eliminated the monopoly position of their state owned gas companies in this respect. So far this has had little direct effect, but if alternative importers emerge, this would presumably spur a debate on responsibility for security of supply.

Recent Developments in the United Kingdom

The United Kingdom is the only European country where there has recently been a real debate on the responsibility for security of supply as a consequence of regulatory changes to introduce competition. Over the last few years it has introduced regulatory changes that in many respects are similar to those in Canada:

■ Comprehensive access to the British Gas (BG) transportation system from 1986 (mandatory third party access) and freedom for anybody to build pipelines.

■ Some degree of unbundling of services in that BG has had to divide its activities into separate units, one of which is the transportation unit.

■ Opening up for competition in the contract market, i.e., the greater part of the industrial market and part of the commercial market.

■ Plans for gradually opening up the residential market to competition from 1996 with a view to a fully competitive gas market from 1998.

Although these changes have already had significant consequences on some parts of the market, it is only recently, in particular in the context of the proposals to introduce competition in the residential market, that security issues have come to the forefront. Under the present arrangements, the size and comprehensiveness of BG offers the consumer a high degree of assurance against risks arising from both network failure and shortage of gas supply, either because of failure to contract for sufficient supplies or through commercial failure. BG's position as the major purchaser of gas from producing fields, its ownership of the pipeline and storage facilities, its plan to meet the highest reasonably expected demand coupled with its responsibility to protect "core" domestic customers in preference to non-domestic customers, are important factors in this context. The cornerstone of the future arrangements for security of supply is the planned Network Code. The proposals for the basic structure of the Code include the following elements:

■ Shared responsibility of all users of the pipeline network for balancing supply and demand.

■ Responsibility of BG Transportation and Storage unit for operating the balancing regime.

■ Responsibility of BG Transportation and Storage for ensuring sufficient pipeline and storage capacity.

■ Priority of supply for domestic customers in case of major supply shortfalls that cannot be absorbed by the market.

No company that wants to operate a public gas network, or to supply the domestic market through a public gas network, can do so unless authorised by licence. In the case of supply to the domestic market, authorisations will be granted only to companies demonstrating to the Director General of Gas Supply (DGGS) through their gas purchase arrangements their ability to meet any reasonable supply obligations they may incur in the light of their business plans. They will also be required to demonstrate to the DGGS their financial soundness, and to undertake a number of other obligations, for example, in relation to the maintenance of supply to customers. They will in addition be required to subscribe to the Network Code.

These obligations on suppliers, taken together with the verification by OFGAS of suppliers' ability to meet their commitments and the provisions of the Network Code to facilitate balancing of available supplies, should, according to the UK Government, provide a large measure of assurance that domestic customers will enjoy continuity of supply. This notwithstanding, there will be a need for a responsible party to act in place of a failed supplier in order to ensure that consumers continue to receive supply for an interim period until they can move to alternative suppliers. The British proposals to solve this problem differ from the ones adopted in Canada on some points, mainly that no individual supplier is required to set aside special volumes of gas either in storage or with producers. As to the responsibility for ensuring last resort supply, several solutions have been proposed: one is to let BG (Transportation and Storage) be responsible; another is to place the obligation collectively on all suppliers, who could in turn nominate one of their number or an agent to take on this role.

Regarding security of supply, the UK gas market is still in transition, and it is very difficult to draw final conclusions on the introduction of competition, with TPA as the most important instrument in that respect. There are, however, at least some indications that security has been enhanced rather than jeopardised:

■ Gas reserves have increased in recent years.

■ The number of producing gas fields has increased (by 9 fields in 1993, bringing the total to 50).

■ Direct supplies from producers to end consumers in the industrial and power generation sector have led to an increase in the construction of pipelines and other infrastructure.

■ The contract structure has become more diverse as regards both time period and forms of indexation, responding to the needs of sellers and buyers.

■ Overcontracting of gas by some large gas buyers has given rise to a market for spot gas, which has some value in security terms.

■ The liberalisation of the market has been instrumental in the realisation of a large market for gas in power generation. This has increased diversity within the electricity sector.

Recent Developments in Germany

Apart from the United Kingdom, Germany is the only country in OECD Europe where there is gas to gas competition. Rather than being a result of a change in regulation, it is an example of a sizeable player exploiting regulation already in place: Wintershall, a gas producer and a subsidiary of the chemicals company, BASF, has used the freedom to build pipelines in Germany to enter the German gas market in a joint venture with Gazprom, the Russian monopoly gas producer and exporter and has actively competed to gain both new and existing gas customers. This venture has solved the problem of access to transportation by building its own pipelines, including storage facilities. This is one way of creating competition, but it requires big players with the financial muscle to build pipelines without much external financing and a large initial baseload of sales. In security of supply terms, the effect of the venture to date has been to introduce one more supply source (the venture imports gas from the UK through the Netherlands), two new pipelines potentially covering a large part of Germany and one big storage facility (with another one planned).

Regulation Concerning TPA on a National Level

The United Kingdom is the only country in OECD Europe having a full-fledged system of mandatory TPA. From the recent debate on TPA in Europe one may get the impression that TPA is a completely new idea in most countries. This is in fact not the case; a few countries already have legislation that creates some kind of TPA:

■ In Switzerland a law adopted in 1963 contains an obligation for pipeline owners to carry gas for third parties on certain conditions.

■ In Sweden, the Pipeline Law of 1978 requires capacity to be made available to a third party, for a reasonable charge, where such action does not cause substantial disadvantage to the owner.

- In Norway, the Government may decide that pipelines owned by one licensee may be used by others, if operational and social conditions warrant and if the government finds that such use would not be to the unreasonable detriment of the licensee's requirements or those of another party already assured the right to use the installation.

- In 1991, a law was passed in Italy that introduced a limited form of open access to the SNAM pipeline system for domestic gas producers using their own gas in own or affiliates' facilities or selling gas to ENEL or to municipal electricity producers. Tariffs and operational conditions for such transport have been laid down in an agreement between SNAM and Unione Petrolifera, an association of petroleum producers.

- In Germany, the "Law against restrictions made on competition of 1957" allows TPA. A company from which TPA is requested however can refuse it when TPA affects the conditions of supply for the customers of the company which is requested to grant TPA.

Although Portugal does not have legislation providing for TPA, it is known to be in favour of TPA. A recent French report on the organisation of gas and electricity markets, the so-called Mandil report, proposed a limited access to GDF's pipeline network for certain user categories. These proposals, however, have not been adopted.

In some countries, for instance in Austria, there are provisions that give third parties the right to participate in the construction of new pipelines. This type of "up-front TPA" has also been used for the construction of the UK-Continent Interconnector and for the Midal-Stegal pipelines in Germany (although in the latter case it has not resulted in any third party participation).

It is also interesting to note in this context that some countries in Central Europe, for instance Hungary and Romania, already have provision for TPA.

Gas Industry Tendency towards Horizontal and Vertical Integration

The fact that there is a debate on competition under way in Europe, to a large extent initiated by the EU directive proposals, has spurred a number of initiatives leading to structural change in the gas industry: expectations of a more open and competitive gas market have led to strategic positioning moves both by traditional gas companies and by newcomers to the gas industry.

At the distribution level, there has for a long time been horizontal integration between gas and electricity companies in some countries in the sense that local utilities offer both gas and electricity (and in some cases also water and other public services). In the Netherlands, for example, two thirds of the local utilities distribute both gas and electricity. In several countries the tendency is towards fewer, but bigger and more diversified local utilities. In the United Kingdom, horizontal integration between electricity and gas has also taken place at a higher level in the gas chain in that Regional Electricity Companies (RECs) have entered into alliances with independent gas companies established after liberalisation of the British gas market. The most important motive behind such alliances is to exploit economies in operations and billing, but such alliances could potentially have a positive effect on security of supply in that production and distribution of gas and electricity could be co-ordinated in shortfall situations. Investments by west European gas distribution companies in gas companies in eastern Europe are an example of horizontal integration in the more traditional sense, though it is more difficult to identify its direct effects on security of supply.

Vertical integration in the gas chain has potentially much more important effects on security of supply. The most notable event in this area over the past few years is no doubt Gazprom's emergence as a potentially sizeable player in European downstream markets. Gazprom's downstream involvement is an explicit part of the Russian Government's energy strategy and reflects a wish to share the rent realised in the downstream part of the gas chain. Gazprom now has joint ventures in a number of countries in both eastern and western Europe, the most well known being that with Wintershall in Germany which involves purchase, transportation, storage and marketing of gas. In Finland, Gazprom has taken a 25% participation in Gasum OY, a joint venture with Neste, the state owned oil and gas company. The new company has a de facto monopoly in the Finnish market and takes all of its gas from Russia. When the company was established, both parties stressed the security aspects of the deal. Neste officials said that "Gazprom now has an interest in maintaining stable gas supplies to Finland and avoiding the conflicts over pricing that have plagued its relations with importers". A Gazprom official stated that "Finland can expect preferential treatment as a result of this agreement. Gazprom now has the incentive to make the terms to Gasum as favourable as possible and contracts as stable as possible".[5]

This type of agreement between gas producers and buyers could enhance security of supply for the buyer in question by giving him preferential access to new supplies. On a daily, operational basis such an agreement gives the producer a strong economic incentive to keep deliveries going, not only because he earns money from selling the gas but also because he shares the revenues and profits earned further downstream. In a shortage situation, however, it would not necessarily be easy to give undue preferential treatment to such an affiliated company if other sales contracts held by the same producer have rules about prorationing in shortfall situations. As long as gas trade under joint venture agreements does not take place to the detriment of other deliveries, it seems clear that this type of vertical integration can only have positive effects on security of supply.

Gas producers in Norway and Algeria also have a strategy of vertical integration. In the Norwegian case, this has so far resulted in downstream participation in the United Kingdom (Statoil and Norsk Hydro participation in Alliance Gas with BP) and Germany (Statoil participation in VNG and Statoil/Hydro participation in a pipeline company with Ruhrgas and BEB Erdgas Erdöl GmbH, and participation by Statoil/Norsk Hydro and other Norwegian producers with Ruhrgas in the Etzel gas storage facilities). The Algerian strategy in this respect has so far not resulted in any conspicuous results, but the will to go in this direction has been clearly stated.

Downstream involvement by gas producers appears to be more common than upstream involvement by transmission and distribution companies, but there are some examples of the latter; for instance the Ruhrgas participation in two offshore gas fields in the United Kingdom. Likewise, British power producers using gas have gone upstream by acquiring shares in gas producing fields and British Gas itself is a major producer. Recently, Gaz de France has announced that it will invest heavily in upstream activity. This kind of move probably reflects two concerns:

■ a fear that profits might move to other parts of the gas chain as a result of regulatory and market driven changes in the industry and

■ a preoccupation with access to gas reserves.

---

5. *Russian Petroleum Investor*, July/August 1994.

Conclusion
Although the regulatory changes that have taken place in the European gas industry over the past 15 years are not as dramatic and as extensive as those seen in North America over the same period, both structural and regulatory changes have taken place that have clearly had effects on gas security of supply. There are indications that the ability to counter gas disruptions in general has improved. Some countries, however, are still vulnerable to disruptions because they rely on only one supplier and/or do not have sufficient storage capacity. For OECD Europe as a whole, dependence on gas as a fuel has increased and the reliance of extra-European supply sources has increased without this being offset to any large extent by increased diversification. On the other hand, the European supply network has become more integrated and more flexible.

While the situation in general as far as security of supply is concerned may be characterised as quite satisfactory at present, future developments towards more competition might have important consequences for security of supply, as discussed below.

FUTURE DEVELOPMENTS IN EUROPEAN GAS MARKETS

The discussion of what the future might bring in terms of the interaction between market and regulatory developments and security of supply for OECD Europe will be based on two assumptions:

a) The market is heading for more competition driven by regulatory changes as well as market forces.

b) Dependence on external supplies will increase.

The North American experience described above indicates that even radical changes towards more competition do not need to jeopardise security of supply in physical terms. The basic principles on which the supply system is based are that the actors in the market are free to enter into the contracts they want and that security of supply is taken care of by letting the actors themselves build the necessary incentives into the contracts. For representatives of the gas industry all over the world, security of gas supply is a major preoccupation; the whole industry is keenly aware that the image of gas is at stake in any disturbances in supplies. This natural incentive to safeguard supplies should not be forgotten in considering regulatory measures in this area.

Market liberalisation in North America appears to have had a positive affect on central indicators of security such as gas deliverability, infrastructure development and price responsiveness. Some of the developments that have taken place are of a general nature and could probably be reproduced in a European context; recent experience in the United Kingdom gives some support to this view. But it is also important to keep in mind that, in some respects, the situation in Europe is very different from that in North America:

■ The number of supply sources is smaller and the potential for an increase in this number is more limited. Indeed, the analysis in Chapter 3 suggests that reliance on the main existing external suppliers is likely to increase. Although for most countries there will be a degree of diversification in the sense of an increase in the number of suppliers, the numbers involved are very small indeed by comparison with North America or even the UK market. In most situations, the European market could only be described as oligopolistic. Furthermore, new supply investments for Europe tend to be very large and take a long time to come on stream, both because of the sheer physical investment and construction effort needed and because lengthy commercial and political negotiations may be needed to establish their viability. Thus many of the potential large sources of supply, such as Nigerian LNG or the Yamal project in Russian, represent resources whose existence has been known about for years, which have been the subject of extensive appraisal and negotiation — even of contracts — but whose contribution to European supply within the timescale of this study remains uncertain. The Yamal project, if implemented in full, could cost upwards of $20 billion, take a decade or more to complete and represent an increment to European supply equivalent to the entire consumption of a major gas consuming country.

■ Europe is dependent on external supply sources. These sources are not intrinsically less secure than indigenous sources; but buyers feel that they have less control and influence over such sources and regard them as more risky. The issues are not solely related to the suppliers themselves. External supply routes are becoming longer and more complex; more countries have to be transited often though areas of rapid political change. On the principle that a chain is as strong as its weakest link, the more complicated a route, the riskier it appears.

■ The European market is less mature and more diverse. It consists of a core of six countries with relatively mature markets, accounting for 90% of total consumption, plus a number of smaller markets still in their infancy where the ability to expand infrastructure and diversification of supplies are probably more important than introducing competition. Even the "mature" markets are relatively young in North American terms. The North American market grew rapidly in the 1950s, developing a Continent-wide infrastructure with multiple pipeline links and interconnections. The European market for natural gas barely existed before the 1970s — consumption was still predominantly local. European gas consumption has tripled since 1971 while North American consumption has remained static. Many major European pipeline connections — e.g. UK-Ireland; UK-Continent; Spain-France; Spain-North Africa —are either very recent or still on the drawing board. This is significant for security in two ways:

a) physical choice of routes and suppliers is inevitably limited by the available infrastructure in natural gas markets. A physical supply link is necessary to enable a commercial transaction to take place, (even if the commercial transaction does not represent an actual flow of gas, e.g., sales from Canada to Mexico).

b) economic gas developments include huge investments of capital which may be put at risk in liberalised markets. For a supply route to develop in the first place there may need to be an assurance that it will be possible to recoup the capital investment involved. Once the capital is amortised, competition may be more acceptable.

The options available for Europe if it seeks to introduce more competition will therefore raise a number of complex issues pertaining to security of supply. The major preoccupation is likely to remain with external supplies and ways to secure these.

More Competition, but Driven by Regulation or by Market Forces?

As indicated above, the European gas industry is at a watershed in that the market actors are expecting regulatory changes and trying to position themselves for them without knowing what exactly will happen. The established market structure is under pressure from a variety of sources. Very simply, the three major driving forces are the expected outcome of the discussion on the EU directives, regulatory developments on a national level and the emergence of new entrants to the gas market like large industrial consumers, electricity producers and service companies.

What will be the impact of these forces on the future structure of the gas industry and the implications for security of supply is of course impossible to predict with precision and beyond the scope of this chapter. Instead it will attempt to describe some of the options with a view to illustrating some of the issues involved.

Table 4.4 summarises one commentator's view of some of the options for intervention in gas markets that have been discussed in recent years, supplemented by some indications of their possible effects on trading patterns, new contracts, price formation, risk and return requirements and security of supply.[6]

All the measures listed in the table could have wide reaching and complex effects, which cannot be discussed exhaustively in this context. Some comments, however, are appropriate:

1. Third Party Access

As stated above, TPA is one key instrument in introducing competition. The IEA has dealt extensively with TPA in its recent transportation study (IEA, 1994). In this context it is important to stress that several forms of TPA are possible and that their effects could be quite different. At least four different forms can be distinguished:

■ Voluntary TPA, where the pipeline companies let out free capacity for a commercially negotiated fee, if they choose to do so.

■ Negotiated TPA, (as proposed by the EU Commission), where the pipeline has the burden of proof if it wants to refuse access.

■ Mandatory TPA, where capacity has to be offered to third parties for a regulated fee (present UK system).

■ US type TPA, where both access and tariffs are regulated and where the pipeline company can not distinguish between transportation of its own gas and that of others because transportation services are unbundled. (The United Kingdom is moving in this direction).

The effects will of course depend on the form of TPA introduced. It is worth noting that EU member countries have so far not agreed on negotiated TPA, as proposed by the Commission.

2. Unbundling or Functional Split-up

In its extreme form unbundling would mean separate companies for production, wholesale sales and purchase transactions, transmission, storage and distribution. For instance, integrated companies would have to split transportation and distribution and/or to split production and transmission. In North America unbundling has been one of the major driving forces behind the construction of storage capacity. This would probably also be the case in Europe if unbundling were introduced. In the United States the objective of competition-induced efficiencies has been considered more important than keeping economies of scope and scale within integrated companies. An advanced form of unbundling in some of the European markets could be more difficult to defend from the point of view of economic efficiency. The latest EU directive proposal contains provisions only on unbundling of accounts.

---

6. The ideas behind this table are further elaborated in Annex 1.

Table 4.4   Possible Effects of Political Intervention in the Gas Market

Measure	Effect on trading pattern	Effect on new contracts	Effect on price formation	Effect on risk and return requirement	Effect on security of supply
Third Party Access	More competition to end users	Split-up	Stability weakened	Higher risk and higher return requirement	Diversification of supplies and risk
Unbundling or functional split-up	More competition on all levels	Split-up	Stability weakened	Higher risk for producers and higher return requirement	Diversification of supplies and risk
Regulation of transportation tariffs	Direct trade between producers and consumers	Split-up	Guaranteed return at transportation level	Higher risk for producers and higher return requirement	Diversification of supplies and risk
Competition at production level	Enhanced role for transportation companies	Split-up of contracts from producers	Lower producer prices	Higher risk for producers and higher return requirement	Diversification of supplies and risk
Competition to final users	Reduced role for transportation companies	Split-up, spot market, futures market	Lower consumer prices	Higher risk for producers and higher return requirement	Split-up of supply responsibility
Horizontal deregulation	Restructuring, oligopoly	Larger contracts	Lower consumer prices	Lower risk for producers and lower return requirement	Diversification of supplies and risk
Vertical deregulation	Integration	Larger contracts	Lower consumer prices	Lower risk for producers and lower return requirement	Direct links between producers and consumers
Horizontal and vertical integration	Integrated oligopoly or monopoly	Larger contracts	Lower consumer prices	Lower risk for producers and lower return requirement	Direct links between producers and consumers
Taxes and duties	Buffer between producers and consumers	Gas less competitive	Higher consumer prices, lower and less stable producer prices	Higher risk for producers and higher return requirement	Weaker incentives for new investments, potentially compromising security of supply

Source: Presented to the IEA in the autumn of 1994 by Øystein Noreng at a seminar concerning future gas market developments.

3. Regulation of Transportation Tariffs

Regulated tariffs at a reasonable level combined with TPA could in some cases make it easier to bring new supplies to the market. The IEA transportation study provides a discussion of the incentive effects of tariff regulation.

4. Competition at Production Level

Measures to encourage more competition at the producer level could in principle lead to a more diversified supply structure but would in practice have limited effects as long as suppliers outside Europe were not affected. Arguably this could weaken the position of European areas.

5. Competition at End-user Level

This would require access to transportation and a clear definition of ultimate responsibility for supply. Experience from Canada shows that these problems can be solved, but the limited number of supply options in most European countries makes it even more important to identify whether the economic benefits really justify the effort. In addition (see below) competition could increase the risks faced by existing companies and reduce their willingness to invest.

6. Horizontal Deregulation

Such a deregulation would imply an elimination of regulation restricting customers in one geographical area from seeking supplies from other areas.

7. Vertical Deregulation

Such deregulation would imply freedom for gas companies to develop business activities both upstream and downstream and could for instance lead to direct links between producers and consumers.

8. Horizontal and Vertical Deregulation

This combination would abolish both horizontal and vertical barriers to participation in the various parts of the gas industry.

9. Taxes and Duties

Taxes and duties represent a political risk in that lower end user prices as a consequence of more competition in the market might be offset by taxes imposed by the government in gas importing countries.

Most of the above-mentioned measures could be implemented both on a European level and on a national level. The number of combinations makes it very difficult to construct a clear picture of the market structure in 15 years time and the implications for security of supply. One possible development path will, however, be sketched to illustrate some phenomena that could affect security of supply. There is of course no implication that this is a path endorsed by or even expected by the IEA.

The most important feature of this scenario of the future European gas market is easier access to transportation than is presently the case in most European countries. This could come about both by introduction of negotiated TPA and general freedom to build pipelines. It could be the result either of regulatory action at the Commission level or the outcome of court cases. Some proponents of TPA claim that present EU legislation is sufficient for new market entrants to obtain access to existing pipelines. Events in the market, for instance the construction and start up of the UK-Continent Interconnector, could present possibilities for testing this proposition. If for instance a power producer or large industrial consumer in Germany, Belgium or France wanted to buy gas from a producer on the UK Continental Shelf, he could probably contract for transportation in the Interconnector but would also need transmission capacity to bring the gas from Zeebrugge, the landing point of the Interconnector, to the point of consumption. In the event of a refusal from the transmission company in question, the would be shipper could seek support from the European Court of Justice. A successful outcome (for the shipper) of such a court case could spur a number of similar cases elsewhere.

Easier access to transportation would in the first phase encourage large customers to try to buy gas directly from producers, although consortia of smaller buyers could also emerge. If customers were required to fight in the courts to obtain access on a case by case basis, the number of prospective buyers would probably be limited. It should be remembered, however, that the volumes needed by a major power producer, for example, could be sufficient to justify the development of a new field.

One of the reasons why the market for gas in power generation has not really been successful in Europe (with a few notable exceptions like the United Kingdom) may be that power producers have not been able to buy gas directly from producers. Power producers have requirements that are different from those of a buyer with a dominant share of household customers in his customer portfolio. Direct contact with the producer would probably make it easier for the power producer to obtain the type of contract he prefers. It is important to note that in most cases demand from power producers would represent new demand in the sense that it would not substitute for existing load. Thus, no take or pay problem would arise in relation to existing contracts. The fact that power generators can sometimes afford to pay a higher price for the gas than other users could also facilitate new field development projects. Freedom to build pipelines and more competition upstream could also imply possibilities for prospective buyers to invest in fields and pipelines. For security reasons and for reasons pertaining to geographical distance, power producers might be inclined to prefer purchasing from Europe, but ventures in other supply areas could also emerge. ENEL in Italy has demonstrated a willingness to seek supplies both in Africa and the Middle East. Other countries may also seek external supplies in the future.

In a number of countries large industrial gas consumers are pressing for a more open gas market that would enable them to buy gas directly and thereby reduce their gas purchase costs. Bulk industrial use of gas is not, however, the highest paying segment of the market, and this group of buyers would probably be more constrained in their choice of supply than power producers. Procurement in nearby geographical areas would probably be dominant, but purchase from producers going downstream would be another solution.

If the recent decisions to proceed towards a competitive residential market in the United Kingdom are successful from the consumer's point of view, a development in this direction in some markets in Continental Europe cannot be excluded. In this case, the issue of who should be the supplier of last resort will emerge, but experience from Canada shows that it is possible to find viable solutions to this problem.

If a large number of residential and industrial gas consumers seek alternative suppliers, it could potentially cause a take or pay problem for the former supplier if his market was eroded. The probability of this causing any problems in physical supply terms is less clear. The fact that a group of customers look for more competitive supplies does not necessarily mean that the existing supplier will lose those customers; however he may have to improve his product or to lower his price to keep them. If he is constrained by take or pay obligations, his marginal cost of gas may be very low so he should in practice be able to compete effectively on price. Since existing contracts normally have a specified duration, and negotiations normally take place some time before expiry, this means that the former supplier would normally have some time to find alternative outlets for his gas if he does lose his contract. In a growing market (which, according to most forecasts, the European market will be) this need not cause significant problems. If, despite all this, easier access to transportation capacity as a result of EU legislation were likely to cause economic problems through the inability to honour take or pay contracts, schemes to solve the problem would need to be developed, as in North America. Another concern voiced in this context is that a sudden introduction of competition could jeopardise cooperation between gas companies and thereby reduce security of supply because the companies are forced to compete for markets to sell contracted gas volumes. Again, as North American experience shows, there are market-based solutions available.

There are already signs that competition could change the exclusive reliance on long term take or pay contracts in European gas contracting. Gas contracting in the United Kingdom seems to be going in the same direction as in Canada, where experience has shown that other ways of sharing risk between sellers and buyers than long term take or pay contracts can be found, and that security of supply can also be ensured under other contract arrangements. It should be kept in mind, however, that the supply situation in Europe is different from the one in North America in that some of the supply sources are remote from the market, are of a large scale and require massive investments. It could be argued that there will be less scope for such megaprojects as the gas industry matures, but there will still be instances where the increase in demand will have to be covered by big incremental projects. In some cases the banks involved in the financing of such projects will require long term take or pay contracts. The main argument from the gas industry against TPA has been that ensuing gas to gas competition in the market would erode the basis for such contracts. It remains to be seen how extensive competition in the European market will become. If there is a problem, long term take or pay contracts with end users like electricity producers might be one solution. Another solution could be to restrict competition in regions being served by new projects for a defined period. This is an idea that has been put forward for countries like Spain where the gas market is still in its early stages of development.

A more open European gas market with easier access to transportation could potentially have a positive effect on vertical integration in the gas chains of countries exporting gas to Europe. As mentioned above both Russia and Algeria are interested in going further downstream in European gas markets, whereas Western companies want to produce in and export from those countries. There are of course obstacles to such developments, but easier access to the European market for Russian companies, for instance, in joint ventures with Western companies could facilitate some opening up. Recently, there has also been discussion in Algeria on the role to be played by foreign companies in production and marketing of gas. Reciprocal moves in the area of access to transportation could therefore be the key to more vertical integration in the gas chain. Seen from a security of supply point of view, vertical integration would obviously give the proper incentives.

It is possible that some degree of unbundling may be part of the future European gas picture. Independently from this, however, more direct contracts between buyer and sellers and increased vertical integration will probably increase the need for pipeline and storage capacity. In the development towards more competition, some of the aggregation effect of the present system would inevitably be lost. Experience from North America suggests, however, that the net effect on security of supply is likely to be positive. The plans to build storage in Germany also point in this direction in that more competition, although not the only factor, has increased the need for, and willingness to build, storage.

A more open European gas market could also give rise to the creation of market hubs where pipelines come together. One possible hub could be Zeebrugge in Belgium where a pipeline from the Norwegian part of the North Sea is landed, where there is already a LNG terminal with storage facilities and where the UK-Continent Interconnector will be landed. Easier access to transportation combined with a not too tight market for gas could give an impetus to a spot market for gas here. Another possible hub is Emden in Germany where several pipelines from the North Sea converge and where there are linkages to storage facilities. Through the Midal/Stegal system owned by Wingas, this area will also have access to Russian gas.

Even under the assumption of a more competitive European gas market in the future, the trends sketched above are only some of the possible developments. It is therefore difficult to draw firm conclusions on the overall effect on the level of security of supply. Combined with the evidence from North America, however, there is nothing in the described trends indicating that a more open gas market would necessarily jeopardise security of supply.

STRUCTURAL AND REGULATORY CHANGES IN THE OECD PACIFIC REGION

The OECD Pacific region consists of countries that represent extremes in terms of dependence on external supply sources and gas market structure. Japan is almost entirely dependent on imports in the form of LNG (although there is some local production of natural gas and production of synthetic gas) and uses around 75% of its gas supplies in power generation. Australia and New Zealand are both self-sufficient in gas, Australia being a considerable exporter of LNG. A conspicuous feature of the gas markets in both of the latter two countries is the high share of gas supplies in the industry sector, either as fuel in energy intensive industries or as feedstock.

When comparing the countries in this region to countries in North America and Europe, Australia and New Zealand are similar to the United States and Canada in that they are self-sufficient in gas, although their markets are much smaller. Japan, on the other hand, is in a situation similar to some European countries in that it is completely dependent on external gas sources. In terms of deregulation and introduction of competition, Australia and New Zealand could be said to be situated somewhere between North America and Europe. Some of the measures adopted in terms of competition are similar to those introduced in the United Kingdom, with the difference that the implementation of the rules is still under way and that it is too early to evaluate their effects. In terms of regulation, Japan has a number of features not very different from those found in many European countries but differs in that formal monopoly power is limited and that negotiated TPA exists.

Japan

Since 1981, gas consumption in Japan has increased by about 70%, and gas's share in TPES has increased from about 6% to about 11%. The sectoral composition of the market, however, has not changed very much: the share of total gas supplies going into power generation in 1980 was 72.6 % and it still remains at about that level. Nor have there been dramatic changes in the composition of final consumption of gas.

In 1981, Japan had four external suppliers, Indonesia, Brunei, Abu Dhabi and the US. At the time, Indonesia supplied around 40% of the total. Today, its share is around 50%, but the number of suppliers has increased, with supplies now also coming from Malaysia and Australia. Since 1980, the number of LNG reception terminals has roughly doubled and is now fourteen. This increase has led to a doubling of total receiving capacity. The terminals are now more dispersed throughout the country; for instance the island of Kyushu has four terminals today (of which one is under construction) but had none in 1980. There is still, however, a heavy concentration of terminals around Tokyo, Osaka and Nagoya.

Most receiving terminals in Japan serve more than one customer and receive gas from more than one exporter. The increase in the number of terminals has meant increased diversification. In recent years efforts have been made to standardise terminal equipment to increase technical ability to receive imports from more than one source.

In 1981, LNG stocks, the only form of gas storage in Japan, amounted to 11 days of average daily consumption for electric utilities and 28 days for gas distribution companies. Total storage capacity is now around 5.6 bcm and amounts to 30 to 40 days of supply. New storage facilities under construction should increase capacity by around 20% by the end of this decade.

The high dependence on gas in power generation makes flexibility in this sector important in terms of total security of supply. One obvious way of reducing the risk of negative effects from gas supply disruptions is to have spare capacity in the generation system. The reserve margin in the Japanese power generation system has, however, fallen over the period considered: in 1981, it was about 16% of total capacity; it is now only around 10%. On the other hand, dual fired capacity in the power stations using LNG increased form 40% in 1981 to about 50% today. This flexibility will, however, decline in the future; new gas-fired generation will generally be single-fired.

The contracts under which gas is supplied to Japan have not changed very much over the period considered: they are still long-term take or pay contracts with gas prices closely linked to crude oil prices. As pointed out elsewhere in this book, this linkage directly exposes the contractual parties to fluctuations in the oil price. In periods of low oil prices, sellers under contracts based on high oil price expectations will suffer and it may be difficult to get new grass root projects off the ground. The Japanese are, however searching for new contract forms that could remedy these problems. Japanese buyers of Australian LNG recently agreed to weaken the link to crude prices somewhat when prices are low.

As pointed out above, a spot market in LNG has emerged in recent years. Japan is playing a double role in this market: on the one hand, the fact that demand has been lower in Japan than expected when some contracts were negotiated has made volumes available in this market. On the other hand, Japanese companies have also been active in this market as buyers. Two factors indicate that the volumes available in this market might increase over time. Firstly, LNG facilities are in many cases able to produce more LNG than indicated by their nameplate capacity and thus have some flexibility. With a number of new facilities planned both in the Asia Pacific region and in the Middle East, bigger volumes might become available on a spot basis. Secondly, a number of existing LNG facilities have been fully depreciated and may be tempted to offer cargoes on a spot basis. From a security of supply point of view this can only be positive.

Japan's dependence on external gas supply sources has led it to become heavily involved in all parts of the LNG chain. Overseas exploration and development have been promoted by financial assistance from the Japan National Oil Corporation (JNOC). The Ministry of Industry and Trade (MITI) encourages LNG development projects by Japanese companies overseas, mainly in Southeast Asia, with an expansion of JNOC financial aid for gas projects. About 38% of LNG imports are JNOC assisted. In a situation where oil prices remain low, involvement by Japanese companies in the LNG chain will probably increase since co-operation and optimisation along the whole chain will become even more important.

Over the period since 1980, gas industry regulation in Japan has remained relatively stable in areas that affect security of supply. Recently, however, the Gas Industry Law underwent some modifications that might affect security of supply: as from March 1995, major users (consuming more than 2 million cubic metres a year) and gas suppliers (of which there are 244, serving 22.8 million customers) can negotiate gas rates directly. There are presently about 500 customers with consumption above the threshold level. Previously subject to MITI approval, their prices will now only need to be reported. A second modification allows gas utilities to serve any industry with gas consumption above a threshold limit outside their designated territory. New market entrants may also supply natural gas to industries meeting the same threshold limit. Access to pipelines is promoted by the legal amendments, but is not mandatory. In both cases approval is required from MITI which requires that the supply does not disadvantage other consumers in the service area.

Australia and New Zealand

Since 1980, gas consumption has more than doubled in Australia and more than quintupled in New Zealand. Gas consumption as a share of TPES increased from 10.6% in 1980 to around 16% in 1992 in Australia, and from 10.2% to 30.7% in New Zealand. Both countries are sparsely populated and are well endowed with other energy sources. Thus, gas has mainly penetrated market segments characterised by bulk uses like power generation and energy intensive industries, including feedstock. In Australia, the share of residential gas use has remained constant at around 14%. The share of gas supplies in power generation and industry has also been relatively stable, at between 60 and 70%. The New Zealand gas market has always been dominated by feedstock and bulk industrial uses. In 1993, 80% of total gas supplies were used as feedstock and for power generation.

Historically, the Australian gas industry has generally developed along the lines of state-based pipeline systems supplying a single major load centre from a single source of supply within each state - Victoria from Bass Strait, Western Australia initially from the Perth Basin and then from the North West Shelf, South Australia from the Cooper basin, Queensland from the Surat/Bowen basin and the Northern territory from the Amadeus Basin. The major exception is the supply of gas to New South Wales and the Australian Capital Territory from the Cooper Basin in South Australia. The length of the pipeline system has increased over time (the length of mains increased from 51,460 kilometres in 1988 to 62,170 kilometres in 1993) and the number of customers has also increased (from 2.1 million in 1988 to 2.5 million in 1993). All the states now have gas reticulation networks, but the load factor varies considerably as a function of the market structure. Storage capacity beyond what is available as linepack is needed, and in 1981 Australia built its first underground storage site. An LNG peak shaving plant has been constructed and the LNG export facilities also comprise gas storage capacity that could be available in emergency situations. Studies have shown that three States have potential for development of underground storage facilities.

The major weakness of the Australian gas supply system today is probably the fact that its various parts are not connected. Future growth in demand is likely to lead to a need for development of new reserve basins and for linking these sources to the rest of the system. New pipeline proposals have been put forward that would link all the States up to an interstate pipeline system.

Multiple sourcing, duplication of, and flexibility in, production facilities, pipelines and compressor stations are ways to enhance security of supply. In spite of the limited economic scope for these measures, the record of the Australian gas industry in maintaining supply is impressive.

The New Zealand gas supply system consists of a very limited number of sources and one single transmission pipeline. Flexibility to meet fluctuations in demand and interruptions is provided by the integrated control system for high pressure transmission lines, line-pack, and interruptible supply to large customers including electricity producers which can use alternative fuels in some of their gas fired generating capacity.

Both Australia and New Zealand are in the process of introducing and implementing regulation intended to create competition in gas markets. In Australia the gas industry has agreed upon a voluntary Code of Practice which provides for negotiated third party access. The Commonwealth Government believes, however, that this Code is not sufficient and that more compelling measures are needed. In 1994, the Commonwealth and State Governments agreed to set up a national framework to achieve free and fair trade in the natural gas sector within and between state jurisdictions. Among the features of this framework are third party access rights to supply networks within and between jurisdictions and franchise agreements consistent with free and fair competition and third party access.

The case of Victoria is a good example of what the State governments want to achieve:

■ multiple producers supplying Victoria on a competitive basis from several basins;

■ access to an integrated gas transmission network covering Southern and Eastern Australia under a system of independent, light-handed regulation which includes unbundled and transparent tariffs, and which will encourage parties to reach commercially negotiated agreements on access terms and conditions. New pipeline additions and interstate trade will be on a competitive basis in response to market demand;

■ direct access to large customers for gas producers, distributors and marketers;

■ an efficient distribution sector with one or more gas distribution businesses;

■ possible future extension of retail competition to smaller customers, subject to technical constraints, with captive customers protected through oversight of tariffs and market conduct by an independent regulator.

Victoria now has one gas producer selling most of its gas to an integrated transmission/distribution/marketing company. One of the first steps in introducing competition will be the disaggregation of this company into separate units for transmission, distribution and marketing.

In recent years, New Zealand has rescinded price regulation and introduced measures aimed at reaching the same goals as those indicated for Australia. There is no explicit legislation providing for third party access, but general competition legislation is in place which is expected to ensure such access in case of failure to reach agreement. The New Zealand regime is based on light handed regulation and information disclosure.

V. GAS USE IN POWER GENERATION AND ITS IMPLICATIONS FOR SECURITY OF SUPPLY

This chapter analyses the long-term prospects for natural gas use in power generation as well as the flexibility of the electricity system in the case of a gas supply disruption, both at present and in the future. The first three sections discuss historical developments and the long term demand outlook. These sections are followed by a discussion of electricity system flexibility and implications for security of supply.

HISTORICAL DEVELOPMENTS

Of the total 7406.9 TWh generated in OECD countries in 1993, 823.6 TWh or 11.1% was generated from natural gas. Gas-based generation grew roughly in line with overall electricity rates throughout the 1970s and 1980s, so that its share has remained relatively stable at around 10%.

However, this overall stability hides some important trends which have shaped the use of gas for power generation in the past. In seven out of 23 IEA member countries, the share of gas in power generation was higher in 1973 than it is now, and in most of these countries, gas will only attain its past share around or after the year 2000 (see Table 5.1). This decline in share over the past two decades was partly due to regulatory impediments. Both in the United States and in Europe, legislative barriers were put in place in the 1970s. In the United States, the Power Plants and Industrial Fuel Use Act (FUA) of 1979 prohibited the use of oil or natural gas as the primary energy source in any new electric power plant or new major fuel-burning boiler installation. This prohibition was abolished in 1987 after abundant supplies of low-cost gas had become available. In Europe, the use of gas was limited by a European Community directive, since it was seen as a specialist fuel, "too noble" to be burnt in large quantities for industrial uses and base-load power generation. The directive was lifted in 1990.

Concern over the long-term availability of gas, i.e., the resource base, was part of the rationale for these barriers. In North America, the ratio of proven reserves to annual production has been within the narrow range of 8 to 12 years for decades. As gas demand grew, reserve estimates were continuously revised upward. This has allayed fears over resource constraints and, among other factors, contributed to a change in attitudes towards natural gas.

Changed attitudes, the abolishment of regulatory barriers to the use of gas and its economic and environmental advantages give reason to expect a larger share of gas-based power generation in the future. Table 5.1 depicts the shares of gas-based power production in OECD countries in 1992 and 1993 as well as historical and projected gas shares in electricity generation.

Table 5.1   Percentage Share of Electric Power Generated from Natural Gas
(Electricity Generation Including CHP and Autoproduction)

	1973	1980	1985	1990	1992	1993	2000+	2010+
Australia	4.3	7.3	9.6	10.6	8.8	9.1	5.2	9.2*
Austria	14.3	9.2	13.1	14.8	13.5	13.4	17.5	22.5*
Belgium	23.7	11.2	4.2	7.7	9.3	9.7	29.3	26.2
Canada	6	2.5	1.5	2.2	2.6	2.6	4.5	5.7
Denmark	0	0	1.1	2.6	2.5	3.7	26.1	38.8*
Finland	0	4.2	2.9	8.6	9	9.1	14.3	23.1
France	5.5	2.7	0.9	0.7	0.7	0.7	3.1	3.7
Germany	10.9	14.2	5.4	7.4	6.2	6.6	14	15.3
Greece	0	0	0	0.3	0.2	0.2	11.5	11.8*
Ireland	0	15.2	50.8	27.7	23.1	28.1	26.9	35.9
Italy	3.1	5	13.6	18.3	15.8	18	36.2**	37.2**
Japan	2.3	14.2	19.2	19.5	21.6	21.5	23.9	19.9
Luxembourg	10.2	23.5	0.8	5.4	4.5	3.4	91.4	91.9
Netherlands	79.5	39.8	60.7	51	56.2	57.2	64.2	59.3
New Zealand	1.4	7.7	20.5	18	25.1	22.2	22.4	8
Norway	0	0	0	0	0	0	0	n.a
Portugal	0	0	0	0	0	0	15.5	n.a.
Spain	1	2.7	2	1	1.1	0.8	16.7	n.a.
Sweden	0	0	0	0.3	0.4	0.6	1.1	1.5*
Switzerland	0	0.6	0.4	0.6	0.6	0.6	0.3	0.9
Turkey	0	0	0.2	17.7	16.1	14.6	25.3	22.7
United Kingdom	1	0.7	1	1.1	1.9	11.1	24.5	46.1
United States	18.6	15.3	11.9	12	13	12.9	14.3	17.3
IEA total	12	11.2	9.7	10.4	11.1	11.5	15.3	n.a.
IEA Europe	7.9	6.9	5.5	6.6	6.4	7.9	16.2	n.a.

Source: IEA, based on country submissions.
n.a. = not available, + estimates, * 2005 values, ** ENEL forecasts.

FACTORS INFLUENCING NATURAL GAS USE IN POWER GENERATION

Economic
Factors

Natural gas as a fuel and, perhaps more importantly, the power plants in which it is burnt, have a number of advantages compared with other power generation options. One of the most important advantages of gas-fired power plants, and especially gas turbines, is that they can be built in small, modular units, and have short construction and lead times - about 3 years, as opposed to 4 to 6 years for coal-fired power stations and 7 or 8, in some cases more than 15 years, for nuclear power plants. Moreover, coal and nuclear power plants are generally designed and built in relation to individual plant sites, whereas gas turbines of up to 150 MW can be preassembled, which allows manufacturers to exploit economies of scale. These factors keep investment costs low and enable power producers to match supply and demand developments closely, thus reducing both the problem of temporary overcapacity due to indivisibility of large generating units, and the need to estimate future demand development many years or even decades ahead. Combined-cycle gas turbines (CCGTs) also have considerably lower operation and maintenance costs, often less than half the cost of coal or nuclear.

The impact of investment on lifetime costs of various forms of power generation capacity depends crucially on the rate used to discount the flow of expenditures occurring over the lifetime of the plant to the date of commissioning. According to the latest NEA/IEA cost evaluation for power generation carried out in 1992 (OECD/NEA, 1993)[1], the investment cost of combined-cycle gas turbines for baseload operation in OECD countries to be commissioned in the year 2000 ranges from US$584 per kW_e in Finland to US$1,292 per kW_e in Japan, assuming a 5% discount rate. At 10%, this figure is US$606 and US$1,448 per kW_e. This compares with US$1,475 (France) to up to US$3,450 (UK) for nuclear power plants at 5%, and US$1,658 and up to US$4,080 respectively, at the higher discount rate of 10%. Coal-fired power stations with flue gas desulphurisation (FGD) are generally less expensive to build than nuclear power stations, with investment costs of US$1,101 (Canada) to more than US$2,000 per kW_e (Japan and Spain) at 5%, and US$1,218 to around US$2,500 at 10%.

Although fuel costs are generally higher for gas than for coal and nuclear, the advantage in investment costs strongly favours gas at higher discount rates. At 10%, gas combined cycle generation is projected to be the least expensive baseload generating option for Belgium, parts of Canada, Denmark, Finland, Portugal, Spain, the United Kingdom and parts of the United States. In the United Kingdom, for example, generation costs from new combined-cycle gas turbines are estimated to be lower than new pulverized coal plants with flue gas desulphurisation as well as new clean coal technology, such as fluidised bed combustion. Despite the fact that steam coal for power generation is much less expensive than gas, the low capital costs of gas-fired combined-cycle units currently make it the most economical generating option in the United States (DOE/EIA, 1994). In France, it has recently been calculated that combined-cycle gas turbines to be commissioned in 2003 would be the most economic generating option for intermediate load (2,000 to 6,000 hours per year), some of which is currently covered by nuclear generation. Since gas is at present used in peak load, this means that it might be expected to be used at higher load factors in France, although not necessarily in baseload.[2]

The favourable outlook for gas depends to some extent on the future development of gas prices. Nearly all of the countries analysed in the NEA/IEA cost study assume real increases in gas prices. In the IEA's 1995 *World Energy Outlook,* the *Capacity Constraints* case assumes that producer gas prices in the United States increase throughout the latter half of the 1990s, and that they stabilise at of US$ 3.30 per thousand cubic feet (tcf) by 2005. Pipeline import prices to Europe and liquefied natural gas (LNG) prices to Japan are also assumed to rise, broadly in line with crude oil prices, which are assumed to increase to US$ 28 per barrel by the year 2005 and remain stable thereafter.[3] LNG imported to Japan is the most expensive form of conventional

---

1. Cost figures are expressed in 1991 US dollars.

2. Ministère de l'industrie, des postes et télécommunications et du commerce extérieur/DGEMP-DIGEC: *Les coûts de référence - production électrique d'origine thermique.* Paris, 1993.

3. Prices are in 1993 US dollars.

carbon-based primary energy used in OECD member countries and is assumed to remain so. Coal prices are assumed to grow moderately, though less rapidly than oil prices, in Europe and Japan. In North America, coal prices are assumed to rise somewhat more swiftly than in Europe and Japan, but not more rapidly than oil prices. Nevertheless, coal is expected to remain the least costly primary energy in all OECD regions.

In Europe and the Asia/Pacific region, gas is traded under long-term contractual arrangements to a larger degree than coal and oil, fuels for which large spot markets exist, and in largely independent regional markets, which makes "world market" price projections less relevant. The price of gas depends very much on contractual arrangements, the supply source and the scale of regional demand. The most important contractual provisions, with respect to their impact on the economics of gas use in power generation, are clauses linking the gas price to developments in the prices of alternative energy sources, and provisions relating to interruptibility. In North America, where a gas spot market does exist, most contracts are short-term, but financial mechanisms have been developed to hedge price risks.

In recent years, flexible pricing concepts for gas sales to power generation have emerged, which link gas prices to the prices of competing input fuels. Under the so-called "indifference" pricing, a gas supplier takes the cost of a power producer's other generating options, including their investment, operation and maintenance costs, into consideration, and adjusts his gas price so that the electricity generator is indifferent between gas and other fuels. When coupled with adjustment clauses, this pricing principle can be a tool to reduce risk both to consumers and producers. Since the other cost components are frequently higher for other fuels, especially for coal, it can also accommodate relatively high gas prices without impairing the competitivity of gas.

According to the 1993 NEA/IEA cost study, natural gas fuel costs in some countries can increase considerably above the assumed price path, which itself already contains an escalation factor, without removing the overall cost advantage for natural gas. At a 10% discount rate, additional gas fuel cost increases of 18 to 26% in the United States to up to 105% in the United Kingdom (PWR) would be necessary to eliminate the cost advantage of gas compared with nuclear power. Fuel cost increases could also be sustained in Belgium and Finland. In comparison with coal, gas costs can increase by 1% in Italy to up to 50% in the United Kingdom without disfavouring gas.[4] Subject to more or less pronounced fuel cost increases, gas would still remain economically attractive compared with coal in Belgium, Denmark, Finland, France, Italy, Portugal, Spain, the United Kingdom and the midwest and northeast regions of the United States.

Gainey (1991) estimates that the input price for gas in Europe could increase dramatically without damaging the competitive advantage of combined-cycle gas power generation, particularly if a carbon tax were to be implemented. According to this estimate, the price could rise as high as US$3.90 per Mbtu without and up to US$5.20 per Mbtu with a carbon tax of US$70 per tonne of carbon in place.[5] Since gas prices delivered to power plants in OECD Europe averaged around US$3.30 per Mbtu in 1993, prices could rise by nearly 20% without a carbon tax and nearly 60% with a carbon tax of US$70 per tonne (IEA, 1995a).

---

4. Assuming international coal prices and flue gas desulphurisation.
5. Figures are estimated for a 600 MW plant, at 65% load factor, 8% discount rate, 25 years lifetime and a tax of $70 per tonne of carbon. The gas prices quoted are prices for gas delivered to the plant.

Fuel Efficiency and Environmental Impacts

Natural gas use in CCGTs has two more important advantages over other power generation options: the high efficiency with which gas is burned and the low emissions of pollutants and greenhouse gases. Whereas a conventional modern coal steam turbine would reach thermal efficiencies just above 40% (approx. 43% for pressurized fluidized bed combustion) and a simple-cycle gas turbine would typically reach thermal efficiencies of 30-35%, combined-cycle gas turbines can achieve thermal efficiencies in the range of 50% or above. This increased efficiency is achieved by extracting the energy exhausted by a simple gas turbine via a heat recovery steam generator. Very efficient new CCGTs, for example those recently built in the United Kingdom or Korea, reach conversion efficiencies approaching 60%; a prototype of a turbine with 60% net efficiency was presented in early 1995. Further increases to 65% or more are expected in the next decade, although the speed of new technological breakthroughs is generally thought to decline in the future.

Natural gas is a low emitter of carbon dioxide because gas has only two thirds the carbon content per unit of energy as does coal, and a larger share of the energy output results from hydrogen burning (IEA/OECD, 1993). Taken together with the higher conversion efficiencies, CO_2 emissions from CCGTs are approximately half as large as the emissions from conventional coal-fired plants.

Natural gas also performs very well with respect to air pollutants. Sulphur dioxide and dust emissions are negligible, and NO_x emissions are only roughly a quarter of those of conventional coal plants. Unlike coal, gas use in CCGTs produces no solid waste, which eliminates the need for waste storage and the potential ground water pollution resulting from it. It also significantly reduces cooling water heat losses. These characteristics make it ideal to meet targets set out by environmental and clean air legislation.

Moreover, the small space requirements of CCGTs help address the problem of the increasing scarcity of plant sites, since they can easily be built at the sites of existing or decommissioned power plants. The Spanish power company Iberdrola is currently considering building a 600 MW combined-cycle plant at the site of its Lemoniz nuclear reactor, which has been mothballed due to a nuclear moratorium.

Some of the advanced coal technologies come close to the low emissions levels of CCGTs. While they offer only limited improvements in terms of carbon dioxide emissions, integrated coal gasification combined-cycle plants (IGCCs), which combine a CCGT with a coal gasifier, actually outperform CCGTs with respect to emissions of nitrogen oxides, emit only roughly a quarter of the sulphur dioxide compared with conventional coal plants, reduce cooling water heat losses, and reach conversion efficiencies of 43 to 46% (IEA/OECD, 1993; IPCC, 1995). However, construction and operating costs for these plants are still relatively high. In the Netherlands, where an IGCC plant has recently been built at Buggenum, investment costs for the year 2000 are estimated to lie roughly 25% above those for conventional coal-fired stations with flue gas desulphurisation and 75-80% higher than those for CCGTs. These high investment costs combined with higher operation and maintenance costs make them more expensive than pulverised coal plants (OECD/NEA, 1993). According to a recent IEA/CIAB survey (IEA/CIAB, 1994), utility managers expressed considerable interest in IGCC technology, but believed that it still needs to demonstrate economic viability and technical and environmental performance if it is to be operated on commercial scale.

The cost of meeting environmental regulations is generally lower for CCGTs than for coal or oil plants, since the former do not require SO_2 removal, and since NO_x control is less expensive. Over the entire lifetime of new plant, natural gas used in combined-cycle turbines appears at present to offer the least cost way of anticipating possible tighter environmental control requirements in the future. Regardless of the plant type, natural gas can be used in multi-firing plants, replacing other fossil fuels for certain periods of time as a strategy to reduce emissions of air pollutants.

Moreover, gas is also seen as environmentally beneficial by the public, which may be one of its most advantageous features, since it represents a viable option in cases where lack of public acceptance hinders the construction of large coal-fired or nuclear power plants.

The Influence of Liberalisation and Privatisation

The current movement towards introducing competition to the electricity supply industry[6] will improve the prospects for natural gas. Firstly, in a deregulated environment, governments will be less capable of imposing fuel choices on the industry which may have been made according to macroeconomic, social, or regional policy goals. In a deregulated, privatised industry, governments can set the legislative framework in such a way that fuel choices are still influenced, but this requires special action and tends to be more transparent to market participants and the general public, which involves greater attention to the potential costs and benefits of government interventions and can limit measures with high social costs.

Secondly, utilities have typically used low discount rates from 5% to 8% to evaluate their investment decisions in the past. Discount rates used in deregulated markets will tend to be significantly higher, because investors in such markets generally bear more risk than utilities in regulated markets. This is due, among other things, to the fact that in a competitive power market, generators will not necessarily be able to pass all their costs through to consumers. This effect is reinforced if the industry is privatised as well as deregulated. Private generators will tend to base their investment decisions on higher discount rates, since their shareholders will exert more pressure on them to earn market rates of return, and since they are less likely to have access to low-cost loans than state-owned companies in a regulated market. Higher discount rates favour less capital-intensive investment, as the previous discussion has shown, and thus will favour gas turbines over investment in nuclear and coal plants.

Thirdly, openly accessible markets attract independent power generators who will seek rates of return on their investment which adequately cover the risks perceived by their sources of finance. Since investors can mitigate their own investment risk by holding a portfolio of investments, they may also have an incentive to minimise their sunk cost in an inherently more risky environment by entering the market with a lower initial investment. Because gas-fired generation capacity can be built in small incremental units and has low investment cost, it will again benefit from this tendency.

---

6.   Recent changes in the industry are described in IEA, 1994a.

Developments in those OECD countries where access to power markets has been liberalised support this view. Virtually all of the capacity under construction after privatisation in the United Kingdom is gas-fired, which has led to a rapid increase in the share of gas-fired capacity to roughly 15% by the end of 1994. This proportion is set to grow to at least 25% by the year 2000 according to forecasts by the National Grid Company. As a consequence, the share of gas-fired power generation has increased from 1.1% in 1990 to 11% in 1993, and is expected to surge to 24.5% in 2000 and 46% in 2010 (see Table 5.1).

In the United States, where the Public Utility Regulatory Policies Act (PURPA) and other legislation improved the conditions for market entry by non-utility power generators (NUGs) after 1978, NUG generation started growing much faster than overall output and investment. Whereas utility power production grew by 23% between 1980 and 1990, independent power generation increased more than 100 fold. This led to an overall increase in the share of gas in electricity generation, since 46% of independent power production was based on gas, compared with only 9% of the public utilities generation (Energy, Mines and Resources Canada, 1993).

Load Management

The natural gas and electricity supply industries are similar in a number of ways. Both depend on a network for transmission and distribution, both are capital-intensive and both face a peak load problem. The similarities, however, do not necessarily make transactions involving both industries more straightforward; they can even create additional difficulties. Although storage is more common in the gas industry than it is in the electricity supply industry, it is expensive for both, and can thus be used for load management only to a certain extent. Other options used for gas load management include seasonal supplies from swing fields and interruptible sales of gas (IEA, 1994c).

The economics of gas extraction and transportation favour an even demand profile for the same reasons as does the electricity supply business, i.e., better load factors for capital-intensive production and transport capacity help to distribute capacity costs over a greater number of revenue-generating energy units supplied to the consumer, and reduce the need to build expensive facilities to supply peak loads. Reducing the peakiness of gas use and creating a stable demand are two important reasons why the gas industry uses long-term relationships, and for which it has developed take-or-pay clauses and interruptible contracts for gas sales.

Baseload power generation from gas would thus be economically attractive for the gas industry, since steady demand of constant quantities would make power generation a baseload gas consumer. In areas where a dense gas transmission and distribution network exists, the pipeline system could be extended rapidly and at low cost to supply a gas-fired power station via a pipeline dedicated to this purpose.

However, natural gas has mostly been used in peak or intermediate load in the past. Baseload use has not been widespread, although it occurred in CHP plants in Europe and in the United States before 1978. LNG is currently used to generate intermediate load electricity in Japan (FEPC, 1994). This pattern of gas use for peak or intermediate demand was due to a mixture of regulatory constraints, like the US Power Plants and Industrial Fuel Use Act mentioned above, technical requirements, and the economics of gas use in a more regulated environment, frequently involving lower discount rates. The cost characteristics, i.e., low capital cost of gas-fired power plants and the relatively high fuel costs of gas, have in the past favoured gas use in peak generation, and the use of capital-intensive coal and nuclear units in baseload. Moreover, gas turbines can be brought on stream very rapidly to meet instantaneous power demand increases. This technical advantage has contributed to the dispatch of gas in peak load.

In countries and regions with simultaneous gas and electricity demand peaks, such as most parts of Europe, the demand patterns of the power supply industry can compound the peakiness of gas demand rather than reduce it. This tends to make construction of dedicated pipelines for individual power plants less attractive. In certain regions of the United States, which have both winter and summer peaks, this has led to a system in which electric utilities often use gas under interruptible contracts or buy it on the spot market. Utilities then switch away from gas to oil in winter, when pipeline capacity becomes scarce due to sharp increases in residential heating demand. This is the case for the Northeast, Middle Atlantic, and South Atlantic supply regions. Fuel switching in the United States is very price-sensitive: 68% of dual-fired power plants switch fuels at price differentials of 5% or less. Independent power producers are even more sensitive to price variability (Makovich and Smalley, 1993). Since Japan has a winter peak for gas demand but a summer peak in electricity demand, it has a relatively stable gas demand for the whole year and thus can use its LNG facilities very economically.

Deregulation and/or privatisation will affect the position of gas in the merit order. As discount rates rise and regulatory constraints are dismantled, gas-based generation can become inexpensive enough to replace or even displace coal and nuclear generation in many countries. Gas-based generation is thus expected to move to baseload operation in Denmark, Finland, Italy, the Netherlands,[7] Portugal, Spain, the United Kingdom and parts of the US, creating stable baseload gas demand by electric utilities.

If gas-based power generation moves away from peak load and into baseload, this will lead to significant increases in the consumption of natural gas and potentially to better exploitation of gas transportation infrastructure. The overall outcome depends on the effects on gas transport cost, wellhead prices, contractual arrangements, and, to some degree, the potential effects of deregulation in the gas markets.

It is, for example, conceivable that the gas industry might want to recoup a larger part of its fixed cost through gas sales contracts with a fixed component, reflecting the capital cost of gas infrastructure, and a separate fuel cost component. To the extent that this would lower variable gas prices, short-term marginal costs of electricity generation from gas would decrease, and gas would move towards baseload.

These issues have led to some insecurity in the electricity supply industry as to what price development they should assume for gas use in baseload. This uncertainty will have to be reduced by better communication between the two industries if gas use in power generation is to realise its strong growth potential.

---

7. In the past, some CHP plants have used gas in baseload operation in the Netherlands. Baseload gas generation will increase significantly within the next two years, since 1,500 MW of gas-fired baseload plant will come on stream.

THE PROSPECTS OF GAS USE FOR POWER GENERATION

The use of natural gas for power generation within the next 15 years will crucially depend on three developments:

a) future electricity demand growth and need for new generating capacity;

b) the development of relative fuel prices, particularly gas prices versus coal prices; and

c) environmental imperatives.

a) Electricity output and demand in the OECD are projected to increase 45% between 1992 and 2010 according to the IEA's 1995 *World Energy Outlook* (*Capacity Constraints* case). This masks higher growth in the OECD Pacific region, where electricity demand is projected to grow at an annual rate of 2.9%, and to increase by 66% over the outlook period. Growth in OECD Europe is expected to average 2.1% per year with a total rise of 46%. Growth will be slightly lower in North America, at 1.8% per annum and an overall increase of around 38% (IEA, 1995b).

Thus, in North America and OECD Europe, additional capacity will be required at a relatively modest pace; in Japan, Australia and New Zealand, new capacity requirements will be somewhat higher. However, the need to replace generating capacity which has reached the end of its economic lifetime or which is retired for other reasons, such as its environmental impacts, technical obsolescence, or lack of public acceptance, and capacity replacement on economic grounds, as in the United Kingdom, increases the potential for the penetration of natural gas into power generation. Among those OECD countries who reported their generating capacity currently under construction, authorised, or planned between 1993 and 2005, natural gas capacity amounted to 30% (IEA, 1994a).

There are various ways in which natural gas use can be expanded, including restarting or using existing gas-fired units at higher load factors (i.e., shifting to baseload), equipping existing coal- or oil-burning facilities with gas boilers in order to gain flexibility or meet environmental regulations, constructing new gas-fired units, repowering uncompleted or retired nuclear units, or adding gas-based power from autoproducers. Retirement of nuclear reactors before the end of their lifetime could play a potentially large role in the United States. Due mainly to unfavourable economic performance, but also a tarnished public image and unsolved nuclear waste problems, a number of nuclear power plants have been shut down, further early retirements are possible, and new nuclear construction is seen as improbable. In the US, this development will primarily benefit coal, but gas used in combined cycle turbines shows favourable economics and is likely to benefit from premature nuclear plant closures as well (INGAA, 1994). In some European countries, such as Sweden and Switzerland, who have a high share of nuclear generation and strong opposition to nuclear power, the same factors could lead to a rapid increase in gas generation in the future, especially since gas capacity can rapidly fill any capacity gap from a phase-out decision.

b) As outlined above, gas prices are assumed to grow faster than coal prices in all OECD regions (IEA, 1995b). This is supported by other sources (e.g., Prior, 1994), although DRI forecasts present a more optimistic view. DRI assumes a decoupling of oil and gas prices in Europe, and stable real gas prices to the power sector between 1994 and 2015. Gas is assumed to become much more competitive for use in the power sector than heavy fuel oil (Slaughter, 1994).

Developments in gas prices are important but not crucial to the future use of gas in power generation, since generators can shield themselves from gas price increases to a certain degree by entering into long-term contractual relationships with their suppliers. These contracts usually contain risk-sharing mechanisms related to prices.

c) The environmental dimension depends on the measures governments will enact in the future in order to limit emissions of acid air pollutants and greenhouse gases. Natural gas offers an inexpensive means of complying with existing clean air standards. However, if environmental imperatives have already been addressed by utilities through the construction of coal-fired power plants with flue gas desulphurisation (FGD), the investment cost for the combination of coal plant and FGD facility is a sunk cost, and the FGD-equipped coal plant will compete against other supply options offering the same environmental standard on the basis of its variable cost only. This will make it less easy for other fuels and technologies to penetrate the market, at least as long as environmental standards are not tightened. However, if continuous tightening of emissions standards can reasonably be expected, power producers will have an incentive to avoid "end-of-pipe" solutions addressing every individual pollutant separately, which could greatly benefit gas use in CCGTs.

These three factors, which indicate significant gas capacity additions, combined with the shift from peak and intermediate load to baseload use discussed above provide for growth rates of natural gas generation which are much higher than overall electricity output growth. Under its *Capacity Constraints* case assumptions, the IEA's 1995 *World Energy Outlook* projects gas-based generation to increase at an annual rate of 6.2% between 1992 and 2010 in the whole of the OECD, which will increase its fuel share from the current level of around 11% to 22% in the year 2010. Growth in the Pacific region is expected to average 4.3% over the period, but with significantly lower growth of 1.9% per annum before the year 2000 and higher growth (6.3%) in the period post 2000. Gas' share in total generation with be roughly stable before the turn of the century at around 18%, but will increase rapidly to 23.3% thereafter. OECD Europe will experience strong and stable growth of 9.2% throughout the whole period, and the share of gas will increase from 6.5% in 1992 to 21.8% in 2010. OECD North America is expected to exhibit 5.4% annual growth throughout the period, with slight acceleration after 2000, and the share of gas almost doubling to 21.8% in 2010.

Other studies also predict considerable growth of natural gas use in electricity generation. The US Energy Information Administration projects that electricity will be the largest growth market for natural gas over the next 20 years. Although according to their estimates, the electricity supply industry currently only represents some 15% of all natural gas demand, it will consume nearly one fifth in 2010 (DOE\EIA, 1995). According to other sources, 70% of all future capacity additions in the United States will be gas-fired.[8]

The average across six recent studies undertaken in the United States indicates an increase in electricity generation from 2,800 TWh in 1990 to 3,600 by 2010. This represents an average annual growth rate of 1.5% over the period. The remainder of the 1990s is expected to show a higher growth rate of around 1.6% per annum, while average growth of 1.1% per annum to 2010 is projected. Independent generation is expected to grow from its 1990 level of 1.0 TWh to

---

8. "Natural Gas as a Powerplant Fuel", special report in: *Power*, February 1994, pp. 35-42.

1.8 TWh by 1995 and more than 4.75 TWh by 2010. The share of natural gas is expected to increase from its current 10% of utility generation to about 15% by 2005, at the expense of nuclear energy and/or oil as well as other fuels, and then to decline to 13% by 2010. Coal's share is anticipated to decrease slightly over the next 10 years, but increase again after 2000 when new coal technologies are available and implemented (Energy, Mines and Resources Canada, 1993).

DRI expects natural gas use for power generation in North America to grow rapidly. From 1990 to 2005, natural gas is chosen over coal as a fuel for power generation, but coal will regain its competitiveness near the end of the period.

Other studies also project a significant rise in the share of natural gas in Western European power generation, which is roughly in line with IEA predictions. According to DRI, there will be an increase in the fuel share of natural gas in power generation from 14% in 1992 to 29% in 2015. Very strong growth is expected in Italy, Sweden, Denmark and the United Kingdom (Enseling, 1994). A Ruhrgas forecast sees the West European power sector's share in overall gas consumption rise from 16% in 1993 to 25% in 2005 (Enseling, 1994). Table 5.2 shows IEA Member countries' projections of natural gas input to power generation in European countries. These have been compared to forecasts from industry sources, which are generally consistent with those shown here.[9]

Table 5.2   Gas Input to Power Generation, OECD Europe (Mtoe)

	1992	2000	2010
Austria	1.83	1.85	1.87
Belgium	1.40	3.40	3.40
Denmark	0.60	2.00*	2.00*
Finland	1.00	1.81	1.84
France	0.00	1.10	1.45
Germany	6.52	13.93	18.89
Greece	0.00	1.11	1.11
Ireland	0.78	0.73	1.10
Italy	7.23	18.20	26.20
Luxembourg	0.01	0.01	0.01
Netherlands	6.05	3.85	4.08
Portugal	0.00	0.75	1.62
Spain	0.52	5.52	6.68
Sweden	0.31	0.46	0.98
Turkey	2.13	6.29	11.63
United Kingdom	2.09	14.65	36.05
Total	**22.97**	**75.66**	**118.91**

Source: Administration and Industry forecasts.
* total input to power generation and CHP, but excluding industrial autoproduction.

9. Some industry forecasts, however, indicate different numbers. For example, Eurogas expects gas input in 2010 in Germany to be 10.1 Mtoe, in Italy 27.7 Mtoe, and in the Netherlands 12.7 Mtoe.

The OECD Pacific countries show relatively low growth rates of 2 to 3% for gas use in power generation according to DRI forecasts (Barret, 1994). This is broadly in line with the IEA's 1995 World Energy Outlook for the time period before 2000, but contradicts results relating to the post-2000 period.

The Japanese electricity supply industry is by far the biggest electricity producer in the OECD Pacific region. In 1992, it accounted for 82% of the region's electricity production. Japan is equally the world's largest importer of liquefied natural gas (LNG), and three quarters of this gas is used in power generation. Electricity production from natural gas was roughly 19.6% in 1992 in public electricity supply, up from about 12.5% in 1979 (IEA, 1994b).

LNG supply to Japan is expensive, and gas is projected to be more expensive than both nuclear and coal for power plants to be commissioned by the year 2000, although according to the IEA/NEA generating cost study, the difference is small, particularly at a 10% discount rate (OECD/NEA, 1994). This view is supported by external cost calculations, which show that baseload LNG-fired generating units show higher costs per kWh produced than new coal-fired and new oil-fired plants (Toichi, 1994).

Nevertheless, Japan plans to increase its LNG-based generating capacity very rapidly from 41 GW in 1992 to 61.6 GW in the year 2000 and 64.5 GW in 2003, which implies an increase of nearly 60% over the period. This capacity increase does not, however, mean that power generation from gas will rise at the same rate: the share of gas is expected to increase from 22.3% in 1992 to 25% in 2000, then fall to 21% in 2010. The reason for this supply picture is that Japan faces an increasingly peaky electricity demand, mainly due to growing air conditioning load, and LNG will therefore be used at lower load factors. Coal-based generation is also expected to increase. Coal capacity is expected to double by the year 2000, and coal generation will increase its share from 14.9% in 1992 to 17.5% in the year 2000 (IEA, 1994b).

SECURITY IMPLICATIONS OF GAS USE IN POWER GENERATION

Short-term Flexibility of the Power Supply System

A high share of gas in power generation at present or in the future could raise issues of security of supply. Some countries, e.g., Turkey and Finland, which depend on a single supplier, Russia, for their gas imports and which envisage increasing the share of gas in their power generation to about one quarter by 2010, would need to ensure enough flexibility in their power supply systems to be able to cope with a gas supply disruption.

Flexibility can in principle be provided in three ways, i.e., through *electricity transfers* within large interconnected areas, such as the UCPTE region[10] in continental Europe, *large reserve margins* within systems, or *multi-firing*. Electricity exchange as a means of coping with gas

---

10. The UCPTE (Union pour la co-ordination de la production et du transport de l'électricité) region is a large region of interconnected and synchronised national power systems, which basically comprises the western part of the European continent except Scandinavia, parts of Denmark, Albania and the former Yugoslavia.

supply shortages requires spare generating and transmission capacity in the interconnected area, which implies that potential power exporters do not themselves suffer from a disruption in gas supply. In Europe, none of these conditions may be fulfilled, at least not if the disruption occurs during periods of peak demand, i.e., between December and February. This is due to the fact that UCPTE countries have nearly simultaneous load peaks: in 1992, the degree of simultaneity was 95.7%. Moreover, spare capacity throughout the whole of the UCPTE is significantly lower than in its individual member countries, mainly due to transmission constraints. In December 1992, guaranteed surplus available capacity was 8.1%, and only 4.4% was available on a long-term basis (UCPTE, 1992).

Individual OECD member countries can have much larger reserve margins than the interconnected region, although generally speaking, margins are declining. There was excess capacity in many OECD countries during the late 1970s and early 1980s, due to overoptimistic demand forecasts, but in the late 1980s, the trend began to change. Although in some countries, like Finland and Ireland, reserve margins have increased between 1985 and 1992, spare capacity in most countries has declined over the period. Two of the countries in Table 5.3 which either envisage large increases in gas use (Spain) or which already have a relatively high share of natural gas (Japan), had very low reserve margins in 1992.

However, in most countries with little spare capacity, flexibility has been introduced via multi-fired capacity. Table 5.4 indicates that virtually all OECD countries which anticipate increases in the portion of gas in power production have high percentages of multi-fired gas capacity, and thus considerable flexibility built into their systems.

Italy, for example, is dependent on imported gas for roughly two thirds of its gas needs and imported 42% of its gas from Algeria in 1993. However, nearly all of its gas capacity is multi-fired. Fuel switching in Italy occurs frequently and in relation to fluctuations in the relative prices of input fuels. In its 1988 national energy plan, the Italian Government foresaw an increase of the share of gas in power generation to around 30% by the year 2000. The new Government has announced that it intends to reduce the growth of gas use somewhat on the grounds of security of supply,[11] but still foresees strong growth. All of Spain's gas plants are dual-fired. Turkey, on the other hand, does not have much dual-firing, but has enormous excess capacity, mostly hydropower from its new South-East Anatolian dam system.

Japan is even more dependent on gas imports than Italy, but has also built a large amount of flexibility into its system, since roughly half of its gas capacity is dual-fired. In the United States, fuel switching in dual-fired facilities occurs regularly, and the share of multi-fired capacity is expected to increase over its already currently high level.

Flexibility in the power supply system through spare capacity and fuel-switching capability can alleviate the impact of a gas supply disruption by shifting energy demand away from natural gas and toward other energy inputs. In the minority of cases, e.g., in Turkey, this would lead to more non-fossil generation, but the bulk of demand for substitute energy would have to be covered by fossil fuels, i.e., coal and especially heavy fuel oil.

---

11. *International Gas Report*, 259, 16 September 1994.

Table 5.3   Reserve Margins in Electricity Supply in OECD Countries
Public Electricity Supply and Autoproduction (Gigawatts)

	1985			1992		
	Peakload	**Peak Capacity**	**Reserve Margin (%)**	**Peakload**	**Peak Capacity**	**Reserve Margin (%)**
Australia	21.0	n.a.	n.a.	28.8	n.a.	n.a.
Austria	n.a.	n.a.	n.a.	3.4	n.a	n.a.
Belgium	8.8	14.1*	60.2	10.7	14*	30.8
Canada	72.0	89.0	23.6	82.5	106.8	29.5
Denmark	5.5	n.a.	n.a.	5.9	n.a.	n.a.
Finland	8.8	12.2	38.0	10.4	16.2	56.8
France	60.0	61.6	2.7	64.0	69.5	8.6
Germany	67.6	90.3	33.7	86.0	109.6	27.4
Greece	4.1	6.2	50.6	5.4	6.4	18.3
Ireland	2.1	2.6	24.6	2.7	3.7	35
Italy#	33.2	48.6	46.4	36.3	44.5	22.6
Japan	109.8	122.1	11.2	150.9	162.4	7.7
Netherlands	9.7	15.2	57.5	10.6	14.7	38.4
New Zealand	4.7	6.1	28.5	5.1	6.5	26.2
Norway	17.3	n.a.	n.a.	17.9	n.a.	n.a.
Spain	21.3	n.a.	n.a.	23.9	32.0##	33.9
Sweden	24.2	27.2	12.2	23.9	n.a.	n.a.
Switzerland	7.8	10.3	32.6	8.5	9.9	17.2
Turkey	5.8	n.a.	n.a.	11.1	20.1+	81.1
United Kingdom	53.0	n.a.	n.a.	51.7	n.a.	26.7**
United States	461.1	n.a.	n.a.	549.2	751.7++	36.9

Source: IEA.

\#   Includes generators other than ENEL.

*   Fédération Professionelle des Producteurs et Distributeurs d'Electricité en Belgique (FPE): *Annuaire Statistique* 1993, Brussels.

\+   government communication.

**   Estimate by the National Grid Company for 1992/3. *Electricity Supply Handbook* 1993.

++   Summer capacity. IEA: *Electricity Information* 1993, Paris, 1994.

n.a. = not available

\#\#   1993 figure.

The impact of a shortfall of gas supply will depend on the circumstances under which it occurs. Chapter six contains a description of what happened in the US during the cold spell of 1994. Total natural gas use in all regions under consideration is winter-peaking. Electricity shows a double peak in the US, with the summer peak around 12% above winter peak demand. This applies for all regions, except for Alaska and six Northeastern states.[12] Natural gas used in power generation shows a clear summer peak, primarily due to the practice of fuel-switching outlined above. Variations in gas input to power generation are large: in 1992, summer gas input was nearly twice as large as winter demand. For this reason, a gas disruption due to a cold spell will tend to occur at precisely the time when it will have the least impact, provided the cold spell

---

12. New York, Vermont, New Hampshire, Maine, Massachusetts, Rhode Island and Connecticut. (NERC, 1992).

Table 5.4   Single-fired and Multi-fired Gas Capacity in OECD Countries
(Public Supply, 1992)

	Total Single-fired Capacity		Multi-fired Capacity				
			Total		of which		
					Dual-fired with:		Triple-fired
					Solids	Liquids	
	MW	**%**	**MW**	**%**	**%**	**%**	**%**
Australia	3400	81.0	800	19.0	0	3.8	15.2
Austria	349	8.7	3679	91.3	26.4	60.2	4.7
Belgium	107	2.4	4282	97.6	4.0	38.6	55.0
Canada	2300	54.0	1957	46.0	36.0	10.0	0
Denmark	211	23.7	678	76.3	0.6	37.8	37.9
Finland	280	13.9	1730	86.1	3.1	46.5	36.5
France	80	8.8	832	91.2	27.4	9.0	54.8
Germany	5850	24.4	18137	75.6	7.8	38.3	29.5
Ireland	257	18.9	1102	81.1	0	81.1	0
Italy	61	0.5	13396	99.5	0	90.7	8.9
Japan	20848	48.9	21777	51.1	1.8	49.3	0
Netherlands	3337	26.0	9505	74.0	16.1	57.1	0
New Zealand	198	10.6	1670	89.4	53.5	35.9	0
Spain	0	0	1928	100.0	0	100.0	0
Turkey	2551	75.4	833+	24.6	0	24.6	0
United Kingdom	1937	100.0	0	0	0	0	0
Unites States	15275	8.5	163754	91.5	14.1	73.4	4.0

Source: IEA.
+   government communication.
n.a. = not available.

does not cause difficulties in the supply of other fuels. The difficulties which the power supply industry experienced during the period of extremely cold weather in January 1994 were due more to the shortage of other fuels, i.e., frozen coal and lack of oil and to insufficient co-ordination between the electricity supply and gas industries rather than disturbances in gas supply as such. In some cases, electric utilities created problems for natural gas pipelines and local distribution companies by cutting their power supplies (DOE, 1995).

In general, timing of a supply disruption is crucial. Japan uses the greatest amount of gas during peak electricity load, i.e., in July, August and September, when generating plants are used almost to capacity. In Europe, the picture is more mixed. Austria, Belgium and Germany have pronounced winter peaks in gas use for power generation, whereas Italy, Turkey and Spain also use larger amounts of gas in summer, partly to compensate shortfalls in hydroelectric generation due to droughts.

Comparison between Tables 5.1, 5.3 and 5.4 shows that the European countries under consideration have enough spare or multi-fired capacity in place to be able to substitute a complete shortfall of gas supplies to power generation even at peak times. Japan seems to be well prepared to compensate for a major supply disruption. Hence, current levels of gas use for power generation do not appear to entail significant security problems for electricity supply. Major increases in gas demand, however, could be expected to alter this conclusion.[13]

Future Flexibility of the Power Supply System

The main trends in the power supply industry, deregulation, privatisation, and the projected increase in natural gas use in power generation, will have implications for the security of natural gas use. The analysis carried out for 1992 has shown that there is enough flexibility in the power sector to avoid electricity supply problems in the event of a gas supply disruption. This is due to the availability of spare generating capacity and/or multi-firing plants, both of which allow substitution of gas by other fuels in the event of a crisis.

In the long run, this situation might change considerably. Several developments will influence the flexibility of the power supply system. Firstly, spare capacity in the electricity supply system might be greatly reduced, as power demand growth and retirement of ageing plants erodes the excess capacity which prevailed in many countries throughout the 1980s. Moreover, due to environmental constraints and public opposition, siting of new power plants is becoming increasingly difficult. As markets open up and potential competitors enter the market, attempts to site new power plants will increase. The low space requirements of combined-cycle gas turbines (CCGTs) can potentially facilitate siting. It is questionable, however, whether a more competitive market will produce excess capacities as large as those built up after the second oil crisis. As indicated in Table 5.3, in 1992, some countries, such as Japan and France had reserve margins of less than 10% at system peak, and peak load showed faster growth tendencies than overall power consumption.

Secondly, system flexibility was to a large degree due to gas use in multi-firing plants. It is uncertain to what extent multi-firing capacity will be built in the future and in a system with more competition. Figure 5.1 shows the historic development of multi-fired gas capacity between 1973 and 1992 in OECD countries. It shows that the share of multi-fired gas capacity stood at roughly 80% of all gas capacity throughout the 1980s, and that extrapolation of historic trends does not indicate a dramatic decrease. The high share of multi-firing may reflect a strong preference for security of supply or a striving to exploit short-term fuel price differentials.

Whether this tendency will remain unchanged in more competitive power markets is unclear. As markets are deregulated, there will be more pressure on generators to lower costs, particularly investment costs. Using gas and other fuels in multi-firing plants is slightly more expensive than running single-fired capacity, but it can be considered an insurance premium to reduce price risk and vulnerability to supply disruptions, not only in relation to gas but also to oil. Installing a multi-fired plant also produces external benefits for others on the system, since fuel switching limits price increases for everyone, not only those who actually invest in multi-fired capacity.

---

13. Chapter 7 discusses the impact of a gas supply disruption to to the power generation and industry sectors on the markets for substitute fuels, i.e., for oil products and coal. See the country annex on Japan for a discussion of gas security issues.

Fuel switching enables generators to exploit price differentials in input fuel prices, gives them negotiating power and improves their position towards gas suppliers. Perhaps most importantly, independent generators, who tend to buy gas on an interruptible basis, may have their supplies switched off during peak gas demand, which, in Europe and in parts of North America, coincides with peak electricity load. Since competitive wholesale power markets tend to operate on the basis of short-term marginal costs, deregulation will create large incentives for generators to continue supplying to the grid even if their gas deliveries are cut, and will thus want to retain the option of using other fuels. For example, high pool prices in the United Kingdom would warrant the use of expensive fuels such as gasoil at peak times, whereas, under normal circumstances, they will continue running on gas as much as possible because of the cost of associated infrastructure and the need to cover gas-related investment cost.

Figure 5.1   Multi-fired Gas Capacity, OECD

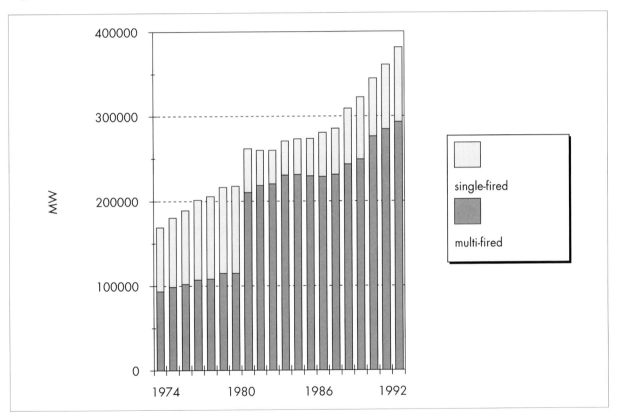

Source: IEA.

As is the case today, competitive markets in the future will encompass utility generators and industrial autoproducers selling excess electricity to the grid. There will also be an increasing number of generators which fall into neither of these categories, i.e., independent or "non-utility" generators in competitive markets. This group will not necessarily apply the same criteria to its capacity choices as industrial autoproducers, but it seems unlikely that multi-firing will decline dramatically. In those OECD countries for which data is available, one third have no multi-firing gas capacity in autoproduction, one third have 100% (Belgium, France, the Netherlands, Luxembourg and Switzerland), and in one third, the share of multi-firing plant ranges between 55 and 80%.

There are examples of countries where multi-firing is expected to decline: in the Netherlands, the share of dual-fired capacity will be drastically reduced from around three quarters to roughly half of the gas generating capacity within the next five years (SEP, 1994). This decline is partly due to the expected surge in combined heat and power production (CHP) from around 14% of total power generation now to roughly 32% by 2000. CHP and multi-firing are not mutually exclusive, neither technically nor economically, but multi-firing can adversely affect the economics of very small CHP plants due to the extra capacity cost. However, within Europe, only Denmark, the Netherlands and Finland have high shares of CHP, compared with total electricity production, and both Denmark and the Netherlands, where the share of small-scale, gas-based CHP is expected to increase significantly, have indigenous gas resources. Moreover, a significant amount of additional gas-fired CHP capacity is expected to come on stream in relatively large plants of 100 MW or more (IEA, October 1994).

These factors do not point to a pronounced decrease in the share of multi-firing. However, the predicted increases in gas use for power generation are to a large degree due to the advantageous economics of combined-cycle gas turbines, which will be responsible for a very large part of gas capacity additions. Taking into account retirement of old gas plant, assuming a move toward baseload, and considering the experience in the United Kingdom, where virtually all plants commissioned or under construction after privatisation (with the exception of the Sizewell B nuclear reactor) were CCGTs, the share of CCGTs in total gas capacity in OECD Europe could increase from its current low level of around 2% of public power supply in 1992 to around 25% in 2000 and to 60% or more by 2010.[14]

Industrial autoproducers already have a significantly higher share of installed CCGTs than public power generators. In 1992, CCGTs accounted for 20% of autoproducers' total capacity. In Greece, the Netherlands and the US, the share of CCGTs in autogeneration was close to one third, in Portugal and Spain the share was around 80%. Autoproducers also have a higher share of simple cycle gas turbines, which account for another 11% of their capacity (compared with 7.5% in public supply).

An increase in the share of CCGTs in the generating system may affect the security implications of gas use, since they can be run as multi-fired plants, but require lighter oil distillates than conventional steam boilers. This will alter the economics of dual-firing, since lighter distillates, such as gasoil, are more expensive than heavy fuel oil, and shift the balance of backup-fuels away from an almost exclusive use of heavy fuel oil to a more balanced mix of both.

Despite the higher cost of light distillates, running CCGTs as multi-firing facilities would be the capacity option of choice as long as the extra cost of installing the necessary equipment combined with higher fuel costs were less than the price differential between firm and interruptible gas supply contracts. Using CCGTs would thus enable generators to exploit inexpensive interruptible gas deliveries. Moreover, if the extra capacity cost of installing dual-firing equipment were very low, such equipment might be installed as an insurance against supply disruptions, even if fuel-switching would not take place on a regular basis for economic reasons.

---

14. IEA Secretariat estimate.

Table 5.5 shows price differentials between firm and interruptible gas supplies in several European countries. The differentials vary across countries, but they are highest in the United Kingdom, where the price of firm gas can be nearly 30% above the price for interruptible gas. Dual-firing should thus be economic in the United Kingdom. Both the experience of PowerGen and National Power, however, indicate that gasoil suitable for CCGTs would not be chosen for fuel-switching. The cost of gasoil is around 12% higher than the equivalent cost of gas, thus ruling out its use for fuel-switching everywhere in Europe except perhaps in the United Kingdom and Belgium. Moreover, equipping CCGTs with dual-firing facilities which use gasoil as a backup fuel requires storage tanks with adequate fire protection as well as a number of design changes in the gas plant. The most expensive change, according to the experience of PowerGen, is to the water treatment plant. NO_x values are excessively high when a plant runs on gasoil, and they can only be reduced to comply with existing air pollution legislation using water injection. This requires a much bigger water treatment plant at significant extra cost. PowerGen considered dual-firing for its 100 MW CCGT at Killingholme, where the gas had to be brought through a 50 km gas pipeline. Design decisions were made in 1989/90 and dual-firing, including five day storage and the required design changes, was estimated to cost an additional £ 5 million. This cost was viewed as uneconomic, and dual-firing was abandoned for this project as well as for the CCGT project at Rye House which takes its gas directly from the British Gas network. The primary reason for abandoning the project was the cost of NO_x control. However, if dry low-NO_x burners were developed, such a project could become economic according to PowerGen.

Table 5.5   Price Differentials between Firm and Interruptible Gas Contracts
(Europe, End 1994)

	Firm (US$ per Mbtu)	**Interruptible**	**Difference**	**Mark-up** (per cent)	**Difference** (cents per kWh)
United Kingdom	4.16	3.23	0.93	28.8	0.17
Spain	3.60	3.40	0.20	5.9	0.04
Germany	5.48	5.39	0.09	1.7	0.02
Italy	4.27	4.21	0.06	1.4	0.01
France	3.61	3.60	0.01	0.3	0
Belgium	3.82	3.25	0.57	17.5	0.11

10 million cm/yr, 90% load - firm.
Source: *World Gas Intelligence*, Vol. V, No. 23-24, 16 December 1994.

According to the expectations of ENEL, the extra cost of dual-firing in CCGTs will lead to a decline in overall gas-based multi-firing in Italy, where gasoil is three times as expensive as natural gas. ENEL expects CCGTs to account for 15% of its thermal capacity in 2002, and intends to equip all its CCGTs with gasoil burners and storage capacity. However, on-site storage will be limited to the equivalent of two weeks' input, which would be too short a time period to be considered multi-firing.

Where CCGTs can be built close to oil refineries, there are other options for backup fuels. The world's largest combined-cycle gas turbine at Teesside in the United Kingdom can be run on propane and naphtha from a nearby refinery. The extra equipment required to operate the Teesside turbines with these fuels included one additional pipeline of less than 5 kilometres linking the power plant and the refinery and specialised fuel nozzles capable of handling liquid fuels. Fuel storage is undertaken by the refinery. According to an IEA Secretariat estimate, the extra capacity cost is only around 0.004 cents per kWh, which could be low enough to warrant the extra equipment as an insurance against unanticipated gas supply disruptions. The most recent gas turbine models are already equipped with fuel nozzles capable of handling liquid fuels without extra cost. Furthermore, propane prices lie within the range of natural gas prices (1992 values). Dual-firing could thus be an economically attractive option at sites where gas and high-voltage electricity grids lie close to oil refineries. There are other sites in Europe, such as Ludwigshaven in Germany, where this is the case, and where dual-firing in CCGTs has been under consideration. Taking into account the envisaged extensions of the gas grid, the number of sites can be expected to rise. Where gasification equipment is installed, CCGTs might also be able to use coal or refinery residue in the future.

It is difficult to discern a clear trend away from or toward more flexibility in the power system as a consequence of increased investment in CCGTs. Moreover, an assessment of the full security implications of increased gas use in a more competitive power market has to account for developments at the level of transmission and supply. It can, for example, be expected that power supply companies offer interruptible electricity supply contracts to a much wider number of consumers, including residential consumers. These contracts may include interruptibility only for certain end uses, such as air conditioning. Curtailment of gas supplies would in this case lead to reduced power supply, but not to system blackouts or brownouts, since only certain uses and certain consumers would be cut off. Larger interconnected areas and increased power exchanges between regions can equally reduce the impact of fuel input disruptions, provided the wider supply offers greater diversification.

Although the above discussion does not indicate a pronounced decline in the power supply system's ability to react to a gas supply disruption, it indicates a need for governments to monitor future developments. It does not, however, mean that the security issues of increased gas use and greater competition are insurmountable, or that concerns over security of supply justify restricting the increased use of gas in power generation. Should the system become more vulnerable to supply shortages, governments have ample scope to develop policy instruments addressing the security issue. Governments could, among other things, create an insurance system, by which generators would be required to provide funds for centralised backup fuel storage or construction and/or maintenance of extra reserve capacity. More intrusive mechanisms could take the form of dual-firing requirements for gas-fired power plants above a certain size and mandatory backup fuel storage.

CONCLUSIONS

Natural gas is generally viewed as a favourable fuel for electricity generation for various reasons, the most important being 1) recent technological improvements in gas turbine technology, i.e., CCGTs, which have dramatically raised conversion efficiencies, 2) low capacity cost, short lead times and the possibility of adding relatively small capacity increments, which enables power producers to follow the dynamics of demand development more closely and to reduce cost, and 3) relatively low emissions of carbon dioxide and environmental pollutants like SO_2, thus enabling generators to meet more stringent environmental regulations at moderate cost.

These combined advantages make natural gas a favourable choice in an electricity market characterised by increasing competition between generators and suppliers on the one hand, and by increasingly stricter environmental requirements on the other.

The economics of natural gas supply are site-specific, but in mature gas markets, the gas supply network should be dense enough to allow the widespread use of natural gas. However, in order to realise the potential that natural gas appears to have, the gas and electricity supply industries need to address their load management requirements and to develop appropriate contractual arrangements in order to minimise cost, and guarantee adequate coverage of demand and sufficient flexibility.

After the turn of the century, coal can be expected to become more competitive compared with gas, since coal prices are expected to rise more slowly than gas prices. Clean coal technology, e.g., IGCCs, might become commercially viable in the same time span, and even in the light of stringent environmental legislation, advanced coal plants combining good environmental performance, small unit size and low fuel cost might have a competitive advantage. The competitiveness of gas versus coal depends, however, on the degree to which pricing mechanisms such as "indifference pricing" will be used, allowing the gas price to reflect the higher capital and operating costs associated with the use of alternative fuels.

Before advanced coal technology can be expected to have a major impact on the electricity supply business, however, natural gas is expected to increase its contribution to power generation considerably. For the OECD as a whole, the IEA's 1995 *World Energy Outlook* predicts the share of natural gas to double from 11% in 1992 to 22% in 2010 in the *Capacity Constraints* case.

Gas use in power generation does not create security of supply problems at present. The discussion in the preceding section shows that while anticipated developments in the electricity market do not clearly indicate whether it will be better or less well prepared for a gas disruption, there is no reason to expect a major deterioration in system flexibility. The power market should be monitored closely in this respect, particularly since it will be the most important gas consuming sector in 2010. Governments, however, will have a number of instruments available to address possible problems in a way which is compatible both with increased gas use and a competitive market.

VI. COPING WITH DISRUPTIONS

INTRODUCTION

The elements of risk identified in this study are long term supply availability and interruptions to supplies caused either by political events or by technical problems such as accidents or extreme weather conditions. This chapter describes the security position of OECD countries with respect to supply interruptions.

The OECD is characterised by a variety of regional gas markets. The range of security issues is unique to each region and imaginable supply disruption scenarios differ.

OECD Europe's gas markets are characterised by a comparatively small number of large transportation facilities and dependence on a small number of outside suppliers. The chapter examines the consequences of supply disruption scenarios.

North America's gas markets are well-developed and have a diversified production and transportation system. No single supply source or transportation route represents a large share of regional supply. This chapter reviews the recent performance of the system at times of peak winter demand.

In the OECD *Pacific* region the security issues are specific to each country. Australia and New Zealand are both self-sufficient in gas. Japan is dependent on LNG imports for more than 95% of its supply and relies on long term contracts with stable suppliers, its modular supply and delivery systems and the possibilities for fuel substitution through the electricity generation system. Since the issues faced by the OECD Pacific region are different for each country their security positions are examined in the individual country annexes.

OECD EUROPE

Introduction

This section examines the consequences of and possible reactions to particular supply disruptions but does not comment on either the likelihood or the precise cause of incidents leading to an interruption in supplies. The analysis is based on the gas market in 1992 but the long term supply and demand figures presented in Chapter 3 are used to analyse how the current market is likely to evolve given changes to both supply diversity and delivery systems as well as to demand structure.

The analysis covers only particular scenarios. The results do not represent the overall security situation for gas supply in the countries concerned. Other plausible scenarios could be envisaged which would have a greater (or lesser) effect on individual countries. It must also be borne in mind that, as discussed in Chapter 3, the share of TPES (Table 3.4) and the sectoral breakdown of gas use vary substantially from country to country. The impact of any disruption would similarly vary between countries.

References to continental Europe refer to all countries within OECD Europe except the United Kingdom and Ireland whose gas grids are, for the time being at least, completely independent of the rest of the continent's network.

Diversity and Flexibility

Supply

Indigenous production in continental Europe is concentrated in the two major exporting countries Norway and the Netherlands. These two countries account for over 70% of the region's production. A further 23% is produced in two large, net importing countries: Germany and Italy.

With the exception of Norway, the Netherlands and Denmark, all OECD countries in continental Europe have to import the majority of their gas supplies. Clearly supply security benefits from a diverse portfolio of sources, but there are limits to the optimal number. Transportation costs are a major component of end-user gas prices and for the development of major new pipelines these costs are more or less proportional to distance. Possibilities for supply diversification, then, are dependent on a country's geographical location - how close it is to supply sources and which countries lie between it and the supplies. But equally important is the size of the local gas market. Gas transportation is subject to significant economies of scale, so a small market may not be able to justify several small pipelines bringing supplies from different sources.

Countries in the centre and north of the continent have access to supplies from three, if not all four, of the major gas exporters (Russia, the Netherlands, Algeria and Norway). Those countries on the eastern and southern edge of OECD Europe, though, are greatly restricted in their choice of suppliers. Austria, in the east, receives almost all of its imports from Russia; Spain, in the south, is dependent on Algerian gas (though is currently diversifying supplies and has a low share of gas in TPES); Turkey, in the south-east has been importing gas exclusively from Russia, although Algerian imports are now commencing.

There are some signs, however, of increasing supply diversity. Both Austria and Spain now have import contracts with Norway whereby the gas is "delivered" through swaps with Gaz de France. ÖMV/Austria Ferngas takes Russian gas destined for France while Gaz de France takes an equivalent volume of Norwegian gas, and Enagas in Spain takes gas produced in the south-west of France in exchange for the Norwegian gas. For the time being these contracts concern comparatively small volumes of gas.

Since gas is heavily used for space heating, demand varies strongly according to season. Gas companies have developed a variety of tools for dealing with these seasonal load variations. The tools fall into three categories: those aimed at increasing the flexibility of supplies, those which provide buffer stocks and those which reduce demand at times of peak gas use.

Table 6.1   Supply to OECD Europe in 1992 (Mtoe)

Destination	Production for own use[1]	Russia	Netherlands	Algeria	Norway	Denmark	Libya	Other[2]	Total
Austria	**1.22**	**4.09**						0.19	5.50
Belgium & Luxembourg			**3.70**	**3.93**	**2.12**				9.75
Denmark	**1.79**								1.79
Finland		**2.41**							2.41
France	1.80	**9.50**	**4.40**	**8.10**	**5.40**				29.20
Germany	**12.20**	**18.19**	**18.11**		**8.42**	1.20			58.12
Greece	**0.06**								0.06
Ireland	**2.07**								2.07
Italy	**13.35**	**11.45**	**4.27**	**12.63**					41.70
Netherlands	**30.69**				2.58				33.27
Spain	**1.12**			**3.20**			**1.72**		6.04
Sweden						**0.63**			0.63
Switzerland		**0.33**	**0.45**					**1.14**	1.92
Turkey	0.16	**3.63**							3.79
UK	**47.78**				**4.74**				52.52
Total	112.25	49.60	30.93	27.85	23.26	1.83	1.72	1.33	248.78

1 Domestic Production less Exports.
2 Includes Germany, France and Italy.
Figures in bold represent > 10% of supply.
Source: Country Submissions.

Swing

Supply flexibility comes either from flexible domestic production or from flexible import contracts. Both imply operation of production and transportation infrastructure at low load levels during certain periods. A measure of supply flexibility is the level of swing, defined here as the maximum monthly delivery divided by the average monthly delivery in a given year. The swings in exports from Russia, Norway and Algeria in 1992 were in the region of 110-115%. Exports from the Netherlands in the same year showed a swing greater than 160%. This exceptionally high swing reflects the fact that the Netherlands has a high production capacity relative to its annual production level, especially from its Groningen field, and that it is comparatively close to its European markets but that its reserves are limited. Further details of the Netherlands' export policies are given in the country annex.

Storage

A country with large storage facilities is able to import gas evenly throughout the year, directing gas into storage during the summer and withdrawing it during the winter. Storage facilities can be broken down into two main types: those used to balance seasonal load fluctuations and peak-shavers used for a few days of high demand. Underground storage, for either seasonal or peak-shaving use, requires specific rock formations which are not found in all countries - hence the presence of such facilities in some countries and not others. France uses its high storage capacity to balance stable imports with varying demand. In Europe, Austria has the highest level of storage in relation to annual consumption and uses its capacity not only for seasonal load balancing but also as a strategic stock against fluctuations in supplies (in 1992, 74% of Austria's supplies came from Russia). Figure 6.1 gives the storage capacities in continental OECD Europe as well as an insight into how these capacities are used.

Figure 6.1   Seasonal Storage Use

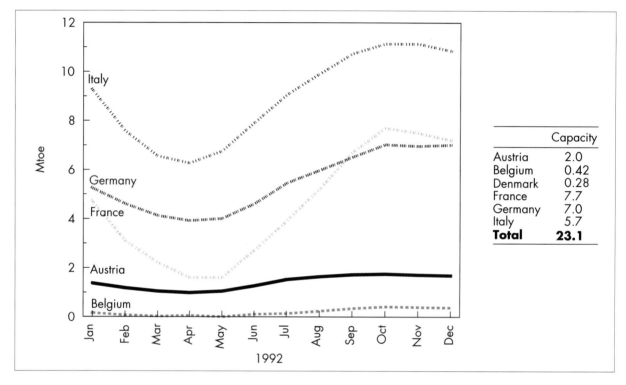

Capacity	
Austria	2.0
Belgium	0.42
Denmark	0.28
France	7.7
Germany	7.0
Italy	5.7
Total	**23.1**

Fuel-Switching

Reducing demand at times of peak gas use involves cutting supplies of gas to selected gas consumers. These consumers can generally switch to alternative fuels such as heavy fuel oil and gasoil or even coal. They are usually industrial consumers or electricity generators who, in exchange for being prepared to lose their supplies, benefit from cheaper gas for the rest of the year. The sales are made under *interruptible* contracts whose conditions can be the subject of individual negotiation. Table 6.2 gives an overview of the general provisions of interruptible contracts in OECD Europe together with their shares of gas sales to the industrial and electricity sectors. For certain countries these data have not been available and estimates have been made.

Reactions to a Supply Disruption

The more diversified a country's supply base, the less impact any single supply disruption will have. Not only does such a country lose a relatively small proportion of its total supplies if one of its sources is disrupted, but it may also be able to seek small additional volumes from its non-disrupted sources to make up for the lost gas.

Table 6.2 Interruptible Sales Contracts in 1992 (Mtoe)

	Total Demand	Interruptible Demand		Contract Conditions
		Industry	Electricity	
Austria	5.2	0.4	0.75	Almost all gas-fired electricity plants are dual- or multi-fired.
Belgium	9.0	0.9	0.9	There exists a very close cooperation between the electricity and gas companies.
Denmark	1.91	0.1	0.1	Interruptions are possible between October 1 and April 30 and require at least 24 hours notice.
Finland	2.4	0.3	0.2	There are just two interruptible contracts. The industry interruptible supplies are routinely cut for several months each winter. Beyond formal interruptions, 90% of demand can easily switch to HFO or LFO, about 3% can switch to LPG and the remaining 7% can be supplied through the pipeline network with a propane-air mixture.
France	27.9	5.6	-	Not usually interrupted in winter. No limit on maximum interruption.
Germany	56.9	6.2	2.9	
Italy	41.0	4.1	-	Contractual interruptions can range from 4 to 16 weeks per year. Most gas-fired electricity generation is multi-fired, even though gas sales for power generation are not formally interruptible.
Netherlands	33.0	-	6.0	Supplies to electricity generators can be interrupted when temperatures drop below 0°C.
Spain	5.2	1.1	0.2	No limit on interruption period. 48 hours notice of interruption required.
Sweden	0.6	-	-	No formal interruptibility. Most gas-fired district heating plants can burn alternative fuels. Some facilities exist for injecting LPG-air mixtures into distribution pipelines.
Switzerland	1.9	0.6	-	Maximum interruptions periods range from 30 to 60 days. Advance notice can be very short (e.g., less than two hours). In the past, cut-off periods have been limited to a few days in winter.
Turkey	4.0	-	1.1	The maximum cut-off period is 6 weeks (although disrupted supplies have to be made up later). The advance notice required is 8 hours.
Ireland	2.0	-	0.8	Most gas electricity generation is dual-fired and can be interrupted under informal agreement with the Electricity Supply Board.
UK	51.1	4.2	0.6	
OECD Europe	242.1	23.5	13.55	

Source: Gas companies, associations and IEA Secretariat estimates.

How can countries/gas companies act when faced with a significant, but temporary, shortfall in gas supplies? The previous section has examined the mechanisms used by gas companies to increase their flexibility on a seasonal basis, but all these mechanisms can, together, be of strategic importance in the event of a supply disruption.

Major production and transportation infrastructure is sometimes built with some spare capacity to allow for increasing demand, but in general capacity is built to be used. In continental Europe this use is almost always linked to specific gas sales contracts. Thus, most major pipelines and production facilities have little, if any, spare capacity at times of peak demand. The spare capacity that exists is in spring, summer and autumn. The size of this spare capacity depends on the swing in the facilities' normal use. The greater the swing, the greater the spare capacity in summer and the more possibilities there are to use a mixture of increased off-peak supplies and storage, together with interruptible sales contracts, to meet firm demand.

The level of monthly swing in both indigenous production and import contracts provides an indication of the surge production capacity of a supply source. But as mentioned above, the use of this spare capacity depends on storage facilities. The scenario analysis presented later in the chapter looks more closely at the dynamics of maximising imports and production by using storage effectively during a supply crisis.

The Netherlands has contracts which foresee it supplying additional volumes to both Germany and Belgium in the event of a temporary shortfall in either of these countries' supplies. There is flexibility in export contracts of 10.5 Mtoe per year as well as an additional back-up capacity of 4.5 Mtoe per year. Further details are given in the Netherlands annex.

Supply Disruption Risks

Political

The principal suppliers of gas into Europe, i.e., non-OECD Europe suppliers, are Russia and Algeria. Together they supplied 39.9% of continental Europe's demand in 1992. Individual countries are not as diverse in their range of suppliers as Figure 6.2 might suggest. Austria, for example, imported 74% of its requirements in 1992 from Russia while Spain received 53% of its gas from Algeria. The greatly differing situations of European countries in terms of supplies and demand flexibility mean that an analysis of the effects of a disruption in supplies must be carried out on a country-by-country basis.

A study commissioned by the IEA (summarised in Annex 2) concludes that neither Russia nor Algeria have an interest, economic or political, in disrupting gas supplies to Europe. The study sees the most likely cause of such a disruption as a breakdown in relations between Russia and the transit countries of the former Soviet Union or a worsening political climate within Algeria. It finds no reason why a deterioration in Russian/Ukrainian relations could aggravate the situation in Algeria or vice versa. On the contrary, were supplies from one to be disrupted, the other would have every incentive both to maximise its income in the short term and to enhance its reputation in the long term by increasing its exports.

Figure 6.2   Supplies to Continental Europe in 1992 (Mtoe)

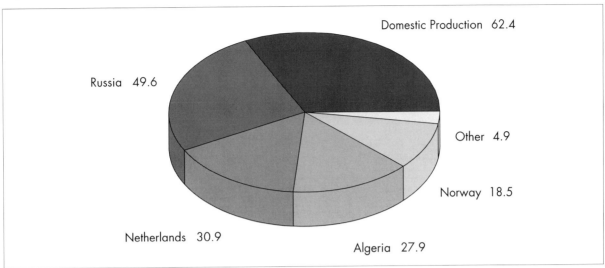

Source: Country Submissions.

Technical

According to a report from a group of European pipeline companies[1], the single largest cause of disruption to pipelines is external interference (i.e., excavation work). Incidents have been reported on transmission pipelines but the vast majority of reported incidents concern distribution pipelines.

On the whole, damage to onshore pipelines can be repaired very quickly (in a matter of days and weeks rather than months) and, therefore, such damage does not pose serious regional security risks. Offshore pipelines are more troublesome to access and repair but this difficulty of access makes them correspondingly less likely to be damaged. Even then, a pipeline in not too deep water can usually be repaired relatively quickly given fair weather conditions.

Perhaps the greatest risk of prolonged interruption comes from the destruction of a major production or processing facility or a deep water pipeline whose replacement might take many months to build. Table 6.3 shows the throughput of such facilities in the European gas supply system. The largest existing facility, Norpipe, brings 16 Mtoe per year of Norwegian gas to Germany and the Netherlands. Its disruption would reduce supplies to Europe significantly less than a total disruption in Russian deliveries (49.6 Mtoe in 1992). The next largest facility, the Transmed pipeline carrying Algerian gas from Tunisia to Italy, had a capacity of 12 Mtoe/year in 1992. A disruption in this line would have similar effects on the Italian gas market to a total disruption of Algerian supplies. The regional consequences of such a disruption would, however, be less serious since supplies to France and to Spain would not be affected.

In fact there appears to be no single facility whose failure would have regional consequences as important as the disruption of Russian or Algerian deliveries.

---

1. *Gas Pipelines: A Report by the European Gas Pipeline Incident Data Group*, April 1988.

Table 6.3   Current Key European Gas Installations

Facility	Capacity		Countries Supplied	Notes
	bcm /year	Mtoe /year		
Norpipe Ekofisk/Emden	19	16	Germany Netherlands	Sub-sea pipeline transporting gas from the Norwegian Ekofisk platform in the North Sea to Emden in Germany.
TransMed pipeline	14	12	Italy	Sub-sea pipeline transporting Algerian gas from Tunisia to southern Italy. Supplies through this line account for over 40% of Italy's gas supply. In the Sicily Channel, where water depths exceed 600 metres, TransMed consists of three separate 20" pipelines (one of which is a spare).
Zeepipe Sleipner/Zeebrugge	13	11	Belgium France	
Zeebrugge LNG import terminal	5	4	Belgium	This terminal is geographically separated from the landfall of Zeepipe.
Arzew LNG export terminal	16	13	Belgium France Spain	
Skikda LNG export terminal	3.2	2.6	France Italy Spain	
Panigaglia LNG import terminal	3.9	3.2	Italy	Originally designed to take Libyan gas, the plant has been modified and is now used below capacity to import LNG from Algeria.
Montoir de Bretagne LNG import terminal	10	8	France	LNG imports from Algeria to western France. Actual throughput is significantly lower than maximum capacity.
Fos sur Mer LNG import terminal	3.5	2.9	France	LNG imports to southern France from Algeria.
Barcelona	8.9	7.4	Spain	LNG imports to northern Spain from Algeria and Libya.
Huelva	3.8	3.1	Spain	LNG imports to southern Spain from Algeria.
Cartagena	0.4	0.3	Spain	Temporarily out of service.
Denmark/Sweden pipeline	1.1	0.9	Sweden	Short sub-sea pipeline.

Supply Disruption Analysis

The Scenarios

The aim of the analysis which follows is to consider the impacts of the largest conceivable disruptions to European gas supplies. The risks identified are both political and technical but the impacts of a political disruption could potentially be far greater than those of a technical disruption. The worst case disruptions are therefore both political.

The basic scenarios considered in this chapter are a total interruption, starting on October 1st, in Russian supplies and, independently, a total interruption in Algerian supplies. Each scenario is considered under two principal variants:

■ Deliveries from non-disrupted sources remain at contractual levels (but include any contracted flexibility such as that described for Germany and Belgium) and supplies to interruptible customers are cut only within general contractual provisions - referred to as the **worst-case scenario**.

■ Deliveries from non-disrupted sources can be increased to capacity, constrained only by the ability of the importing countries to store the volumes delivered during low demand season that are beyond their immediate needs. Supplies to customers with interruptible contracts or dual-firing can be cut for the duration of the supply shortage. This is referred to as the **best-case scenario**.

The countries included in the analysis are those which import gas from Algeria and/or Russia, namely Austria, Belgium, Finland, France, Germany, Italy, Luxembourg (indirectly), Spain, Switzerland and Turkey. The Netherlands and Norway are considered in their role as exporters to several countries affected in these scenarios. Denmark is taken account of only by way of any spare export capacity to Germany. Sweden is excluded altogether.

As noted above the scenarios have particular impacts on certain countries but are not wholly representative of the overall security situation. Different scenarios could have been chosen. The ones selected affect multiple countries at the same time. Other scenarios could be envisaged for particular countries (e.g., terrorist actions) with greater or lesser impacts than those shown.

Methodology

At the outset it was realised that any analysis of gas supply disruptions must take into account several industry characteristics.

■ Demand is seasonal. Any shortfall would probably occur in or immediately after winter.

■ Storage facilities do not always operate as a strategic reserve; their levels can fluctuate during the year when they serve a load balancing function.

■ Gas is traded, for the most part, under long term contracts which specify maximum deliveries and delivery rates. It is these contracts which normally determine infrastructure capacity.

The analysis is based on monthly supply and demand data for 1992 and, where available, for 1993. Supply data are broken down by source, and demand figures split between firm and interruptible customer categories. Details of where the data have been estimated are presented after the results. From these data the following have been inferred:

■ actual storage levels, month by month, in 1992 (and for some cases in 1993 as well);

■ monthly production and import "capacity" by source - assumed to be equal to the maximum monthly levels.

For the scenarios defined above the following calculations were made for each of the consecutive 27 months (i.e., until the end of December two years later):

■ available supply from indigenous production and imports
  "best-case" includes extra-contractual (but within capacity) imports
  "worst-case" imports are those actually reported in 1992/3
  both cases include maximum capacity indigenous production

■ demand to be met
  "worst-case" includes interruptible demand that has already been cut for the length of its contractual conditions in a calendar year

■ export commitments (1992/3 figures are taken as contractual obligations)

■ supply deficit or surplus - any deficit is withdrawn from storage and a surplus is fed back into storage, leading to a new storage level for the start of the following month.

The "cut-off" point when supplies to firm customers have to be cut is the month when the supply/demand gap exceeds storage volumes. For those countries without significant storage facilities, this "cut-off" point corresponds to the first month during the disruption when demand exceeds available supply from production and imports.

The analysis is not, and probably never could be, exhaustive. A number of issues, which are beyond the scope of this project, have not been tackled.

■ The data are based not on detailed contract information (which are confidential) but on actual 1992 supply figures. Contracts include provisions for some flexibility in annual deliveries, usually around 10-15% of annual contracted quantities. The analysis does not take account of 1992 deliveries in relation to contracted levels.

■ No account is taken of system bottlenecks experienced during days of peak demand.

■ Gas quality issues have been ignored.

Results

As emphasised above, the results of this analysis must not be taken in isolation: they do not represent the whole gas security situation of the countries in question or the relative impact of gas disruptions. Table 6.4 shows a variety of indicators for the countries affected by either of the two scenarios to underline the point that no single indicator is illustrative of the gas security position. One of these is the "cut-off" point when there is a risk that supplies to firm customers may need to be curtailed because the supply/demand gap exceeds storage volumes. In practice in an emergency extra measures are likely to be taken which affect the course of the shortfall.

The analysis suggests that those countries with diversified supply options could, on the whole, maintain supplies to their firm customers for over a year if either Russian or Algerian supplies were disrupted; those countries on the south and south-east ends of Europe, that is Spain and Turkey, whose gas markets are new and dependent on supplies from either Russia or Algeria could face early supply shortages; Austria, on the eastern end of Europe, has the highest ratio of storage capacity to annual consumption in Europe; even without supply diversity this storage buffer could delay a serious impact on firm customers by about four months.

Even under the "best-case", with all interruptible demand cut indefinitely and non-disrupted sources supplying at maximum capacity, some countries might need to disrupt firm customers within a few months. But the impact on firm customers would not necessarily be great. Belgium, for instance, could exhaust stored volumes after just three months in the "worst-case" Algerian disruption. Some firm customers would have to be cut for about three months but over the year the extra-contractual cut-backs represent only 1% of total demand. So the "cut-off" point should not be interpreted as meaning widespread disruptions in all cases.

Table 6.4   Security Indicators for Countries Supplied by Russia or Algeria

Country	Gas[1] Share of TPES (%)	Number of Significant[1] Suppliers	Russia's Share of Supplies (%)	Algeria's Share of Supplies (%)	Months Prior to Supply Curtailments	Disruption
Austria	20.8	2	74	–		Russian
Belgium/Luxembourg	17.7	3	–	40		Algerian
Finland	8.8	1	100	–		Russian
France	12.1	5	32	27		Russian / Algerian
Germany	16.7	4	31	–		Russian
Italy	25.8	4	27	30		Russian / Algerian
Spain[2]	6.2	5	–	51		Algerian
Switzerland	7.6	3	17	–		Russian
Turkey	6.9	2	95	–		Russian

Scale: 0   10   20   30+

1. Significant suppliers representing more than 5 % of total (includes domestic production).
2. Refers to data for 1994.

■ Worst Case
□ Best Case

Source: Country Submissions and IEA Secretariat Estimates.

Table 6.4 should only be read in conjunction with explanations of the scenarios and results given above and the data and assumptions shown on the following pages. A summary of the data and assumptions is given on an annual basis in Table 6.5 for the Russian disruption and Table 6.6 for the Algerian disruption. Under the Russian disruption 25% of the region's supplies are cut, but even under the worst-case set of assumptions the final shortfall of gas to end-users represents just 2.5% of total demand.

Table 6.5   Response During First Year to a Total Disruption in Russian Supplies Starting on October 1st (Mtoe)

| Country | "Worst-Case" | | | | | | "Best-Case" | | | | | | Total Demand | Annual Shortfall Annual Demand (%) | |
	Supplies Lost	Increased Imports	Increased Domestic Production	Interruptible Demand Cut	Stock Draw[1]	Shortfall in First Year	Increased Imports	Increased Domestic Production	Interruptible Demand Cut	Stock Draw[1]	Shortfall in First Year			"Worst" Case	"Best" Case
Austria	4.2	-	0.2	1.2	1.8	1	-	0.2	1.2	1.8	1		5.2	19.2	19.2
Finland	2.5	-	-	0.5	-	2.0	-	-	2.5	-	-		2.5	80	0
France	9.5	-	0.1	5.6	3.8	-	2.8	0.1	5.6	1	-		27.9	-	-
Germany	18.2	9	4.5	3.7	1	-	9	4.5	4.6	0.1	-		56.8	-	-
Italy	11.2	-	-	0.8	10.4	-	1.7	-	4.1	5.4	-		41.0	-	-
Switzerland[2]	0.3	-	-	0.1	-	0.2	-	-	0.3	-	-		1.9	10.5	-
Turkey	3.6	-	-	0.1	-	3.5	-	-	1.1	-	2.5		3.8	92.1	65.8
Total (OECD)	49.5	9	4.8	12.0	17.0	6.7	13.5	4.8	19.4	8.3	3.5		189.6	2.5	1.8

1. The volumes withdrawn from storage over and above net withdrawals in the reference year 1992.
2. Russian gas is delivered to Switzerland under a contract with Ruhrgas.
Source: Country submissions and IEA Secretariat estimates

Table 6.6   Response During First Year to a Total Disruption in Algerian Supplies Starting on October 1st (Mtoe)

Country	"Worst-Case"						"Best-Case"					Total Demand	Annual Shortfall Annual Demand (%)	
	Supplies Lost	Increased Imports	Increased Domestic Production	Interruptible Demand Cut	Stock Draw[1]	Shortfall in First Year	Increased Imports	Increased Domestic Production	Interruptible Demand Cut	Stock Draw[1]	Shortfall in First Year		"Worst" Case	"Best" Case
Belgium & Luxembourg	3.9	1.8	-	1.8	0.1	0.2	2	-	1.8	0.1	-	9.5	2.1	-
France	8.1	-	0.1	5.6	2.4	-	1.5	0.1	5.6	0.9	-	27.9	-	-
Italy	12.5	-	-	0.8	10.3	1.4	2.9	-	4.1	5.5	-	41.0	3.4	-
Spain[2]	3.7	0.3	-	0.6	0.7	1.5	1.1	-	1.1	0.6	0.3	5.8	25.9	5.2
Total (OECD)	27.7	2.1	0.1	8.8	13.6	3.0	7.5	0.1	12.6	7.1	0.3	189.5	1.6	0.2

1. The volumes withdrawn from storage over and above net withdrawals in the reference year 1992.
2. Based on data for 1994 (Note that in 1994 Spain's supply was significantly greater than its consumption. The difference is accounted for by cushion gas injected into storage. It is assumed that in the event of a disruption the injection of cushion gas would have been suspended, liberating extra supply for firm customers.)

Source: Country submissions and IEA Secretariat estimates

Data and Assumptions

Austria

In 1992 Austria imported 74% of its gas needs from Russia. Most of the remainder came from domestic production. A small volume from Germany currently supplies the area in the west of the country which is not connected to the bulk of the Austrian grid.

Given this high dependence on a single import source, a large storage capacity has been built. This ratio of storage capacity to annual consumption is the highest of any country in the region (130 days of average consumption). This capacity is used not only for seasonal load balancing, allowing the importing company ÖMV to purchase spot gas in summer to supplement its long term contracts, but also as a strategic stock to guard against irregularities in supply.

Indigenous production in 1992 was 1.2 Mtoe and the monthly supply swing[2] was 118%, implying a spare production capacity of about 0.2 Mtoe.

Figure 6.3   Effects of a Russian Supply Disruption Starting October 1st, Austria

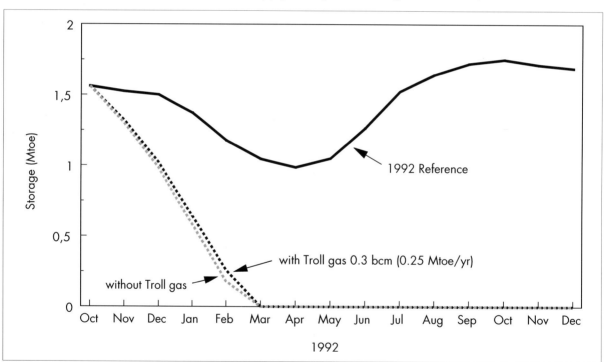

Source: Secretariat estimates based on 1992 data from the Federal Ministry for Economic Affairs.

On the demand side there is considerable flexibility. Industrial demand in 1992 accounted for 30% of total consumption. Hard data on interruptibility in the industrial sector is not available, but estimates put the level at around 25%. Another 20% of demand is accounted for by power generation where virtually all facilities have dual-firing capabilities. The distinction between interruptible and firm gas for power generation is not always clear since some of the power

---

2.   Peak monthly figure divided by average monthly figure.

generators are themselves gas wholesalers. All gas to power generation in Austria is assumed to be interruptible. This puts interruptibility at around 25-30% of total demand. It is assumed that this demand could be cut indefinitely.

In a scenario where Russian supplies were totally disrupted for a prolonged period, Austria's options would be extremely limited. All surrounding countries are themselves heavily dependent on Russian gas and would therefore be unlikely to supply spot volumes. Austria would have to cut all interruptible demand, maximise indigenous production and draw the balance down from storage. Since there are no further extra-contractual measures that could be taken, such as additional supplies from non-disrupted sources, the "best-case" and "worst-case" are identical.

In 1993 Austria received its first supplies under the new Troll contract with Norway. Although Norwegian gas is not physically delivered to Austria[3] under normal circumstances, were Russian supplies to be disrupted the gas would be transported through Germany. Initial annual deliveries of 0.3 bcm (0.26 Mtoe) should grow to 1 bcm (0.86 Mtoe) by the year 2000. Figure 6.3 includes a line showing the small difference these Norwegian volumes would have made in the disruption scenario based on 1992 data.

Additional measures for dealing with a major energy supply crisis are contained in the "Energy Steering Law" which allows the Ministry to order the interruption of supplies to the different customer categories.

Belgium

Belgium's gas supply in 1992 came from Algeria (3.93 Mtoe), the Netherlands (3.7 Mtoe) and Norway (2.12 Mtoe). There is no indigenous production. Belgium re-exported 0.6 Mtoe to Luxembourg (most of Luxembourg's supply). Storage capacity of 0.4 Mtoe, which is used for seasonal load balancing, represents just 17 days of average consumption.

Monthly swing in imports from Algeria and Norway was about 115% in 1992 - but the swing in Dutch imports was almost 190%. Back-up arrangements between Gasunie of the Netherlands and Distrigaz of Belgium allow for a considerable increase in supplies in the case of need. This contractual flexibility probably represents around an extra 1.8 Mtoe on an annual basis, with most of the increased deliveries being available outside the middle of winter (when there is little spare capacity). Beyond contractual levels, were Norway and the Netherlands to export gas to Belgium at maximum rates all year round this would provide an additional 3.3 Mtoe from the Netherlands and 0.3 Mtoe from Norway above 1992 levels.

Of total demand 10% was interruptible in industry and 16% was consumed in power generation, most of which has dual-firing capabilities. The level of formal interruptibility in gas sales for power generation is thought to be around 65%. It is assumed that this demand can be cut indefinitely.

It is unclear to what extent Belgium could handle the large additional volumes of low-calorific Groningen gas from the Netherlands implied under the "best case" scenario.

---

3. The contracted volumes of Norwegian gas are delivered to France, and Austria takes an equivalent volume of Russian gas destined for Gaz de France.

Figure 6.4   Effects of an Algerian Disruption Starting October 1st, Belgium

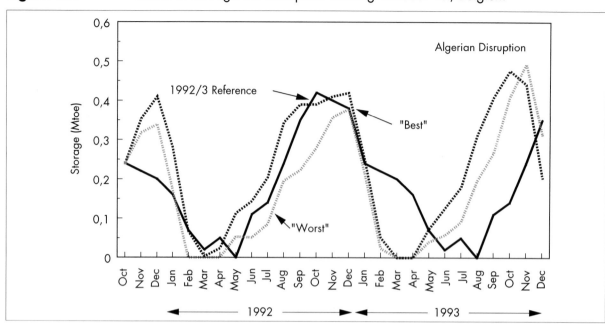

Source: Secretariat estimates based on 1992 and 1993 data from Distrigaz.

France

In 1992 France received 31% of its total gas requirements (including re-exports) from Russia and 27% from Algeria with the balance coming from Norway (18%), the Netherlands (15%) and domestic production (9%). The storage capacity of 7.7 Mtoe, which is the largest in absolute terms of any country in the region, allows Gaz de France to import gas at a fairly constant rate all year round. There was some swing in imports from the Netherlands and Norway in 1992 (about 130%), but imports from Russia and Algeria showed a swing of 110%.

There is no public power generation from gas but 20% of consumption falls in the interruptible industry sector. Supplies to interruptible customers are almost never cut, but under contractual conditions they can be cut for an indefinite period.

Table 6.7   Assumptions Behind Political Disruption Scenarios for France (Mtoe)

	"Worst Case"	"Best Case"
Russian Disruption		
Interruptible demand cut	5.6	5.6
Increased imports from		
Algeria	-	1.1
Netherlands	-	0.7
Norway	-	1.0
Increased production	0.1	0.1
Algerian Disruption		
Interruptible demand cut	5.6	5.6
Increased imports from		
Russia	-	0.7
Netherlands	-	0.4
Norway	-	0.5
Increased production	0.1	0.1

Figure 6.5   Effects of a Russian Disruption Starting October 1st, France

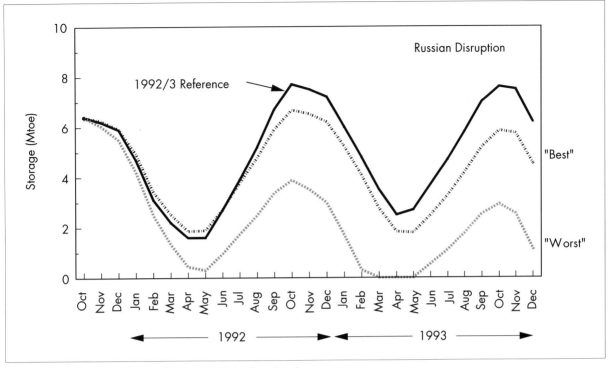

Source: Secretariat estimates based on 1992 and 1993 data from Gaz de France.

Figure 6.6   Effects of an Algerian Disruption Starting October 1st, France

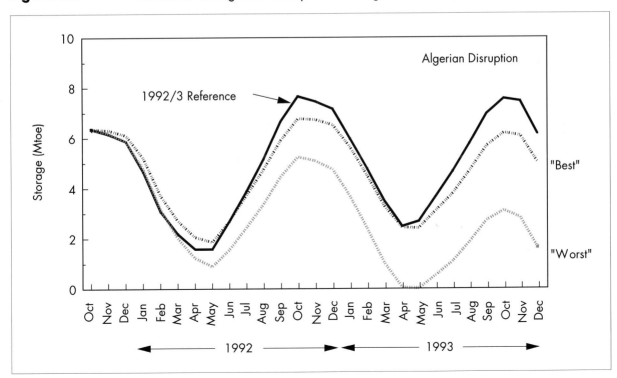

Source: Secretariat estimates based on 1992 and 1993 data from Gaz de France.

Finland

All gas in Finland is delivered from Russia and the country has no gas storage facilities. There are two interruptible contracts, one for supplies to public power generation, the other for power in a chemical plant. These sales are cut in winter to reduce peak demand.

All gas users can, however, switch to alternative fuels. Just over 90% of consumption can be switched to heavy or light fuel oil, 2-3% can use LPG and the remainder can operate on a propane-air mixture supplied through the gas transmission system from a plant next to Neste's Porvoo oil refinery.

Germany

Of total 1992 gas requirements (59.5 Mtoe including re-exports and stock filling) Germany received 23% from indigenous production, 31% from Russia, 30% from the Netherlands, 14% from Norway and 2% from Denmark. Storage capacity at 7 Mtoe represents 44 days of average consumption.

Monthly import data for Germany were not available. The data used in this analysis have been taken from countries reporting exports to Germany. Production operated at a monthly swing level of 130%, between that of imports from Norway and Russia at 110% and nearby Denmark (160%) and the Netherlands (180%).

Figure 6.7   Effects of a Russian Disruption Starting October 1st, Germany

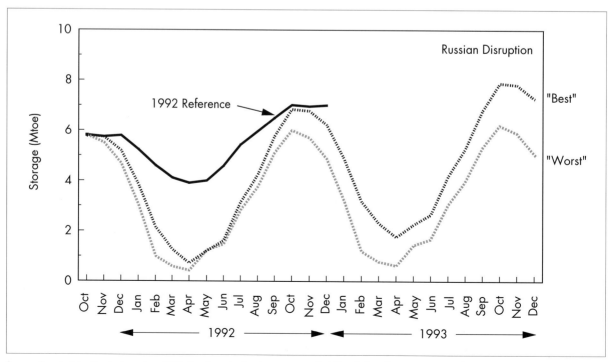

Source: Secretariat estimates based on 1992 data from the Bundesministerium für Wirtschaft, industry estimates and supplying countries.

Demand for gas in 1992 was 6.5 Mtoe for electricity generation and 24.7 Mtoe for industry. The working assumptions used in the analysis are that 25% of industrial demand and 45% of demand for power generation are interruptible and that all of total interruptible demand can be cut under contractual conditions for three months each year and only 20% can be cut for the whole year. Peak winter interruptible demand has been assumed to be double the summer level. These last two assumptions are arbitrary.

Italy

Supplies to Italy of 42 Mtoe in 1992 came from indigenous production (32%), Algeria (30%), Russia (27%) and the Netherlands (11%). Imports from Russia, Algeria and the Netherlands were all fairly even throughout 1992, with monthly swings in the range of 115-130%. Production was flat over the year. Most of the seasonal load balancing requirements (peak monthly winter demand was over three times minimum monthly summer demand) was met by storage.

Figure 6.8   Effects of a Russian Disruption Starting October 1st, Italy

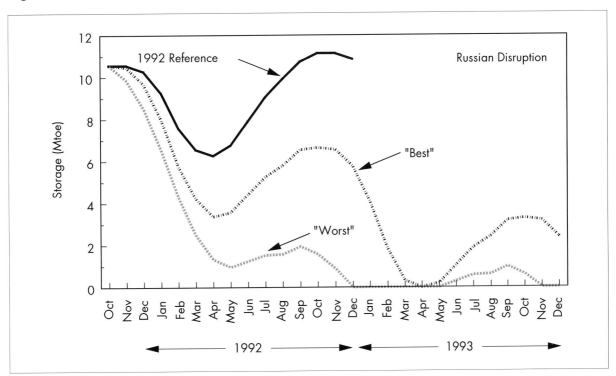

Source: Secretariat estimates based on 1992 data from the Ministry of Industry.

About 10% of total demand, in the industrial sector, is formally interruptible and contractual conditions allow for interruptions of between 4 and 16 weeks per year. Demand for electricity generation is not formally interruptible, although most gas-fired power plants can burn other fuels. In the analysis that follows no interruptions have been assumed to gas destined for power generation.

Figure 6.9 Effects of an Algerian Disruption Starting October 1st, Italy

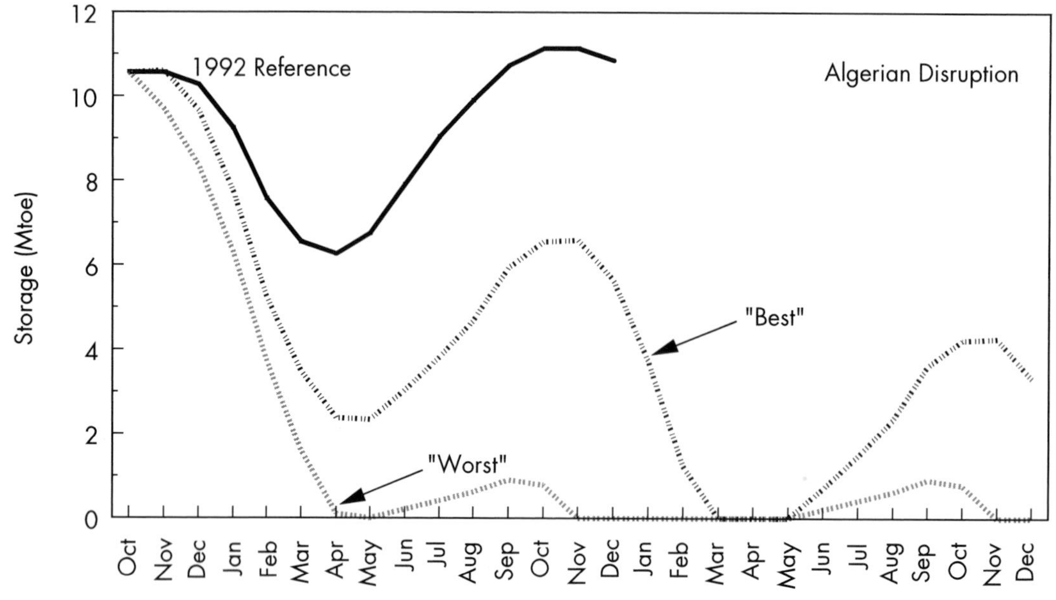

Source: Secretariat estimates based on 1992 data from the Ministry of Industry.

Spain

Spain's gas market is expanding rapidly and since 1992 has undergone important changes affecting its gas security. These changes include the development of seasonal storage capacity (of which there was none in 1992) and the diversification of supply sources, with new gas coming from Norway and even Australia and Abu Dhabi. Under such rapidly changing conditions it is impossible for one base year to be representative of the country's security position. The disruption analysis is therefore based on 1994 data, i.e., the latest data available prior to publication of this study.

In 1994 Spain received 51% of its gas supplies from Algeria (all in the form of LNG), 18% from Libya, 12% from Norway, 10% from domestic production and 9% from Australia and Abu Dhabi. Imports from Norway were being built up during the year and it is assumed in the "best" case that these imports could have been increased to their maximum monthly level throughout the year. The swing in imports from Libya was about 125% and the "best" case assumes that monthly Libyan imports could have been increased to their maximum monthly levels. No additional supply from Australia, Abu Dhabi or other spot LNG is assumed.

Underground gas storage capacity had reached 0.4 Mtoe of working gas by 1994 (in the field at Serrablo) and further storage was (and still is) under development. This means that Spain's total supply in 1994 was significantly higher than its total consumption since both cushion gas and working gas were being injected into storage during the year. It has been assumed in the analysis that, in the event of a disruption to Algerian supplies, all available gas would be made available to customers instead of being injected into storage. This means that seasonal storage use as well as any supply loss in 1994 may not be representative of future years. However, Spain's plans for storage expansion imply that this supply "excess" is likely to remain for several years.

Underground storage is supplemented by a buffer stock of LNG (equivalent to 0.12 Mtoe) maintained at the two active LNG reception terminals. Although smaller than the underground storage, this capacity is important because its daily send-out capacity is greater than that of Serrablo.

Interruptible demand accounted for about 14% of the industrial sector and almost 50% of the demand by the power sector (in total, interruptible demand made up 10% of overall demand). In a disruption, supplies to all power generators and feedstock users would probably be cut, doubling the level of interruptibility (the scenario used for the "best" case).

In January, 1995, Enagas signed a storage agreement with Gaz de France for a total capacity of 0.4 bcm (0.33 Mtoe) with a maximum delivery capacity of 0.1 bcm/month (0.08 Mtoe/month). Although this contract was not in force during the base year, it has been included in the disruption analysis in order to illustrate the most up-to-date picture possible of Spain's situation.

The results in Figures 6.10a and 6.10b show storage levels falling to zero after 9 to 10 months but curtailments to firm customers beginning after 2 1/2 to 5 months. This results from the limited withdrawal capacity of the Serrablo storage (2.5 mcm/day, 0.06 Mtoe/month; this should be expanded to 3.5 mcm/day by 1997).

Figure 6.10a   Effects of an Algerian Disruption Starting October 1st, Worst Case, Spain

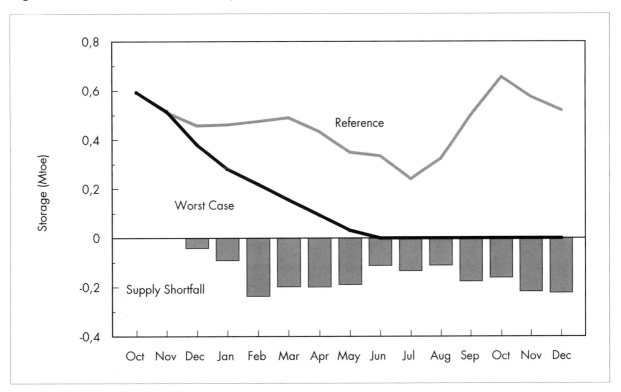

Source: Secretariat estimates based on 1994 data from the Ministry of Industry.

Figure 6.10b   Effects of an Algerian Disruption Starting October 1st, Best Case, Spain

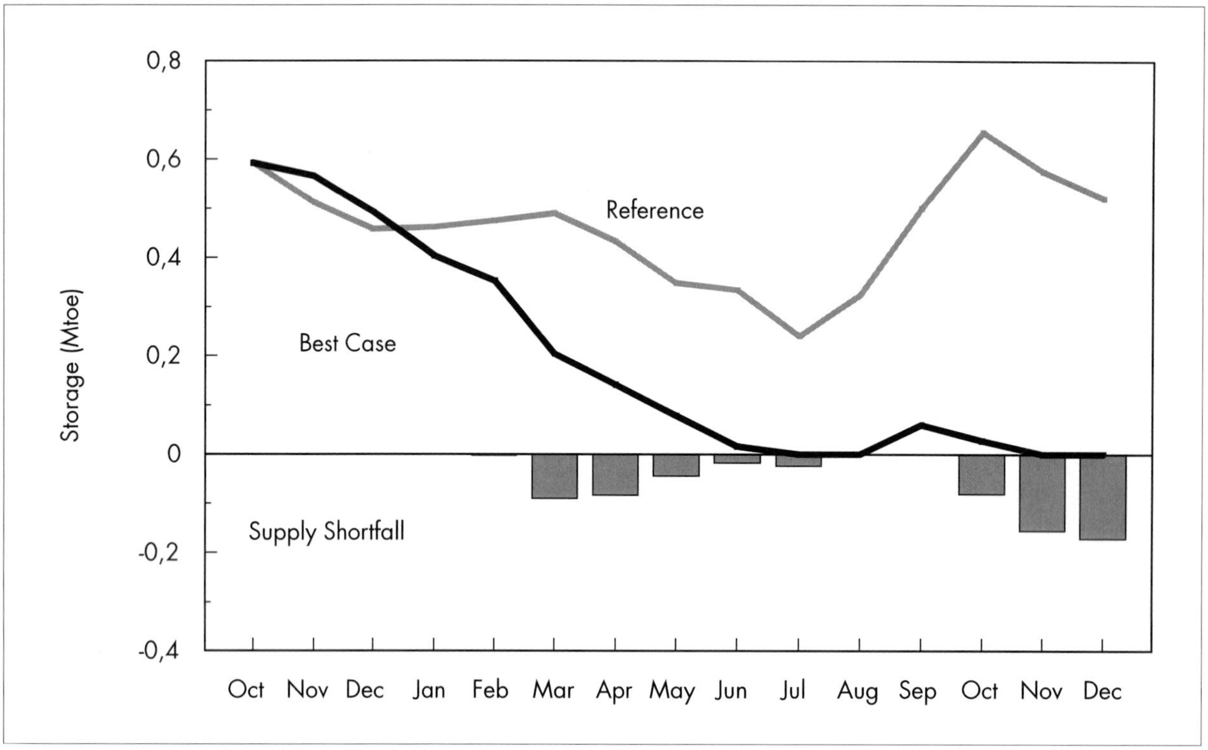

Source: Secretariat estimates based on 1994 data from the Ministry of Industry.

Switzerland

Gas supplies to Switzerland in 1992 came from Germany (44%), the Netherlands (24%), Russia (17%), France (14%) and Italy (1%). Switzerland has no storage facilities of its own and is dependent on Germany to provide load balancing services. The contract for Russian gas is, in fact, a contract between Swissgas and Ruhrgas. Russia delivers gas to Ruhrgas in Germany at a high load factor; Ruhrgas then delivers the gas to Swissgas according to Switzerland's seasonal needs. Switzerland is effectively dependent on Germany for 61% of its supplies - how these deliveries would hold up in the event of a disruption to supplies from Russia is unclear.

Approximately 30% of total demand is interruptible. Contractual interruption periods range from 30 to 60 days. No data on the seasonality of interruptible demand were available - it has been assumed that peak monthly winter demand in the interruptible sector was 30% greater than in the summer.

The assumption taken in the analysis is that given a disruption to Russian supplies, deliveries of "German" gas would continue but volumes under the "Russian" contract would be interrupted. In Figure 6.11 the "worst-case" assumes that no additional volumes are available from non-disrupted sources and the "best-case" assumes an additional 10% are available from the Netherlands.

In a scenario of disrupted supplies under the Russian contract there would not have to be a cut in deliveries to firm customer categories. A prolonged cut in Russian gas would, however, entail sales to interruptible customers being cut beyond their contractual periods.

Figure 6.11   Demand and Available Supply in the Event of a Russian Disruption, Switzerland

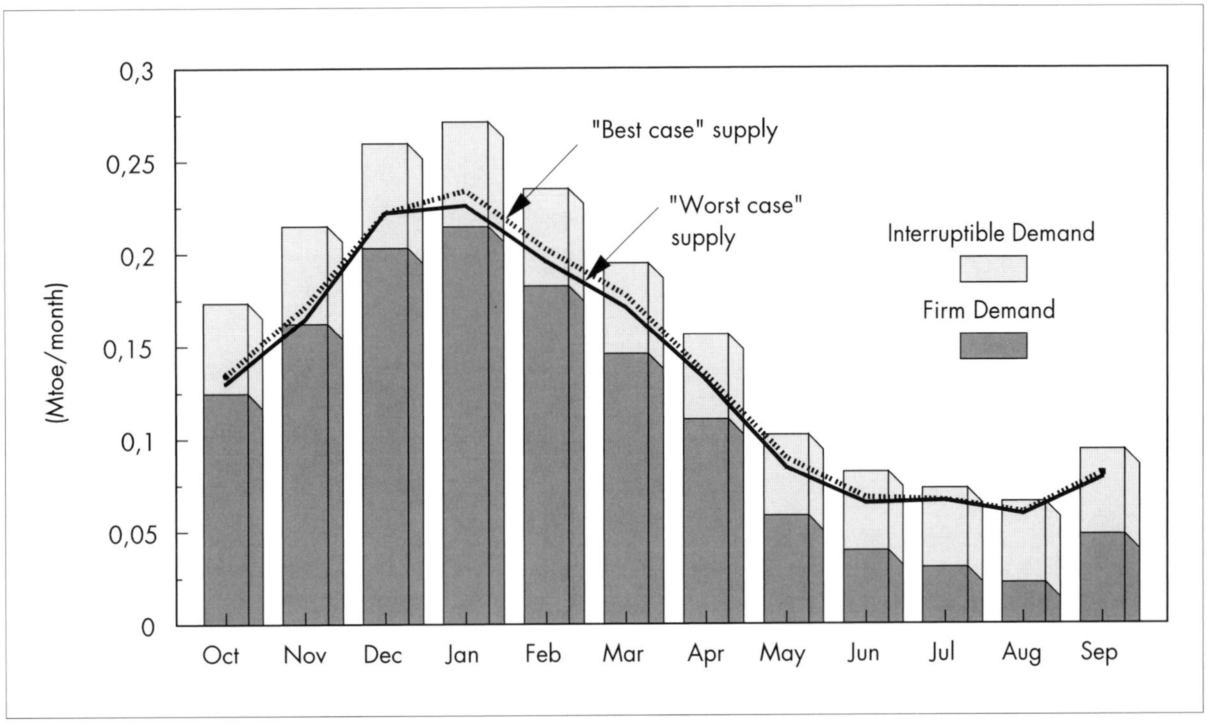

Source: Secretariat estimates based on IEA and Swiss Gas Association data.

Turkey

Over 95% of Turkey's gas supplies came from Russia in 1992, the balance being made up by a small domestic production. Supplies to the Ambarli power plant (which made up 30% of total gas demand) are interruptible. With no seasonal storage and no alternative suppliers (in 1992) a total disruption in Russian supplies would cut deliveries to firm customers almost immediately.

In 1994 deliveries of Algerian LNG began to the new reception terminal at Marmara Ereğlisi (near Istanbul). Annual volumes should reach a plateau of about 1.6 Mtoe/year (compared with existing Russian deliveries of 3.6 Mtoe/year). The LNG terminal has storage capacity of 0.26 mcm of LNG (just over 0.1 Mtoe of gas - about 2 weeks of average consumption). This new development would enable Turkey to deal with a short disruption, but after a month or so of lost Russian supplies, significant sales to firm customers would have to be cut.

Prospects for Future Security from Disruptions

Supply Diversification

This section draws on the analysis carried out in Chapter 3 on supply contracts, demand forecasts and additional supplies beyond existing contracts. The ability of individual countries to cope with a supply disruption varies greatly and so the analysis in Chapter 3 is expanded here to cover supply on a country-by-country basis.

Demand forecasts collected from member states put OECD Europe demand at 325 Mtoe in 2000 and 396 Mtoe in 2010. These figures compare to contracted levels of 298 Mtoe in 2000 and 263 Mtoe in 2010. Existing contracts cover 93% of forecast demand in 2000 and 66% in 2010. Contract extensions could increase the share of demand covered to almost 88% in 2010. Gas demand is therefore almost completely covered in 2000, but the sourcing of a significant share of supplies in 2010 remains speculative.

For the region as a whole, existing contracts cover Russian deliveries of 49.6 Mtoe in 1992 and just 12.1 Mtoe in 2010; most Russian contracts will probably be renewed, pushing Russian exports up to 59.8 Mtoe in 2010. Algerian contracts cover 27.9 Mtoe in 1992 and 38 Mtoe in 2010. The largest increase comes from Norway, whose exports are scheduled to grow from 23.3 to 54.5 Mtoe and make up 21% of the region's already contracted supplies in 2010, up from just 9% in 1992. The slowly declining production in most countries should be more than offset by an increase in UK output which could exceed 80 Mtoe by 2010. Production for national use could then rise from 112 to 138 Mtoe (a decline in the share of total supply from 45 to 35%).

Table 6.8 gives an overview of the European supply contracts that are known to the IEA. Comparison of these contracted levels with the demand forecasts given in Chapter 3 suggests a need for additional supplies described in Table 6.9.

Table 6.8   Existing Supply Contracts and Production Forecasts (Mtoe)

To	From	1992	2000	2010
Austria	Germany	0.19	0.20	
	Norway		1.29	1.29
	Production for own use	1.22	0.42	0.42
	Russia	4.09	4.18	2.09
Austria Total		**5.50**	**6.10**	**3.80**
Belgium	Algeria	3.93	4.02	
	Netherlands	3.70	3.23	3.23
	Norway	2.12	5.32	5.84
Belgium Total		**9.75**	**12.57**	**9.07**
Denmark	Production for own use	1.79	3.50	3.47
Denmark Total		**1.79**	**3.50**	**3.47**
Finland	Russia	2.41	3.62	3.18
Finland Total		**2.41**	**3.62**	**3.18**
France	Algeria	8.10	9.26	7.91
	Netherlands	4.40	4.31	
	Nigeria			0.42
	Norway	5.40	15.00	17.58
	Production for own use	1.80		
	Russia	9.50	10.03	
France Total		**29.20**	**38.60**	**25.91**
Germany	Denmark	1.20	2.10	2.10
	Netherlands	18.11	2.51	2.51
	Norway	8.42	20.90	23.17
	Production for own use	12.20	11.69	7.59
	Russia	18.19	15.59	
Germany Total		**58.12**	**52.79**	**35.36**

Table 6.8   Existing Supply Contracts and Production Forecasts (Mtoe) (continued)

To	From	1992	2000	2010
Greece	Algeria		0.51	0.51
	Production for own use	0.06		
	Russia		1.71	1.88
Greece Total		**0.06**	**2.22**	**2.39**
Ireland	Production for own use	2.07		
Ireland Total		**2.07**		
Italy	Algeria	12.63	20.84	20.84
	Netherlands	4.27	4.66	4.66
	Nigeria			2.93
	Production for own use	13.35	16.79	12.28
	Russia	11.45	17.14	
Italy Total		**41.70**	**59.42**	**40.71**
Netherlands	Norway	2.58	3.44	4.81
	Production for own use	30.69	31.14	31.97
	UK		0.50	0.50
Netherlands Total		**33.27**	**35.08**	**37.28**
Norway	Production for own use		0.52	1.12
Norway Total			**0.52**	**1.12**
Portugal	Algeria		2.07	2.07
Portugal Total			**2.07**	**2.07**
Spain	Algeria	3.20	8.09	4.98
	Libya	1.72	1.29	
	Nigeria		0.42	0.84
	Norway		1.81	1.81
	Production for own use	1.12		
Spain Total		**6.04**	**11.60**	**7.62**
Sweden	Denmark	0.63	0.92	0.92
Sweden Total		**0.63**	**0.92**	**0.92**
Switzerland	France	0.27	0.53	
	Germany	0.85	1.59	1.59
	Italy	0.03	0.08	0.08
	Netherlands	0.45	0.47	
	Russia	0.33	0.33	
Switzerland Total		**1.92**	**3.00**	**1.67**
Turkey	Algeria		1.65	1.65
	Production for own use	0.16		
	Russia	3.63	4.91	4.91
Turkey Total		**3.79**	**6.56**	**6.56**
UK	Norway	4.74		
	Production for own use	47.78	59.83	81.37
UK Total		**52.52**	**59.83**	**81.37**
OECD Total		**248.78**	**298.40**	**262.53**

Source: Country Submissions, Cedigaz.

Table 6.9   Future Supply Requirements (Mtoe)

	Forecast Demand		Forecast Production & Contracted Supply		Additional Requirements		Possible Contract Renewals[1]		Need for New Supplies	
	2000	2010	2000	2010	2000	2010	2000	2010	2000	2010
Austria	6.4	8.3	6.1	3.8	0.3	4.5		2.3	0.3	2.2
Belgium & Luxembourg	13.4	14.7	12.6	9.1	0.8	5.6		3.6	0.8	2.0
Denmark	3.5	3.5	3.5	3.5						
Finland	3.6	4.3	3.6	3.2		1.1		1.1		0.0
France	34.0	39.5	38.6	25.9		13.6		11.4		2.2
Germany	71.5	79.5	52.8	35.4	18.7	44.1	18.0	39.3	0.7	4.8
Greece	2.6	3.2	2.2	2.4	0.4	0.8			0.4	0.8
Ireland	1.5	2.0			1.5	2.0			1.5	2.0
Italy	56.5	69.6	59.4	40.7		28.9		17.1		11.8
Netherlands	35.9	37.0	35.1	37.3	0.8		0.8		0.0	
Norway	0.5	1.0	0.5	1.1						
Portugal	1.6	3.0	2.1	2.1		0.9				0.9
Spain	12.8	14.7	11.6	7.6	1.2	7.1	0.4	4.9	0.8	2.2
Sweden	1.0	1.8	0.9	0.9	0.1	0.9			0.1	0.9
Switzerland	2.5	3.2	3.0	1.7		1.5		1.5		0.0
Turkey	16.4	25.1	6.6	6.6	9.8	18.5			9.8	18.5
UK	61.0	85.5	59.8	81.4	1.2	4.1	1.2	3.3		0.9
Total	324.7	395.9	298.4	262.5	34.8	133.7	20.5	84.5	14.4	49.2

1. In practice some contracts may not be renewed and others, which are excluded here, may be renewed.

Note that for some countries (forecast production) + (contracted supply) exceeds (forecast demand).

Source: Secretariat estimates.

In speculating on the possible sources of gas to meet these additional requirements the point of departure has been that countries will, to a large extent, conclude new contracts with their existing suppliers and will do so in such a way as to maximise the diversity of their new supply portfolios.

The figures in Table 6.10 show one way in which the supply gaps might be filled. The reasoning behind the supply allocation is given below:

a. **Austria** has traditionally been supplied from domestic production and from Russia but has recently signed up for Norwegian gas under the Troll contract. Under normal circumstances the Norwegian gas is swapped for Russian gas to avoid transportation across Germany. For this reason deliveries from Norway are likely to remain relatively small. The balance of requirements will have to come from Russia.

b. **Belgium's** suppliers have been Algeria, the Netherlands and Norway. Given the large appetite for new gas in southern Europe, Belgium is not an obvious market for additional Algerian volumes. Exports from the Netherlands are unlikely to grow further and the country shows little interest in Russian gas. This leaves either the UK (via the new Interconnector) or Norway as the most likely suppliers of all additional volumes.

Table 6.10   Possible New Supplies for OECD Europe (Mtoe)

To	From	2000	2010
Austria	Norway	0.1	1.1
	Russia	0.2	1.1
Belgium	UK	0.8	2.0
France	UK		2.2
Germany	UK	0.7	4.8
Greece	Russia	0.4	0.8
Ireland	UK	1.5	2.0
Italy	Algeria		5.0
	Russia		6.8
Portugal	Algeria		0.9
Spain	Algeria	0.5	1.2
	Norway	0.3	1.0
Sweden	Denmark	0.1	0.9
Turkey	Algeria	0.4	0.4
	Qatar	2.3	2.3
	Russia	7.1	7.1
	Turkmenistan		8.7
UK	Production for own use		0.9
Grand Total		**14.4**	**49.2**

Source: Secretariat estimates.

c. **Germany** could import new supplies from any of its current suppliers except the Netherlands. In practice increased Danish production may stay in Denmark and Sweden. This would leave the UK, Russia and Norway as likely supply candidates.

d. **Ireland** is now connected to the UK gas grid. UK gas will probably replace dwindling domestic production and meet growing demand.

e. **Italy's** current supplies come from Algeria, the Netherlands, Russia and domestic production. The electricity company ENEL has concluded a contract for Nigerian LNG. The limited extra production capacity in Algeria will be sought especially by Spain (see below). Nevertheless, some additional Algerian gas may be available for Italy. The Netherlands is unlikely to be increasing exports beyond existing contracts. When the Nigerian project has been completed, there may be some spare capacity but the balance of Italy's requirements will probably have to come from Russia.

f. Algeria is likely to remain **Spain's** largest supplier. Increased imports of Norwegian gas (swapped for French/Russian gas) may be possible. Further LNG supplies will probably be obtained from countries such as Nigeria and Trinidad and Tobago.

g. **Sweden's** gas demand is forecast to rise by a relatively small volume to 1.8 Mtoe in 2010. This means that Denmark will probably remain the country's sole supplier.

h. **Switzerland's** additional requirements will be small and will probably come from the country's existing suppliers.

i. The supplies listed for **Turkey** are all under negotiation.

j. The **UK** is more or less self-sufficient in gas, but currently imports small volumes from Norway under a depletion contract. The estimates presented above assume that the legal disputes surrounding the Frigg pipeline will be resolved and that Norwegian exports to the UK will be extended. These imports could free up production capacity for exports to the continent via the Interconnector.

Table 6.11 shows how European supply diversification could evolve over the forecast period and is based on the contracts in Table 6.8 and the new supplies discussed above. It should be noted that gas supply diversification by itself does not necessarily reduce dependence on individual countries where the share of gas in TPES is expanding. The analysis points to the following trends:

a. Dependence on **Russian** gas is likely to fall in Austria, France, Germany and Turkey. Italy, however, will import an increasing share of its needs from Russia. In fact, the total share of gas in TPES in Italy is expected to rise from 25% in 1992 to 34% in 2010, and gas from Russia will increase its share of the Italian market.

b. Dependence on **Algerian** supplies should fall in Belgium and France and rise moderately in Italy. Algeria is set to maintain a high share of the Spanish market.

c New **Norwegian** supplies are expected to increase market share significantly in northern Europe as total exports climb from 23 Mtoe in 1992 to possibly 69 Mtoe in 2010.

d. With stagnant or falling **domestic production** and exports, the **Netherlands** will lose significant market share, from 12% in 1992 to possibly 6% in 2010.

e. Diversification should improve very substantially in **Turkey** with new supplies from Algeria, Turkmenistan and Qatar. The gas from Turkmenistan, however, may be dependent on transit through Russia.

Two reservations in the results shown in Table 6.11 should be noted:

a. Exports from the Netherlands are assumed to fall modestly over the forecast period as some contracts expire. The continuation of exports at the level in Table 3.18 in Chapter 3 includes some provision for contract renewals and will depend on new reserve discoveries.

b. Production in the UK is assumed to keep track with domestic demand which is forecast to rise from 50.7 Mtoe in 1992 to 85.5 Mtoe in 2010. Current forecasts of UK gas production span a large range and lead to some uncertainty as to which way and how much gas will physically flow through the Interconnector in 2010.

The contracts already signed, together with those likely to be renewed, cover around 100 Mtoe of the forecast growth between 1992 and 2010. Much of the infrastructure required for this increase is already under construction or in the planning stage. These projects include the new Norwegian Troll platform, expansion of the Transmed pipeline from Algeria to Italy, the Maghreb-Europe pipeline from Algeria to Spain and the UK-continent Interconnector.

Table 6.11   Forecast Supply Diversification (per cent)

	1992	2000	2010
OECD Europe			
Algeria	11.2%	14.2%	13.5%
Denmark	0.7%	0.9%	1.0%
France	0.1%	0.2%	0.1%
Germany	0.4%	0.5%	0.5%
Italy	0.0%	0.0%	0.0%
Libya	0.7%	0.4%	0.3%
Netherlands	12.4%	8.7%	6.2%
Nigeria		0.1%	1.1%
Norway	9.3%	16.1%	17.4%
Production for own use	45.1%	37.2%	35.1%
Qatar		0.7%	0.6%
Russia	19.9%	20%	19.1%
Turkmenistan			2.2%
UK		1.0%	2.9%
By Country			
Austria			
Germany	3%	3%	2%
Norway		22%	29%
Production for own use	22%	7%	5%
Russia	74%	68%	64%
Belgium			
Algeria	40%	30%	25%
Netherlands	38%	24%	22%
Norway	22%	40%	40%
UK		6%	14%
Denmark			
Production for own use	100%	100%	100%
Finland			
Russia	100%	100%	100%
France			
Algeria	28%	24%	23%
Netherlands	15%	11%	
Nigeria			1%
Norway	18%	39%	45%
Production for own use	6%		
Russia	33%	26%	25%
UK			6%
Germany			
Denmark	2%	3%	3%
Netherlands	31%	23%	20%
Norway	14%	33%	40%
Production for own use	21%	16%	10%
Russia	31%	24%	21%
UK		1%	6%

Table 6.11   Forecast Supply Diversification (per cent) (continued)

	1992	2000	2010
Greece			
Algeria		19%	16%
Production for own use	100%		
Russia		81%	84%
Ireland			
Production for own use	100%		
UK		100%	100%
Italy			
Algeria	30%	35%	37%
Netherlands	10%	8%	7%
Nigeria			4%
Production for own use	32%	28%	18%
Russia	27%	29%	34%
Netherlands			
Norway	8%	12%	13%
Production for own use	92%	87%	86%
UK		1%	1%
Norway			
Production for own use		100%	100%
Portugal			
Algeria		100%	100%
Production for own use			
Spain			
Algeria	53%	67%	64%
Libya	28%	10%	9%
Nigeria		3%	6%
Norway		20%	22%
Production for own use	19%		
Sweden			
Denmark	100%	100%	100%
Switzerland			
France	14%	18%	17%
Germany	44%	53%	51%
Italy	1%	3%	3%
Netherlands	24%	16%	20%
Russia	17%	11%	11%
Turkey			
Algeria		13%	8%
Production for own use	4%		
Qatar		14%	9%
Russia	96%	73%	48%
Turkmenistan			35%
UK			
Norway	9%	2%	4%
Production for own use	91%	98%	96%

Given the rapidly growing dependence on Norwegian supplies it should be noted that much of the planned capacity will be concentrated in relatively few pieces of infrastructure. The Troll platform in the North Sea will be particularly important and could be producing over 30 bcm (25 Mtoe) in 2010, making it responsible for a third to a half of Norwegian exports. Any failure of this platform could have serious consequences for the gas markets it serves in northern Europe. Nevertheless, the volumes lost in such a failure would be slightly lower than current imports from Algeria.

Assuming that in the event of a disruption to Troll gas all available Norwegian supplies would be distributed on a pro-rata basis among importing countries, the losses would be most serious in Belgium, France and Germany. At worst the resulting supply reduction to France and to Belgium could be comparable to a total loss of Algerian gas. The supply loss to the German market, however, would be only half the volumes lost in a total disruption to Russian deliveries.

Supply Flexibility

Assessment of future supply flexibility must look not only at supply diversification but also at trends in utilisation rates and load factors of production and import facilities and their implications for spare capacity. Current load factors (implied from 1992 monthly production and trade data) fall into three broad categories:

a. **Low-load** (30-60%) covers contracts between the Netherlands and Belgium and Germany as well as the supplies to countries with very limited load management of their own (i.e., Finland, Sweden and Switzerland which have no storage).

b. **Medium** (65-75%) covers other contracts involving limited transportation distance, principally exports from the Netherlands to France and Italy, German supplies from domestic production and from Denmark and UK production.

c. **High-load** (75-95%) covers most other contracts, where long distance transport by pipeline or LNG is involved or where domestic production capacity is being maximised (and therefore being operated at a more or less constant rate).

The analysis of possible responses to supply disruptions presented here uses these load factors to estimate physical supply capacity - the volumes that could be supplied if production and transportation facilities were operated at full capacity all year round. Countries must be able to store gas if they are to take advantage of any additional capacity, most of which arises in summer.

Table 6.12   Assumed Load Factors in 2010 for Supplies to OECD Europe (per cent)

Source	Load Factor	Source	Load Factor
Algeria	85	**Denmark**	75
Russia	85	**UK**	75
Netherlands	75	**Other LNG**	85
Norway	90	**Indigenous Production**[†]	100

† for countries which import the majority of their gas (i.e. excludes Denmark, Netherlands, Norway and UK).
(Load factor = peak month/average month)

The trend in supplies is towards stagnant domestic production and stagnant exports from the Netherlands, two of the principal sources of low and medium load supplies. The supply outlook shows an increasing dependence on supplies from more distant sources (especially Norway) which will probably fall into the high-load category, since the economic viability of long-distance transportation projects usually demands high usage.

At the same time as dependence on more distant high-load supplies is increasing, the peak production capacity of most European production is falling as fields mature and their pressures drop. This is particularly true of the Groningen field in the Netherlands which has traditionally served as Europe's swing producer. The low-load contracts between the Netherlands and Belgium and Germany have been possible only as a result of the high swing available from Groningen.

The implications of these trends are that spare capacity from domestic production and from the Netherlands will fall in absolute terms, the spare capacity from more distant supplies will remain a small percentage of actual deliveries from these sources (around 10-15%) and consequently spare capacity as a proportion of total supplies will decrease.

The following analysis looks at the impacts of supply diversification and reduced supply flexibility on security of supply. Tables 6.13 and 6.14 give estimates of spare supply capacity available in the event of disruptions to deliveries from Russia or Algeria. They also show the percentage of demand that would have to be made available through stock withdrawals and interruptions to customers. The figures for 1992 are those presented in the analysis of disruptions earlier in this chapter. The estimates for 2010 are based on the supply balances in the previous section and assumptions of future supply load factors (given in Table 6.12).

The overall trend is one of reduced supply flexibility (in terms of spare production capacity) being more or less offset by improved supply diversification.

The countries showing major gains are Austria, France and Belgium (as well as Turkey if a new supply route from Turkmenistan can be realised) - countries which are all likely to reduce the share of Russian or Algerian gas in their supplies. Some countries, particularly those in the south of Europe with fewer supply options, are likely to become more dependent on storage and interruptibility.

It should be noted, however, that in the 1992 "best" case spare capacity for some countries is higher than the increase in production and imports assumed, especially for the countries receiving supplies from the Netherlands. The "best" case assumes some seasonality in imports for 1992 while the spare supply capacity for 2010 assumes maximum capacity is maintained throughout the year. This indicates an increasing reliance on storage and interruptibility in the event of a disruption, even for those countries diversifying their supplies.

Storage

Storage capacity in OECD Europe is planned to expand by around 60% between 1992 and 2000, compared with demand which is forecast to rise by 35%. There are a number of driving forces behind this rapid growth. The largest growth is in Germany where dependence is shifting from domestic production and highly flexible imports from the Netherlands to imports under high load contracts, especially from Norway.

Table 6.13   Spare Supply Capacity: Possible Response to a Russian Disruption (Mtoe)

| | 1992 ("Best" Case) | | | | 2010 | | | | | Missing Supplies[1] ÷ Demand | |
	Demand	Supplies Lost	Increased Production & Imports	Missing Supplies[1]	Demand	Supplies Lost	Spare Supply Capacity[2]	Missing Supplies[1]		1992	2010
Austria	5.2	4.1	0.2	3.9	8.3	5.3	0.3	5.0		**75%**	**60%**
Finland	2.4	2.4		2.4	4.3	4.3		4.3		**100%**	**100%**
France	27.9	9.5	2.9	6.6	39.5	10.0	4.4	5.6		**24%**	**14%**
Germany	56.8	18.2	13.5	4.7	79.5	17.0	11.2	5.8		**8%**	**7%**
Greece	0.1				3.2	2.7	0.1	2.6			**81%**
Italy	41.0	11.5	1.7	9.8	69.6	23.9	6.6	17.3		**24%**	**25%**
Switzerland	1.9	0.3		0.3	3.2	0.3	0.2	0.1		**17%**	**4%**
Turkey[3]	3.8	3.6		3.6	25.1	12.0	2.3	9.7		**96%**	**39%**
Total (OECD)	241.8	49.6	18.3	31.3	395.9	75.5	25.2	50.4		**13%**	**13%**

1. Required from storage, interruptibility and curtailments to firm customers.
2. Potential supply capacity from increased production and imports from non-disrupted sources derived from load factors in Table 6.12.
3. Spare capacity for 2010 includes a contribution from Turkmenistan which may be dependent on transit through Russia.

Table 6.14 Spare Supply Capacity: Possible Response to an Algerian Disruption (Mtoe)

| | 1992 ("Best" Case) | | | | 2010 | | | | | Missing Supplies[1] ÷ Demand | |
	Demand	Supplies Lost	Increased Production & Imports	Missing Supplies[1]	Demand	Supplies Lost	Spare Supply Capacity[2]	Missing Supplies[1]		1992	2010
Belgium & Luxembourg	9.5	3.9	2.0	1.9	14.7	3.6	2.4	1.2		20%	8%
France	27.9	8.1	1.6	6.5	39.5	9.3	4.5	4.7		23%	12%
Greece	0.1				3.2	0.5	0.5	0.0			1%
Italy	41.0	12.6	2.9	9.7	69.6	25.8	6.3	19.5		24%	28%
Spain[3]	5.8	3.7	1.1	2.6	14.7	9.4	0.7	8.6		45%	59%
Turkey[4]	3.8				25.1	2.0	4.1				
Total (OECD)	241.8	28.4	7.6	20.8	395.9	53.6	18.5	37.1		9%	9%

1. Required from storage, interruptibility and curtailments to firm customers.
2. Potential supply capacity from increased production and imports from non-disrupted sources derived from load factors in Table 6.12.
3. Refers to 1994 data.
4. Spare capacity for 2010 includes a contribution from Turkmenistan which may be dependent on transit through Russia.

Table 6.15   Storage Development Plans - OECD Europe (bcm)

	1992	2000	2010
Austria	2.3	3.2	n.a.
Belgium	0.5	0.8	1.00
Denmark	0.3	0.8	0.8
Finland	-	-	-
France	10.2	12.7	n.a.
Germany	9.8	17.2	21.5
Greece	-	-	n.a.
Ireland	-	0.1	0.1
Italy	13.0	19.0	n.a.
Luxembourg	-	-	n.a.
Netherlands	0.1	4.0	5.0
Norway	-	-	-
Portugal	-	-	n.a.
Spain	0.5[†]	1.4-2.5	n.a.
Sweden	-	-	-
Switzerland	-	-	-
Turkey	0.2	1.2	n.a.
United Kingdom	3.5	n.a.	n.a.
Total	**39.5**	**~ 61**	**n.a.**

Source: Country submissions.
† In 1994
As a rule of thumb, 1 Mtoe is approximately equal to 1.27 bcm.

The Netherlands has traditionally relied on swing production from its Groningen field to meet seasonality in both demand and export requirements. It is estimated that by 1997 Groningen will no longer be able to meet those peak requirements. The new storage under development will allow the Netherlands to maintain production volumes by making greater use of capacity outside peak demand times.

In Denmark (which used to store some gas for Sweden), France and Italy the development of storage is in line with the growth in demand levels. Austria is increasing its storage capacity more quickly than its demand and plans to sell storage services to its central European neighbours. Both Austria and Italy are expected to maintain a high share of strategic gas storage - i.e., those volumes beyond needs for seasonal load balancing.

The construction of storage facilities is particularly necessary in the new gas markets of Spain and Turkey where it will enable improved load management and provide some buffer against temporary delays to or reductions in deliveries. It is important that these plans be realised and that further developments be made for 2010.

Demand Structure

Forecasts collected from countries in Europe show gas demand rising by 70% between 1992 and 2010. Much of this growth takes place in the power generation sector. The projected growth in demand from the residential/commercial sector, which accounts for most of the seasonality in demand, is just 36%. Since gas use in power generation is expected to move towards base load use, the trend is towards some reduction in the overall seasonality of demand.

Table 6.16   Gas Demand Forecast - OECD Europe (Mtoe)

	1992	2000	2010
Industry	85.2	113.2	128.4
share of total	*35%*	*35%*	*32%*
Power Generation	34.7	73.6	113.3
share of total	*14%*	*23%*	*29%*
Residential/Commercial	115.0	127.2	141.4
share of total	*48%*	*39%*	*36%*
Unattributed	6.2	10.7	12.8
Total	**241.1**	**324.7**	**395.9**

Source: Country forecasts (reproduced from Chapter 3, Table 3.5a).

There are two possible reasons why switching capabilities may decline:

a. increasingly strict environmental regulations are likely to limit fuel choices in boilers to natural gas and electricity, where previously fuel oil and coal might have been options;

b. steam boilers are being displaced by more efficient gas turbines and combined cycle configurations. Steam boilers typically use fuel oil for back-up, but the secondary fuel for gas turbines is usually limited to more expensive gasoil or LPG. The same tendencies can be found in power generation, where heavy fuel oil will increasingly be displaced by gasoil as a backup fuel.

The attractiveness of investment in dual-fired facilities will depend on the price differential between firm and interruptible gas and hence on the commercial strategy of gas companies. The decisions of gas companies will probably be made on the basis of the deferred costs of storage to cope with seasonal demand fluctuations. It should be noted, though, that in the event of a prolonged supply disruption the protection afforded by storage lasts a limited time. Supplies to interruptible customers with dual-fired facilities, however, can technically (if not contractually) be cut indefinitely.

Other Factors

Spot LNG

LNG spot transactions have been taking place over the last three years. In 1992 only five such deals were completed but by 1994 this activity had doubled. Spot deals in 1994 represented 2 bcm, of which 1.2 bcm was delivered to European markets. Some of these deals represent trade between partners to existing long term contracts. An interesting development, however, has been the delivery of LNG from "new" suppliers. In 1994 Enagas of Spain, for example, purchased 500 mcm from the Australian North-West Shelf. Deliveries from Abu Dhabi have also been taking place in 1995.

The volumes delivered to Europe so far have been comparatively small but have been valuable, especially in Spain, during the revamping of Algeria's liquefaction plants. Whether the LNG spot market develops will depend on the availability of spare liquefaction and transport capacity, the level of gas prices and transportation costs. According to Petrostrategies, the recent Abu Dhabi deliveries benefited from a 35% discount on transit fees through the Suez Canal, down from US$ 0.22-0.24 per Mbtu to US$ 0.17 per Mbtu.

Interconnection

Each of the disruption scenarios considered in the analysis above affects only some of the countries in OECD Europe. For example, a disruption to both Russian and Algerian supplies at the same time in 1992 would have affected nine countries whose supply loss would have represented 50% of their demand, but only 31% of demand in OECD Europe. There could be scope for increased interconnection and market flexibility to allow the effects of any supply disruption to be absorbed by a larger demand volume and to make use of spare capacity in countries that are not directly affected by the disruption.

Conclusions   Supply diversification is expected to increase in most major markets although this may be offset by a reduction in supply flexibility. The dependence on storage, demand interruptibility and dual-firing in the event of a disruption is likely to increase. Plans for storage are already well-advanced but particular attention should be paid to the level of interruptibility in the rapidly growing power generation sector.

NORTH AMERICA

As a whole, the OECD North America region (including Mexico) is basically self-sufficient in gas (the only import flow being minor LNG volumes into the United States). Canada exports close to half of its total production to the United States, and these import volumes constitute about 11% of total US gas availability. Moreover, there is some gas trade between Mexico and the United States. The present gas trade in the region does not rely on any third countries for transit, and the NAFTA agreement has created a commercial and political framework which should favour a steady flow of gas. The concerns about politically conditioned disruptions in gas supplies are therefore less acute than in Europe.

North America has a very diversified supply structure in that the United States has around 9000 gas producers and Canada around 1000. Reserves are concentrated in a small number of regions, but the number of deposits and the integrated nature of the supply infrastructure to a large extent outweigh this. In general, gas buyers in North America have a much wider choice between sellers than in Europe.

The United States and Canada have gone through a liberalisation of their gas markets in which price deregulation and the introduction of competition through third party access (TPA) and unbundling were the major features. This has meant a more market driven and more decentralised responsibility for security of supply. The existence of short term markets for gas in North America means that prices are allowed to play a role in allocation of scarce supplies in a shortfall.

All these factors imply that simulation of the effects of politically conditioned disruption scenarios are less relevant for North America than for Europe. It is therefore more important to study gas deliverability in situations where the supply system comes under stress for other reasons, for example, as a result of extreme weather conditions.

After the recent regulatory changes in North American gas markets, questions were raised about the ability of the gas supply systems to react adequately in stress situations. Recently, both the Canadian and the US gas delivery systems have been exposed to weather conditioned tests, in both cases with honourable results. In the winter of 1992/93, Canada experienced a severe cold spell. The National Energy Board (NEB) produced a study in 1993 on experience from this period which is drawn upon in the following sections. In January 1994, a bitter cold spell in the United States exposed the gas delivery system to extreme strain one year after implementation of Order 636. Several institutions have made their own analysis of how the system performed, and these studies will also be referred to below.

CANADIAN EXPERIENCE DURING THE WINTER OF 1992/93

Since natural gas deregulation in late 1985, the Canadian gas industry has experienced a number of important developments.[4] The demand increase and associated expansion of most of the pipeline systems serving the Western Canadian Sedimentary Basin have reduced the excess productive capacity that existed at the time of deregulation. Figure 6.12 illustrates how natural gas travels from the wellhead to the burner tip in Canada, changing ownership several times under different contracts and at different prices.

Since deregulation, marketable gas production from the Western Canada Sedimentary Basin increased by almost 50% by the winter of 1992. The cold winter of 1992/93 led to production increases of around 10 bcm both in 1992 and 1993 (total production for the whole of 1992 was about 120 bcm). The tightness in the gas supply/demand balance was reflected in sharp increases and volatility in short term gas prices. From a level of around $1 per gigajoule one year earlier, short term gas prices went as high as $4.50 per gigajoule during the winter of 1992/93.

The production, transportation and contractual difficulties that buyers and sellers encountered during the cold spell of the winter 1992/93 are briefly described below.

Supply Difficulties

The physical production of marketable natural gas normally includes the extraction, gathering and processing of raw gas. The most serious problem experienced by producers and supply aggregators during late 1992 and early 1993 was the failure of certain wells to produce at expected levels of production for extended periods of time, in most cases due to lack of

---

4.   Some of these are described in the IEA's study on gas transportation (IEA, 1994).

Figure 6.12   Typical Flow of Natural Gas

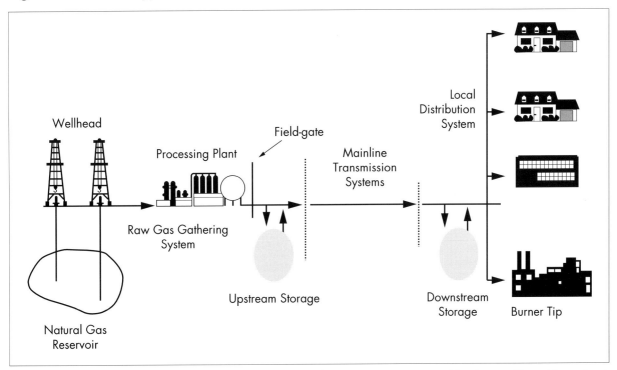

Source: Natural Gas Market Assessments, Canadian Natural Gas Market Mechanisms: Recent Experiences and Developments, National Energy Board, November 1993.

systematic testing and cost saving measures taken during the preceding surplus period. A second problem at the wellhead was "freeze-offs", i.e., icing that restricts the flow of gas; the probability of which increases when temperatures drop far below 0 degree Celsius. During the first three weeks of December 1992, western Canadian gas producers were producing at record levels and when temperatures dropped to very low levels across western Canada in late December and early January, natural gas production was curtailed by 6% due to wellhead freeze-offs.

Western Canadian producers have a great deal of experience with operating gas wells during periods of harsh climatic conditions and even during the coldest days in December 1992 and January 1993, producers and aggregators indicated that the number of well freeze-offs was not out of the ordinary. However, the significantly reduced excess deliverability and higher prices compared with previous winters made it more difficult and costly for producers to arrange for alternative gas supplies.

Canada operates some of the biggest gathering, transmission and distribution pipeline systems in North America. With all pipelines it is necessary to curtail the operation of specific segments of the lines for short periods of time for scheduled and sometimes unscheduled maintenance or to allow new facilities to be installed. Outages on gathering and distribution systems typically only affect relatively small volumes compared with outages on transmission systems which can affect or interrupt very large volumes. In case of outages, the remaining capacity (if any) is first allocated to firm service shippers affected by the outage and then to interruptible shippers. Fortunately, there were no significant outages on the transmission system during the cold spell studied here.

The efficient and safe operation of a pipeline system requires that the pipeline's linepack be maintained within a specified range. Linepack is the amount of gas which is maintained in the pipeline system. If the linepack drops below a specified level, the delivery capacity and the efficiency of the pipeline declines. If it exceeds design levels, the security and safety of the pipeline may be compromised.

Prior to December 1, 1992, transmission pipelines balanced their receipts from shippers (i.e., deliveries into the pipeline) and deliveries (i.e., withdrawals from the pipeline) once a month. Under this regime, on any single day during a month, a shipper could withdraw contracted quantities from the system but deliver little or no gas into the system, in effect drawing down the pipeline's linepack, a practice referred to as "drafting".

The problem caused by this system was that when certain shippers experienced difficulties that restricted their ability to deliver into the system over short periods of time, they continued to nominate and withdraw full contract quantities at the delivery points. Widespread "drafting" tolerated under monthly balancing often reduced the linepack below the acceptable range. The pipeline operator was then forced to restore the linepack by requiring other shippers to increase deliveries into the system and/or curtail deliveries out of the system to all shippers on a *pro rata* basis. In effect, the responsibility for resolving certain producers' short-supply situations was indiscriminately shifted to all system users. To respond to the difficulties created by drafting, one major pipeline operator introduced daily balancing on 1 December 1992. This requires each shipper's receipts and deliveries to balance on a daily basis. Daily balancing shifted the onus for resolving short-supply situations to the parties that created them.

The introduction of daily balancing was widely supported within the industry. However, most of the parties surveyed felt that its introduction in December 1992 at the beginning of a period of peak demand made it more difficult for individual shippers experiencing short-supply situations to respond because the option of "drafting" had been eliminated. At that time, many of the other alternatives used to deal with short-supply situations, such as storage, the daily spot market and pipeline inventory transfers were still in the developmental stage and, as a result, many producers and marketers experienced difficulties maintaining full gas flows during periods of peak demand in late 1992 and early 1993.

It is not uncommon for natural gas to change ownership five or six times between the wellhead and the burner tip. The allocation of the physical flow of gas between different buyers and markets is determined by contract terms and conditions, contract prices and transportation arrangements. Typical contractual problems identified by those surveyed that created difficulties for buyers and sellers in 1992 and early 1993 were inappropriate or inadequate contract terms and conditions, sudden changes in market prices and inadequate transportation arrangements.

In late 1992 and early 1993, short term prices increased to levels considerably above one year or longer-term contract prices, and producer netbacks under contracts with aggregators. As a result, in a number of cases, sellers allocated gas away from longer term contracts and into the spot market. This practice became known as *price majeure*. When it occurred, it often left buyers under longer-term contracts in a short-supply situation. While it is difficult to know with any precision how widespread this practice was in 1992 or 1993, it was most prevalent under contracts that did not include either a commitment to deliver backed by a corporate warranty or strong penalties for failure to deliver, such as seller indemnification or the buyer's cost of make-up gas. The risk of *price majeure* underscores the importance of good contracting practices, particularly if the contract includes a fixed price over an extended period when price volatility may be experienced. The fact that *price majeure* may occur illustrates the difference between contracting culture in North America and in Europe, where such a phenomenon has been hardly conceivable.

Options Used to Maintain Gas Flows to End-Users

The responsibility for resolving a short-supply situation will depend on whether the problem is created by a circumstance of *force majeure*. In any event, there is a wide range of options available to both buyers and sellers, including local distribution companies (LDCs), who have a need for make-up gas supplies. In 1992/93, in most instances when the responsibility was on the end-user to resolve the problem, the difficulty was shifted to LDCs which have more experience dealing with short-supply situations and a wider range of alternative sources of supply. No cases were identified where either a firm or interruptible end-user was forced to curtail its gas consumption because gas supplies were inadequate. A brief overview of the mechanisms used to keep the gas flowing is given below.

In the event of a supply disruption that is not caused by an event of force majeure, the onus is typically on the seller to resolve the difficulty with a minimum of disruption to the buyer. In a competitive marketplace such as the Canadian gas market, the seller's reputation as a reliable supplier may be at risk. Sellers who encountered supply difficulties in 1992 and early 1993 relied on the following options to maintain gas flows to end-users:

Curtailment in deliveries A common situation in 1992 and early 1993 was that many producers experienced less than the anticipated production dedicated to an aggregator and were unable to meet in full the aggregator's (i.e., buyer's) nominations. In reviewing their portfolio of contracts, several producers determined that there was often no financial penalty for failing to deliver nominated volumes under long-term, reserve-based contracts with supply aggregators, nor was there an obligation to provide make-up volumes from other non-dedicated fields. In this situation, producers typically continued to meet their commitments under their non-aggregator contracts, including spot contracts and allowed a shortfall against the aggregator's nominations. The aggregator would then be faced with the obligation to cut sales and/or purchase additional supplies. Unless deliveries to buyers were designed to be interrupted, most producers and marketers sought out alternative supplies to maintain gas flows rather than curtail buyers. Failure to deliver even under *force majeure* conditions can jeopardise the seller's reputation and create opportunities for competitors. Therefore, delivery curtailments, particularly for an extended period of time, were seldom viewed as an attractive option by sellers.

Pipeline tolerances Prior to introduction of daily balancing, the use of pipeline tolerances or "drafting" to resolve short-supply situations was widespread practice. It is still available today on most pipelines and distribution systems as an option to "buy time" to resolve relatively small or isolated supply problems for short periods of time.

Spot gas purchases The most common option used by sellers to maintain gas flows in 1992 and early 1993 was to purchase supplemental gas supplies on the spot market, particularly after the introduction of daily balancing on one of the major pipeline systems. There are four spot gas options: spot gas purchases at the field, spot gas purchase at an upstream storage site, spot purchase at typical delivery points; and so-called inventory transfers under which some shippers put more gas into a pipeline than they are withdrawing and transfer their positive balance to other shippers who are short. Spot gas is almost always available as an alternative source of supply, but sometimes only at a very high price. Many producers and marketers incurred large financial losses in 1992 and early 1993 by purchasing higher priced spot gas to maintain deliveries under lower priced firm contracts.

Upstream and downstream storage Withdrawal of stored gas from upstream storage and especially from downstream storage facilities were used as make-up supplies during the cold spell in 1992/93.

Special arrangements In many cases, special or unique arrangements were made to deal with short-supply situations, for instance, short term gas "loans" . Similarly, several sellers made backhaul and swap arrangements with buyers located in the United States in December 1992 and January 1993, in effect importing US gas into Western Canada to meet the peak demand caused by very cold weather. For many buyers and sellers, the difficulty with such arrangements is that, unless they have been arranged in advance, they can take up to two or three days to organise and in a volatile market, prices can swing widely, suddenly undermining the economics of such arrangements.

If a buyer's gas supplier declares *force majeure* and is unable to arrange alternative gas supplies, the responsibility for resolving the short-supply situation shifts to the buyer. In a *force majeure* situation, the supplier is relieved of any financial obligation to the buyer and it is the buyer's responsibility to arrange alternative supplies and to minimise its costs. The options available for keeping gas flowing are very much the same for the buyer as for the seller. If the buyer is an end-user, he may curtail his own consumption at the burner tip if possible. In cases where this was not possible, the LDCs were key players in resolving many of the short-supply situations experienced in 1992-93 since they have options not readily available to typical end-users. Such options include for instance "uptick" rights i.e., the right to nominate as much as 25% above the daily contract quantities under special long term contracts, and prearranged peaking services under which the LDC has the right to redirect the end-users' gas supplies into its system.

US EXPERIENCE DURING THE COLD SNAP OF JANUARY 1994

In January, 1994, the United States experienced a period of exceptionally low temperatures which severely tested the nation's gas delivery system. The outcome of the test was followed all the more closely as the winter of 1993/94 was the first winter under Order 636 which to a large extent restructured the gas industry.[5]

In the view of FERC, responsible for drafting and implementing Order 636, the Order passed a very difficult test, and the gas industry performed very well. In a testimony before the House of Representative Subcommittee on Energy and Power, FERC Chair, Elizabeth Anne Moler, said the following about why the industry performed so well under Order 636:

---

5. For a description of Order 636, see IEA, 1994.

The keys are communication, flexibility and accountability. Order 636 provides for strong communication among all segments of the industry. Electronic Bulletin Boards (EBBs) are key. The EBBs provide both an early alert to changing conditions and a channel for instantaneous communication throughout an emergency. Pipelines can address problems before they become crises, and transporters can monitor gas supply, storage withdrawals and customer demand in time to respond as needed. We have issued rules that will make EBBs even better.

Order 636 provides flexibility both at the wellhead and in pipeline operations. Gas prices rose quickly during the worst of the emergency and have fluctuated since then in the face of continued cold. Price signals for gas work better then ever before. Natural gas is now priced as a commodity.

Order 636 also gives the pipelines the flexibility they need to meet unusual conditions. As demand intensified, some pipelines exercised stricter control than usual over their system operations. They declared "alert days", "critical times", or imposed "operational flow orders" to discipline receipts and deliveries. These let the pipelines get the most out of their systems when they are stretched near their limits.

Finally, Order 636 provides accountability. All parties know what their rights and obligations are. This helped the industry respond during January. Furthermore, we have heard of very few disputes arising from the emergency. This suggests that the industry solved the problems as they developed. That is as it should be.

After the emergency in January 1994, several institutions have done their own analysis of what really happened and what lessons can be learned.[6] A summary of this material, mainly based on the analysis done by the DOE, is presented below

Background

During the week of January 16-22, 1994, extreme meteorological conditions - bitterly cold temperatures, often following severe ice storms - affected both transportation and energy supply and necessitated controlled, manually implemented disruptions in energy supplies in States in New England, the Mid-Atlantic, and the Midwest, and as far south as Alabama. Electric power transmission, distribution and generation suffered disruptions, as did flows of natural gas, propane, kerosene and fuel-oil supplies. Electric power outages further exacerbated energy delivery problems by de-energizing the petroleum pipeline pumps and natural gas pipeline compressors needed to continue to operate at full capacity. An analysis of heating degree-days indicates that January 1994 was a relatively cold month throughout the United States (6% below normal) and that the temperature in the Mid-Atlantic regions was much colder than usual (Washington, for instance was 20% colder than normal).

Effects on the Gas Industry

Natural gas demand during the week of January 16, 1994 reached record levels. The 2538 billion cubic feet (bcf) consumed in January 1994 was the highest level since January 1973. On average, natural gas use in consuming regions in January is about twice that of August; during the winter months, any significant departure from normal temperatures will directly and immediately increase demand for natural gas.

---

6. See for instance: *Interstate Natural Gas Pipeline Performance During the Cold Snap of January 1994, Background Report*, March 1994, Interstate Natural Gas Association of America and *Fact Sheet on Natural Gas Industry Actions, January 1994*, American Gas Association, February 4, 1994.

In a survey of 21 pipeline companies that supplied the Eastern United States during the week of January 16-22, the Interstate Natural Gas Association of America (INGAA) found that the throughput level for the week represented an all-time high and was larger than the sum of the historic peaks from any year for the 21 pipelines surveyed. Four pipelines also met or set all-time highs for the week for storage withdrawals.

New all-time daily highs were also set: the INGAA survey reported new records for send-out, market deliveries, scheduled transportation and throughput, and eight pipelines set all-time records for individual days. On average, these records were 8% higher than previous records. Deliverability, particularly during demand surges, depends heavily on the availability of natural gas in storage. Energy Information Administration (EIA) statistics show that 723.8 bcf of gas was withdrawn from storage in January 1994 for the entire US. This is a monthly record and a 30-percent increase over January 1993.

The American Gas Association (AGA) surveyed several of its member local distribution companies in the area affected by the cold to determine their send-out volumes during the January 18-20 period. All seven of the LDCs surveyed equalled or exceeded their design day at least twice, and five LDCs equalled or exceeded their design day for the 3-day survey period. A design day generally refers to a 1-day send-out that would occur no more than once in 25 years.

Fortunately, the cold weather of January 1994 did not significantly affect gas production in the major producing regions. Some downstream storage fields experienced storage withdrawal problems due to frozen valves. These were fixed quickly, and their overall impact on production and service was limited.

General Natural Gas Industry Operations during Peak Demand Periods

Figure 6.13 illustrates natural gas flows during peak periods of demand. In physical terms, the flows are similar to those under the same conditions in Canada and in Europe, although the organisational and contractual aspects of some of the transactions are different in the latter. Since this general picture is well-known, only features specific to the US situation will be pointed out.

Natural gas is moved from major producing regions, such as the Gulf of Mexico and East Texas, to major consuming regions through large interstate pipelines. Pipelines must carefully coordinate receipts from producers and withdrawals from storage to ensure a balance between these inputs and gas taken from the system by consumers. For balancing purposes, traditional instruments like storage, linepack, peak shaving facilities (including LNG, propane-air and compressed natural gas (CNG) stored in aboveground tanks) and interruptible contracts are used. In an emergency, pipelines can issue operational flow orders (OFOs) requiring a shipper to inject or withdraw gas into or from the system at specific receipts or delivery points to ensure the continued flow of gas through the pipeline. Several hours to a full day's notice must be given before pipeline companies can implement an OFO.

Curtailment is the most severe control strategy. Under curtailment, pipeline companies may cut off transportation or storage service to their shippers in the event of a major supply or capacity disruption. However, curtailments are not used for firm transportation (service offered under

Figure 6.13   Natural Gas Flows during Peak Periods

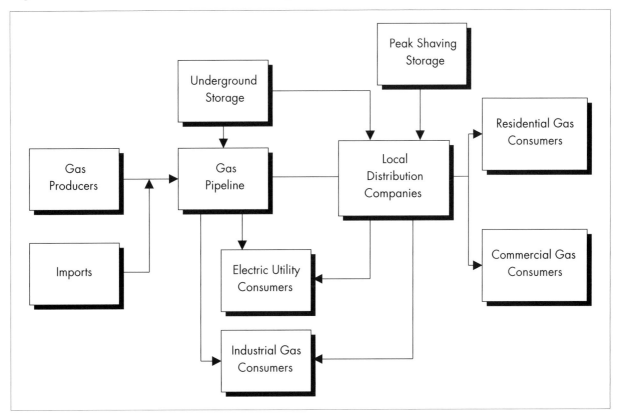

Source: DOE (1995).

contracts that anticipate no interruptions) except under *force majeure.* Order 636 provides protection to high-priority users in the event of a pipeline emergency. As part of the Order 636 restructuring filing, each pipeline company was required to submit for FERC approval a priority schedule for curtailment to firm transportation shippers.

Industry Actions during January 1994

During the week of 16 January 1994, the record demand for natural gas was met by a combination of sustained maximum production, record import levels and optimisation of all available storage.

Production

As noted above, domestic natural gas production was not hampered to any degree by the cold temperatures. Of the few disruptions in service that took place, none can be attributed to a disruption of natural gas production.

Monthly natural gas production displays little seasonal variation. Typically, January production may exceed July production by only about 5 or 6 percent. The ability to increase natural gas production on a month-to-month basis is very limited. January 1994 production, estimated at 1620 bcf, exceeded January 1993 production by about 3%.

Imports

For the United States as a whole, imports of natural gas in 1993 constituted 11.2% of total consumption. Some US regions, however, have a much higher dependency on imported gas. Table 6.17 shows the share of imports in January 1994 in the regions that were most severely affected by the cold spell. Canadian imports accounted for nearly one-third of the total gas supply in New England and nearly one quarter of the supply in New York. Canadian gas is delivered to US markets in the East by Transcanada Pipelines Ltd. (TCPL). Primary transportation routes from the Canadian border to eastern US markets are through the Iroquois and Tennessee Gas pipeline systems, which account for about 90% of the supply to eastern US markets. During the middle of the January 1994 cold spell, TCPL reported a single-day record for exports to the United States of 3.3 bcf. TCPL aggregate deliveries to Canada and the United States for the month of January also established a new record, reaching 221 bcf, an increase of 17% over January 1993.

Table 6.17   Natural Gas Imports as a Percentage of Total Gas Deliveries by State, January, 1994 (mmcf)

State	Canadian	Mexican	Algerian	Total Deliveries	Imports as % of Total Deliveries
New England					
Connecticut	4,835	0	556	16,780	32.1
Maine	246	0	0	777	31.7
Massachusetts	8,774	0	4,431	43,328	30.5
New Hampshire	445	0	384	2,904	28.9
Rhode Island	2,784	0	336	8,761	35.6
Vermont	1,181	0	0	1,181	100.0
Total	**18,275**	**0**	**5,707**	**73,731**	**32.5**
Mid-Atlantic					
New Jersey	4,358	325	78	82,479	5.8
New York	27,679	522	172	122,809	23.1
Pennsylvania	641	0	16	102,982	0.6
Total	**32,678**	**847**	**266**	**308,270**	**11.0**

Sources: Import data: filings submitted by importers to Office of Fuels Programs, Fossil Energy; total deliveries data: Energy Information Administration (EIA) form EIA-857. See EIA's Natural Gas Monthly (DOE/EIA-0130(94/09), Table 22.

The cold spell offered some interesting examples of the role international cooperation can play in an emergency situation. The 1993-94 winter was the first in which additional Canadian supplies via the Iroquois interconnection with TCPL were made available to New York and New England. The normal operating capacity for the Iroquois pipeline is 670 million cubic feet per day (mcf/d). However, during January 16-22, 1994, Iroquois was able to operate all its compressors (not a normal operating procedure) to provide an additional 140 mcf/d above its firm transportation requirements. Most of the additional volume went to electric power generators. TCPL was able to provide Iroquois with additional natural gas in part because of cooperation from eastern Canadian LDCs.

Canadian gas supplies via Iroquois were extended further south through an interconnection with the Tennessee Gas pipeline system. By the use of displacement with Tennessee Gas, additional gas service was made available in Pennsylvania and New Jersey.

New England is at the terminus of the only two major pipelines that transport gas from producing regions in the Gulf Coast and southwest to the northeastern United States. Because this reduces possible alternative supply options in the event of any supply disruptions to the south or west, New England is usually one of the first regions to experience reductions during peak-demand periods and seasonal termination of interruptible service. This unique situation has made imported LNG from Algeria an important supply source in eastern New England, particularly during peak periods. LNG can also be stored and transported, further adding to its versatility as a peaking supply source.

DISTRIGAS of Boston, which imports LNG from Algeria, supplied a record 6.06 bcf of firm supply to New England during January 1994; it also recorded its highest daily send-out during the week of January 16. An additional tanker of Algerian LNG was delivered to DISTRIGAS on short notice to supplement normally scheduled deliveries at Boston. DISTRIGAS noted that vaporised LNG not only helped to meet the region's peak demand but also made a major contribution to maintaining the system integrity of the Iroquois and Tennessee Gas pipelines.

Storage

Storage comprised approximately 29% of the January 1994 natural gas supply, as compared with 25% for January 1993. Table 6.18 lists the actual sources of supply for January 1994. However, storage accounted for 37% of total supply for the 1-week period beginning on January 15. Thus, storage is an important instrument indeed when it comes to supplying gas in a tight supply situation.

Table 6.18   Sources of Natural Gas Supply, January, 1994 (bcf)

Source	1994 Volume	Percent of Total	1993 Volume	Percent of Total
Conventional Production	1,634	62	1,584	66
Underground Storage	755	29	607	25
Peak Shaving	13	<1	13	<1
Imports	220	8	198	8
Total	**2,622**	**100**	**2,402**	**100**

Source: DOE (1995).

Problems Encountered at the Transmission and Distribution Level

The biggest number of problems caused by the cold spell arose in the distribution part of the gas chain. Only one interstate pipeline, Texas Eastern, reported an interruption in firm transportation service. The interruption only lasted 16 hours and was due to a mechanical-electrical problem when electricity supplies were curtailed and Texas Eastern's backup electricity generators failed to operate. This event highlights the need for coordination among electric and gas utilities in a crisis and the importance of reliable backup systems ready for use.

Failing electricity supply also caused some problems in the gas distribution sector. In some areas rolling blackouts caused electrically operated compressors to shut down, created difficulties in gas system control-room operations and reduced operations at some peak-shaving plants.

Several LDCs reported sporadic deliverability problems, and in a few instances firm service was interrupted. Most of these interruptions were related to system capacity limitations - i.e., demand simply exceeded pipeline design throughput capacity. LDCs and state and local officials made appeals for conservation of natural gas to prevent a tight situation from getting worse, and frequent news media broadcasts requested consumers to lower thermostats and reduce hot-water use.

A key element in managing demand for most LDCs was the enforcement of interruptible contracts. Exercising interruptibility provisions to ensure the integrity of service to firm customers, however, was not always straightforward. When customers who buy gas under interruptible contracts do not stop using gas when asked to do so, higher priority customers such as residential households are in jeopardy of losing their gas supply. The fact that a significant number of interruptible gas users continued to consume gas when they were asked not to do so proved to be a widespread and serious problem. There were limited reports of LDCs having to go to the interruptible customer and physically shut off the supply. One reason for the reluctance of some interruptible customers to stop using gas was the shortage of reserve fuel, caused either by inadequate stocks or by delivery problems as a consequence of the cold.

Government Actions during the Cold Spell

To a large extent, under the present organisation of the natural gas market in the United States, actors in the market ensure security of supply. In emergency situations, however, there is also some scope for government action. During the January 1994 cold spell, few problems were observed in the parts of the gas supply system under federal jurisdiction. Only one interstate pipeline experienced problems, and no problems arose that required FERC assistance. FERC activities were therefore limited to monitoring and surveying pipelines. The events related to LDCs were monitored by DOE offices such as the Office of Emergency Management.

Responses at the state level varied widely. Although only one state issued a formal request to reduce natural gas consumption, other states issued general appeals to reduce energy consumption overall. Most of the time, however, the LDCs issued their own appeals to reduce consumption.

Natural gas at the state level is a highly regulated commodity and, consequently, most LDC actions usually require some type of approval from or coordination with state public utility commissions (PUCs). This was the case during the January cold spell with most PUCs closely monitoring - and approving when necessary - LDC actions. LDCs generally were proactive in contacting their respective PUCs as problems became evident.

State governments activated emergency management agencies which, for the most part, are designed to respond to all types of emergencies but typically deal with natural disasters. Most of their energy-emergency experience dealt with spot fuel-oil and propane shortages; prior experience with a natural gas emergency was almost nonexistent. In some states the emergency management offices played a pivotal role in coordinating fuel-oil deliveries to interrupted gas consumers.

Lessons Learned

The difficulties that arose during the January 1994 cold spell spurred analysis to determine what really took place and what measures could be taken in the future to improve preparedness for similar situations. The report from DOE (1995), which deals with the whole range of energies, issued the following recommendations concerning natural gas as a result of the review:

- The communication within the gas industry itself during the emergency functioned well, but information to the public, especially in the beginning, was deficient in both timing and content and mechanisms to improve it in the future should be put in place.

- LDCs and pipelines should work closely with their supplying electric utilities to make them aware of the crucial nature of certain gas facilities to avoid disruptions as a consequence of rotating blackouts. In some cases, replacing electrically operated compressors with natural gas-fuelled ones should be considered.

- Utilities, PUCs and state energy offices should review eligibility criteria for gas customers wanting interruptible service, and natural gas suppliers must ensure that consumers with interruptible contracts understand and abide by the terms of their agreements. State energy offices should require all high-priority gas users who elect to stay on interruptible contracts to have adequate backup fuel supplies.

- Each LDC has a design day based on weather probabilities for its specific geographical area. During 1994, several LDCs exceeded their design day more than once in the same week. LDCs may need to plan their systems for colder weather. The fact that an LDC has exceeded its 25-year design day in more than one cold spell in the past few years may indicate that weather norms have changed and that design-day criteria may need to be re-examined.

One general recommendation from the DOE review of the 1994 cold spell is that each state prepare, exercise and use when appropriate an emergency supply crisis plan. The experiences from the cold spell have also spurred the gas industry to put more emphasis on reliability issues. For instance, the Natural Gas Supply Association, representing companies that produce and market over 90% of the domestic gas consumed in the US, has urged the gas industry and its regulators to incorporate pre-arranged mutual assistance agreements into their contingency plans. As reported elsewhere in this study, TCPL in Canada already offers services to facilitate the implementation of such contingency plans.

Conclusions

The overall conclusion from the recent involuntary tests of the United States and Canadian deliverability systems for natural gas is that these systems perform very well under stress and that the entire gas industry works very well together especially when the image of gas in the public opinion is at stake. The tests have, however, been useful in identifying weaknesses in the systems that should be remedied. Some of the measures identified are found to be on the borderline between public and private responsibility. In the United States there seems for instance to be some discussion as to who should be responsible for emergency or contingency planning. It is interesting to note in this context that the experiences during the cold spells described above have led to new services being offered by the gas companies to reduce the strain during shortfalls and to reduce the probability of shortfalls occurring.

Since both the United States and Canada have recently gone through a period of gas surplus, the performance of their gas deliverability systems may not necessarily be representative of a future situation. Future gas demand is of course uncertain, and considerations about future deliverability and reliability of the gas system have to be based on a number of assumptions. At least one attempt, however, has been made to think systematically about how reliability could be maintained, reasoning within the framework of one specific forecast for the future physiognomy of the US gas market. This attempt will be dealt with below.

MAINTAINING RELIABILITY IN THE NATURAL GAS DELIVERY SYSTEM IN THE FUTURE

In 1994, the Gas Research Institute undertook a study of the future reliability of the natural gas system (GRI, 1994). Its overall forecast for the US gas market suggests that demand will grow from 17.4 Quads (614 bcm) in 1989 to 23.9 Quads (843 bcm) in 2010. How this growth in annual gas demand translates into future seasonal gas load profiles will be an important factor in gas system planning. It is clear that the gas industry must make substantial investments in new pipeline, storage, and peak-shaving facilities to serve expected growth in seasonal gas demand. The study estimates that the industry must increase its annual (pipeline -based) delivery capacity by 14.7 billion cubic feet per day (bcf/d), its market-area underground storage capacity by 2.9 bcf per day, and its peakshaving capacity by as much as 8.5 bcf/d by 2010. Based on current plans, the industry has shown itself willing and able to undertake the needed investment in new facilities.

Future seasonal load profiles, and future gas delivery requirements will depend on the demand in each end-use sector, changes in the mix of functional end-uses within the sectors (e.g., space heating versus water heating) and the penetration of gas technologies with new seasonal load profiles (e.g., space cooling, electric power production and natural gas vehicles). The GRI study uses a methodology for projecting seasonal load profiles that was specifically designed to relate the annual demand outlook of the GRI Baseline Projection to the load profiles of each functional end-use.

Figure 6.14 summarises the annual demand growth in the 1994 edition of the GRI Baseline Projection using functional groups that reflect the general patterns of seasonal gas use. While annual demand increases by 6.5 Quads (236 bcm) by 2010, temperature-sensitive end-uses (primarily residential and commercial space heating) show no net growth in annual demand. Gas end-uses with baseload or off-peak seasonal profiles - such as residential and commercial appliances, space cooling, natural gas use in vehicles, and industrial sector process gas use - are expected to grow by 3.9 Quads (138 bcm). Gas used for electric power production in commercial and industrial sector co-generation, and by electric utilities and independent power producers, is projected to grow by 2.6 Quads (92 bcm).

These trends imply that future seasonal profiles of gas use will grow most rapidly in the baseload and off-peak portions of the year. As a result, future needs for new delivery capacity will

Figure 6.14   Growth in Seasonal Gas Demand from 1989 to 2010

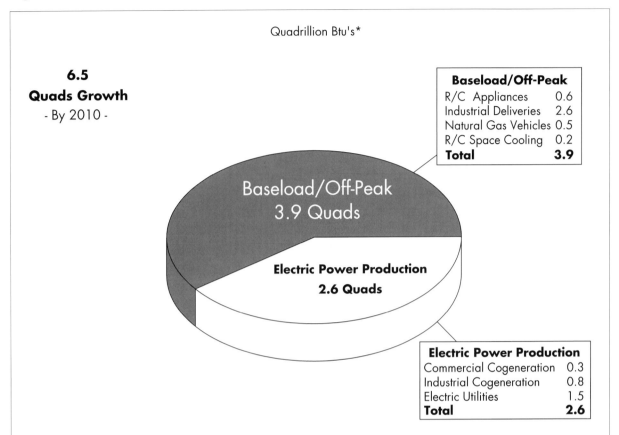

Quadrillion Btu's*

6.5
Quads Growth
- By 2010 -

Baseload/Off-Peak
R/C Appliances	0.6
Industrial Deliveries	2.6
Natural Gas Vehicles	0.5
R/C Space Cooling	0.2
Total	**3.9**

Baseload/Off-Peak
3.9 Quads

Electric Power Production
2.6 Quads

Electric Power Production
Commercial Cogeneration	0.3
Industrial Cogeneration	0.8
Electric Utilities	1.5
Total	**2.6**

* 1.03 Quadrillion Btu's (Quads) is the energy equivalent of 1.0 Trillion cubic feet (Tcf) of natural gas.
Source: GRI (1994).

generally emphasise annual delivery capacity. However, there are uncertainties associated with many determinants of seasonal gas use. Two in particular will have important implications for future underground storage and peakshaving capacity requirements:

a) Gas Service in Power Generation Markets

Currently, most gas used for electric power generation is interruptible and follows a counter-cyclical profile of increasing demand in the summer air-conditioning season. In contrast, much of the projected growth is expected to occur in combined-cycle gas turbine units serving base and intermediate load electric generation needs. To the degree new gas-fired power generation select firm gas service, the natural gas industry will require additional annual delivery capacity and gas storage services to meet the annual and wintertime fuel needs of these customers. If, however, a large proportion chooses interruptible gas service, the need for new delivery capacity will be reduced, and the seasonal sharing of annual delivery capacity between power generators and LDCs may substitute for market-area storage services.

b) Evolution of Residential and Commercial Load Profiles

The 1994 GRI Baseline Projection expects gas use per customer in the residential and commercial space heating market to decline 25% by the year 2010. If peak-day use per customer declines in proportion to annual use, the future design-day demands of the residential and commercial sectors will not increase. However, the recent experience of many gas distribution companies suggests that the peak-day gas demands of residential and commercial space-heating customers are not declining as rapidly as their annual use. If the future trends in peak-day gas use per customer are consistent with recent industry experience, a significant increase in the peak-day demands of the residential and commercial sectors can be expected.

FUTURE LOAD PROFILES AND CAPACITY REQUIREMENTS

Figure 6.15 shows the projected profile of seasonal gas loads and the delivery capacity required in the Lower-48 gas system in 2010 based on the annual demand projections in the 1994 GRI Baseline Projection. On an annual basis, average daily gas demand in 2010 is 17.6 bcf/d (or 37%) above current levels. Gas loads increase in all periods of the year, reflecting the predominantly base-load nature of annual demand growth. Average daily gas demand during the winter period increases 17.5 bcf/d, and during the off-peak season 18.5 bcf/d. The non-coincident design day demand for gas increases 14 to 28 bcf/d over current levels, depending on the effects of conservation on peak-day heating demand.

Figure 6.15   Profile of Gas Loads and Delivery Capacity for 2010

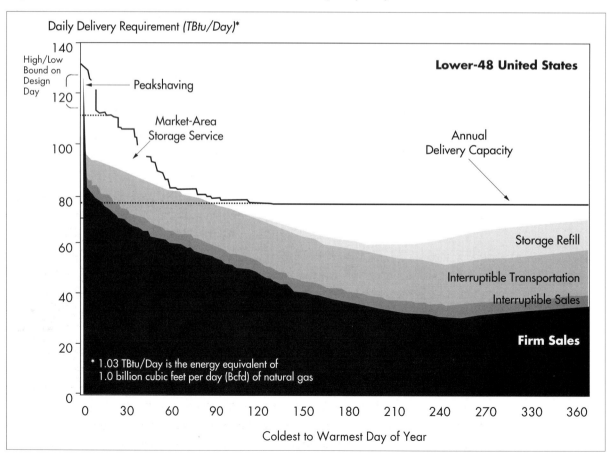

Source: GRI (1994).

Figure 6.16   Requirements for New Delivery Capacity by 2010

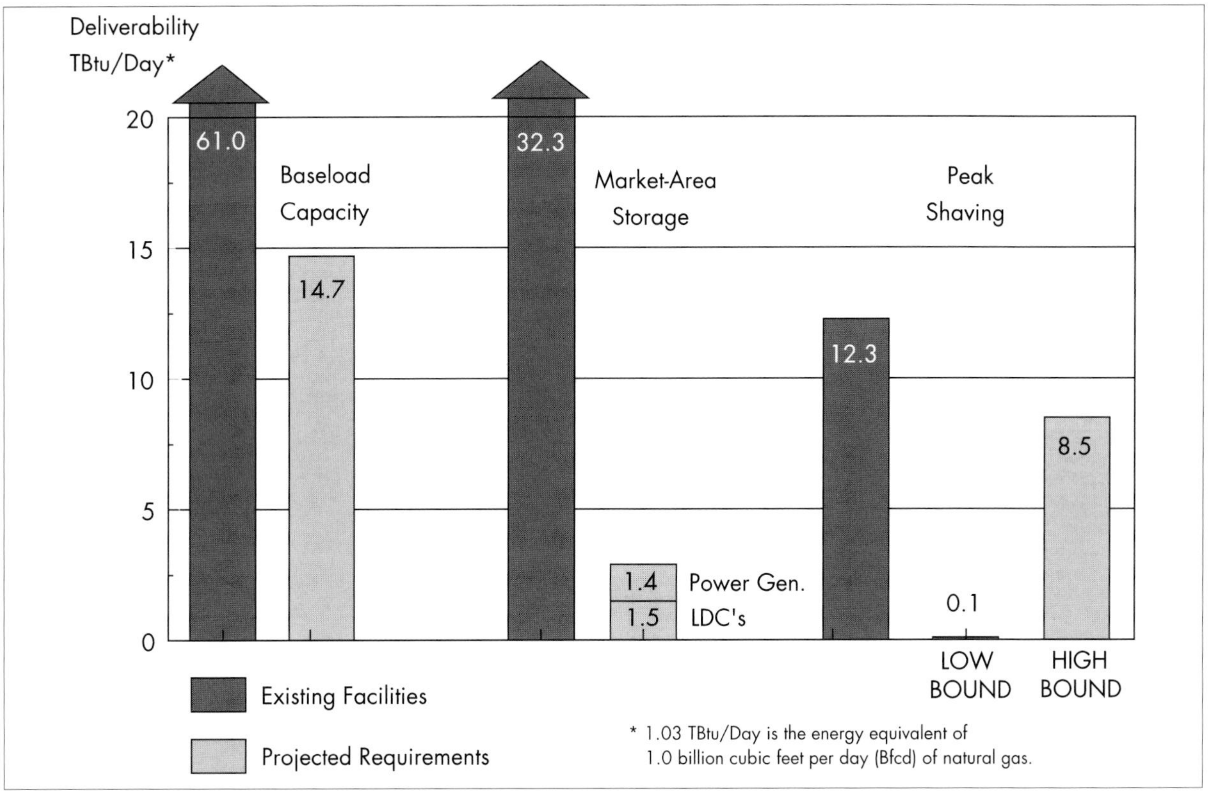

Source: GRI (1994).

To meet this increased load, the Lower-48 gas delivery system will require continued new pipeline, storage, and peakshaving capacity. Figure 6.16 summarises the future requirements for new delivery capacity in comparison with the existing capability of the Lower-48 delivery system:

■ Future needs for new delivery capacity will be predominantly baseload in nature. A total of 14.7 bcf/d of new annual capacity will be required to serve growth in firm loads over the next 20 years, an increase of 24% in existing annual delivery capacity.

■ Future needs for new market-area underground storage are less than for annual delivery capacity and will depend significantly on the gas purchase strategies of future electric power generators. An additional 2.9 bcf/d of seasonal deliverability from underground storage (an increase of 9%) is required by 2010, with almost one-half needed to serve firm electric power generation loads. If electric generators purchase gas on an interruptible basis, no new market-area storage would be needed to support gas sales to power plants. Because gas space-heating loads, which traditionally have driven storage needs, are not expected to grow on an annual basis, LDCs are expected to require only an additional 1.5 bcf/d of new market-area storage service by 2010.

■ Future requirements for gas peakshaving depend critically on design-day requirements of residential and commercial space-heating customers. If design-day demands decline in proportion to annual use per customer, the industry will need new capacity only to replace retired facilities and to maintain current levels of reserve capacity. In contrast, future requirements for new peakshaving capacity will be significantly greater if recent peak-day trends on distribution systems continue. As much as 8.5 bcf/d of new peakshaving capacity could be required in the Lower-48 by 2010, 70% of current capacity.

FUTURE DELIVERY CAPACITY REQUIREMENTS AND INDUSTRY CONSTRUCTION PLANS

Since the base year of the GRI study (1989), the US gas industry has completed several major pipeline expansion projects and has announced many additional pipeline and underground storage projects to provide increased delivery capacity for regional markets. These plans show the willingness and ability of the industry to undertake the investment in the new facilities needed to serve future load growth. In fact, gas storage in North America is experiencing unprecedented growth.[7] According to a recent Canadian study, US deliverability from storage is expected to increase by 17 to 26% by the end of this decade (NRC, 1994). Current US storage development proposals involve capital costs of $2.2 billion, compared with undepreciated interstate pipeline storage assets in 1991 of $2.7 billion.

The situation in Canada is similar: the decline in excess wellhead deliverability in 1992 and the introduction of daily balancing on the NOVA pipeline system have increased the demand for storage. Large increases in storage capacity are being developed in Western Canada. Deliverability from Alberta storage more than doubled between 1991 and 1994. Canadian natural gas producers and consumers use storage on both sides of the Canadian/United States border. According to Natural Resources Canada (NRC, 1994), the rapid pace of development raises the question of whether too much storage is being added and what effect this new capacity will have on North American natural gas markets and prices.

A more detailed look at the estimations done in the GRI study reveals that in the US, pipeline expansion projects in service as of 1993 have added almost 40% of the new annual delivery capacity projected to be required by 2010 (using 1989 as base year). Announced plans for pipeline construction during the next several years will provide an additional 30% of the future need. Given the 5-year planning horizon typical for pipeline construction, it is likely that the remaining annual delivery requirements can be planned and constructed in time to serve future market requirements.

As shown in Figure 6.17, new market-area storage services are only one aspect of current industry plans. Storage developers also are planning many new facilities in production areas and at developing market hubs to support pipeline system operations. Substantial additions of high-deliverability storage are planned to provide gas balancing services, to enhance gas supply and system reliability and to serve power generation markets. Of the total planned storage expansion, only that designed for market-area storage is directly comparable to the storage requirements projected in the GRI study.

Nationally, the 0.8 bcf/d of market-area storage capacity completed since 1989 provides almost 30% of the new market-area storage requirements projected for 2010. The industry's completed and planned total of 4.2 bcf/d for new market-area storage services nationally is more than adequate to provide for all future storage requirements through 2010.

---

7. See the Canadian and US annexes for additional detail.

Figure 6.17   Future Requirements and Industry Construction Plans for
New Underground Storage

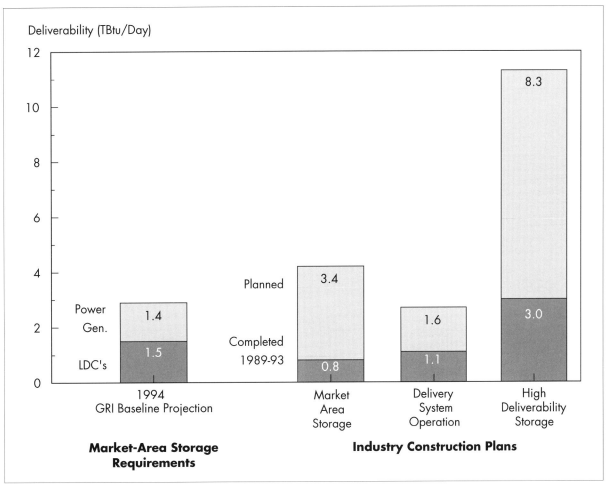

Source: GRI (1994).

Perhaps the most striking outcome of the GRI study is the potentially large need for new peakshaving capacity to serve the future peak-day demands of firm residential and commercial gas loads. At least some new peakshaving capacity will likely be required across a wide range of trends for peak day and annual gas use, and these needs could be very large if recent peak-day demand trends continue. However, few new gas peak-shaving facilities have been constructed since the late 1970s, and some existing facilities have been retired. The industry has no current plans for the expansion of gas peak-shaving capacity, except a proposal to provide gas peaking services based on LNG to be stored in the Cove Point LNG import terminal.

The above considerations illustrate the difficulties involved in simulating the gas market at a future point in time. Such simulations will always have to be based on a number of assumptions that can be questioned. The conclusion to be drawn from this analysis, however, is that gas markets in North America have built-in incentive mechanisms that will see to it that sufficient capacity is installed to cater for reliable gas supplies.

VII. EFFECTS OF GAS SUPPLY DISRUPTIONS ON MARKETS FOR OTHER FUELS

This chapter examines the short-term substitutability of gas outside of the power sector, the overall effect of potential gas supply disruptions on the demand for other fuels - mostly oil products - and the broader impact on international oil markets. Analysis of the substitutability of gas in the power sector is covered in Chapter 5.

SUBSTITUTABILITY OF GAS OUTSIDE THE POWER SECTOR

Overview

In many natural gas-consuming OECD countries, the existence of customers with dual- or multi-firing equipment confers a significant potential for substituting gas with other fuels at short notice. In general, this flexibility has come about as a result of two main factors:

■ End-users of energy can gain a competitive advantage by switching fuels to profit from movements in fuel price differentials, thus providing a form of insurance against an adverse movement in the price of a particular fuel.

■ Gas companies in many instances have been prepared to offer gas supplies under interruptible contracts, whereby the gas supplier reserves the right to interrupt the gas supply when required for an agreed maximum period and number of times per year. In return for the inconvenience of accepting an interruptible supply, the customer pays a lower gas price than those customers with firm supply contracts. Many gas companies offer interruptible gas supplies because of the flexibility this conveys in meeting seasonal demand peaks and the cost saved in building additional storage capacity.

Although the primary reason why gas suppliers often offer interruptible contracts is to match peak demand (usually lasting no more than a few days each year) from firm customers with available supplies, interruptible customers with dual-firing also provide a greater degree of security for firm customers in the event of a major and prolonged gas supply disruption. Interruptible contracts normally stipulate the conditions under which supplies can be interrupted, including the minimum notice period prior to interruption, the maximum number of days of interruption and maximum single period for interruption; negotiated contracts may also place take-or-pay obligations on the buyer. During a supply disruption, the gas supplier could interrupt supplies initially in line with the terms of such interruptible contracts; were it deemed necessary to interrupt for longer periods than specified in the contracts, the supplier could declare *force majeure*. Depending on the seriousness and expected duration of the disruption to supplies, the supplier might interrupt all or a significant proportion of its interruptible customers for an indefinite period in order to conserve remaining gas supplies from indigenous production, imports or storage for its firm customers.

The importance of interruptible customers and therefore the degree of short term fuel-switching potential varies considerably among OECD countries according to the flexibility of gas supplies and the availability and cost of building and maintaining storage facilities. In the Netherlands, for example, there are no interruptible customers because Gasunie, the national gas utility, is able to meet all peak demand through the low cost flexibility of the indigenous Groningen field. By contrast, the UK relies heavily on interruptible customers because of the limited amount of gas storage and the pronounced seasonality and unpredictability of demand.

Although the terms and conditions of interruptible contracts vary markedly between countries and gas suppliers, in all cases only large consumers are encouraged or allowed to sign such contracts for reasons of administrative efficiency: at times of peak demand, it is less costly to contact and arrange to interrupt a small number of large customers than a large number of small customers. Gas suppliers typically place minimum requirements on annual contract volumes and/or peak day consumption and often also insist on customers installing and maintaining dual- or multi-firing equipment, which is normally only economic for medium to large gas consumers. These requirements mean that, in general, interruptible supplies are limited to medium to large industrial consumers, though some large customers in the commercial sector, such as public buildings and large office blocks, may qualify for interruptibility in some countries (e.g., the United Kingdom).

While in no case in OECD countries are residential customers supplied under interruptible contracts, there may in practice be a limited amount of potential fuel-switching capability. For space heating in particular electricity could in many cases provide some back-up through the use of portable, relatively inexpensive and easy to install convector heaters. However, in countries where interruptible contracts are available to the large consumers, residential customers would normally be the last category of customer to be interrupted in the event of a major disruption in supplies to those countries.

Interruptible gas prices are set typically on the basis of approximate parity with heavy fuel oil. In most OECD countries where such supplies are available, prices are set at a slight premium to heavy fuel oil to reflect lower handling costs and environmental benefits. Firm gas prices for large industrial and commercial consumers tend to be set in line with gasoil and heavy fuel oil prices. Indexation arrangements were modified in many OECD European countries after the 1986 oil price collapse to ensure that gas prices respond more quickly to movements in oil prices. Typically, firm and interruptible gas prices for large consumers in Europe are recalculated every three months. Thus, in the event of a gas supply disruption, any increase in gas prices would depend on the effect of the loss of gas supplies on the demand for heavy fuel oil and gasoil and therefore oil prices. Paradoxically, there may be some short-term incentive for customers with dual-firing capacity to switch to gas (unless supplies are cut) for as long as gas prices lag behind any increase in heavy fuel oil prices.

Fuel-switching capability has developed in most OECD countries not primarily because of gas suppliers' concerns about how to respond to a major supply disruption but mainly in response to gas suppliers' need to find the most economic option for balancing peak demand with available supply. The existence of interruptible customers with the capability of switching quickly to an alternative fuel can nonetheless complement the flexibility provided by stocks and the 'swing' in indigenous output and/or imports in meeting an unexpected gas supply disruption and, therefore, significantly enhance overall gas supply security.

Fuel-Switching in Industry

The potential for fuel-switching in industry varies considerably according to the type of industrial activity and historical trends in end-user prices of competing fuels. For technical reasons, some industrial applications lend themselves to the use of different types of fuels making the installation of dual-firing equipment a practical (if not economic) proposition. Steam-raising is particularly suited to dual-firing. Other applications typically require the use of one particular fuel, e.g., electricity in aluminium smelting.

Table 7.1 illustrates the typical alternatives to natural gas in primary industrial energy-using applications. Alternatives to natural gas exist in all broad categories of energy use. The capital cost of equipment to use each type of fuel, the price of the fuel and, in some instances, environmental regulations determine which fuel is used in practice. Many firms provide for the option of switching fuels at short notice, either to benefit from relative fuel price movements or to qualify for interruptible gas supplies at a lower price than firm gas. Fuel switching is generally made possible by the installation of dual or multiple firing equipment on the same unit (on-system). However, in some cases, there may be a second back-up or under-utilised unit fired with a different fuel, enabling a certain degree of switching from one to the other (off system).

Table 7.1   Possible Alternatives to Natural Gas in Primary Industrial Uses

Alternative fuel	Direct process	Process steam	Space heating	Autogeneration /CHP
Heavy fuel oil	✓	✓		✓
Gasoil	✓	✓	✓	✓
LPG	✓		✓	
Coal	✓	✓		✓
Electricity	✓			

✓ widespread alternative   ✓ alternative in some cases

Multi-firing is most common in steam-raising and autogeneration. In general, heavy fuel oil is the main competing fuel and back-up fuel in steam raising, because of the price advantage over other oil products and electricity and the ease of handling and storage compared with coal and LPG. Gasoil or heavy fuel oil is the most common back-up fuel in autogeneration, depending on the type of turbine technology. The collapse in oil prices in 1986 reinforced the position of oil products as the main competing fuels to natural gas, and back-up fuels where dual-firing exists (see Table 7.2). In most OECD countries, heavy fuel oil is the least expensive fuel and electricity the most expensive including taxes.

Although considerable short-term fuel-switching potential exists in many OECD countries, the potential to switch away from gas is limited by the degree to which other fuels are already the preferred fuel choice. Where dual coal/gas-firing equipment is installed, coal is generally the preferred main fuel and natural gas the back-up fuel since the cost of the coal is typically lower than that of gas. There are thought to be few instances where a company using natural gas could quickly switch to coal, though in some cases environmental regulations such as emissions limits or sulphur content in fuels introduced after the installation of dual-firing may compel the use of natural gas. Where fuel oil or gasoil is the alternative to natural gas, the choice of main fuel is determined by the prices prevailing at any given time. In the United States, for example, there is considerable switching between natural gas and heavy fuel oil according to relative price

Table 7.2   Energy Prices for Industry, 1992 (US$ per toe)

	Natural gas	Heavy fuel oil	Gasoil	Electricity	Steam coal
Australia	141.1	na	na	532.7	na
Austria	204.3	135.5	266.8	813.2	126.3
Belgium	160.5	102.5	226.9	744.5	na
Canada	93.0	107.2	204.1	460.7	na
Denmark	na	129.3	288.4	774.8	165.6
Finland	143.9	150.2	285.4	662.5	75.8
France	169.8	123.3	320.6	670.1	141.3
Germany	222.8	136.6	291.0	1081.6	285.9
Greece	na	169.5	491.1	809.5	na
Ireland	376.0	150.5	335.2	808.8	na
Italy	196.8	197.0	907.0	1308.6	75.2
Japan	484.6	219.1	318.2	1652.0	87.8
Luxembourg	na	141.9	267.2	na	na
Mexico	73.9	61.6	218.9	576.6	na
Netherlands	na	182.9	na	na	na
New Zealand	205.4	226.0	263.3	342.0	na
Norway	na	421.4	439.6	na	58.3
Portugal	na	204.6	802.1	1682.7	na
Spain	169.3	137.8	402.6	1218.3	na
Sweden	na	381.6	470.6	642.9	na
Switzerland	331.4	143.0	243.4	1103.9	90.1
Turkey	149.3	171.4	na	1075.8	125.0
United Kingdom	175.1	115.9	227.9	887.4	121.3
United States	118.2	89.3	196.7	564.0	57.4

na = not available

Note: Prices include non-refundable taxes

Source: *IEA Energy Prices and Taxes* (IEA, 1994).

differentials. In Europe, gas is most often the preferred fuel; switching to fuel oil normally only occurs when gas supplies are interrupted during peak winter demand periods. LPG is rarely a back-up fuel (and almost never the main fuel) where dual gas/LPG-firing is possible because of the relatively high price of LPG: its use as a back-up fuel is mostly limited to the production of process heat in special applications requiring a clean, constant heat source comparable to that provided by natural gas.

Potential for Switching from Natural Gas in Industry in OECD Countries

North America

United States

Gas is used in a range of industrial applications: boiler fuel, feedstock, process heat and for combined heat and power generation (see Figure 7.1). There is a highly developed capability in US industry for short term fuel switching, particularly between natural gas and heavy fuel oil.

Fuel switching behaviour is driven by competition and profit: companies will often switch from one fuel to another, sometimes for only a few days, to benefit from a sudden shift in fuel price differentials. In practice, delivery costs and state environmental laws and regulations may constrain the degree to which natural gas is backed out by oil products. However, it is technically possible for a large amount of natural gas consumption in industry - mostly in boilers - to be replaced by oil at short notice. Moreover, in a gas supply emergency, Federal and state emissions restrictions might be suspended or relaxed to protect jobs and industrial competitiveness.

Figure 7.1   Industrial Gas Use, United States, 1992

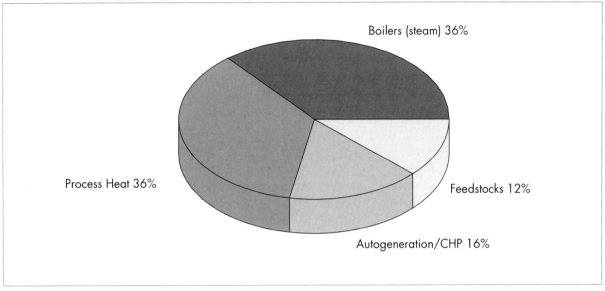

Source: PIRA (1993).

At present, natural gas is usually the preferred fuel in multi-fired industrial plant, and the greatest fuel switching potential is from natural gas to other fuels. According to a DOE study completed in 1991, manufacturers in 1988 could only have increased their consumption of natural gas by a maximum of 14% through a complete switch to natural gas - regardless of economics. Conversely, by exercising all possible switching opportunities away from natural gas, its consumption could have been cut by 39% (see Table 7.3).

Table 7.3   Natural Gas Consumption, United States (billion cubic feet)

	1988	**1992**
Industrial natural gas consumption	5141	6156
Share of industrial energy demand	35 %	39 %
Maximum switchable consumption	2008	na
Maximum possible consumption	5840	na
Minimum possible consumption	3133	na
Discretionary use rate*	74 %	na

* Natural gas consumption as share of maximum possible
na = not available
Source: DOE/EIA (1991); DOE/EIA (1994).

The 1991 DOE/EIA study provides considerable detail on the capability of different industrial sectors to switch between fuels. Table 7.4 shows the capability of industry to switch from natural gas to other fuels in 1988. The greatest potential for substituting gas lies in the textile, paper and food industries: energy use in these sectors is mainly for steam raising which is typically multi-fired. The least potential for switching from gas is in chemicals, partly because gas used as a feedstock in ammonia, methanol and hydrogen production (around 10% of total gas use in the chemicals industry) is not substitutable.

Table 7.4   Capability to Switch from Natural Gas to Alternative Fuels, United States (1988 estimates)

Industry group/ Census region	Natural Gas Cons. (bcf)	of which Switchable (%)		Alternative fuels where switching is possible (%) *					
		bcf	%	Heavy fuel oil	Gasoil (distill-ate)	LPG	Coal and coke	Elec.	Other
I. INDUSTRY									
Chemicals	1 465	340	23	42	49	24	5	6	6
Primary metals	720	264	37	39	31	29	8	3	na
Oil refining etc	666	258	39	33	35	71	neg	5	7
Food & related	475	268	56	46	54	25	3	3	1
Stone/clay/ glass	451	247	55	17	51	43	10	2	1
Paper	415	237	57	64	38	5	8	5	1
Fabricated metal	197	60	30	18	40	52	3	7	2
Transport equip.	134	53	40	36	36	40	4	8	neg
Ind. machinery	123	38	31	24	47	47	5	13	na
Textiles	111	71	64	52	38	35	4	1	1
Rubber & plastic	107	60	56	50	63	12	3	3	2
Electric equip.	82	38	46	18	53	40	3	5	neg
Printing	47	16	34	31	44	56	neg	12	neg
Other	148	59	40	24	34	24	neg	2	2
Total	**5 141**	**2 008**	**39**	**39**	**44**	**33**	**5**	**4**	**3**
II. REGION									
Northeast	490	241	49	49	46	25	2	3	2
Midwest	1 389	586	42	38	44	33	8	4	2
South	2 724	899	33	37	42	36	5	5	5
West	538	282	52	40	50	32	4	5	1
Total	**5 141**	**2 008**	**39**	**39**	**44**	**33**	**5**	**4**	**3**

*   The proportion of natural gas consumption which could have been replaced within 30 days by alternative fuels. The alternative fuels combined exceed 100% because more than one alternative fuel exists in some cases.

neg = negligible (less than 0.5%)

na = not available

Source: DOE/EIA (1991).

DOE data indicate not only how much natural gas could be replaced by alternative fuels but also the degree of flexibility in selecting replacement fuels in each industry. In most cases, boilers fitted with heavy fuel oil firing equipment could also operate on gasoil (distillate). Most plants would choose to run on heavy fuel oil in practice except in the unlikely event that the price differential between fuel oil and gasoil narrows sufficiently to make gasoil a more attractive option. Similarly, many units are able to operate on LPG as a back-up fuel; a third of all natural gas use could technically be replaced by LPG. However, the normally much higher price of LPG would probably mean that in many cases either heavy fuel oil or gasoil would be selected ahead of LPG as the replacement fuel. Similarly, while purchased electricity could potentially replace 4% of natural gas consumption (according to DOE data), cheaper alternatives such as LPG might in practice reduce the actual amount of gas switched to electricity.

The actual pattern of fuel-switching in the event of a disruption in natural gas supplies would, thus, depend to a large extent on the relative prices of the alternative fuels. Figure 7.2 shows the likely approximate share of each fuel in replacing natural gas in US industry in a serious gas supply disruption assuming relative fuel prices remain close to current levels. LPG and gasoil are estimated to account for over half of the fuel-switching from gas, mainly in direct heat and energy and in small boilers.

Figure 7.2   Fuel Switching from Natural Gas in Industry, United States

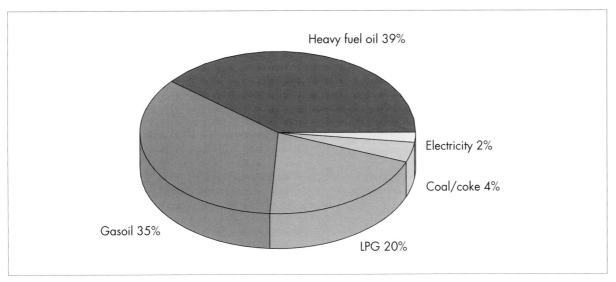

Source: DOE/EIA (1991).

There are pronounced regional differences in the capability of industry to switch from natural gas. The Northeast has the highest proportion of gas consumption which is immediately replaceable by other fuels - just under half. At the other extreme, industry in the South is only capable of switching a third of its consumption of gas.

Canada

Outside of Alberta, most gas suppliers offer gas under interruptible contracts. The National Energy Board estimates that around 25% of industrial gas sales, which are handled by local distribution companies (LDCs), are switchable to other fuels at present. This equates to around 12% of total gas sales in Canada. Heavy fuel oil is the main alternative fuel. The use of interruptible contracts, which are usually offered by LDCs on condition that the buyer has the capability to switch fuels at short notice, varies widely by region. There are few interruptible sales to customers in the vicinity of the producing areas in western Canada, because of the low cost of providing for winter demand peaks. LDCs in eastern Canada offer low interruptible prices to encourage consumers to maintain a multi-fuel capability. In reality, however, there are few interruptions. The amount of dual-firing in industry is thought to have declined significantly in recent years because, with the emergence of surplus gas deliverability, gas suppliers have had less incentive to offer interruptible gas as a way of meeting peak winter demand. The Government believes that fuel-switching capability is unlikely to decline further.

OECD Europe

Dual- or multi-firing of industrial boilers and furnaces/kilns is common-place in most countries in OECD Europe. In most cases, multi-firing equipment has been installed since the mid-1970s as a result of the increased availability of natural gas and increased volatility of oil prices. Where the capability to switch between gas and other fuels exists, the preferred fuel in use at present is almost always gas. This is largely because gas is sold in most European countries under contracts of at least one year with minimum take-or-pay obligations, limiting the scope for short-term fuel switching for economic reasons. Thus, dual-firing is normally only installed when gas is intended, at least initially, to be the primary fuel. This means that considerable flexibility to switch to other fuels in the event of a supply disruption currently exists in Europe. Table 7.5 shows the amount of gas sales in those countries with a gas market which could be switched at short notice to other fuels.

Among the European countries with the highest gas sales, the *United Kingdom* has the largest potential for fuel-switching away from gas. At present, around 50% of industrial sales and 15% of commercial sales could be switched to other fuels. This has come about primarily because British Gas - until the late 1980s the monopoly gas supplier to industry - opted for interruptible gas contracts to large consumers over building high-cost storage facilities to meet peak winter demand. In *France*, close to half the sales of gas to industry could be switched. In practice interruptions to gas supplies are extremely rare, casting doubt on whether all customers which claim to be able to switch fuels adequately maintain this capability. Gaz de France is at present surveying its interruptible customers to ensure that this is the case. Fuel-switching potential is smaller in Italy and Germany: *Italy* relies more heavily on storage while *Germany* depends to a large extent on swing in its gas imports - particularly from the Netherlands - to meet seasonal demand peaks.

In the *Netherlands*, the low-cost swing afforded by the large Groningen field means that there is less need for Gasunie to maintain storage capacity. Since all industrial customers are supplied under firm contracts, there is no requirement for them to maintain a dual-firing capability. A small number of large industrial companies who currently contract for firm gas are nonetheless thought to have dual-firing to enable them to switch at short notice to heavy fuel oil should relative prices provide an economic incentive to do so. *Denmark* relies on the limited flexibility of output from its offshore gas fields and use of onshore storage to meet peak winter demand. Around a quarter of industrial gas sales are interruptible: with the recent introduction of natural gas in Denmark, many industrial customers have switched to gas while maintaining the capability of switching back to the fuel used previously - in most cases heavy fuel oil. No interruptions have yet occurred. In *Sweden*, fuel switching capability is largely confined to customers consuming more than 5 mcm, who are legally obliged to maintain dual-firing equipment and store minimum volumes of back-up fuel.

The extent of dual-firing capability in OECD Europe is thought to be highest in *Finland, Turkey* and *Switzerland,* which have no significant gas storage. Although industrial customers in Finland and Turkey are not supplied under formal interruptible contracts, almost all such customers are thought to have dual-firing capability as a protection against a disruption to supplies from Russia - the sole supply source.

Table 7.5 Fuel-switching Capability in Industry, OECD Europe
(Gas sales to industrial customers with dual-/multi-firing equipment, 1992 estimates)

	Mtoe	% of total industrial sales*	% of total gas sales**
Austria	0.40	30	8
Belgium	0.93	31	10
Denmark	0.13	25	7
Finland	1.21	100	50
France	5.60	55	20
Germany	6.17	27	11
Greece	0	0	0
Ireland	0	0	0
Italy	4.09	27	10
Luxembourg	n.a.	n.a.	n.a.
Netherlands	0	0	0
Spain	1.14	36	22
Sweden	neg.	n.a.	n.a.
Switzerland	0.58	81	30
Turkey	0.82	100	34
United Kingdom	4.22	50	8

* Excluding feedstocks   n.a.= not available
** Including feedstocks   neg.=negligible
Source: Country submissions; IEA estimates.

Table 7.6 Alternative Fuels to Natural Gas in Industry, OECD Europe
(per cent of switchable gas sales)

	Heavy Fuel Oil	Gasoil	LPG	Coal	Electricity
Austria	95	2	0	2	1
Belgium	90	10	0	0	0
Denmark	90	10	0	0	0
France	90	3	0	2	5
Finland	40	50	10	0	0
Germany	90	10	0	0	0
Ireland	-	-	-	-	-
Italy	98	2	0	0	0
Luxembourg	n.a.	n.a.	n.a.	n.a.	n.a.
Netherlands	-	-	-	-	-
Spain	95	2	0	2	1
Sweden	n.a.	n.a.	n.a.	n.a.	n.a.
Switzerland	6	90	0	4	0
Turkey	90	5	0	3	2
United Kingdom	85	10	0	2	3

n.a. = not available.   - = not applicable
Note: In practice, more than one alternative is often available; estimates show only the primary back-up fuel, such that percentages add to 100. Includes industrial combined heat and power.
Source: Country submissions; IEA estimates.

Table 7.6 shows the main alternative fuels to natural gas for industrial customers with multi-firing installed in OECD Europe. Unlike in the United States, fuel switching in industry is not surveyed regularly and reliable data on fuel switching potential is not readily available. Estimates have been compiled on the basis of information provided by gas utilities and governments. In many cases, more than one back-up fuel is possible (particularly in large industrial boilers). The table shows only the likely actual substitute fuel which would depend to a large extent on relative prices. The estimates shown are based on energy price differentials prevailing in 1992. It has also been assumed that environmental regulations, that in some instances prevent the use of high sulphur fuel oil or steam coal, would be relaxed to facilitate a switch to such fuels in the event of a major supply disruption.

Heavy fuel oil is by far the most common substitute for natural gas in industry, because of price (see Table 7.2) and ease of handling compared with coal and LPG. The importance of gasoil as the main back-up fuel in each country depends on two main factors:

■ The frequency and duration of gas supply interruptions for seasonal load balancing: where interruptions are frequent but normally short-lived (e.g., in Switzerland), gasoil is often the preferred substitute fuel.

■ The amount of gas turbine Combined Heat and Power (CHP) capacity, gasoil being the main alternative to natural gas in gas turbines.

Coal and LPG are rarely significant as back-up fuels. Where coal/gas dual-firing exists, coal is normally the primary fuel. There are, however, thought to be in some countries a small number of old coal boilers which have been replaced with more efficient gas-fired boilers but have been kept in reserve as insurance in case of a gas supply disruption or a major problem with the main boiler. These boilers could probably be brought into service within days or weeks, depending on how well they have been maintained. Direct use of electricity by industry in the event of a gas supply interruption is also thought to be minor.

OECD Pacific

In *Japan*, around 67% of the supply of natural gas (96% of which was imported) was accounted for by the power generation sector in 1992. The residential sector accounted for around 17%, industry about 11% and the commercial sector 5%. Most of the gas used in the residential, commercial and industrial sectors is city gas, a mixture of imported natural gas (which makes up approximately 45%) and locally-manufactured town gas. Unlike in power generation where about half of gas-fired capacity is dual-fired, there is thought to be limited fuel-switching potential in the industrial and commercial sectors in Japan. There are no interruptible supply contracts as such, though contracts with some individual customers contain *force majeure* clauses. An estimated 20% of larger city-gas consumers, which account for a small proportion of total demand, have dual-firing, but this proportion is declining. Heavy fuel oil is the main back-up fuel for most of those consumers with dual-firing.

In *Australia*, there are not thought to be any industrial or commercial gas customers currently supplied under formal interruptible contracts. A small amount of dual-firing capacity is nonetheless likely to exist as a result of recent conversions to gas from other fuels where oil- or coal-firing facilities have been retained; in these cases gas could probably be replaced by an alternative fuel at fairly short notice. In *New Zealand*, there are a number of large industrial gas consumers with dual-or multi-firing capability to provide flexibility in the event of a technical disruption to deliveries or a shift in relative fuel prices. It is not known what proportion of current gas sales are potentially substitutable by other fuels at short notice. Gasoil is thought to be the main alternative fuel.

Prospects for Multi-firing in Industry

Although reliable data is limited, it is thought that the proportion of energy consumed in industry which could technically be switched at short notice by means of installed multi-firing equipment has increased in recent years. This has been prompted by the much greater volatility and particularly relative volatility of fuel prices since the early 1970s, which has provided large energy consumers with a strong incentive to improve flexibility in terms of the fuels they can use. At the same time, tighter environmental regulations in many countries have reduced the ability of industrial consumers to switch to alternative fuels on economic or price grounds. Such regulations include air toxic emission limits and ceilings on sulphur content in fuels. In the United States, for example, though 40% of current industrial gas use could theoretically be switched to other fuels, only 10% is thought to be vulnerable to switching under normal circumstances due to emissions restrictions affecting the use of high sulphur heavy fuel oil and high taxes on oil products. Although, in the event of a gas supply curtailment, industrial end-users could use low sulphur fuel oil or distillate, the economic incentive for industry to install dual-firing has been reduced by tighter environmental restrictions on fuel-burning.

Unless governments intervene to halt the trend, industrial fuel-switching capability is expected to contract gradually over the next decade or two in OECD countries generally due to two key factors:

■ Increasingly restrictive laws and regulations concerning industrial plant airborne emissions are likely to limit fuel choices for investments in boilers, furnaces and kilns to natural gas and electricity and preclude the use of fuel oil and coal in many instances. Given that gasoil and LPG are, at current relative prices, generally less competitive with natural gas, the additional cost of installing dual-firing equipment may not be justified in such cases.

■ The displacement of traditional steam boilers (back pressure, pass-out and condensing) with more efficient gas turbine and combine-cycle systems will make dual- or multi-firing less economic because the back-up fuel options are limited to gasoil or LPG. Lower cost heavy fuel oil is typically the back-up fuel for existing dual-fired steam boilers operating on natural gas.

The commercial strategy of gas suppliers will, nonetheless, play a key role. The attractiveness of investment in dual-firing by industrial gas consumers will depend to a large extent on the price differential between firm and interruptible supplies. That differential will, in turn, be driven by the need for additional flexibility in meeting peak demand and the cost of alternative methods (e.g., storage). The greater the need for and the higher the cost of new storage, the more incentive gas suppliers will have to encourage industrial consumers to accept interruptible supplies.

EFFECTS OF GAS SUPPLY DISRUPTIONS ON MARKETS FOR OTHER FUELS

Introduction

This section analyses the effects of possible gas supply disruptions in OECD Member countries on the markets for other fuels, particularly oil products, based on the preceding assessment of fuel switching capability in the industrial/commercial and power sectors. An assessment is made of the extent to which any sudden increase in demand for substitute fuels caused by a disruption to gas supplies might be constrained by existing distribution and logistical capacities, and the likely impact of such demand increases on international oil markets in terms of supply flexibility, trade patterns and price. The analysis is focused on OECD Europe, where the volume increase in demand for substitute fuels under the two central disruption scenarios is quantified.

OECD Europe

Potential Impact of Gas Supply Disruption on Demand for Other Fuels

A country-by-country analysis was made of the volume effects on demand for other fuels in OECD Member countries in Europe based on the two gas supply disruption scenarios defined in the core analysis (see Chapter 6): a total disruption in Russian supplies and, independently, a total disruption in Algerian supplies. No distinction is made between the best and worst case variants of each scenarios since they both assume that all supplies to interruptible customers are cut completely, on the grounds that gas supply companies would seek to conserve gas solely for their firm customers and maintain firm supplies for as long as possible regardless of whether some scope exists for increased supplies from other sources. All OECD Europe countries supplied by Russia and/or Algeria were included in this analysis, namely: Austria, Finland, France, Germany, Italy, Switzerland and Turkey under the Russian disruption scenario; and Belgium, France, Italy and Spain under the Algerian disruption scenario. Countries not supplied by Russia or Algeria are assumed to be unaffected by a curtailment in supplies from either country. The data used was for 1992.

The methodology for estimating the increase in demand in the industrial/commercial sectors for each substitute fuel in the event of gas supplies being cut to interruptible customers is summarised in Figure 7.3. Interruptible demand is broken down according to the primary back-up fuel. Interruptible supplies used as feedstocks are assumed to have no substitute: any curtailment of these supplies would thus result in the shut down of the processing plant. The demand for the substitute fuel in each case takes account of differences in efficiency of the boilers/burners. It has been assumed that on average oil boiler/burners are 3% less efficient and coal boilers/burners 5% less efficient than gas-fired equipment. These calculations were performed for each country, resulting in an estimate of the total volume demand increase for heavy fuel oil, gasoil, LPG, coal and electricity.

For the power generation sector, a slightly different methodology has been used.[1] The figures for the use of back-up fuels in electricity generation were based on 1992 figures for monthly gas input into power generation and were calculated under the assumption that gas supplies to the

---

1. Substitutability of natural gas use in the power sector is discussed in detail in Chapter 5.

power sector are cut completely wherever multi-firing capacity is in place, regardless of contractual arrangements. Substitution by oil products and coal was calculated according to the amount and type of multi-firing capacity in place. No changes in relative prices were assumed for the sake of simplicity. Conversion efficiencies for burning secondary fuels were assumed to be 3 percentage points below those for primary fuels in multi-fired capacity. Due to the small share of gas turbines and CCGTs currently in use, heavy fuel oil was assumed to be the predominant substitute oil product.

Figure 7.3   Methodology for Calculating Effect of Gas Supply Disruption Scenarios on Demand for Other Fuels

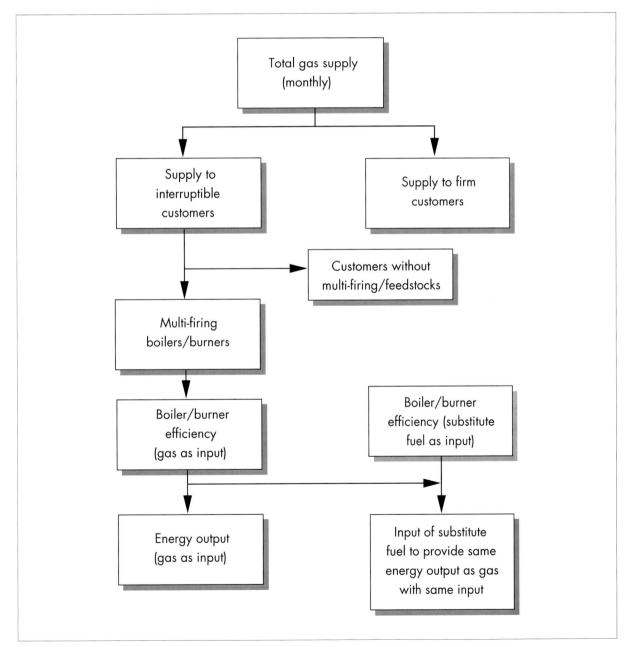

The results for the industrial/commercial and power generation sectors were aggregated to provide estimates of the total increase in demand for each fuel by country in the peak winter month (January) and for a full year (were the disruption to last that long). These estimates, which should only be considered as indicative given the difficulties encountered in compiling country-specific data on fuel-switching capabilities and boiler/burner efficiencies, are summarised in Table 7.7. A more detailed breakdown of heavy fuel oil and gasoil demand by country is shown in Table 7.8.

Table 7.7   Effect of Gas Supply Disruptions on Demand for Other Fuels, OECD Europe (IEA estimates based on 1992 data)

		Units	Peak month*	Year
SCENARIO 1 (Russian Disruption)				
Incremental demand in industrial sector:	Heavy fuel oil	000 tonnes	1777	16477
	Gasoil/diesel	000 tonnes	205	1932
	LPG	000 tonnes	11	103
	Coal	000 tonnes	30	285
	Electricity	GWh	351	3330
Incremental demand in power sector:	Heavy fuel oil	000 tonnes	1144	11949
	Diesel	000 tonnes	0	0
	Coal	000 tonnes	204	1935
Total incremental demand:	Heavy fuel oil	000 tonnes	2921	28426
	Gasoil/diesel	000 tonnes	205	1932
	LPG	000 tonnes	11	103
	Coal	000 tonnes	233	2219
	Electricity	GWh	351	3330
SCENARIO 2 (Algerian Disruption)				
Incremental demand in industrial sector:	Heavy fuel oil	000 tonnes	1127	11131
	Gasoil/diesel	000 tonnes	33	345
	LPG	000 tonnes	0	0
	Coal	000 tonnes	24	231
	Electricity	GWh	341	3232
Incremental demand in power sector:	Heavy fuel oil	000 tonnes	758	8537
	Diesel	000 tonnes	0	0
	Coal	000 tonnes	0	0
Total incremental demand:	Heavy fuel oil	000 tonnes	1885	19668
	Gasoil/diesel	000 tonnes	33	345
	LPG	000 tonnes	0	0
	Coal	000 tonnes	24	231
	Electricity	GWh	341	3232

* January
Source: IEA estimates.

The results of this analysis show that the impact of either a Russian or an Algerian supply disruption would be felt largely in terms of a significant increase in demand for heavy fuel and, to a much lesser extent, gasoil/diesel. The effect of a Russian disruption would be greater than that of an Algerian disruption due to the larger number of countries currently supplied with Russian gas. The impact on fuel oil demand is estimated to amount to over 28 million tonnes

Table 7.8   Effect of Gas Supply Disruptions on Demand for Heavy Fuel Oil and Gasoil/Diesel, OECD Europe
(thousand tonnes, IEA estimates based on 1992 data)

		Heavy fuel oil		Gasoil/diesel	
		Peak month*	**Year**	**Peak month***	**Year**
SCENARIO 1 (Russian Disruption)					
Incremental demand in:	Industry	1777	16477	205	1932
	Power	1144	11949	0	0
	sector	2921	28426	205	1932
	TOTAL				
of which:	Austria	154	1270	1	8
	Finland	135	1190	59	572
	France	544	5149	17	160
	Germany	918	8251	68	582
	Italy	1003	10785	8	77
	Switzerland	18	123	48	495
	Turkey	148	1657	4	38
SCENARIO 2 (Algerian Disruption)					
Incremental demand in:	Industry	1127	11131	33	345
	Power	758	8537	0	0
	sector	1885	19668	33	345
	TOTAL				
of which:	Belgium	212	2397	7	86
	France	544	5149	17	160
	Italy	1003	10785	8	77
	Spain	126	1337	2	22

* January
Source: IEA estimates.

over a full year (an average of around 540 thousand barrels per day) and just under 3 million tonnes in the peak month (660 thousand barrels per day). Table 7.9 shows the estimated incremental demand for heavy fuel oil under each scenario as a percentage of actual demand in 1992. It is clear that the volume demand effects of gas supply disruptions vary considerably from country to country. Under the Russian supply disruption scenario, incremental fuel oil demand is equivalent to almost 30% of total deliveries in OECD Europe. Finland experiences the biggest proportionate increase in fuel oil demand, though the largest absolute increase in demand is in Italy. Under the Algerian supply disruption scenario, Belgium experiences the largest proportionate demand increase.

Incremental demand for gasoil/diesel is small in relation to actual deliveries, even under the Russian gas disruption scenario: the total increase in all seven countries affected amounts to under 2 million tonnes, equivalent to only less than 1% of total OECD European demand in 1992. Finland is the only country that experiences a significant percentage increase in demand (around 20%). All of the increase in gasoil/diesel demand comes from industry, since the amount of natural gas-fired turbine power generation capacity for which diesel could be the back-up fuel was negligible in 1992. The increase in demand for coal, LPG and electricity would be relatively small; even under scenario 1 (Russian disruption), the increase in demand would amount to less than 0.5% for LPG, less than 1% for coal and 0.15% for electricity.

Table 7.9   Incremental Increases in Demand for Heavy Fuel Oil as Proportion of Total Sales (1992)

	Inland consumption (000 tonnes)	Incremental demand (000 tonnes)	Incremental demand (%)
SCENARIO 1 (Russian Disruption)			
Austria	1 981	1 270	64
Finland	1 071	1 190	111
France	7 997	5 149	64
Germany	10 418	8 251	79
Italy	26 129	10 785	41
Switzerland	473	123	26
Turkey	7 295	1 657	23
Other OECD Europe	43 894	-	-
TOTAL	99 258	28 426	29
SCENARIO 2 (Algerian Disruption)			
Belgium	2 966	2 397	81
France	7 997	5 149	64
Italy	26 129	10 785	41
Spain	9 775	1 337	14
Other OECD Europe	52 391	-	-
TOTAL	99 258	19 668	20

Source: IEA estimates.

The large potential incremental demand for oil products in the event of major supply disruptions raises questions about the ability of oil distribution systems to cope. There has never been a major gas supply disruption in any European country, so the flexibility of oil distribution systems has never been tested fully. Few countries have assessed in any detail on a regular basis whether there would be any severe logistical constraints on the delivery of incremental volumes. Such constraints might include bottlenecks or capacity shortages in oil pipelines, insufficient storage capacity at oil and coal distribution terminals and too few road tankers, trucks and railcars. Studies that have been carried out in European countries by oil companies and gas utilities tend to show that sufficient flexibility exists to respond to a demand surge caused by fuel switching by interruptible gas customers. For example, throughputs could be increased significantly at loading terminals and road tankers could be used for two rather one daily delivery round, which is the general practice in many Western European countries. Deliveries of heavy fuel oil to industry have fallen by over 60% from 1980 to 1992 in OECD Europe; while part of the delivery infrastructure has been removed or converted to other activities, there is still significant overcapacity. If necessary, military transport facilities and personnel might also be available. In addition, stocks of oil products held by industrial end-users would help to cushion the immediate impact of any increase in oil demand caused by switching away from gas. No detailed information is available on these stocks in European countries, though anecdotal evidence suggests that they would be sufficient to meet much of the immediate increase in demand for several weeks.

The UK miner's strike in 1984/5 provided a useful case study in how oil product deliveries can be boosted in a sustained manner in emergencies. The loss of supplies of coal from indigenous coal mines led the Central Electricity Generating Board, the monopoly power generating company at that time, to substitute much of its coal inputs for heavy fuel oil by burning a mixture of coal and oil at its coal-fired plants, bringing into service mothballed oil-fired plant and maximising inputs at operating oil plants. Over the 12 months of the strike, heavy fuel oil deliveries to UK power stations totalled 24 million tonnes, compared with around 2.5 million tonnes in 1983 (Ledger and Sallis, 1994). Much of this huge increase in deliveries was effected by road tankers. A sharp increase in tanker freight rates encouraged road haulage and oil distribution companies to bring a large number of old tankers, many of which had not been used for many years, into service.

The relatively modest increase in demand for LPG and coal that would be associated with any type of gas supply disruption would not pose any major difficulties for distributers. There is ample flexibility within existing LPG and coal distribution networks to handle a sudden, modest increase in demand. The increase in electricity demand would also easily be covered within existing reserve capacity margins.

Potential Impact of Gas Supply Disruption on International Oil Markets

The potential impact of the most severe disruption discussed above, the Russian gas supply disruption, is defined as an average demand increase of 540 thousand barrels per day in total oil demand (or 660 thousand barrels per day in the peak month, January) comprised of 500 thousand barrels per day of fuel oil (mainly low sulphur fuel oil) and 40 thousand barrels per day of heating oil. The effect on the oil markets needs to be considered from two perspectives, total oil demand and the demand for individual fuels.

Although the increase in demand would occur only in Europe, as discussed below, the effect of the increase would be felt in the oil markets world-wide and therefore the surge in demand needs to be considered in a global context. In these terms, 540 thousand barrels per day is a fairly small volume representing only 0.8% of global oil demand. The nearest equivalent in terms of a sudden surge in oil demand is a period of extremely cold weather. For example, in January and February 1994 oil demand in North America was on average 1.54 million barrels per day higher than a year earlier and a large part of this can be attributed to the extremely cold weather which occurred on the north eastern seaboard.

An important distinction between a *demand* surge, whether caused by a period of unexpectedly cold weather or a sudden shut down of Russian gas *supplies* and a supply problem such as a cut-back in Middle East crude oil supplies is the time factor. Whereas a demand surge leads to an almost immediate requirement for extra oil products, the physical effect of an equivalent cut-back in Middle East crude oil supplies is not felt for many weeks, reflecting the total number of days in the supply chain. Thus the initial effect on cargo market of a demand surge will normally be more extreme than if the same volume of oil was lost through a crude oil supply disruption. This would particularly be the case in the example of the cut-off in Russian gas supply as fuel oil would be essentially the only product affected. As already discussed, the increase in global oil demand is only 0.8%, but the 500 thousand barrels per day increase in fuel oil represents over 3% of global fuel oil use and nearly a quarter of total European fuel oil demand (including bunker and refinery use). The resultant total fuel oil demand would be the highest level since 1983. Fuel oil prices would surge while the price of lighter products would actually go down either immediately or once new supply patterns were in place (since a continuing increase in refinery margins would not be sustainable). The greatest price increase would clearly be for low sulphur fuel oil (LSFO) since this would be the grade most affected. This effect was illustrated in the UK miner's strike in 1984/85 when power station demand for HSFO increased by 380 thousand barrels per day. The heating oil/HSFO price differential decreased from $7.40 per barrel in July 1983 to $2.10 per barrel in January 1985 with the fuel oil price increasing by $3.80 per barrel and the heating oil price decreasing by $1.50 per barrel. Figure 7.4 illustrates graphically the main likely effects of increased heavy fuel oil demand caused by a gas supply disruption.

Figure 7.4   Impact of Increased Heavy Fuel Demand Caused by Gas Supply Disruption

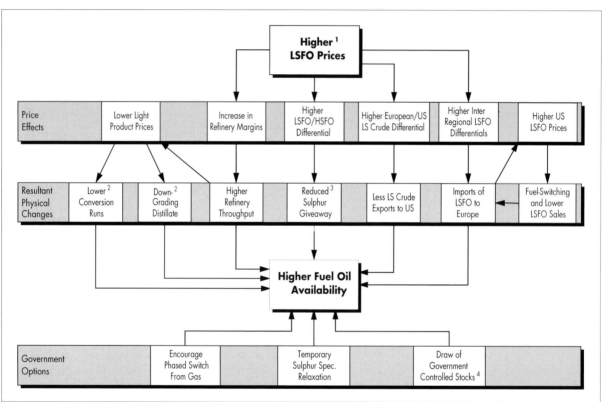

1 Magnitude of rise influenced by pre-disruption fuel oil stock level and distillate (gasoil)/heavy fuel oil spread.
2 Subject to magnitude of distillate/fuel oil spread.
3 To the extent that it exists in base case.
4 To the extent that this can lead to additional LSFO availability by reducing sulphur giveaway.

The extent of the fuel oil price surge is clearly impossible to predict as it would be highly dependent on the oil market position at the moment when the gas supply disruption occurred. As an example, the weather-induced demand surge in North America in January 1994 mentioned above led to increases in weekly average New York Harbour prices of over $4 per barrel on heating oil and $5 per barrel on fuel oil.

The most immediate source of additional oil in the gas supply disruption case would clearly be the drawdown of industry fuel oil stocks. Thus, if the disruption occurred at a time when European fuel oil stocks were at historically high levels and the price differential between light products and fuel oil was also high, the effect on fuel oil prices would be far less than if it had occurred, for example, in December 1994 when fuel oil stocks were low and the average heating oil/LSFO differential was at the lowest level for over seven years.

As in all demand or supply disruptions, the surge in LSFO prices as suppliers attempted to cover the surge in demand, would immediately set in train the necessary steps to meet the potential fuel oil shortfall. The sharp increase in fuel oil prices would lead to an increase in refinery margins in Europe. As a result crude runs (primarily low sulphur crude runs) would be increased, increasing supplies of fuel oil and clean products. The higher refinery margins would simultaneously increase the value of crude in Europe in relation to other regions which would be expected to lead to a reduction in exports of low sulphur crude to the United States from the North Sea and North and West Africa, thus making available the crude oils needed for the increased European low sulphur crude refinery throughputs.

In addition to the narrowing of the distillate/fuel oil spread, there would be a significant increase in the LSFO/HSFO spread (assuming there were no temporary relaxations of fuel oil sulphur specifications). This would provide an incentive to increase LSFO production at the expense of HSFO where there was originally sulphur giveaway (for example at a refinery where the LSFO/HSFO price differential had previously been insufficient to justify a marine freight differential involved in replacing low sulphur crude with high sulphur crude). The lowering of the heating oil/fuel oil spread could be expected to make marginal conversion capacity unattractive (as in the 1984 UK miner's strike) and conversion runs would be decreased, again increasing fuel oil availability. Depending on how tight the fuel oil supply position was at the beginning of the disruption and how the heating oil/LSFO spread developed, some downgrading of distillate to fuel oil (viscosity giveaway) could become attractive. This could not only increase fuel oil supply but also assist in meeting fuel oil sulphur requirements.

While it would probably be technically possible to meet the surge in demand wholly from European refineries, in practice, it would be more economic to cover part of the requirement by imports. The higher fuel oil prices in Europe would increase the price differentials between Europe and other regions, thus leading to increased net imports of fuel oil and further increasing European supplies. This would increase fuel oil prices in other regions though not sufficiently to make the export of fuel oil to Europe unattractive. In general, it can be assumed that the price effects in Europe (the lower heating oil/fuel oil spread and the higher LSFO/HSFO spread) would occur throughout the global oil market. In simple terms, the effects would be more muted as distance from Europe and hence logistics costs increased, but the resultant price signals would contribute to the increase in supply of low sulphur crude and LSFO to Europe. One example of possible effects of the higher global LSFO prices might be *increased* use of natural gas in the United States (assuming this was not already maximised) at the expense of LSFO, thus effectively using natural gas in the United States to overcome a natural gas shortfall in Europe through the mechanism of inter-regional LSFO movements. A recent example of this type of readjustment of inter-regional flows to assist in meeting a surge in demand in response to changes in price differentials was in January 1994. The sharply higher demand in North America induced by the extremely cold weather resulted in the differential between New York Harbour and Rotterdam heating oil prices swinging from minus $2 per barrel in early December to plus $2 per barrel in early January. As a result, shipments of distillate from the United States to Europe in December 1993 were replaced by shipments in the other direction in January 1994.

In the event of a prolonged suspension of Russian gas supplies, the initial sharp changes in price differentials would tend to diminish as the increased supplies of fuel oil and low sulphur crude were made available in Europe and a new "equilibrium" was established. The price differentials at this stage would be dependent on a variety of factors, notably the amount of sulphur giveaway prior to the gas supply disruption and how and when the increased global crude requirements to make the additional 540 thousand barrels per day of oil products were made available. Theoretically, if there were adequate sulphur giveaway prior to the crisis the optimal way to meet the additional fuel oil requirement would be to increase heavy crude production to make more barrels and to replace some light crude production by heavy crude (e.g., increasing Arabian Heavy production at the expense of Arabian Light) to make fuel oil at the expense of light products. If this could be done to the extent required, no reduction in refinery conversion runs would be needed. However, it is unlikely that sufficient sulphur giveaway would exist and, in addition, heavying up the crude mix would be the reverse of Saudi Arabia's current strategy. In practice it seems likely that any available spare OPEC low sulphur crude capacity (e.g., in Nigeria) would be used and any scope to delay North Sea maintenance work safely would be considered. The remaining crude shortfall would be expected to be primarily made up with higher sulphur, heavier crude. The net effect would continue to be higher LSFO/HSFO and lower heating oil/LSFO differentials than before the cut-off of Russian gas supplies occurred. However, as already mentioned, the magnitude of the changes in differentials would be much smaller than in the first few days of the crisis, reflecting the various steps which had been taken to adjust the global supply demand balance.

Oil transportation would also clearly be affected. Marine fuel oil transportation would increase sharply, leading to an increase in the relevant freight rates. Although the volume of fuel oil demand would be no greater than in the early 1980's, rationalisation of the fuel oil distribution system has taken place since then and it is possible that in some cases there could be problems in delivering to customers the full additional volumes by road or rail.

As already discussed, if fuel oil stocks were at low levels at the time of the gas supply disruption, the initial effect on oil markets of a prompt increase of 500 thousand barrels per day of fuel oil demand could be severe. Governments would have various options to reduce the severity of the impact if they so wished. One would be to encourage the phased switch over of interruptible contracts, providing the balancing natural gas volumes through gas stock drawdown. However, this would clearly reduce gas stocks and could even lead to the subsequent failure to supply firm gas customers if the gas supply disruption was sufficiently long. A second option would be to take the opportunity of higher fuel oil prices to drawdown some government-controlled fuel oil stocks in countries where these exist, replacing them with crude oil or lighter products, incidentally improving security in the case of a subsequent oil supply crisis. A third option would be to consider some temporary relaxation of fuel oil sulphur specifications. The appropriateness of adopting any of these options would depend on the oil market situation at the time.

North America

In view of the diversity of the sources of gas supply in North America, we have not attempted to define a specific gas disruption scenario to quantify the volume effect on demand for alternative fuels. Any major supply disruption, whatever the cause, would probably be of very short duration. The extensive gas storage and highly developed pipeline system would also limit the effect of a disruption on gas deliverability. Given the extensive fuel-switching capacity in industry and in power generation in the United States and Canada (much greater than in Europe), a sudden loss of gas supply in any region would quickly lead to an increase in demand for LPG, gasoil, heavy fuel oil and coal. There could also be a 'knock-on' effect on the demand for condensate and naphtha as competing petrochemical feedstocks to LPG. The precise demand effect would depend on the length of the disruption, the level of oil stocks held by end-users at the start of the disruption, the source of the disruption and the regions affected.

Past experience of sudden oil product demand surges suggests that the North American oil product distribution system generally could cope with a demand surge induced by a gas supply disruption, though bottlenecks could occur in some parts of the system. Difficulties are likely to be most acute when a major gas supply disruption in North America is caused by extreme weather or a natural disaster, which could also disrupt oil distribution at least temporarily (e.g., due to closure of distribution terminals or roads). The extreme cold weather in the eastern United States in January 1994, for example, caused some temporary distribution problems mainly due to frozen rivers and blocked roads, though stocks of oil products held by industrial companies and utilities helped to cushion the effect of these disruptions (DOE, 1995).

The impact of a North American gas supply disruption on international oil markets would depend on the magnitude of the demand increase, the pattern of demand across the product range and the extent to which the affected regional markets are able to be supplied economically by imported products and supplies from other regions. Nonetheless, a major disruption to gas supplies affecting oil demand in one region would almost certainly impact on oil prices throughout North America and internationally. Since the incremental oil demand would likely be less focused on heavy fuel oil and more evenly spread across the product barrel (LPG, distillate and jet kerosene) than would be the case in Europe, demand could more easily be met by simply increasing refinery throughputs assuming sufficient spare refining capacity is available. Increasing throughputs would probably be most difficult in summer when capacity utilisation is typically at its peak.

OECD Pacific

As with North America, we have not attempted to define specific gas disruption scenarios for Japan, Australia or New Zealand to quantify the volume effect on demand for alternative fuels since considerable supply-side flexibility exists in most cases. Furthermore, the effect of any major supply disruption on gas deliverability and demand for other fuels would probably be more regionalised than in Europe or North America, where the gas distribution networks are more interconnected. In Japan, oil distribution systems combined with oil stocks held by utilities and industrial companies are thought to be adequate to cope with a surge in demand that would be associated with the loss of part of Japan's gas supply (e.g., through the disruption to LNG imports). Although we have not analysed in detail the oil distribution infrastructure in Australia and New Zealand, there is no reason to believe that the distribution system generally could not cope with a surge in demand caused by a gas supply disruption, though bottlenecks could occur in some parts of the system - particularly in the early stages of a supply disruption.

SUMMARY AND CONCLUSIONS

Our analysis of fuel switching capability in the industrial and power generation sectors shows that considerable flexibility exists in most OECD countries for gas to be substituted at very short notice for other fuels - mainly heavy fuel oil and gasoil - in the event of a gas supply disruption. Our detailed analysis of the volume effects of a major supply disruption in OECD Europe suggests that while the incremental demand for oil products would be significant, in most cases it would probably not exceed existing distribution capacities. The effect of a Russian gas supply disruption would be greater than that of an Algerian disruption due to the larger volume of gas involved and the larger number of countries currently supplied with Russian gas: the impact on fuel oil demand based on 1992 data is estimated to amount to around 28 million tonnes over a full year (an average of around 540 thousand barrels per day) - equivalent to just under 30% of total deliveries in 1992. Taking into account stocks of heavy fuel oil and gasoil held by end-users, it is likely that the oil distribution system could handle such a surge in demand - even were it to last for many months.

In the power sector, the increased share of CCGTs may affect the markets for substitution fuels in a favourable way. Whereas the overall increase in the demand for oil products from the power sector appears manageable, the emphasis on heavy fuel oil for power generation could create supply problems depending on available stocks.

At present there is thought to be sufficient spare capacity within the global refining industry in general to deal reasonably comfortably with the incremental demand for oil products induced by a major gas supply disruption such as the total loss of Russian or Algerian gas exports to OECD Europe. A sharp increase in heavy fuel oil prices as suppliers attempted to cover the surge in demand - especially for low sulphur fuel - would immediately provoke market responses to meet the potential fuel oil shortfall. The extent of the fuel oil price change would be highly dependent on the oil market position at the time of the gas supply disruption. Increased refinery runs in Europe - induced by higher fuel oil prices and refinery margins - would probably meet only part of the incremental demand, with imports accounting for the rest. The ease with which a sudden increase in demand could be met in the future will depend critically on the amount of spare refining capacity and refiners' flexibility in responding to a sudden shift in oil product demand patterns. Although it is difficult to predict the long term availability of oil and global refining capacity, the shift towards light distillates and natural gas liquids suggests that a higher share of CCGTs will reduce problems with the product spread which refineries face at present, and improve the possibility of increasing crude runs and producing the required amount of backup fuels.

ABBREVIATIONS AND CONVERSION FACTORS

ABM   Aggregators, Brokers and Marketers

ABU   Abu Dhabi

ACQ   Annual Contract Quantity

AGA   American Gas Association

ALG   Algeria

AUS   Australia

bar   Unit of pressure: 1 bar = 0.9869 standard atmosphere = 750 mm mercury

bcm   billion cubic metres

BG   British Gas

BOL   Bolivia

BRU   Brunei-Darussalam

CAN   Canada

CCGT   Combined-Cycle Gas Turbine

CIF   Cost, Insurance, Freight

CIS   Commonwealth of Independent States

CNG   Compressed Natural Gas

DCQ   Daily Contract Quantity

DEN   Denmark

DOE   Department of Energy, United States

EIA   Energy Information Agency of the DOE

ENEL   Ente Nazionale per l'Énergia Elettrica, State-owned Electricity Utility, Italy

EU   European Union

FERC   Federal Electricity Regulatory Commission, United States

FGD   Flue Gas Desulphurisation

FOB   Free on Board

GdF   Gaz de France

GER   Germany

GFU   Gassforhandlingsutvalget, Norwegian Gas Negotiating Committee

GJ   Gigajoule = 10^6 joules

GW   Gigawatts

IEA   International Energy Agency

IGCC	Integrated Coal Gasification Combined-Cycle
IND	Indonesia
INGAA	Interstate Natural Gas Association of America
JNOC	Japan National Oil Company
LDC	Local Distribution Company
LIB	Libya
LNG	Liquified Natural Gas
LPG	Liquified Petroleum Gas
MAL	Malaysia
mcm	million cubic metres
MCS	Minimum Conditions of Supply
MEX	Mexico
MITI	Ministry of Industry and Trade, Japan
Mbtu	million metric British thermal units
MOA	Mandatory Open Access
MW	Megawatt = 10^6 Watts
NAFTA	North American Free Trade Agreement
NEB	National Energy Board, Canada
NETH	The Netherlands
NOR	Norway
NOVA	Canadian Pipeline Company, Alberta
OECD	Organisation for Economic Cooperation and Development
Ofgas	Office of Gas Supply, UK
OFO	Operational Flow Orders
ÖMV	Austrian Oil and Gas Company
REC	Regional Electricity Company
SEP	Dutch Electricity Generating Board
SHR	Sharjah
SNAM	Italian Gas Company owned by ENI
TCPL	TransCanada Pipeline
TOP	Take-or-Pay
TPA	Third Party Access
TPES	Total Primary Energy Supply
UCPTE	Union pour la Co-ordination de la Production et du Transport de l'Électricité
UK	United Kingdom
USA	United States of America
WACOG	Weighted Average Cost of Gas

ANNEX 1

STRUCTURAL CHANGE IN THE EUROPEAN GAS MARKET:
Implications for Industry and the Security of Supply

by

Oystein Noreng

Gas Markets Under Pressure

The established order in the European gas markets is under increasing pressure. The question is no longer when the historical structures of West European gas trading will give way, but when, in what circumstances, into what and with what sequence of events. Pressure is mounting from political authorities, first of all the European Commission pushing for transparency and competition, and increasingly from large consumers desiring competition and lower end user prices. This is especially the case in Germany. In brief, it seems fairly clear that the pattern of gas trading on the European continent will change, but it is less clear in what direction.

The North American pattern with unbundling and mandatory third party access is an important reference, but it represents only one of many possible outcomes to Europe's gas problems. Contrary to the situation of North America, gas supplies to continental Europe are concentrated on four major sellers, Algeria, the Netherlands, Norway and Russia, two of whom are external. In all four cases, the sales of gas are handled by a single company, for which a giant gas field plays a pivotal role. Algerian gas sales are handled by Sonatrach, a state owned gas monopoly, whose major source of gas is Hassi R'mel. Dutch gas sales are monopolised by Gasunie, owned conjointly by the Dutch state, Exxon and Shell, with the major source of gas at Groningen. Norwegian gas sales are handled by GFU, the gas negotiating board, dominated by Statoil, the national oil company, dependent upon the Troll field. Russian gas sales are monopolised by Gazprom, entirely owned by the state, and whose major source of gas is Urengoi.

With only four large sellers, the continental European gas market is dominated by an oligopoly. The counterpiece has been made up by gas purchasing monopolies, monopsonies, historically in the United Kingdom, still in the major continental countries. On the continent, gas sales from outside have historically encountered a single purchasing consortium, a monopsony, with German Ruhrgas as the key element, joined by Gaz de France, Gasunie of the Netherlands and Distrigaz of Belgium. Historically, the relationship between these few gas traders has been marked by non-confrontational bargaining rather than by outright competition and conflict. The major advantage of the historical market structure was the ability to secure long-term deals for large volumes on take-or-pay contracts. Recent examples are the gas contracts from Troll and Urengoi. This market structure combined security of supply for the consumers with secure outlets for producers. The major disadvantage was the high cost. As mutual monopolies usually do, the European gas giants shared the economic rent. One effect was an unusually high profit in gas transportation. This led to high gas prices for consumers, while depressing prices for producers, compromising the economics of new gas supplies. This was the European gas scene in the old world, until the fall of the Berlin Wall and the collapse of the Soviet Union in 1989-1991.

Subsequently, everything has changed. The new Russia has expressed dissatisfaction with the low income from the traditional arrangement for selling her gas, especially in the German market. By changing partners, Russia has introduced an element of competition into the German gas market. In the United Kingdom the monopoly has been brought to a close, but the government seems to intervene directly in the market. In Germany rival groups currently compete for markets and supplies although there are strong incentives for understanding.

Limited reserves mean that any incremental gas demand on the European continent has to be covered from outside, i.e., from Algeria, Norway, Russia or new, distant sources. Due to reserve depletion, dependence upon outside supplies is increasing even with stagnant demand. Rising dependence upon outside sources in the longer run means rising supply costs, essentially because of longer transportation distances. Giant fields with low extraction costs imply fairly stable marginal costs at the well-head. Hence the cost of gas transportation, eventually also gas transit, rather than that of gas extraction is the key problem for continental Europe[1]. Gas transportation costs are essentially a function of capital investment, linked to distance and volume, the load factor and merchant profits. Fixed costs are predominant in the overall cost of transporting gas, but pipeline construction costs seem to be between fifty and one hundred per cent higher in continental Europe than in comparable densely populated areas in the United States[2]. Discount rates and assumptions about capital life significantly influence cost figures[3]. In gas transportation economies of scale are considerable, because an increase of pipeline diameter yields a disproportionate capacity increase[4]. The unit cost of gas transportation is also heavily dependent upon the load factor. Load figures for the European gas grid are generally kept confidential, but it is a legitimate question to what extent pipeline companies in a monopoly or semi-monopoly position have strong incentives to raise the load factor in order to reduce unit transportation costs. Finally, even if figures are not readily available, it seems that profits in gas transportation in many cases are higher than in gas extraction. Indeed, pipeline companies that are also gas merchants seem to enjoy higher than usual profits once their investment has been depreciated.

Self-sufficiency, based on a large number of smaller fields, provides the gas market of the United Kingdom with a supply structure more similar to that of North America. Short distances mean low transportation costs, even if extraction costs at small fields may be high. Hence for the UK the main economic problem related to gas is rising cost at the well-head, not in transportation. Politically, the problem is to extend the duration of self-sufficiency. For infrastructure reasons,

1. This is the conclusion of a recent study carried out by L'Observatoire Méditerrannéen de l'Énergie for the International Energy Agency. (See *Oil, Gas and Coal Supply Outlook*, Paris 1995, OECD/IEA, p. 102 ff.)
2. The German Wintershall Midal pipeline and the US Tenneco New England pipeline have roughly comparable dimensions and capacities, but the construction cost per km and mm of the German line are about 80 per cent above that of the US line. The reason may be stricter environmental rules in Germany, more infrastructure to cross or a less competitive construction industry. Due to more compressors, the technical cost of transporting gas in the German case seems to about 50 per cent above the US case.
3. *Oil, Gas and Coal Supply Outlook*, op.cit., p. 93.
4. Jerome D. Davies, Blue Gold, London 1984, George Allen and Unwin, p. 23 ff.

the small UK gas suppliers are currently confined to the domestic market. Potentially they could have a considerable impact upon the gas market of Northwest continental Europe weakening the traditional oligopoly in European gas supplies. Limited reserves and rising well-head costs means that the impact eventually could be of a fairly short duration.

The historical system of gas trading in Europe can be described as de facto mutual monopolies either under government ownership or government guarantee. The reality of monopoly trading has been ever present, in spite of formal differences and apparent diversity in organisation. Indeed, the difference between the French vertical integration and the German vertical control has been more formal than real. The model was in many ways the electricity industry. In order to foster gas trade, the gas merchant companies, which were also transporters, were either by law or in practice given exclusive rights. At the same time, local gas distribution has also been exempt from competition.

The reason has been that gas trade, from production through transportation and storage to distribution, is a highly risky business in its early stage, requiring huge investment at the various stages. Indeed, a gas chain overwhelmingly consists of capital, meaning high fixed cost and low variable cost. This means that a gas market usually goes through a development of distinct stages, dependent upon the depreciation of the infrastructure. At a first stage, before the infrastructure has been depreciated, marginal cost is rising, risk is high and return on investment low. A guaranteed monopoly, either through public ownership or legal exemptions from the general rules of competition, is often seen as an appropriate way to attract capital to the gas industry and to secure supplies to consumers. Hence, concerns for security of supply and industry profits have not been only compatible, but mutually supportive.

Subsequently, in a second stage, after the infrastructure has been depreciated and markets and supplies have been established, marginal cost declines quickly, risk is reduced and return on investment rises significantly, at the same time as incentives to reduce costs are limited. Prices are usually not transparent and transportation cost indistinguishable from merchant profits. Consistently high profits and low risk invite both criticism from gas users and competition. Security of supply becomes less of an issue as new suppliers enter the market.

In a third stage, the monopoly system comes under increasing attack because of high profits and lack of flexibility. The solution to supply security is found in competition rather than in monopolies. Even at this stage, capital requirements represent formidable barriers to entry, meaning that in the gas market, a *de facto or de jure* monopoly will be replaced by an oligopoly, unless political authorities intervene to enforce competition, as in North America. In any case, this is the stage of rising political and institutional risk.

The dynamics of the development of a gas market can be shown by the table below.

Table 1 Stages of a Gas Market

STAGE	Infrastructure	Marginal cost	Profits	Risk
Establishment	Not yet depreciated	Rising	Low	High
Established	Depreciated	Falling	High	Low
Under Attack	Further investment	Rising	Falling	Rising

Rising Institutional Risk

The historical system has been marked by gas trading in large volumes, covering large areas and long time horizons, based on *take-or-pay*, TOP, deals. Traditionally, European gas trade, at least across borders, was a business of a small number of companies, sellers, buyers or transporters, each with a monopoly position in its area of business. Merchant and transporter margins have been substantial, also offering producers stable outlets and low risk, but with comparatively low returns on investment, at least with present low oil prices.

Prospects are that monopoly positions will become obsolete in one way or another and that consequently European gas trade will be disaggregated, with smaller deals, covering smaller areas and shorter time horizons. There is the evident market risk of competition, by newcomers investing in parallel pipelines to the extent that is legally feasible. At this stage, the political risk is considerable for all parties in the gas business, but perhaps especially so for the established suppliers. If the historical system of reciprocal monopolies is to crumble, it is of a critical importance for bargaining positions whether competition at first will be introduced in gas sales or in gas purchasing, or simultaneously at both levels, as well as the form of competition.

The main elements of political and institutional risk are shown in the table below.

ELEMENTS OF POLITICAL RISK IN THE GAS MARKET:

1) **Third party access to pipelines**

2) **Unbundling, functional disaggregation of pipeline companies**

3) **Regulated transportation tariffs**

4) **Competition among producers, dependent upon third party access**

5) **Gas-to-gas competition to final users**

6) **Horizontal and/or vertical deregulation of the gas industry**

7) **New taxes in conjunction with one or more of the above measures**

Third party access to pipelines generally means that the merchants and transporters no longer can monopolise gas sales in their historical markets, but have to transport the gas of potential competitors[5]. The concept of third party access needs to be differentiated, as the impact is conditioned by the supply structure. It could take the form of pipeline companies **voluntarily** selling free capacity. The effect could be a supplement to existing deliveries, but not necessarily compromising price stability. In the market this could mean an oligopoly with a leading firm able to keep discipline. Third party access could also take the form of a **negotiated use of capacity**. Likewise, the effect would be a supplement to existing deliveries and an oligopoly in the market, not necessarily at the expense of stability, as a few large firms would be able to co-ordinate supplies. Alternatively, third party access could take the form of the disposal of a **mandatory part of capacity**, e.g., also for smaller UK producers. The effect in the market could be an alternative to existing deliveries and competition at a lower level of aggregation, with price

---

5. Jonathan Stern, *Third Party Access in European Gas Industries*, London 1993, Royal Institute of International Affairs, p. 21 ff.

transparency, most probably compromising price stability. Finally, third party access could take the form of a public regulation, accompanied by a disaggregation of existing deliveries. The effect would be competition at a much lower level of aggregation and price transparency and consequently less price stability.

Table 2   Forms of Third Party Access

Form	Organisational Effect	Market Effect	Price to End Users
Voluntary free capacity	Supplement to existing deliveries	Oligopoly with a leading firm	Stable prices
Negotiated	Supplement to existing deliveries	Oligopoly	Fairly stable prices
Mandatory part of capacity	Alternative to existing deliveries	Competition at a lower level of aggregation, price transparency	Falling prices
Public regulation	Split-up of existing deliveries	Competition at a much lower level of aggregation, price transparency	Falling and unstable prices

Unbundling or functional disaggregation of pipeline companies means that integrated gas companies are forcibly broken up into different companies in gas production, transportation and distribution. An unbundling of the gas industry would mean a politically enforced separation of the production, transmission, storage and distribution functions, in principle with a symmetry of competition at the various stages of the process. If symmetrically enforced, the effect would be transparent prices, probably a volatile market and a radical disaggregation of the trade, with considerable price risks. There would be more competition at all stages. The enhanced risk for producers would mean higher requirements for return on investment. For consumers, a disaggregation of supplies would mean a risk diversification.

Regulated transportation tariffs means that governments or supra-national European Union, EU, authorities decide the prices and returns on gas transportation, upon examination or assumption of costs. Regulated transportation tariffs would remove uncertainty and price risk from gas transmission, but enhance the price risk for producers and consequently lead to a requirement for a higher return on capital invested upstream. The immediate effect would be direct trade between producers and end users or final sellers. For the consumers, the effect of a disaggregated supply pattern would be risk diversification.

Competition among producers would mean breaking up the present gas monopolies, especially in the Netherlands and Norway, subject to EU legislation[6]. Competition among producers would enforce the role of pipelines, disaggregating contracts from producers, leading to lower producer prices, enhanced price risk for producers and a higher return on capital required. For the consumers, also in this case, the effect of a disaggregated supply pattern would be risk diversification.

---

6. Even if Norway is not a member of the European Union, the country is a member of the European Economic Area, essentially subject to EU rules and legislation. Norway has accepted the EU licensing directive, affecting its upstream oil and gas activities.

Gas-to-gas competition would mean that final users could choose between competing suppliers. Gas-to-gas competition at the end-user level would weaken the role of pipelines, but could also lead to a disaggregation of supplies, especially if smaller UK suppliers get access to the continental market. Possibly, the disaggregation could lead to a spot market and a futures market for gas. Lower prices to end users could mean enhanced risk for producers, requiring a higher return on capital. Again, for the consumers, the effect of a disaggregated supply pattern would be risk diversification.

Horizontal and/or vertical deregulation is a more complex issue. Horizontal and/or vertical deregulation would give the gas industry the ability to expand into new areas and new businesses, so that gas producers could invest i transportation and distribution and the merchant companies could invest upstream. A horizontal deregulation would lead to a restructuring of local distribution companies in countries such as Germany, possibly leading to an oligopoly. In the market, the effect would be larger contracts, lower prices to end users, less producer risk and lower return on investment required. For the consumers, the effect could be a diversification of supplies and risk Stronger incentives to investment would reduce the supply risk.

A vertical deregulation would lead to enhanced integration, both larger contracts and more trading of gas within company groups. More direct trading between producers and consumers could lead to lower prices to end users. Direct trading in large volumes would reduce risk for producers and eventually imply a lower return required on investment. Also in stronger incentives to investment would reduce the supply risk.

A horizontal and vertical deregulation could lead to an integrated oligopoly or monopoly. The effect would be larger contracts and lower price to end users. Less producer risk could lead to lower return required on upstream investment.

Table 3   Effects on Company Structure of Horizontal and Vertical Deregulation (Example: Germany)

	Horizontal barriers	**Horizontal deregulation**
Vertical barriers	Unbundling, reciprocal and local monopolies	Unbundling into reciprocal monopolies
Vertical deregulation	Integrated monopolies	Integrated oligopoly or monopoly

New taxes represent a persistent risk in conjunction with one or more of the above measures.. If for example competition at any level should put a downward pressure on final gas prices, there would be a strong temptation for consumer country governments to capture most or all of the price decline by new taxes. New taxes would raise the buffer between producers and consumers, weakening the competitiveness of gas. The effect would be higher prices to end-users, lower and less stable prices to producers, implying a higher return required on investment. Weaker incentives to investment could lead to a deteriorating supply security for consumers.

Any such measure represents a potential threat to established producers, transporters and distributors of gas, if not to all of them, not the least because their effects are largely untried in a European context. The various measures discussed above could have a limited impact on the market to the extent that the oligopolistic supply picture is retained. To the extent that smaller UK suppliers get access to the continental market, the different measures of liberalisation could have a more profound impact.

In the end, the risks of unstable prices and eroding market shares for the established sellers should be weighed against the potential benefits of a more open and more flexible gas market, with gas gaining in share of the overall energy market, especially in market segments able to pay high prices, such as e.g., power generation. The North American and UK experiences of liberalisation through unbundling and third party access seem to have favoured consumers more than producers, at least in the short term. The market impact seems to be that competition first drives gas prices down, subsequently that low prices lead to rising gas demand, and in a third stage that rising demand leads to new price rises. The United States apparently has gone through the whole cycle, with the UK now finding itself in the second stage, with competition driving prices down. Especially in the United States the point of departure was detailed government regulation, not monopoly trading. There is an evident political risk that Europe will attempt to imitate a US system of hyper-regulation, in spite of a different supply position. This is not the only feasible outcome for Europe. In both the United States and in the UK intermediary margins, i.e. transportation costs and merchant profits seen to have come down substantially. In both cases enhanced flexibility has helped gas gaining market share from other energy sources. These issues remain important for Europe.

Driving Forces   The historical European system of gas trading is under attack from several corners. The key element of change is demand for energy in general. As the European economies grow and become technologically more advanced, with employment increasingly in services, the bulk of energy demand moves from industry to the residential and commercial sector. More than a volume growth, this represents a qualitative change in the sense that energy demand becomes decentralised on a large number of consumers with individual requirements and load patterns, taking out a rising part of their energy consumption in the form of electricity. Such a heterogeneous market is more difficult to service by a monopoly than a more homogeneous market with the bulk of demand in industry with more even load patterns. At least at intermediary stages, technical progress enhances competition between the various sources of energy, leading to a progressive integration of energy markets. The requirement is flexibility, as technical potential for substitution and competition precedes the institutional arrangements. Hence with increasing substitution, the problem is increasingly how to meet an overall demand for energy rather than the demand for specific energy sources. This has profound implications for the security of supply. Within this overall picture, there are rigidities, especially with motor fuel in the transportation sector, which will not be discussed in this context.

Electricity deserves a special mention. In OECD Europe as a whole, electricity demand seems to be rising at 2.5-3 per cent annually, more or less regardless of short-term economic conditions. To some extent the rising power demand represents a substitution away from other fuels, to some extent incremental energy demand. The major exception is Germany, where consumer electricity prices have not (yet?) come down. Hence Europe faces a rising problem of capital investment and organisation in the electricity industry. As the demand growth essentially is in the residential and commercial sector, the load curve becomes increasingly uneven, at the same time as the price elasticity of demand tends to decrease. Flexibility against this backdrop becomes increasingly important. Short lead times represent a major advantage for gas turbines in power generation, as opposed to the long lead times and rigidity of nuclear power and large coal fired thermal power station. The investment need represents a strong argument for opening the electricity market to industrial generators. Indeed, the argument now seems to be less on the principle than on the form, whether through open access to the grid or a single buyer. For industrial power generators, as for smaller power companies,. the low capital cost of gas turbines represents another strong argument in favour of gas in power generation.

The UK precedent is important in this respect, as competition in the electricity market has strongly favoured gas in power generation. In continental Europe, as has been the case in the UK, chances are that a liberalisation of the electricity market will set an irresistible precedent for the gas market. The issue seems less to be the principle of more open markets than the form and the sequence of measures. The overall prerogatives of openness and competition, prevalent world-wide as in Europe, reinforce practical considerations in the same direction.

In Europe, the looming regional imbalance in gas trade constitutes another argument in favour of more open markets and slimmer intermediary margins. Prospects are in the mid 1990s that North-west Europe, including the UK, whose gas markets are mature, if not saturated, will be flooded with more gas from the North Sea, eventually also from Russia, leading to depressed prices unless the oligopoly acts efficiently. By contrast, Southern Europe, whose gas markets are still growing strongly, risk insufficient supplies from potentially more unreliable sources. Hence the issue of supply security is not identical in these two parts of Europe. Overcoming this cleavage will demand both incremental investment in infrastructure and lower intermediary margins.

Changing Structures in Gas Trade

The prospect of rising gas demand and rising import dependency, with gas having to be transported ever longer distances, distinguishes the continental European market from the US or the UK one. For continental Europe, the issue is simultaneously to reduce intermediary margins and to maintain strong groups which can organise and finance investment in long-term long-distance supplies.

Presently, there are multiple and partly contradictory tendencies in shaping the gas market. Concurrently with the tendencies of opening the market to more competition, there are trends in the direction of vertical and horizontal integration. These differing political tendencies correspond to different requirements. Indeed, gas policy priorities vary according to circumstances, the key variable being the maturity of the market and the import dependence. In an immature gas market with low imports, priorities are to develop production and infrastructure and to maintain production. This is the situation in e.g., Denmark or Ireland. In an immature market with high imports, priorities are to secure supplies and diversify risk. This is the case in e.g., Greece, Portugal or Spain. In a mature market with low imports, the priority is cost effectiveness. This is the case e.g., in the UK. In a mature market with high imports, priorities are to also to secure cost effectiveness, but at the same time to hedge bargaining power and diversify risk. This is the case in France and Germany.

Table 4 Gas Policy Priorities under Different Circumstances

	Immature market	Mature market
Low imports	Develop production and infrastructure	Improve cost effectiveness, maintain production
High imports	Secure supplies, diversify risk	Improve cost effectiveness, secure bargaining power and supplies, diversify risk

Different priorities require different policy instruments. In an immature market with low imports, monopoly and integration could be appropriate tools, with .high imports, centralisation of purchases and monopoly. In a mature market with low imports, appropriate instruments could be decentralisation and competition through a mandatory TPA, public regulation of transport tariffs and a functional split-up. In a mature market with high imports, the suitable instruments could be a controlled decentralisation, through an oligopoly, deregulation and integration. as well as controlled competition through a negotiated TPA.

Table 5 Potential Gas Policy Instruments

	Immature market	Mature market
Low imports	Monopoly and integration	Decentralisation and competition through a mandatory TPA, public regulation of transport tariffs, functional split-up
High imports	Centralisation and monopoly	Controlled decentralisation (oligopoly), deregulation and integration. competition through a negotiated TPA

The diversity of situations in Europe makes a uniform gas regime hard to imagine, at least in the short or medium term. On the other hand, a wave of change is imaginable, where reforms commencing e.g., with the electricity sector in one continental country after a few years has profound repercussions on the gas industry in other countries. The driving forces is the need for industry and other businesses to compete on fairly equal terms. Even if energy at the outset was excluded from the general competition rules of the EU, it is hard to imagine that it will remain so forever.

Against this backdrop, some kind of negotiated TPA seems more feasible on the continent than unbundling. Indeed, integration seems to be in vogue to overcome supply and market risk. In the longer run, secure outlets are as important as secure supplies. Even with a mandatory TPA, gas producers with interests in distribution networks or power stations will have an advantage over those who are not in such a position. Concurrently, gas distributors and power companies with upstream interests will have an advantage over those without upstream interests, other factors being equal. Hence, consumers served by distributors linked to producers are likely to enjoy a higher degree of supply security than others.

As for the transactions, the critical factor will be the eventual access of smaller UK suppliers to the continental market. Without such an access, the spot market for gas will most likely remain a UK phenomenon, continental gas deals remaining fairly aggregated. With such an access, however, a spot market and eventually a futures market are likely to emerge in the continent.

A spot market could be strongly influenced by an effective oligopoly in spite of marginally important small scale traders. A futures market is more troublesome, as it would essentially be a paper market, trading in options, where physical supply security does not count. Hence a futures market could compromise the security of supply by deterring investment through low prices based on anticipations and appearances. The capital requirements, the lead times and the rigidity of transportation make the gas markets much less flexible than the oil market. Hence a futures market, linked to a spot market where disaggregated UK supplies had a key part, could give short-term price signals quite contrary to the long-term trend in supply costs due to rising transportation distances.

Challenges to the Industry

The continental gas industry faces two sets of challenges: how to safeguard the current deals and how to position for a more open market in the future? The various forms of gas market opening would have different effects on the *take-or-pay* contracts dominating the present supply picture. A functional split-up and regulation would mean that historical TOP contracts would have to renegotiated with new buyers, leading to disaggregation of deals. Eventual new TOP contracts would be disaggregated. By contrast, a deregulation and integration would lead to an adaptation to a new framework for existing TOP deals, possibly transferring economic rent from the transporters to the producers. There would be continued incentives for new TOP deals.

Table 6   Third Party Access and Take-or-Pay Contracts

Form	Effect on existing contracts	Effect on new contracts
Voluntary free capacity	Little	Continued basis
Negotiated	Limited	Continued basis
Mandatory part of capacity	Weaken	Weaken
Public regulation	Undermine	Difficult

Likewise, the different forms of third party access would not have the same effects on the *TOP* contracts. A voluntary or negotiated use of free capacity would have little effect on existing contracts and imply a continued basis for new contracts. By contrast, a mandatory use of part of the capacity would weaken the basis for historical contracts as well as for new contracts. A public regulation of pipeline use could undermine the historical contracts and render new TOP contracts difficult. Needless to say, historical partners would have an advantage, but a complete restructuring of the gas trade would imply severe risks for all parties.

Table 7   Effects on Take-or Pay Contracts of Various Forms of Gas Market Opening

	Effect on historical TPA - contracts	Effect on eventual new TPA- contracts
Unbundling and regulation	Renegotiation with new buyers, disaggregation	Disaggregation, major problems for long-term contracts
Deregulation and integration	Adaptation to a new framework	Continued incentives

The arena of competition would be strongly influenced by radical changes. In case of deregulation and integration, to the extent that the monopolies are retained or replaced by a duopoly or an oligopoly, the importers would remain the arena of competition. A mandatory or regulated Third Party Access, TPA, would replace it to wholesalers and large end users. A regulation and unbundling with a duopoly or an oligopoly would transfer the arena of competition to wholesalers, with a TPA to retailers and large end-users. Against this backdrop, the producers should prepare for marketing their gas further down the chain to a larger variety of customers with more heterogeneous needs, whereas transporters and distributors should prepare for closer links with producers.

Table 8   The Arena of Competition

	Monopoly	**Duopoly/ oligopoly**	**Mandatory or regulated TPA**
Integration	Importers	Importers	Wholesalers and large end-users
Unbundling	Importers	Wholesalers	Retailers

Implications for security of supply

Security of supply can be seen as a private commercial or as a public regulatory issue. As a private commercial issue, the task is to diversify risk and eventually pay a premium for priority deliveries in case of a crunch. Monopoly trading on the continent makes this difficult. Most users have no choice of supplier and monopolies have few incentives to offer premium contracts. As a public regulatory issue, the question is what customers are to have priority in case of a crunch, eventually in what way and at what cost. In this perspective, competition may imply an enhanced risk through uncertainty and reduced investment. Instead of competing suppliers, the solution may be regulations and emergency plans, including storage requirements. The priority among users then becomes a question of substitutability and alternatives.

Table 9   Supply Security as a Commercial and a Regulatory Issue

Point of view	Issue	Solution
Commercial problem	Risk diversification	Premium payment
Public regulatory problem	Priority of customers, substitution potential and security requirements	Regulations, emergency plans and storage

In principle, households and service institutions such as hospitals and schools have the highest priority, because substitution is the least advanced. Power generation could have the second priority, because gas in electricity generation in many cases can be replaced by fuel oil, distillate or coal, also assuming that in an emergency environmental restrictions will be lifted. Industry would have third priority, because of fairly general substitution facilities.

Such considerations could also work out in a market, based on the ability and willingness to pay and the competition among multiple sellers for a variety of clients. This has to be seen against the types of supply risks. It is usual to distinguish between **long-term risk** in the gas market, due to insufficient investment in new production and transportation, and **short-term** risk, due to accidental or political disruption of existing supplies. A third type of risk should be introduced, **medium-term risk**, due to unexpected rises in demand because of weather, economic conditions, shortfall of competing fuels, etc.

Table 10   Substitution Potential and Supply Requirements

Market segment	Alternative energy source	Substitution potential	Supply requirements
Industry	Fuel oil, coal	Easy	Interruptible
Power stations	Distillate	More difficult and costly	Less interruptible
Households and small busilses	Electricity	Very difficult and costly	Not interruptible

The long-term risk can be dealt with through higher prices to producers, transporters or both. The short-term risk can be dealt with through emergency plans and extensive storage. The medium-term risk can best be dealt with through a flexible market, where rising demand in relation to constant supplies leads to gradually rising prices, providing incentives for users with good substitution facilities to switch to alternatives. If medium-term risk can be dealt with in such a way, short-term risk could also, provided the system is integrated through sufficient infrastructure.

Table 11   Types of Supply Risk in the Gas Market

Type of risk	Risk element	Cause	Precaution
Short term	Supply shortfall	Accident, sabotage, political crisis	Storage, excess capacity. supply diversification
Medium term	Rising demand in relation to contracted supplies	Comparatively low consumer prices	Storage, excess capacity. supply diversification,price consumer rises
Long term	Insufficient investment	Insufficient producer prices or transporter profits	Higher producer prices or transportation margins or both

In principle, there is little difference between demand rising in relation to constant supplies or supplies falling in relation to a constant demand. Differences in timing and abruptness will at first be abstracted. In both cases a shortfall should lead to price rises. The question is whether the cost should be distributed by regulators or by the market. The market solution may be more brutal, but also more efficient and less costly in the longer run. Provided the system is sufficiently integrated through infrastructure and general access to storage facilities, a shortfall at one point should be distributed fairly evenly and the cost be limited for any single user. The problem in today's European gas market is, however, that insufficient infrastructure between the various gas importers and the reliance on bilateral TOP contracts enhance the supply risk for each importer through a low degree of actual diversification and a low degree of potential diversification in case of a crisis. Hence the combination of infrastructure development and more flexible trading could lead to a considerable reduction of both short-term and medium-term risk for all gas users, enhancing the attractiveness of gas as a fuel. The discrepancy between market prospects for Northwest and Southern Europe mentioned earlier makes such measures even more urgent.

Indeed, the countries of Southern Europe and eventually those of Central Europe, because of their quickly rising gas demand and consequent need for supply diversification, could have an interest in measures reducing transportation costs through intermediary countries with large territories in a key position, essentially France and Germany. Such measures could also be in the interest of the established suppliers.

Indeed, the gas market is not a zero-sum game. The interest of the suppliers is to reach a large market at low transportation cost. The interest of the buyers is to diversify supply risk and hedge bargaining positions. For a gas buyer it is from both points of view more advantageous to a be a gas transit country than to be at the end of a gas chain. Hence it could also be in the interest of the large gas importing countries to encourage gas transit through their territory, essentially by reducing gas transportation costs. For example, France is currently at the end of four gas chains, from Algeria, from the Netherlands, from Norway and from Russia. It could be in France's interest to be a gas transit country, e.g., for Algerian gas to Germany and the UK, for Norwegian gas to Italy, Portugal and Spain and for Russian gas to Portugal, Spain and the UK. This would require a different gas regime with lower transportation costs, but France could benefit from an enhanced bargaining position and an improved supply security. Also for Germany, rising gas transit trade from north to south and east to west because of lower transportation costs would enhance the security of supply. Likewise, Spain would benefit from being a transitor of Algerian gas to France and eventually other countries further north, instead of being at the end of gas chains from Algeria, Libya and Norway.

In the present, segmented European gas market, where different areas are served by different TOP contracts, often with limited diversification the supply today in each case is unnecessarily high, due to insufficient infrastructure and rigid trading patterns. In a market more integrated by infrastructure, freer access and more open trading, the risk connected with each supplier would be spread out on a much larger area, with much smaller potential effects of a shortfall. Such a development could especially be in the interest of the countries of Southern Europe with a quickly rising gas demand.

Conclusion

The alternative for continental Europe is not necessarily the US or the UK model. The political problem is the bargaining position, potentially also the security of supply, as demand rises, facing a small number of sellers, implying a weaker bargaining power and a higher concentration of supply risk. The economies of scale in gas transportation and the need to finance large new projects in gas extraction and transportation with an increasing dependence upon outside sources are in a European context legitimate arguments against breaking up the gas industry on the US model[7]. The major economic risk is that in Europe price instability would lead to higher risk premiums and hence rising capital cost on both production and pipeline projects. The argument does, however, deserve some critical examination.

First, there is the question whether large new production projects like Troll and Urengoi will be needed in the next years. From Algeria, delivery capacity will be expanded by the new Maghreb-Spain pipeline. Norwegian capacity will increase as smaller and medium sized fields offshore are

---

7. Jonathan Stern, *European Gas Markets*, London 1990, The Royal Institute of International Affairs, p. 90 ff.

developed. Russian capacity could expand as energy conservation progresses in the home market, eventually supplemented by the development of smaller and medium sized fields. Later on, the likely development candidates are giant gas fields in the Middle East, at a far distance, with low unit cost, but a high political risk unaffected by the structures of European gas trade. This again stresses the importance of transportation costs.

Second, transportation costs can be kept in check by competition, eventually also by a more competitive construction industry. This could be an argument for parallel competing pipelines, eventually combined with vertical integration in order to reduce risk for both producers, transporters and distributors. The alternative could be to guarantee a fixed return on pipeline investment, as is the case in the United States, in order to reduce risk, discount rates and capital cost, eventually combined with a mandatory TPA. The problem in Europe, so far at least, is that there is no authority able to set pipeline transportation tariffs, guarantee a fixed return and supervise an eventual mandatory TPA. By the mid 1990s Europe does not yet seem politically mature for such a solution. The supranational institutions for such a task are lacking and the relationship with Russia, the major gas producer of the neighbourhood, is as unclear as the development within Russia herself. In the meantime, vertical integration with a negotiated third party access may be a reasonable outcome for continental Europe, adding flexibility and some competition to the present system and gradually reducing transportation costs, but at the same time maintaining a gas industry able and willing to finance new long distance pipelines. The major political risk for the European gas industry is a chain of events leading to an uncontrolled deregulation and more open competition, especially with smaller UK producers entering the continental market, at first leading to a supply pressure and falling prices, but subsequently to rising demand, unless new taxes are imposed, but in the meantime with insufficient investment in production and transportation.

Table 12 Potential Effects of Various Political Measures in the European Gas Market

Measure	Effect on trading pattern	Effect on new contracts	Effect on prices	Effect on risk and discount rates	Effect on supply security
Third party access (mandatory or regulated)	More competition to final users	Disaggregation	Instability	Higher risk, higher discount rates	Diversification of supplies and risk
Unbundling	More competition at all levels	Disaggregation	Instability	Higher risk, higher discount rates	Diversification of supplies and risk
Regulation of transportation tariffs	Direct deals between producers and consumers	Disaggregation	Guaranteed return in gas transportation	Higher risk for producers, higher discount rates	Diversification of supplies and risk
Competition at producer level	Strengthening the role of pipelines	Disaggregation of producer contracts	Lower producer prices	Higher risk for producers, higher discount rates	Compromising long-term supplies

Table 12   Potential Effects of Various Political Measures in the European Gas Market (continued)

Measure	Effect on trading pattern	Effect on new contracts	Effect on prices	Effect on risk and discount rates	Effect on supply security
Competition at end user level	Weakening the role of pipelines	Disaggregation, spot market, futures market	Lower consumer prices	Higher risk for producers and transporters, higher discount rates	Compromising long-term supplies and short-term supply responsibility
Horizontal deregulation	Restructuring, oligopoly	Larger contracts	Lower consumer prices, more stability	Less risk for producers, lower discount rates	Diversification of supplies and risk
Vertical deregulation	Integration	Larger contracts	Lower consumer prices, more stability	Less risk for producers, lower discount rates	Direct links between producers and last sellers, direct supply responsibility
Horizontal and vertical deregulation	Integrated oligopoly or monopoly	Larger contracts prices, more stability	Lower consumer	Less risk for producers, lower discount rates	Direct links between producers and last sellers, direct supply responsibility
Taxes and duties	Buffer between producers and consumers	Gas less competitive	Higher prices to consumers, lower and less stable prices to consumers	Higher risk for producers and transporters, higher discount rates	Compromising long-term supplies and short-term supply responsibility

ANNEX 2

FUTURE NATURAL GAS SUPPLY FOR EUROPE, THE ROLE OF TRANSIT COUNTRIES AND SECURITY OF SUPPLY: Executive Summary[1]

by

Observatoire Méditerranéen de l'Energie

Several studies carried out recently forecast a significant natural gas deficit for Europe by 2005-2010. The present study does not proclaim the possibility of such a scenario, but analyses some related issues.

Unless new major discoveries are made in the countries of the European Union, which seems unrealistic, those countries will have to increase their natural gas imports considerably:

■ either from neighbouring countries, e.g., Norway and Algeria (or rather: North Africa), which are already major suppliers. Today's known reserves are finite but new exploration efforts and/or technological progress may, however, produce positive results;

■ or from more remote countries like Russia or the Middle East, with their substantial natural gas reserve potential, but where supply routes stretch out over thousands of kilometres and often cross several transit countries (Figure 1).

In either case, a growing dependence on natural gas imports, will increase interest in European security of supply. Those security of supply issues have several facets, depending on whether one looks at the actions taken by consumer countries, possible developments in supply countries, or the "attitudes" of transit countries.

In the present study we look both at the future natural gas supply potential for Europe and at the security aspects of those potential supplies. A special emphasis has been put on transit issues, where very little literature exists.

Supply Curve of Future Natural Gas Potential for Europe

In relation to natural gas supply potential, we analyzed the various possible future gas exporting countries, their reserve potential, their export capacity, their production cost, transportation cost and total supply cost for gas imports into Europe.

---

1. This is the summary of a study produced by the Observatoire Méditerranéen de l'Energie for the IEA. The views expressed are those of the Observatoire Méditerranéen de l'Energie and are not necessarily shared by the IEA.

Figure 1   Long Distance and Long Term Supply of Natural Gas to Europe

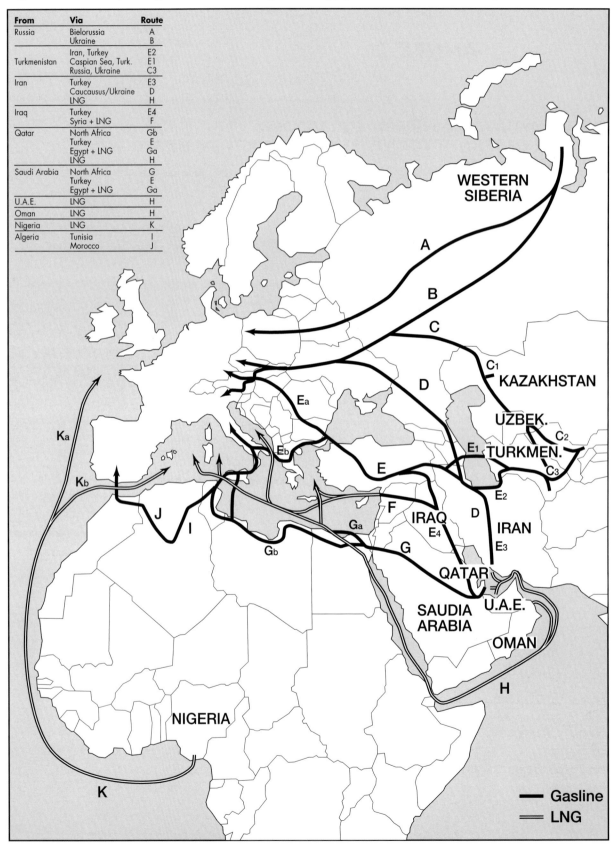

From	Via	Route
Russia	Bielorussia	A
	Ukraine	B
Turkmenistan	Iran, Turkey	E2
	Caspian Sea, Turk.	E1
	Russia, Ukraine	C3
Iran	Turkey	E3
	Caucausus/Ukraine	D
	LNG	H
Iraq	Turkey	E4
	Syria + LNG	F
Qatar	North Africa	Gb
	Turkey	E
	Egypt + LNG	Ga
	LNG	H
Saudi Arabia	North Africa	G
	Turkey	E
	Egypt + LNG	Ga
U.A.E.	LNG	H
Oman	LNG	H
Nigeria	LNG	K
Algeria	Tunisia	I
	Morocco	J

The aim of this part was to draw a tentative supply curve for potential future natural gas supplies to Europe.[2] This curve gives, for each potential exporting country and supply route (Figure 1), supply capacity to Western Europe by 2010 as well as the supply cost (excluding royalties for producer countries).

Two different discount rates, 10% and 15%, were used. The higher rate reflects a risk premium for the investor willing to invest in the more risky projects (several transit countries, political instability, etc.).

Whereas production costs and technical transportation costs are real costs with identifiable cost elements (even if they are not always easy to quantify), transit taxes are more like royalty payments than charges; it is therefore even more difficult to estimate them, especially when they refer to possible future routes. In order to evaluate the attitude of potential future transit countries towards transit taxes, a number of variables, such as the transit country's need for gas, its foreign exchange needs, its institutional framework, its economic and local political power and its negotiating power, have been systematically evaluated for each country. It goes without saying that the determination of these fees is to a certain extent based on subjective evaluation, but a systematic attempt has been made at analysing the issue in some detail.

The supply curve for the additional, not yet contracted, natural gas potential for Western Europe by 2010, shows that the cheapest new supplies are by pipeline from North Africa (between 1.50 and 1.80 $/Mbtu, depending on the discount rate), followed by LNG from North Africa and submarine pipelines from Norway (between 2.20 and 2.80 $/Mbtu). Intermediate supply costs (3.00 to 3.60 $/Mbtu) are those by pipeline from Russia or by LNG from the ARAB-Persian Gulf and Nigeria. Long distance pipeline supplies from the Arab-Persian Gulf and Central Asia are the most expensive options (3.30 to 4.30 $/Mbtu).

Excluding royalties for the producing countries, some 90 billion cubic meters of not yet contracted gas could be available for Western Europe by 2010 at a cost lower than or around 2.30 $/Mbtu using a 10% discount rate, and lower than or around 2.80 $/Mbtu using a 15% discount rate. Available not yet contracted export capacity by 2010 would increase to some 170 billion cubic meters, for supply costs below 3.00 and 3.60 $/Mbtu depending on the discount rate.

The Role of Transit Countries for Security of Supply

The recent emergence of several long distance transportation projects to supply Europe with gas from remote regions makes the subject of transit increasingly important. Moreover, due to recent geopolitical and geoeconomic development, most potential transit countries are today in "transition", both from an economic and from a political (domestic and international) point of view. Those countries present a variety of different situations, with major uncertainties about their future attitude towards natural gas transit.

In order to analyze potential transit countries, we have suggested a system of classifying transits, which specifies the nature of transits (single crossing, multiple crossing and its different

2. The supply curve is illustrated in Figure 3.1 in Chapter 3.

subdivisions, (quasi) obliged crossing, alternative crossing, etc.). For each country concerned, the following aspects are examined: political, military, and economic power, economic interdependence with neighbour countries, existence of ethnic and religious minorities (which can be active or passive), natural gas and energy net importing, exporting or self-sufficient country, institutional framework, etc.). It is clear that these factors affect the policy of countries towards transit. A typology of transit events consisting of four levels has been proposed: negotiations, threats, irregularities, supply cuts.

It is uncertain whether there is a real risk of gas supply cuts due to transit issues. Because of the novelty of gas transit, little historic data is available (besides transit of former communist Eastern European countries, which were formerly politically dominated by the Soviet Union and whose experience is therefore not necessarily representative of their future attitude). On the other hand, international oil pipelines have been built extensively, especially in the Middle East, which is also one of the potential major supply regions for future natural gas for Europe. A previous OME study analyzed all international oil pipelines in the Middle East from 1931 (first oil pipeline in the region) until now (1994). None of the 8 international pipelines in the region has operated continuously since it was built. In fact, of the 250 "pipeline years", representing the cumulative age of international export pipelines in the Middle East, only some 133 pipeline years of actual operation (or 53%) have been recorded. Those supply cuts were rarely due to wars or military intervention; most of the time they were due to political hostilities and conflict between neighbouring countries.

A concise security of supply review is given for all existing and potential exporting and transit countries in relation to future possible European natural gas supplies (see Figure 1). Some forty countries have been analyzed, taking account of the strategic geographic position of each country, energy and natural gas dependence of the country on the gas route, economic factors, geopolitical aspects and disputes, minority problems, etc. Special emphasis has been put on the Maghreb countries, Ukraine and Middle Eastern countries.

Ukraine as a Major Natural Gas Transit Country

For this study we were asked to analyze in more detail the case of Ukraine as a transit country. At present, all gas from Russia and from Turkmenistan to Western Europe crosses Ukraine. On the other hand, Ukraine imports some 60 to 80% of its natural gas consumption from Russia, and some 10 to 20% from Turkmenistan (this gas has to cross Russia in order to reach Ukraine). Besides Ukraine, which is doubtless the most important gas transit country of the CIS, other major CIS transit countries include: Russia, Kazakhstan, Belarus and Moldova.

Whereas during the USSR era there was an economic and geopolitical equilibrium which made transit work smoothly, since the breakup of the USSR, this equilibrium has been disturbed:

■ From a geopolitical point of view, the new independent States are reviewing their relations with Russia. Until a new order is installed, some friction is possible.

■ From an economic point of view, the real cost or opportunity cost approach creates considerable problems for transit countries since their energy bills have skyrocketed and have to be paid in hard currency. These countries were neither prepared nor able to adapt to this new situation.

Using our typology of transit, we have assessed 27 natural gas "transit events" between January 1, 1992 and December 31, 1994. Of those 27 events, Russia was directly involved with 19, Ukraine with 18, Turkmenistan with 10, Moldova with 2, the Baltic States with 2 and other Central Asian countries with 2. Concerning the level of these events, 10 correspond to negotiations or renegotiations, 8 to supply cut threats, 3 to irregularities and 8 to actual supply cuts or reductions (of which 2 were accidents).

Most transit events between Russia and Ukraine were linked to Ukraine's energy debt. In fact, Ukraine's debt toward Gazprom evolved from less than 300 million dollars in early 1993 to well above one billion dollars during 1994. It is understandable that Gazprom reacted with supply cut threats (3 events) as well as with actual supply cuts or reductions (2 events).

During those supply reductions, Ukraine continued to offtake gas from the transit pipelines towards Europe. This offtake is made possible by the nature of Ukraine's transport configuration, where big industrial clients are directly connected to the transit pipelines. It was therefore not necessarily a deliberate reaction by the Ukrainian government. Heavy Ukrainian withdrawals forced Gazprom in early 1994 to pay fines to its European customers who saw significant reductions in their supplies.

Due to the common history of Ukraine and Russia it is understandable that recent relations between the two countries have been by no means easy. Major disputes since independence in 1991 between the two countries include: the Crimea peninsula, the Black Sea fleet, the nuclear arsenal, the more than 10 million Russians living in Ukraine, the debt issue, the oil and gas transit issue.

Even if the transit events are sensitive to the political relations between Russia and Ukraine, it seems that the energy debt issue is a major driving force. For instance, in mid 1994 the energy debt fell from 900 to 600 million dollars due to a transit agreement (negotiation). However, by the end of 1994 it had climbed to 1.4 billion dollars.

The first conclusions on the relations between Russia and Ukraine are that both countries are conscious of the mutual interdependence and that they try, as far as possible, to avoid conflict. In fact, Russia and Gazprom are very well aware of the crucial and symbolic importance of the security of supplies to Europe and do everything to maintain their image as a secure supplier.

Ukraine does not have any interest in pushing its powerful neighbour too far. It depends heavily on Russia to satisfy its domestic energy supplies. Both countries are progressively building the basis for a sustained cooperation on their own terms.

Security of Maghreb Natural Gas Supplies

We were also asked to study the Maghreb in detail. Algeria, as a major producing country, and Tunisia and Morocco, as transit countries, account for about one third of European natural gas imports. The durability of the security of these supplies depends mainly on the political, economic and social stability of the region and especially Algeria.

The study therefore discusses the different actors who shape the present Algerian situation as well as their mutual relationship:

- the army, and its internal divisions;

- the major political parties: National Liberation Front (FNL), Socialist Forces Front (FFS) and the Islamic Salvation Front (FIS), outlawed since April 1992;

- the different islamic forces and their own internal power struggle: the FIS with its two main divisions (the Salafists of Ali Benhadji and the Djezaarists of Abdelkader Hachani); the competing movements (Hamas, En-Nahda and El-Ouma), which have, however, a smaller audience than the FIS, the pro-FIS Islamic Army Movement (MIA) and the terrorist Islamic Army Group (GIA);

- the ethnic minorities (mostly Berber constituted of Kabylies, Chauias and Tuaregs) and their backing from political parties (Union for Culture and Democracy (RCD) and FFS).

One of the major constraints which faces Algeria is the extremely high dependence of its economy on world markets. The hydrocarbon sector is the backbone of Algeria's economy, accounting for 95% of export earnings, 25% of GDP, and 57% of government revenues. 3 billion dollars per year (equivalent to 6% of GDP) have to be spent just for basic food imports (cereals, meat and milk), and the same amount has to be invested every year just in order to maintain present industrial activity. Burdened by a huge external debt (amounting to 27 billion dollars) and the collapse of world oil prices which plunged the country into a severe recession, Algeria, one of the most centrally planned economies in the Arab world, was forced in 1992 to launch a comprehensive, IMF-supported program to achieve microeconomic stabilization and to introduce market mechanisms into the economy.

Due to the economic consequences of the recession the painful structural adjustment measures and the low credibility of the regime (supported by the army), the islamic forces were able to win widespread support among the population. After the cancellation by the government of elections expected to be won by the FIS in 1990, Algeria faced political turmoil. In 1993, a new government was formed, one of whose priorities was the resumption and acceleration of the structural adjustment process.

It is important to note that all political forces (including and especially the islamists) are very much in favour of a stronger integration of Algeria into the world economy. Moreover, all political forces are extremely conscious of the important strategic role of the hydrocarbon sector for Algeria's economy. No political force envisages a review of the oil and gas export programme.

Special emphasis was put on developing a possible scenario of a FIS government and its consequences for European natural gas supplies. With such a scenario, we do not think that gas supplies would be interrupted, for the following three main reasons:

- First, because the hydrocarbon sector accounts for almost all Algeria's export earnings and no government, whatever its political colour, could afford to ignore it if it wishes to maintain a minimum economic and social equilibrium. Without strong economic diversification, which is not likely to occur in the short term, this constraint will continue to exist for many years ahead.

- Second, because the economic principles of Algeria's islamists are liberal and in favour of free trade with the rest of the world. The FIS has always declared that it would honour the heavy external debt of the country.

■ Third, because of the nature of the social base of the FIS, which is mainly constituted of presently marginalised classes, who will put pressure on any islamic government to see their economic conditions improve. Of course, the FIS could take some populist measures, e.g., a strict moral regime, so as to offset economic frustrations, but those measures will not work unless accompanied by substantial economic improvements.

The major danger threatening European natural gas supplies from Algeria in the event of an islamic government, is rather due to the risk of a progressive upheaval of the political, economic and social environment: minority revolts, flight of technicians and managers, strikes, etc., which could lead to a paralysis of the economy and therefore affect the hydrocarbon export sector.

Concerning the other two Maghreb countries, Tunisia and Morocco, we do not believe in a "domino theory", i.e., Algerian islamism being exported to those countries. Both Tunisia and Morocco have, in recent years, had positive economic growth with, at the same time, social structuring favouring the emergence and the widening of a middle class linked with the present political regime. On the other hand, political adjustment to absorb a potentially growing islamic radicalism, is likely to be slow, even if there have been indications both in Morocco and Tunisia of some cautious conciliatory moves towards opposition parties.

COUNTRY ANNEXES

AUSTRALIA

GAS POLICY

Australia is rich in natural resources but many of the reserves are offshore and distant from domestic markets and are as yet undeveloped. Because of concern over security of supply, the legislative and regulatory regimes of the states and territories have in the past restricted the building of interstate gas pipelines and the transfer of onshore gas resources across state borders. This has contributed to the development of regional, rather than national, markets for gas. Efforts are currently underway to free up Australia's gas industry. A range of federal and state government as well as industry initiatives are in place or under development that will have the effect of creating a competitive, national gas industry.

Australia's gas industry is growing and Australia is the third largest exporter of liquefied natural gas (LNG) in the Asia-Pacific region. Australia does not import natural gas.

The policy of the Federal Government has been to establish a framework to facilitate industry investments in the natural gas industry by the private sector on a commercial basis. One outcome of this policy could be increased linkages between gas resources with gas markets across state/territory boundaries and to encourage the interstate trade in gas.

In February 1994 the Council of Australian Governments (CoAG - representing the federal, state and territory governments) agreed to implement free and fair trade in gas between and within their respective jurisdictions by 1 July 1996. Features of the agreement include:

■ removal of state/territory legislative and regulatory barriers to trade within and between regions (e.g., Victoria and South Australia have had restrictions on the sale of gas outside of their respective states);

■ third party access to pipelines;

■ harmonisation of pipeline construction standards;

■ commercialisation of publicly owned utilities;

■ removal of restrictions on gas use (e.g., Victoria has had restrictions on the use of gas for electricity generation).

The federal, state and territory governments have established a Gas Reform Task Force to develop a national policy framework to implement the CoAG gas reform initiative. Consistent with the CoAG approach, in June 1994 the Australian Government sold its only interstate gas pipeline, the Moomba-Sydney Pipeline (MSP), to a consortium of private companies. The MSP had, until the sale, been owned and operated by a federal authority, The Pipeline Authority (TPA). TPA is due to be wound-up by December 1996. Other state/territory governments are also seeking to place their pipeline operations onto a more commercial basis. South Australia has sold to a private company the pipeline assets of the Pipeline Authority of South Australia (PASA), and Western Australia has corporatised the gas pipeline from Dampier to Perth, previously operated by the State Energy Commission of Western Australia. Queensland has recently announced that a private company will build, own and operate a new pipeline to deliver gas to Brisbane.

Federal regulation of LNG exports has also eased. LNG export contracts are now subject only to price approval.

GAS DEMAND

The main use of gas in Australia is in the industrial sector, which accounted for 57% of demand in 1992/3. The balance of consumption was split evenly between electricity generation and the residential/commercial sectors.

The Australian Bureau of Agriculture and Resource Economics (ABARE) has projected that gas consumption in Australia could grow rapidly over the next five years, at an average rate of 5.4% a year compared with 3.2% over the past five years. ABARE has said that the projected growth over this period is driven mainly by a number of new natural gas consuming projects coming on stream as well as by some existing energy intensive operations switching to natural gas or increasing capacity. Growth in the use of natural gas is expected to be particularly strong in electricity generation and cogeneration.

Over the longer term, to 2009-10, ABARE projects gas consumption to continue to grow strongly, albeit at a slower rate of 3.5% per year. However, more rapid growth is possible if further new investments, especially in pipelines and new fields, go ahead and gas becomes more widely available at competitive prices. Further investments in gas supply and consumption projects are more likely as the details of the policy setting, particularly as a result of the CoAG process, become available.

Strong growth is also expected in the demand for LNG in the Asia-Pacific region and this should create opportunities for further supplies from Australia.

Table 1   State by State Demand Forecast (bcm)

	1992-93	**1999-2000**	**2009-10**
New South Wales	2.53	3.50	5.37
Victoria	6.22	6.97	9.04
Queensland	1.02	1.47	1.63
South Australia	2.65	3.44	3.57
Western Australia	5.28	9.29	11.91
Northern Territory	0.33	0.42	1.02
Total	**18.04**	**25.48**	**32.93**

Source: ABARE.

GAS SUPPLY

Australia's gas regions are relatively unexplored. The comparatively small markets, often distant from reserve basins, have not provided sufficient commercial incentive for expanded exploration. Many of the past discoveries have been a result of exploration for oil. But markets for gas are expanding (2009-10 demand should be almost double 1991-2 levels). If reserves continue to decline - particularly in the southern and eastern states - there should be incentives for greater exploration. The lack of past exploration suggests a potential for significant additions to known reserves. Grid integration and the easing of government controls are also expected to increase investor confidence and hence exploration effort.

Table 2 — Production and Recoverable Reserves

Basin	Proven and Probable Reserves as of 31.12.92 (BRS Figures in Petajoules)	Production 1992-1993 (ABARE Figures in Petajoules)	Approximate Reserves-to-Production Ratio in Years
Adavale	23	0	na
Amadeus	684	13.7	50
Bass	374	0	na
Bonaparte	7,244	0	na
Bowen/Surat	276	36	8
Browse	18,992	0	na
Carnarvon	40,384	507	80
Cooper/Eromanga	4,437	208.3	21
Gippsland	9,642	221.3	44
Otway	37	3.7	10
Perth	144	14.7	10
Total	**82,238**	**1,004.7**	**82**

Sources: Australian Gas Association, Gas Industry Statistics 1995, Canberra, BRS, Petroleum Resources Assessment Branch 1994, *Oil and Gas Resources of Australia 1993 Canberra.*
ABARE *Quarterly Mineral Statistics*, September Quarter 1994.

Most Australian states/territories have significant gas resources within their boundaries. With the exception of New South Wales and Tasmania, each state/territory produces sufficient gas for its own uses. Reflecting state/territory regulation and the often vast distances between gas supply sources and gas markets, the gas supply and transportation systems have developed more or less independently from one another. Although the overall reserve-to-production ratio for Australia is high (40 years for demonstrated commercially recoverable reserves and a further 40 years for proven but as yet uneconomic reserves, see Table 2), the relatively low level of pipeline interconnection between states means that the reserve picture should be reviewed on a state-by-state basis.

The State of Western Australia (WA) and the adjacent offshore areas has very large reserves of natural gas, including over 70% of Australia's proven and probable (with 50% probability) recoverable reserves. The gas is transferred to the market in the south of the Sate by Dampier-Perth pipeline and the Western Australian Natural Gas (WANG) pipeline. The North West Shelf (NWS) project provides most of WA's needs (4 bcm in 1992-93), with a number of smaller projects including the Harriet and Griffin projects supplying the balance. The Goldfields Pipeline currently being constructed will transport gas from the NWS and East Spar projects to the mineral rich central parts of WA from 1996. There is considerable scope for the discovery of increased reserves in areas offshore WA. The NWS project is also the source of Australia's gas for the LNG export industry.

Australia's largest state in terms of population, New South Wales (NSW), imports its gas from South Australia (SA) and Queensland through the Moomba-Sydney Pipeline (MSP). The MSP is currently Australia's largest natural gas pipeline. Gas for the pipeline is sourced from the Cooper-Eromanga Basin, the bulk of which is in SA. A part of the Cooper-Eromanga Basin is located in the southeast of Queensland and a smaller interstate pipeline links this part of the basin with the MSP processing facilities at Moomba in SA.

Plans for two other proposed interstate gas pipelines from Victoria to supply the NSW market are currently being evaluated. A pipeline proposal to link the Gippsland Basin gas fields to the Sydney market along the eastern seaboard (Eastern Gas Pipeline Project) is being evaluated by the Australian Company, BHP, and the Canadian company, Westcoast Energy. Another proposal to link the Victorian grid at Wodonga with the Moomba-Sydney Pipeline spur to Wagga-Wagga is being considered by East Australia Pipeline Ltd (EAPL) and the Victorian Gas Transmission Corporation (GTC).

Both of these pipeline proposals could provide the foundation for an eastern seaboard gas pipeline grid linking Victoria and NSW, with the future possibility of also linking South Australia and Queensland.

SA is supplied by gas pipeline exclusively from the Cooper Basin which lies in the isolated north east of the State. In 1988 an agreement was reached between the SA Government and the Cooper Basin gas producers to maintain a rolling ten year reserve cover. The subsequent exploration schedule should maintain supplies well beyond 2010. The establishment of a contract for 7.7 bcm of gas over ten years from 1994 from southwest Queensland has led to enhanced exploration in that part of the State. The gas is transported to Moomba through an interstate pipeline. There is a possibility that SA may in the future also be supplied from resources in the Otway Basin, offshore of Victoria.

Victoria's gas supplies are sourced mainly from the Gippsland and Otway Basins, which are located offshore but relatively close to the areas of consumption. Reserves of over 100 bcm in the Gippsland Basin have not yet been committed under contract. The reserve/production ratio is over 40 years.

Queensland's main gas consuming region is in the southeast of the State around Brisbane but the majority of its reserves are in the Cooper-Eromanga basin, in the southwest of the State. Queensland's supply currently comes from the Bowen-Surat Basin. While the reserve/production ratio of total available Bowen-Surat reserves approximates eight years, reserves which are currently commercially recoverable are almost depleted, with a reserve/production ratio of about two years. However, from October 1996 a new 760 km pipeline will operate from southwest Queensland to Wallumbilla, where it will connect to both

Figure 1   Location of Natural Gas Reserves and Natural Gas Transmission Pipelines, Australia 1995

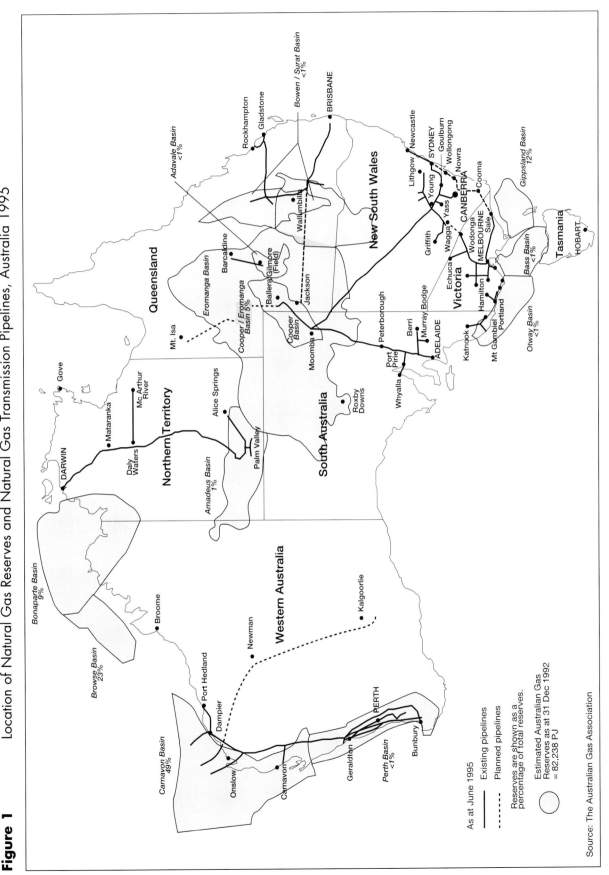

As at June 1995

———— Existing pipelines

-------- Planned pipelines

Reserves are shown as a
percentage of total reserves.

◯ Estimated Australian Gas
Reserves as at 31 Dec 1992
= 82,238 PJ

Source: The Australian Gas Association

the Roma to Brisbane pipeline and the State gas pipeline to serve the Brisbane, Rockhampton and Gladstone markets. Another planned pipeline will supply gas from the southwest Queensland region to Mt. Isa in the State's northwest from 1997.

The Northern Territory's Darwin market is supplied from the Amadeus Basin in the Territory's isolated south, through the Alice Springs-Darwin pipeline. Although this basin only accounts for 1% of Australia's known reserves, the small market in the Northern Territory means that the Territory's reserve/production ratio is greater than 50 years.

Tasmania obtains 60 terajoules of gas from the mainland in the form of LPG, which is reticulated to about 2,000 customers.

Exports

The NWS LNG Project has recently been able to increase its maximum production capacity to 7.5 million tonnes per annum (mtpa). The NWS Joint Venture Partners (JVP) have long term contracts with eight Japanese utilities to supply 7 mtpa of LNG until the year 2009. Negotiations are currently under way with the Japanese utilities to supply an additional 0.5 mtpa.

A portion of the excess production capacity from the NWS LNG Project is currently being sold on the world spot market. The bulk of this has been sold to ENAGAS of Spain but there have been some recent sales to South Korea and to Turkey. In 1994 all of the spot sales (13 shipments totalling 428,000 tonnes) were to Spain. During 1995 it is expected that eight cargoes will go to Spain (totalling 248,000 tonnes), one to Korea (56,000 tonnes) and approximately three to Turkey (170,000 tonnes). If the Japanese utilities contract an extra 0.5 mtpa, the NWS Project's capacity for spot sales will be significantly reduced without the further expansion of infrastructure.

The NWS JVP are currently investigating the viability of expanding the production capacity of the project by up to 7 mtpa through the introduction of two additional LNG liquefaction trains. This would maintain Australia's position as a major LNG supplier in the Asia-Pacific region.

INFRASTRUCTURE

The Australian gas market is characterised by consumers being linked to remote gas producing regions by large and lengthy transmission pipelines. In most cases each state/territory sources its gas from one producing region through a single strategic pipeline, such as the MSP. At present there is no national interconnected transportation grid.

Major pipeline additions linking reserves in the north and west of the country to markets in the south and east are considered possible within the time horizon of the next 40 years, but actual construction will depend on a number of factors, including: the proving of sufficient new gas reserves closer to the major markets, gas prices relative to other fuels, the demand for gas, the amount of gas used for production of LNG for exports and the economic cost/benefit of new pipeline infrastructure development.

COPING WITH DISRUPTIONS

Over 70% of Australia's production in 1992/3 came from two offshore producing areas - the Gippsland basin in the Bass Straight (where there are multiple production facilities) and the NWS project where production from a single platform was supplemented by a second in 1993.

Each gas market is dependent on single and long pipelines (see Table 3). There is storage of marketable gas at Moomba, providing peak load balancing and a back-up for South Australia and New South Wales. The only storage close to market is an LNG facility near Melbourne used for peak shaving.

There has been very limited experience of pipeline failure in Australia. The linepack on the long pipelines represents a significant volume of gas which could maintain supplies to markets for several days in the event of an incident near a producing area. The gas companies' strategies in the event of a disruption are to cut supplies to interruptible customers and to maintain the ability to repair damaged pipelines quickly.

Table 3   Major Supplying Pipelines (km)

State Supplied	Route	Approximate Length
New South Wales	Moomba-Sydney	1300
Northern Territory	Palm Valley-Darwin	1600
Western Australia	Dampier-Perth	1400
South Australia	Moomba-Adelaide	800
Queensland	Wallumbilla-Brisbane	440
	Wallumbilla-Gladstone	530
Victoria	various	up to 270

Source: Australian Gas Association.

CONCLUSIONS

In conclusion, Australia has plentiful reserves of natural gas and has good prospects for major new finds. The current reserve-to-production ratio of 40 years for commercially recoverable reserves and 82 years for proven and probable reserves provides for a secure future. While some of Australia's gas reserves are located in distant offshore basins, such as those in the Browse and Bonaparte Basins to the north and are judged to not be commercially viable at this stage, there are sufficient reserves in the developed, producing basins to meet short-to-medium term requirements.

AUSTRIA

GAS POLICY

Responsibility for importing gas in Austria is shared between the oil and gas company ÖMV and the association of regional gas companies Austria Ferngas (AFG). It is AFG's responsibility to coordinate both the demand and storage requirements of its eight member companies. The regional company operating in Tyrol, whose pipelines are not connected with the rest of the country, is not a member of AFG and buys German gas through ÖMV.

The government has no targets for the development of gas in Austria and there are no current plans to change the organisation of the industry.

GAS DEMAND

In 1992 gas accounted for 21% of Austria's energy demand. Gas sales are not expected to grow substantially in the power generation or residential/commercial sectors. The development of gas sales outside cities is restrained by competition from subsidised biomass district heating schemes. The most active sector is expected to be industry.

Table 1 Forecast Gas Demand (bcm)

	1992	**2000**	**2010**
Total Consumption	**6.11**	**7.48**	**7.6-8.3**
Industry	1.89	3.06	n.a.
Power Generation	2.13	2.15	n.a.
Residential/Commercial	2.08	2.26	n.a.

Source: Association of Gas and Heat Utilities, Austria Ferngas.

GAS SUPPLY

In 1992 indigenous production of gas amounted to 1.44 bcm - 24% of total gas supply. The remaining supplies came from Russia, from where Austria has been importing gas since 1968.

Austria's gas fields are mostly depleted; remaining proven reserves are 11.3 bcm and a further 6.2 bcm are considered possible, giving a reserves to production ratio in the region of 10 years.

Austria tried for 20 years to diversify its supply base and succeeded only in 1986 with the signing of the Troll contract covering Norwegian deliveries. Deliveries under this contract started in 1993 at an initial level of 300 mcm/year, but should plateau at 1 bcm/year by 2000. ÖMV/AFG have taken an option for another 0.5 bcm/year under the contract; the start date for delivery of this extra gas is still under negotiation but will probably be around 2000. The Norwegian gas is not physically delivered to Austria. Instead, the gas is delivered to Gaz de France and the importers ÖMV/AFG take an equivalent volume of Russian gas destined for France.

A small supply gap exists now (200-300 mcm/year) between demand and supplies under long term contracts. These supplies are being supplemented by spot deals, usually gas from Russia bought during the summer and used to fill storage. The gap between already contracted gas and demand is expected to reach 0.8-1.6 bcm just before deliveries under the Troll option begin at the end of the century. The Troll option should reduce, but not fill, this gap.

INFRASTRUCTURE

Existing storage of 2.3 bcm represents 133 days of average 1992 consumption, the highest of any OECD country. This relatively high storage capacity has been built up as a consequence of the country's high dependence on imports from Russia (74% of supply). This storage provides not only a security margin in the event of a supply disruption, but is also the main load management tool for matching seasonal demand with fairly constant imports and production. All the storage is in depleted gas fields, mostly around Vienna. The storage facility at Puchkirchen is being expanded from 90 mcm to 500 mcm during 1995 and a new site at Zwerndorf, with a working gas capacity of 500 mcm, is planned for 1997.

Austria is an important transit country with a total of 18.8 bcm of Russian gas passing through its pipelines in 1992 to Germany, France and Italy. There are two major transit lines: WAG runs from the Slovak border at Baumgarten to Germany and TAG (which itself consists of two parallel pipelines) runs from Baumgarten to the Italian border.

All Russian gas, imported or transited, passes through the Slovak/Austria border station Baumgarten. There are, however, five separate pipelines at this point.

The Hungary-Austria Gasline (HAG) is being built by ÖMV in cooperation with the Hungarian company MOL. It will link Baumgarten with Györ towards the end of 1996. No supply contracts have yet been signed for the use of this pipeline, but Hungary is expected to buy storage services from Austria.

A project based on importing LNG to the Adriatic port of Krk is under investigation jointly by ÖMV and seven other European gas companies. A north-south pipeline crossing Austria (the Pentaline) is part of the proposal. Suggested total volumes for the project are around 10 bcm, of which Austria might eventually take 1 bcm. The project's future is uncertain (and not at all likely before 2005).

COPING WITH DISRUPTIONS

In the event of a gas supply crisis the Energy Steering Law can be invoked to order interruptions to customers. The gas industry, however, has its own emergency supply plan, a cooperative agreement drawn up by AFG, ÖMV, RAG and the local distribution companies, which foresees interruptions to particular sectors in the event of a supply problem.

The large storage facilities provide a significant degree of short term flexibility and have in the past allowed the gas industry to cope with winter reductions in Russian deliveries. To date, the Russians have always made up lost volumes the following summer.

Additional short term flexibility comes from interruptible sales contracts. The policies of the different regional gas companies on interruptible contracts vary considerably. One quarter of sales to industrial consumers probably fall into this category. Most gas-fired generating plant can, and often does, burn other fuels.

Production from domestic fields offers little flexibility; they are operated near their production capacities for most of the year.

In the event of Russian supplies being disrupted, the Troll contract stipulates that Norwegian gas would be physically delivered to Austria (with the Troll partners taking responsibility for the transit through Germany).

BELGIUM

GAS POLICY

Supply of gas in Belgium is the responsibility of the transmission company Distrigaz. The company has been privatised but the state will retain a "golden share" with which it will retain a veto in matters related to national energy policy. The Government has a strong influence on the choice of supply sources.

The government is considering the establishment of a new national body to promote CHP within the framework of the Belgian National Policy Programme for reducing CO_2 emissions.

The treaty covering construction of the UK-Belgium pipeline (the Interconnector project) has been finalised by the Belgian and UK governments. More details of this project are given below.

GAS DEMAND

Gas made up 17% of TPES in 1992 and sales are still expanding. In 1994, for instance, 45000 new customers were connected. The policy of promoting CHP schemes as well as the electricity supply industry's plans for new CCGT plants implies a significant rise in the share of total gas supply being used for power generation - forecast by Distrigaz to rise from 16% in 1992 to 24% in 2010. In 1994, two CCGTs of 460 MW went into production and further projects are planned.

Table 1　　　Gas Demand Forecast (Mtoe)

	1992	2000	2010
Total	**9.03**	**12.8**	**14.0**
Industry[1]	3.50	4.1	4.5
Electricity Generation	1.40	3.4	3.4
Residential/Commercial	4.12	5.3	6.2

1. Includes CHP
Source: Distrigaz.

GAS SUPPLY

In 1992 Belgium imported 3.7 Mtoe from the Netherlands (38%), 2.12 Mtoe from Norway (22%) and 3.93 Mtoe from Algeria (40%). Of these imports 0.4 Mtoe are re-exported to Luxembourg (to which Belgium is the principal gas supplier). There is no domestic production in Belgium.

Over the forecast period Belgium is expected to remain dependent on the same three suppliers, with some additional volumes from the UK through the Interconnector. The major source of incremental gas should be Norway. Its share of Belgium's supply is forecast to increase from 22% in 1992 to 36% in 2010 as new volumes under the Troll contract and a separate power generation contract are delivered through the recently completed Zeepipe. Absolute levels of supplies from Algeria and the Netherlands are expected to stay more or less stable. Thus by 2010 Belgium's supply should be split more evenly among its three major suppliers.

One of the contracts signed with the Norwegian producers is backed by a further contract between Distrigaz and Electrabel (the major electricity producer) made possible by adapting terms in a way favourable to power generators. The supply is intended for base load power generation and the gas price is indexed to coal and inflation, ensuring competitiveness with coal over the duration of the contract. Deliveries under this contract are due to begin in 1996 and reach a plateau of 1.9 bcm (1.5 Mtoe).

INFRASTRUCTURE

The gas transport network is connected with those of the Netherlands, France, Luxembourg and, through the new Zeepipe, Norway. Belgium is also an important transit country for gas from the Netherlands and Norway to France and Spain. The routing of the main transmission lines cross the country in line with this transit role. There are separate pipelines dedicated to transporting low-calorific Groningen gas.

The Zeepipe links the Troll/Sleipner fields in the Norwegian North Sea to Zeebrugge and was completed in 1993. It has a capacity of 13 bcm/year (10.8 Mtoe/year).

The LNG reception terminal at Zeebrugge receives tankers from Algeria. It can handle the largest LNG tankers (130,000 cubic metres) and has in the past received such tankers from Australia on behalf of Enagas in Spain (which in turn received shipments of Algerian LNG in smaller tankers that could be handled by the Spanish terminals) and from Abu Dhabi.

The UK-Continent Interconnector project was agreed upon in December 1994. It is designed to carry up to 20 bcm/year between Bacton and Zeebrugge - initially from the UK to the continent and possibly in the other direction in the next century. Completion of the pipeline is planned for 1998. Distrigaz has an ownership share in the project. The geographical convergence of the Zeepipe, Algerian LNG deliveries and the Interconnector should make Zeebrugge an important point on the European gas network[1].

Underground storage capacity is 0.465 bcm working gas. Distrigaz plans to increase this capacity to 0.745 bcm in 2000 and 1 bcm in 2010.

---

1. Although the throughput of Zeebrugge is set to increase substantially, the LNG terminal and the landfall of the two pipelines are at different sites. There are, however, all located in the harbour area.

COPING WITH DISRUPTIONS

In the event of a disruption to supplies Belgium could call on its underground storage and above-ground LNG stocks, its backup supply agreement with Gasunie of the Netherlands and its reserve of interruptible customers.

In 1992 27% of total industry consumption (3.5 Mtoe) was interruptible and it is understood that 60-70% of the 1.4 Mtoe delivered to Electrabel can also be interrupted (even if those supplies are not formally labelled as interruptible). This means that in total, approximately 20% of demand is interruptible. In industry the main backup fuel is heavy fuel oil, while most of the existing gas-fired plants are triple-fired (heavy fuel oil/coal/gas). New CCGTs are planned to be able to use gasoil, but for limited time periods only.

Distrigaz' planning criteria are that, in the event of a disruption to its largest supply source, it should be able to maintain supplies to all its firm customers for a year.

CANADA

GAS POLICY

Canada perhaps has the most unfettered natural gas market in the world. This is a consequence of a series of deliberate policy actions stemming from a general economic policy of relying on market forces. On the other hand, the competitive regime existing in Canada is the result of very deliberate regulation by both Federal and Provincial Governments.

From a situation in the 1970s where TransCanada Pipelines Ltd. had a monopoly on gas transmission from Western to Eastern Canada and a virtual gas purchase monopoly, and prices all along the gas chain from wellhead to citygate were regulated on a cost plus basis, the industry has gone through a number of radical changes. Today's industry is characterised by keen competition among producers (of which there are around 1000) and among suppliers of gas to end consumers. For instance, Canada is probably the only country in the world where residential consumers can choose their supplier. The transmission part of the gas chain, being a natural monopoly, has kept its monopoly position but is regulated by the National Energy Board on a cost plus basis (although introduction of incentive mechanisms as a substitute for competition is being considered for pipelines in general). The most important steps taken to deregulate the industry have been the scrapping of wellhead gas price regulation, the lifting of gas export restrictions, and the implementation of mandatory open access to pipelines coupled with unbundling of the purchasing, transportation and sales activity of TransCanada Pipelines Ltd.

Up to the second half of the 1980s when deregulation took place, a "tin on the shelf" concept governed Canadian depletion policy. In this era, an inventory of up to 25 years of annual gas production was required before exports were allowed. Since Canada traditionally has exported a significant share of its production to the US (close to 50% in 1993), it was natural to link resource policy to export policy. Natural gas reserve levels in the ground are now, however, a function of industry investment rather than government regulation. The reserves to production ratio has now fallen to around 19 years. It is thought that the R/P ratio will settle at about 10 years which is near the level that the US has had for the last 25 years. This "just in time gas" approach represents a considerable savings in present value terms as far as total development costs are concerned.

In spite of a general tendency towards deregulation, both imports and exports of natural gas are regulated by the NEB. Gas can be exported under the authority of a short term order (less than 2 years) or a long term licence (up to 25 years). Short term export orders are easily obtained, and once attained routinely renewed, while licences may require a public hearing under the Market-Based Procedure (MBP). This Procedure is the Board's current mechanism for fulfilling the NEB Act's requirement that the Board "finds exports to be in the public interest". Thus, when considering a licence application the Board shall "satisfy itself that the quantity of gas to be exported does not exceed the surplus remaining after due allowance has been made for the reasonably foreseeable requirements for use in Canada having regard to the trends in the discovery of gas in Canada "(Export Licensing Criteria, Section 118 of the NEB Act). The public hearing component of the MBP for examining export licence applications consists of a complaints procedure, an export impact assessment and a public interest assessment (all other matters that the Board considers relevant). The principle underlying the complaints procedure is that gas should not be authorised for export if Canadian users have not had the opportunity to buy gas on similar terms and conditions (including price) as the proposed exports. But this principle also presumes that there is nothing preventing potential Canadian buyers from doing so.

Canada is a signatory to both the Free Trade Agreement and NAFTA. These agreements abide by the provisions set out in the GATT principles. The GATT contains a basic prohibition against quantitative restrictions, but there are exceptions to the basic prohibition, the so-called "domestic shortfall" exceptions. According to the Canadian Government the export licensing procedure is not at odds with the GATT rules.

Natural resource ownership in Canada is vested in the provinces. This means that the gas producing provinces have a strong influence on gas reserve dispositions. The "pre-emptive right of Alberta" is an example of this. This refers to Alberta's right to refuse a removal permit for gas leaving the province (which accounts for more than 80% of the total Canadian gas production).

Through its responsibility for the regulation of pipelines, the NEB plays an important role when it comes to making decisions that could indirectly influence security of supply. This can be illustrated by two issues that have been discussed recently: Add-on vs. Rolled-in tolls and incentive regulation for pipelines. The first issue deals with the way in which tolls or tariffs for incremental system developments are calculated. The second issue deals with alternative ways of fixing the pipelines' rate of return. Decisions concerning these issues could change the weight of commercial incentives for exploration and development and thereby influence the security of supply. By and large, industry prefers the export hearing process and prefers the rolled-in approach to toll-setting but would like the pipeline companies to be subject to greater discipline to cut costs.

In 1994, Canadian gas export revenues totalled more than CDN $6 billion.

GAS DEMAND

The National Energy Board (NEB) staff has looked at two different scenarios for future gas demand as a function of the future development in gas production costs reflecting different degrees of technological progress in exploration and production of natural gas. After a long period of surplus gas production capacity, the emergence of a more balanced and more integrated North American gas market makes future gas production cost a more crucial factor than in the past. The Current Technology case of the Board staff assumes that gas exploration and production technology will basically remain the same as today but with some reduction in costs. Gas supply costs will increase over time as more costly reserves will be exploited. In the

High Technology case, however, it is assumed that technological progress to a large extent will compensate for the increase in gas supply cost that otherwise would occur. The difference in natural gas supply costs between the two cases (and the resulting differences in field and end user prices) lead to appreciable variations in North American energy demand, fuel shares by end users, Canadian export levels and fuel choices by electric utilities. The total amount of natural gas used in Canada will be influenced, perhaps strongly, by the extent to which it is used in electricity generation. The analysis made by the Board staff suggests that if price increases are moderate, gas use in power generation could increase substantially from 119 PJ (= 4.5 bcm) in 1992 to 535 PJ (= 12.7 bcm) in 2010. Under this scenario the gas share in total primary energy use would increase from around 25% today to 29% in 2010. Primary gas demand is projected to grow from 2.2 tcf (= 62.2 bcm) in 1992 to 3.7 tcf (= 104.7 bcm) (2.8 tcf or 79.2 bcm in the Current Technology case). The annual growth rate for the two projections are 1.3% and 2.2%, respectively. Growth rates for residential and commercial demand are slightly lower than average in both cases, whereas industrial demand shows a slightly higher than average growth.

As a significant share of Canadian gas production is exported to the US, future demand for gas in the US will heavily influence future total demand for Canadian natural gas. The NEB has made demand and supply projections for the US using the same scenarios as for Canada. Not surprisingly, the increase in demand is greater in a world characterised by relatively low gas supply costs and prices. The higher demand case generates total annual US gas use of over 25 tcf (707.5 bcm) in the years to 2005, but the NEB analysis suggests that levels as high as this are unlikely to be sustainable with the Current Tech view of supply. After 2005, rising prices of gas relative to oil increasingly result in energy users switching away from gas. With a High Tech view of supply, US production averages about 22 tcf (622 bcm) in the last five years of the period up to 2010. This implies a Canadian export level of some 3 tcf during this period. Should an incremental source of low-cost supply, such as Mexico enter the North American market, Canadian gas would face stiffer competition. It is possible that, in these circumstance, Canadian exports could decline somewhat for a period of time. The development of such an incremental supply source is unlikely to occur before the turn of the century. According to the NEB, a plausible range for Canadian exports of gas over the study period is between 2 and 4 tcf (56.6 and 113.2 bcm).

GAS SUPPLY

For most of the past decade the natural gas industry in Canada has been in a state of transition. During the late 1970s and the early 1980s natural gas prices in Canada had been regulated at sufficiently high levels that the use of gas was discouraged but producers had a strong incentive to explore for new reserves. In Canada, the NEB's use of quantitative surplus tests in its regulation of gas exports tended to restrict access to US markets by Canadian producers. By the mid 1980s, productive capacity greatly exceeded the demand for natural gas and large volumes of gas were shut in.

In 1986 administered prices for natural gas were eliminated in Canada; a gradual phase-out began in the US in 1978, resulting in complete deregulation of wellhead prices in 1993. Price deregulation was accompanied by the opening up of access to pipelines and revision of the NEB's export surplus determination procedures in 1987. Natural gas is now traded in an increasingly integrated and competitive North American marketplace.

Because price deregulation occurred at a time when there was a large surplus of productive capacity (the so-called gas "bubble"), natural gas prices subsequently declined precipitously in North America, falling by about one-half between 1986 and 1992. The decline in prices induced an appreciable increase in the demand for natural gas, especially in the US. Producers met the increase in demand by drawing on existing productive capacity; the very low prices combined with large excess productive capacity effectively eliminated any incentive for producers to search for and develop new gas reserves. These phenomena produced a gradual decline in excess productive capacity so that, at present, natural gas markets in North America are roughly in balance. The decline in excess productive capacity was mirrored in a steady decline in the ratio of remaining reserves to production in Canada and the US as the distortions induced by price and export regulation were worked off. Over the past two winters there have been increasing signs of price firmness. On an annual average basis, natural gas fieldgate prices in Alberta increased in 1993 by 27 cents, the first increase in 10 years.

Canada's natural gas resource base, i.e., the in-place inventory of conventional and unconventional gas resources, is immense. Table 1 shows the distribution of resources by category and by geographical location.

In the time frame of this study, the greatest contribution to gas supply will continue to come from conventional gas resources in the Western Canadian Sedimentary Basin (WCSB). The NEB's total marketable resource potential for the WCSB amounts to 7.2 trillion cubic metres of which 43 remains to be found. The NEB draws the conclusion that "the WCSB will be reliable source of natural gas for some time to come".

In addition to conventional resources, Canada has enormous unconventional resources like coal bed methane and tight gas. Both these sources of gas require specialised completion and production techniques. There has been only limited development of these resources to date and much of the industry activity is directed towards research or pilot projects. While the NEB recognises that there are substantial volumes of shale gas and hydrates in Canada, these are not likely to be exploited within the study period due to lack of commercial technologies.

Perceptions of the size of the resource base are linked to current opinions on possible trends in the cost of incremental supply. Though analysts have generally assumed that finding and production costs of gas will increase in the future, according to the NEB there is limited and ambivalent evidence of such a trend in the historical record; the presumed date for the commencement of increasing costs of resource exploitation continues to be pushed back into the future. In fact, exploration and production costs for natural gas have declined in recent years. For instance, finding and production costs for Alberta in 1991 appear to have been considerably lower than in 1981.

The view taken by the NEB in its High Tech scenario described above (claiming that advances in technology and geological knowledge will prevent cost of finding and developing gas reserves from rising appreciably) is that Canada will remain a low cost gas producer for a long time to come.

Table 1   Marketable Conventional Gas (bcm)

Western Canada Sedimentary Basin

	Cumulative Production[1]	Remaining Reserves[1]	Discovered Resources	Initial Discovered	Undiscovered Resources	Ultimate Resources
Alberta	1832	1586	—	3418	2127	5545
British Columbia	252	238	—	490	940	1430
Saskatchewan	71	79	—	150	62	212
South YT/NWT	8	6	—	14	15	29
Sub-Total (WCSB)	2163	1909	—	4072	3144	7216

Frontier and Other

	Cumulative Production[1]	Remaining Reserves[1]	Discovered Resources	Initial Discovered	Undiscovered Resources	Ultimate Resources
Territories[2]	—	—	19	19	279	298
Mack/Beaufort	—	—	362	362	1575	1937
Nova Scotia	—	—	154	154	362	516
Grand Banks/Lab	—	—	245	245	1032	1277
Arctic Islands	—	—	407	407	2269	2676
Other Frontier[3]	—	—	—	—	2538	2538
Ontario	32	9	—	41	—	41
Sub-Total (Frontier and Other)	32	9	1187	1228	8055	9283
Total for Canada	**2195**	**1918**	**1187**	**5300**	**11199**	**16499**

Notes:
1. Cumulative production and reserves as of 31 December 1992.
2. Excludes that portion assigned to the Western Canada Sedimentary Basin.
3. Other Frontier includes: Georges Bank; Laurentian Basin; E. Newfoundland Basin; S. Grand Banks; Maritimes Basin; Hudson Bay; Baffin Bay and offshore British Columbia.

Source: WCSB production and reserves from provincial agencies and NEB. Frontier and other production, reserves and resources from NEB, CNSOPB and CNOPB. Undiscovered resources estimates: All estimates are NEB 1993, however, studies by the provincial agencies and Geological Survey of Canada were used in deriving estimates.

Canadian gas production could reach close to 7 tcf a year by 2010. The NEB does not see any deliverability problems related to this level of production. Having studied other sources of supply outside the WCSB like LNG, unconventional gas and gas from the frontier regions of Canada, it concludes that the supply costs of these sources, together with environmental concerns in the case of LNG and frontier regions, are likely to preclude them from becoming more than marginal sources of supply in the next two decades.

In Canada, unlike countries like Norway and Algeria, contracted gas volumes are not a good indicator of future gas deliveries. The most important reason for this is that short term sales hold a high share of total volumes sold. This is illustrated by the distribution of exports to the US by contract type. In 1993, about half these exports were short term in nature (of which about 30% were firm and 20% interruptible) and the remainder were sold on long term contracts.

INFRASTRUCTURE

Although there is considerable consumption of natural gas in the producing provinces, the Canadian gas industry is still characterised as "production in the west, consumption in the east". This is clearly reflected in the gas infrastructure in that most of the production fields, gathering pipelines and processing plants are located in the west with the major west-east transmission pipeline in the middle and the regional and local distribution pipelines in the east. The export points for gas to the US are, however, spread out all along the Canadian-US border.

Canadian gas reserves are spread over a large number of pools. Up to 1992, reserves had been identified in 26,900 different pools. The initial reserves in these pools totalled more than 4,000 bcm, but the average size was only 151 mcm. 195 of the pools (0.7% of the total number) contained more than 2.8 bcm of marketable gas and accounted for 52% of total reserves. The average reserve size in the pools having more than 2.8 bcm each, was 10.9 bcm. This means that Canadian reserves are spread over a very large number of relatively small reservoirs, a situation different from the situation found for instance in the Norwegian part of the North Sea.

At the end of 1992, Canada had 555 gas processing plants of which 507, representing 94% of the capacity, were located in Alberta. In 1992, the gas processing plants on average ran at only 65% of capacity.

Although the discrepancy between productive capacity and actual production has been diminishing, recently there was still a capacity margin of some 15% in gas production. Further, the large number of gaswells being drilled in Western Canada implies that the discrepancy will begin to grow again, particularly if new exit pipeline capacity is not soon constructed. NEB analysis suggests that estimated productive capacity is currently in approximate balance with estimated pipeline capacity. Looking ahead, the NEB analysis suggests that peak day capacity will exceed pipeline capacity each year by a narrow margin. More recently, on the NOVA system in Alberta peak production capacity including storage withdrawals is expected to be 16% higher than peak-day demand. This implies that a shortfall in production in one place could probably be replaced by production somewhere else.

The major pipeline systems which transport gas within and from the producing provinces in Western Canada to Canadian domestic markets and export markets are expanding in response to increased demand for and supply of gas from this region. Each of the major pipeline systems which provide take-away capacity of Western Canadian production has expanded since deregulation and most are expected to expand over the next few years.

Pipeline capacity utilisation in Canada is generally high. According to the NEB, average capacity utilisation is around 90%. This is higher than in the US and Europe.

The most vulnerable part of the Canadian pipeline system seems to be the TransCanada pipeline between Alberta and Ontario which is the only direct east-west connection.

The pipeline, however, is looped in many places, and disruptions could also be countered by using storage in Eastern Canada.

Currently, there are 16 pipeline interconnections between Canada and the US with a total annual maximum capacity of 3032 bcf. The six largest points represent 88% of export capacity. During the gas year 1992/93, the average load factor for all the pipelines to the US was 91%. On the six biggest ones the load factor varied between 79% and 105%. Flows in these pipelines are not reversible.

The Canadian Government has forecast an increase in daily export capacity to 9.2 bcf/day by the year 2000 (annual export capacity of 3358 bcf). There are also 3 pipelines through which gas is imported into Canada from the US, having a total capacity of 500 mcf/day.

Total storage capacity in Canada is 438 bcf; the maximum daily sendout rate 7.0 bcf/day. As one of the responses to the tighter supply and demand conditions, upstream storage capacity is being expanded in the producing regions. Since deregulation, actual annual output from storage has more than tripled. Construction of upstream storage capacity has increased strongly and is expected to continue to increase in the near future. The increased availability of upstream gas storage will increasingly enable such marketing tools as gas exchanges, gas parking, backstopping and pipeline balancing to take on a greater role. These factors contribute to a more flexible and efficient marketplace.

According to a study recently done by the Canadian Government, total storage capacity is expected to increase by 13% by the year 2000.

COPING WITH SUPPLY DISRUPTIONS

The fundamental, underlying principle of the Canadian government's approach to security of supply is to ensure a healthy, open natural gas market, freedom of access to markets coupled with access to supply. Nevertheless, the Energy Supplies Emergency Act contains provisions that in an emergency situation could be applied to natural gas. One of its central elements is compulsory allocation of energy supplies.

Since deregulation in 1985, the number of players active in the marketplace as buyers, sellers, including producers, demand and supply aggregators, marketers and end users, has increased dramatically, resulting in a highly decentralised marketplace for Canadian natural gas. As long as excess deliverability persists, the industry has had little difficulty managing the dislocations caused by wellhead freeze-offs, pipeline outages or contract breakdowns without disrupting gas flows despite the growing number of players. The purpose of the following is to identify the changes that are occurring that will enable both buyers and suppliers to effectively manage supply dislocations and surges in demand, particularly during peak demand periods where there is little or no excess productive capacity.

Prior to 1992, many gas fields in western Canada had not produced at maximum levels nor had they been rigorously tested for several years. As a result, many operators did not have an accurate measure of their fields' sustainable productive capacity at the beginning of the 1992/93 gas year. However, during the record cold winter months of late 1992 and early 1993 and 1994, many fields were operated at maximum capacity for extended periods providing operators with an accurate measure of their field's capability. (Experience during the cold spell in 1992/93 is described in Chapter 6.) This information has enabled producers to more accurately match their contractual commitments with their actual productive capacity. At the same time, in the absence of excess deliverability across the WCSB many producers and marketers have increased the proportion of their total gas supply that is sold on a short-term or spot basis. This enables them not only to backstop their longer term commitments more readily, but also to take advantage of any short-term price spikes. Use of storage in producing regions has allowed producers to have backstop supplies in storage, allowing them to meet peak demand and/or contractual commitments.

LDCs have used downstream storage facilities located near their markets for many years as a valuable tool to manage their gas supply portfolios as well as their customers' gas supplies efficiently and to manage peak demands during the heating season. Downstream storage is increasingly used not only by LDCs, but by end-users, marketers and pipeline companies as a valuable means of increasing the reliability of gas supplies.

Over the last decade, western Canadian producers, supply aggregators and marketers have not required large quantities of upstream storage to manage their gas supply. Parties were able to utilise the relatively large surplus deliverability that existed during this period to mitigate any supply disruptions or to meet demand during peak periods. However, as the excess productivity capacity has declined, upstream storage facilities have been expanded. Upstream storage will allow buyers and sellers to respond more readily to pipeline outages and production difficulties. In addition, its widespread use should reduce the volatility exhibited in short-term prices.

An important aspect of reliable supply management is the anticipation of possible difficulties and the advance preparation of contingency plans that allow parties to respond promptly and effectively to difficulties. Buyers and sellers have implemented a range of contingency plans, including backstopping arrangements between producers and marketers, upstream and downstream storage, exchange agreements with parties that have access to alternative sources of gas supply such as downstream storage or other supply basins. Also, agreements have been made with large end-users located in Canada and the US that can burn alternate fuels, such as cogeneration plants, that allow end-users' gas supply to be diverted to other markets if necessary.

To facilitate the implementation of some of these contingency plans, on 1 November 1993, TransCanada implemented a new service that allows shippers to immediately implement a plan of action in the event of an interruption of upstream supplies. Under TransCanada's Curtailment Contingency Plan, shippers can instruct the pipeline in advance how to curtail markets or where to nominate for alternative sources of gas supply if and when a curtailment occurs. Through this plan shippers can be assured that their lower priority markets will be curtailed before higher priority markets or that backstop supplies will be nominated to avoid curtailments.

Several US Northeast and central Canadian LDCs are negotiating a Mutual Assistance Agreement in conjunction with TransCanada to increase the reliability and security of gas supply to their firm customers. If a gas supply curtailment occurs that threatens firm gas supplies to a participating LDC's customer, other participating LDCs have agreed to use their best efforts, including curtailing interruptible customers, to provide back-up gas supplies to the affected LDCs.

While it is unlikely that it would be necessary to activate this agreement to resolve a short-supply situation encountered by a single producer or marketer, it will be a valuable means to enhance the reliability of firm gas service in the event of a major unscheduled curtailment on a transmission system such as NOVA or TransCanada.

Canadian end gas consumers are among the few in the world that are free to choose their supplier. Many Canadian LDCs have imposed minimum supply conditions on small end-users buying gas on a direct purchase basis. These conditions typically require such buyers to contract for firm gas supplies for periods as long as ten years. They also require the contract to be supported by firm transportation service (not pro-ratable firm or interruptible service). In addition, several utilities require that the delivery capability of the buyer's supplier be assessed by a qualified independent consultant. The supplier must also indemnify the buyer as part of the contract against the incremental cost of alternative gas supplies in the event of a gas supply failure. Finally, the supplier under the gas contract must agree to give the LDC the right to nominate up to 10% above the buyer's DCQ (Daily Contract Quantity) to provide an additional source of back-up gas to the LDC in the event that the gas supply to other small users is interrupted or curtailed.

Until October 1993, large volumes of western Canadian gas were sold under firm contracts with fixed prices for one year and often longer. When gas prices suddenly increased to much higher levels in late 1992, the risk of interruptions to a buyer's gas supply due to "price majeure" (the fact that the seller may want to sell the gas to somebody else for a higher price) also increased. In response to the greater price volatility associated with tighter gas supply/demand balances, many buyers and sellers have indexed their firm gas contract prices to spot prices. By indexing the price, the risk to the buyer and the seller of the price being significantly above or below the market and, hence, the risk of supply disruptions due to "price majeure" are decreased.

A highly decentralised, tightly balanced market with a large number of active participants trading gas 24 hours a day at several different points along an integrated system from the wellhead to the burner tip requires efficient and accurate communications between the players. Producers, aggregators, pipelines, storage operators, LDCs and many end-users require early and detailed information about potential or actual supply disruptions. Parties requiring incremental gas supplies must be able to quickly locate sellers with gas available. Similarly, sellers with excess supplies need to identify buyers requiring gas. Both buyers and sellers must be able to obtain timely and reliable information on current gas prices. To facilitate this exchange of information new services are being offered. At least two companies are offering electronic gas trading systems that are expected to be fully operational in the near future. Using these systems, it will be possible to buy and sell gas anonymously on hourly, daily, monthly or longer terms at different delivery points twenty-four hours a day, seven days a week. The operators of these systems guarantee the delivery of gas purchased through their systems, enhancing the reliability of supply.

A second development is the use of electronic bulletin boards. Bulletin boards are designed to allow pipeline companies, shippers, buyers and sellers and other market participants to communicate information easily and quickly regarding pipeline curtailments, nomination changes, available pipeline capacity/requests for pipeline capacity, and gas supplies required or available.

In addition to the measures and instruments mentioned above, which are to a certain extent the result of the recent restructuring of the Canadian gas market, traditional measures like supply diversification and interruptible contracts are also used to enhance security of supply. Large gas purchasers, particularly LDCs in central Canada and British Columbia, have diversified their gas supply portfolios to include gas from US supply basins, which in some cases has entailed the construction of new pipelines.

The use of interruptible contracts is widespread in Canada, but precise estimates of the potential for switching between fuels does not seem to exist. The Government indicates that 20% of industrial LDC sales, or 10% of total sales, are switchable. Other estimates are somewhat higher. The use of interruptible contracts varies widely by region; it is very low in areas where end-users are located near production. In eastern Canada, LDCs have low interruptible rates to encourage a proportion of end-users to maintain a multi-fuel capability. There are, however, few curtailments to interruptible customers, as curtailments generate loss of revenues.

The Canadian Government believes the multi-fuel capacity has stopped declining and will remain constant in the future. Because it considers the choice of fuel to be a commercial matter, the Government no longer has policies or programmes aimed at encouraging multi-fired capacity.

The NEB collects statistics on pipeline incidents in Canada. In 1993 it registered 65 different incidents. The data collection is done as part of the NEB responsibility for pipeline safety regulation. However, nobody seems to keep a precise record of events resulting in supply disruptions. The evidence in this area is therefore rather anecdotal. The historical record of the Canadian gas supply system seems to be good in the sense that supply interruptions normally are mitigated very quickly.

DENMARK

GAS POLICY

In 1992, gas constituted 11% of TPES and accounted for 2.5% of electricity production in Denmark. The share of TPES is expected to increase to around 20% by the year 2000 and remain at that level. The Danish gas market is thus still in a development phase. The Danish government has strongly encouraged the use of natural gas. Since its inception, the Danish Natural Gas Project, i.e., the downstream part of the Danish gas industry, has been assisted financially by a tax exemption on gas sales and a formula linking the price of gas to the price of oil, including taxes and duties. In 1993, this *de facto* subsidy was estimated at DKr 2 billion. Natural gas use, particularly in industry, large power plants and small-scale CHP for district heating, is expected to continue to rise significantly to the end of the 1990s as a result of government measures. These measures include the promotion of a small scale CHP programme, the exemption of gas from the recently introduced carbon tax and the requirement that electric utilities draw up capacity plans consistent with the objectives of "Energy 2000", an action plan for a sustainable energy development in Denmark published in 1990. The follow-up plan published in November 1993 includes several new measures to increase connections to natural gas.

GAS DEMAND

The Danish gas market is expected to reach its maturity by the year 2000. Domestic sales are expected to increase from 2.3 bcm in 1993 to 4.1 bcm in 2000. As there is limited potential for further expansion in the residential sector, most of the growth will take place in the industrial sector (up from 693 mcm in 1992 to 1,050 mcm in 2000), in power generation (up from 84 mcm in 1992 to 950 mcm in 2000) and in CHP and DHP plants (from 572 mcm in 1992 to 1500 mcm in 2000).

In 1993, Denmark exported 1.54 bcm of natural gas to Sweden and Germany. As a consequence of new contracts, export volumes are poised to increase to 3.5 bcm annually from 1997. Total sales from the Danish continental shelf are thus expected to reach 7.5 bcm annually around 2000, but might decline somewhat during the period up to 2010.

GAS SUPPLY

Production from the Danish continental shelf is so far the only source of supply. Based on expected gas reserves of 202 bcm in 2000, the production level can be maintained for about 27 years. The Danish government pursues an active exploration policy to increase the reserve base. The Government leaves decisions about exports to Dansk Olie & Naturgas A/S (DONG). Gas production beyond 7.5 bcm with a view to increasing exports would necessitate large investments in new infrastructure.

In 1993, Dansk Naturgas A/S (DANGAS), a subsidiary of DONG, concluded a new purchase agreement with the Danish Underground Consortium (DUC) which increased the total volume to be delivered to 130 bcm of which 24 bcm had been delivered by the end of 1993. The deliveries will have an annual plateau level of 7-7.5 bcm which will be upheld for a minimum of nine years. The contract does not stipulate a fixed total volume but rather a fixed annual volume that will be supplied as long as it is technically and financially feasible to carry on production at this level.

DANGAS has a contract with Swedish buyers for deliveries of 20 bcm over the period 1985 to 2010, implying annual deliveries of 1.1 bcm annually up to 2002. An additional contract with German buyers will increase annual volumes from 0.7 bcm a year to 2.5 bcm annually from 1997. This volume could, however, be reduced if there is a need for this gas to supply the Danish market.

New supplies from the Danish Continental Shelf beyond what is foreseen today would imply increasing costs as this would necessitate significant investments in new infrastructure. For security of supply reasons DANGAS wants new supply sources outside the Danish continental shelf. A link to the Norwegian pipeline system has been considered in the context of possible exports from Norway to Sweden with Denmark acting as a transit country. Another possible solution is taking supplies from the British part of the North Sea through a pipeline to Poland or Germany.

INFRASTRUCTURE

In 1993, a total of 6.3 bcm was produced on the Danish continental shelf. Of this, 4.0 bcm were sold to DANGAS and 1.87 bcm was reinjected. The remainder was consumed or flared on the platforms. The Danish gas production takes place in nine different fields, of which Tyra is the most important, accounting for about 60% of total production. Gas from all the DUC fields passes through the Tyra complex before it is shipped through one single offshore pipeline to the Nybro gas treatment plant located onshore. The increase in gas sales from 1997 means that new compression facilities will have to be installed at the Tyra platform. These facilities can also be used for injecting gas into the Tyra reservoir in periods with low gas sales.

The Nybro terminal has been dimensioned particularly with security of supply in mind. Its gas processing facilities will be expanded by a new production line from 1997, increasing the daily gas processing capacity from 16 to 25 mcm.

The onshore transmission pipeline system is simple, having one West-East line through which gas is exported to Sweden, and one North-South line through which gas is also exported to Germany. The pipeline from Nybro to Egtved, where the two lines cross, will be doubled before

1997. As far as storage is concerned, the philosophy has been to locate such facilities as far out on the two transmission axes as possible given the constraints that geology imposes on such location. For the time being there are two storage facilities that are operative, Ll.Torup in Jutland and Stenlille on Zealand. Both facilities are currently being expanded. At Ll.Torup, six caverns have been established in a subterranean salt dome with a total capacity of 300 mcm of natural gas. A seventh cavern will be added, bringing total capacity to 375 mcm.

At the Stenlille storage facility, a total of 400 mcm of natural gas was injected into the aquifer of a sandstone structure at the end of 1994, giving a possibility to withdraw approximately 150 mcm from this storage facility in the winter of 1994/95.

To keep storage in line with the growth in demand, DONG is considering the expansion of storage facilities, including the possibility of new storage facilities at Toender in the south of Denmark close to the pipeline to Germany.

COPING WITH DISRUPTIONS

Denmark has a general law on measures concerning distribution and rationing of goods in the case of shortages caused by international circumstances ("Lov om forsyningsmessige foranstaltninger"), but there is no legislation dealing explicitly with security of gas supply. It has therefore been up to the actors in the gas industry to provide for security of supply. Given the circumstances under which the Natural Gas Project was created, DANGAS has very strong commercial incentives to assure its customers a high degree of security of supply.

The objectives of DANGAS in the area of security of supply are:

■ In a normal situation DANGAS aims at being able to supply the total market, although all interruptible customers — including the major power plants — can be interrupted if needed.

■ To cope with emergency situations DANGAS aims at establishing sufficient storage volume and withdrawal capacity for securing supply to the uninterruptible market during the period it will take to re-establish the supply, e.g., for the repair of a breakage of the offshore pipeline.

Historically, the reliability record is very good. Maximum down time on offshore facilities has been 6 to 8 hours. The gas treatment facilities at Nybro have never been down for more than 10 minutes.

When there is an interruption in supplies, a procedure will be followed under which deliveries will be based on linepack until gas from storage can be released and deliveries to the interruptible customers can be established. The interruptible customers are obliged to keep backup facilities. Deliveries to the interruptible customers have never been interrupted.

In addition to using storage and interruptibles, there are also other flexibilities in the system. In a case where there is a cutoff in supplies from only one platform, such shortfalls can be met by reducing reinjection of gas on other platforms.

The effect of a disruption in supplies varies considerably depending upon when it occurs. At present, daily demand can be as low as 4 mcm a day in the summer, whereas peak winter demand can rise to 21 mcm a day.

During the coldest month of 1993, about 5 mcm a day on average was delivered from storage. The maximum sendout from storage was 15 mcm/day in 1993 increasing to 18 mcm/day in 1994. In case of a complete interruption in gas supplies in a situation with a daily consumption over 20 mcm, it would be difficult to continue to supply all firm customers if the cold weather persisted for several days. Expansion of storage and sendout capacity will enable DANGAS to tackle such situations better in the future.

FINLAND

GAS POLICY

In 1993, gas constituted 8% of Finland's TPES. The share of gas in electricity generation was 8.1% and 26% in the production of district heat and power. By imposing differentiated energy taxation and subsidising interest payments for the construction of a gas transmission network, the Government has encouraged the increase in natural gas consumption observed over the last 20 years. Today the gas market in Finland is in many ways at a crossroads in that from an energy policy point of view the circumstances are favourable for a further gas expansion, but this is on the condition that one more source of supply in addition to present Russian supplies is found. In 1994, an agreement was entered into with Gazprom which will allow volumes from Russia to increase to 4 bcm during the 1990s. The Government has decided against a further nuclear expansion and gas is an obvious alternative in power generation. The Government therefore actively supports efforts to establish a pan-nordic gas transmission system based on gas from Norway.

GAS DEMAND

Natural gas consumption in Finland totalled 2.9 bcm in 1993. Demand forecasts vary considerably as a function of the role seen for gas in power generation. With no major breakthrough for gas in power generation, total demand is expected to be 4.2 bcm in 2000 and 5.0 bcm in 2005. The major growth will then take place in district heating and in industry. With access to one new supply source and a decision to increase gas use in large scale power generation, demand could total 8 bcm in 10 years' time.

GAS SUPPLY

Finland has no gas production of its own and started importing Russian gas 20 years ago. Since then it has received 27 bcm of gas from Russia which is still the only import source. Recently, Neste, the state oil and gas company, concluded a joint venture agreement with Gazprom, creating a new company called Gasum of which Neste owns 75% and Gazprom 25%. This company concluded a new supply agreement with Gazprom allowing it to increase its present imports to more than 4 bcm annually by 2000. The 20 year agreement is expected to further enhance the price stability and predictability of Russian gas exports to Finland. Gazprom considers that it now has the incentive to make the terms to Gasum as favourable as possible and contracts as stable as possible, and that Finland can expect preferential treatment as a result of this agreement.

A few years ago, Neste discussed the possibility of importing gas from Norway. Real negotiations were never initiated, because there was not enough demand in Sweden to justify a pipeline from the North Sea. If the attitude to gas in Sweden becomes more favourable, the Finns will make a new attempt to import gas from Norway. LNG imports into Finland were considered, but the idea was abandoned for cost reasons.

INFRASTRUCTURE

The gas transmission system in Finland is a simple one, consisting of one East-West axis branching off towards the North and South in the Western part of the country but without reaching the West coast. The system includes two compressor stations and 170 delivery points (pressure reduction stations). About half of Finland's population lives within reach of the distribution system.

The gas from Russia is taken from Urengoy through the Northern Lights pipeline, and thus only crosses Russian territory so that no transit problems arise. The Russian compressor station at Severnaja, 150 km from the Finnish border, can be fed via two pipeline strings. There are also two routes for taking gas to St. Petersburg through which gas to Finland has to pass.

Finnish geology lends itself badly to construction of storage facilities and there are no such facilities so far. A 350 MW air-propane plant with an underground propane storage, designed to meet the energy needs of "gas specific customers" in the event that normal gas supplies are completely interrupted, does exist.

COPING WITH DISRUPTIONS

The Emergency Preparedness Act gives the Ministry of Trade and Industry the powers to ration energy in emergency situations. According to the Act on Economic Security Stockpiling, stockpiles can be created and maintained for raw materials, equipment and commodities indispensable to the livelihood of the population and the unbroken production of output in the case of disturbances in foreign trade. Under the Act on Compulsory Stockpiling of Imported Fuels the importers of coal, crude oil and oil products shall maintain mandatory stockpiles. The increased importance of natural gas in Finland (in areas where gas is distributed its share of primary energy consumption is estimated to reach 20% during the 1990s, and it could reach more than 60% of fuel consumption in district heating and CHP) has led to efforts in favour of bringing gas under this act. A proposal to this effect (a draft concerning all fossil fuels including natural gas) is now before Parliament and is expected to be adopted in January 1995 and enforced by July 1995. In practice this would mean that gas users supplying electricity and heat to communities and consuming more than 15 mcm of natural gas a year would have to maintain stocks of replacement fuels corresponding to 3 months' consumption to be used in the event of an interruption in gas supplies. No such obligation will be imposed on industry. Industrial customers are expected to store one week's consumption of alternative fuels under their contracts with Gasum. Household customers are covered by the gas importer's obligation to store alternative fuels in gaseous form (e.g., propane for the air-propane plant).

Because Finland has no storage facilities it has been necessary to install facilities to burn alternative fuels. About 90% of gas consumption can easily be replaced by petroleum products, 50% by LFO and 40% by HFO. The remainder of natural gas end users are gas-specific, for whom replacing gas with liquid fuels is either impossible or very difficult. In the event of a gas supply interruption 3% of the total gas volumes could be substituted by LPG and 7% by air-propane mixture.

What would typically happen in a situation where there is a shortfall in gas supplies is that big industrial consumers will switch to oil, power stations to oil or coal. When the pressure on the gas distribution network has become sufficiently low an air-propane mixture can be introduced to feed the gas specific customers. For this purpose an air-propane plant has been built adjacent to the Porvoo refinery. The linepack in the transmission system, at a pressure of 40 bar, would be sufficient for the needs of gas-specific users for nearly a week. The air-propane mixture, however, can only be introduced when the transmission pipeline pressure has fallen to 8 bar.

Historically, the reliability record of Russian supplies has been very good. Over the 20 year period of Russian deliveries to Finland there have been two interruptions. In both cases they were due to technical problems arising when starting gas shipments in new loops. In both cases it took less than 36 hours to sort out the problems, and the Russians made admirable efforts to do it as efficiently as possible. In some instances during cold spells there have been unforeseen pressure falls on the pipeline to Finland, but these have not caused major problems.

Investment in the air-propane plant mentioned above has been made in the hope that it will not have to be used. If the plant had been in existence over the entire period since the introduction of natural gas in 1974, it would in fact never have been used.

FRANCE

GAS POLICY

State-owned Gaz de France (GDF) dominates the gas industry and has a monopoly over all imports and exports. Gaz du Sud-Ouest (GSO), which is 70% owned by Elf Aquitaine and 30% by GDF, operates the gas transmission network in the southwest of France where it exploits domestic production. Compagnie Française du Méthane (CFM) plays a gas marketing role in central France but the network in this region is still operated by GDF. CFM is owned by GDF (50%), Elf Aquitaine (40%) and Total (10%). As the main actor, GDF is the body to which the government delegates the responsibility for maintaining the supply/demand balance.

There is no stated policy on the sources of future imports and levels of supply diversification, although all import agreements are subject to government approval.

A recent report commissioned by the government proposed major changes in the organisation of the gas industry. These proposals included:

- Removal of GDF's import and export monopoly (to be replaced by a system of import authorisations for gas network operators and large industrial consumers);

- Changes in ownership structures of GSO and CFM to give a single majority shareholder in the two regions served by the companies;

- Removal of the requirement that transportation companies be at least 30% state-owned;

- Allowing those communes not yet served with gas to choose the concessionary that will build and operate the distribution network.

The report does, however, foresee a role for a single body to manage the transportation network and ensure a balance between supply and demand. The conclusions and recommendations of the report are under consideration.

The short term market outlook and gas policy are described by the *Contrat d'Objectifs* - a planning agreement between GDF and the government that covers a three year period. The current *contrat* covers the period 1994-96 and sets targets for sales growth, performance, tariffs and investment.

Gas suppliers in France (GDF as well as the other regional/local distributors) are under a public service obligation to supply any customer within their authorised supply areas. In addition, an operator must set its prices in such a way that its customers with the same demand characteristics pay the same rates, wherever they are located geographically.

GAS DEMAND

In 1992 natural gas demand was 28 Mtoe, almost all of which was consumed by industry and the residential/commercial sectors. Gas penetration in the industrial sector was 22% and 27% in the residential/commercial sector.

The *Contrat d'Objectifs* foresees gas reaching 45-55% of the market for new residential buildings[1] and the network's geographic coverage increasing from 70% to 75% of all homes. In the longer term combined heat and power is being encouraged and is likely to account for roughly 4% of gas consumption by the year 2000.

Industry estimates project total gas demand to grow from 28 Mtoe in 1992 to 33.5-34.5 Mtoe in the year 2000. After 2005 there is considerable uncertainty surrounding the possible role of gas for electricity generation. This uncertainty is reflected in the large range of estimated demand levels for 2010 which vary from 35 to 44 Mtoe.

GAS SUPPLY

About 9% of supplies are met by domestic production (mainly from the Lacq field in the southwest) while the vast majority is imported from Russia (32%), Algeria (27%), Norway (18%) and the Netherlands (14%).

Domestic production is tailing off and is expected to be negligible by 2000. GDF's most recent supply contract covers deliveries from the Norwegian Troll/Sleipner fields which began in October 1993 and are due to reach plateau volumes of 8 bcm (6.4 Mtoe) by 2004. Existing contracts cover projected demand up to 2000. Assuming that existing contracts will be renewed, a further 9-10 Mtoe will be required in 2010 if demand reaches the upper scenario, although under the low gas demand growth scenario no significant new supplies will be needed.

Table 1   Supply and Demand Balance (Mtoe)

	1992	2000	2010
Demand	28	33.5 - 34.5	35 - 44
of which: CHP		1.8 - 1.9	1.3 - 2.1
Contracted Supply (estimate including probable renewal of existing contracts)	28	35	35
Potential Supply Gap	0	0	0 - 9

Source: Gaz de France.

---

1.   Electric heating is very common in France and in 1992 electricity made up almost 40% of total residential energy consumption.

INFRASTRUCTURE

The transmission pipeline network is well interconnected, with supplies entering the network in five separate regions:

■ Dutch and Norwegian gas arrive at the Belgian border in the north of the country;

■ Russian gas arrives at the German border in the northeast;

■ Algerian gas is delivered to the two LNG terminals in the south and west;

■ French gas is produced in the southwest.

The new volumes of gas contracted under the Troll deal will entail the construction of a new pipeline from the North Sea. It has recently been decided that the landing point for this pipeline will be Dunkerque in France. This decision will determine which parts of the French grid will need reinforcement.

Further projects include the construction of a pipeline from the LNG reception terminal at Fos to Toulouse scheduled for completion in 1997. This line will complete a loop around the south of the country and will facilitate the delivery of Algerian gas to the southwest as production from the Lacq field declines. There is also a possibility that a new reception terminal will be built at Fos. Given today's contract portfolio, though, and the fact that demand should be covered for several years by these contracts, no major new works are planned between now and 2000.

Storage capacity of 8 Mtoe at 15 sites around the country represents 104 days of average consumption. Capacity should be expanded by another 2 Mtoe before 2000 - in line with the forecast growth in demand.

The French gas system of import contracts, production and storage is designed so that it can continue to supply all of its customers continually during a 2% winter - or, in other words, the coldest winter that is statistically probable in any 50 year period. Such a winter, were it to occur now, would increase annual demand by about 1.5 Mtoe/year above average levels. It is this criteria which determines whether additional storage capacity is necessary.

France recently began "transiting" Norwegian gas to Spain with the construction of a new pipeline crossing the Pyrenees. The Norwegian gas is not physically delivered to Spain; it is swapped for an equivalent quantity of French gas. Initial loads are 2 bcm/year (1.6 Mtoe), although the pipeline could carry up to 6 bcm (4.8 Mtoe).

COPING WITH DISRUPTIONS

With the largest storage capacity of any country in western Europe, France is able to import gas at a consistently high load factor. While minimum monthly summer demand is about a quarter of maximum monthly winter demand, imports remain more or less level throughout the year.

Storage levels at the end of the winter heating season are typically below 2 Mtoe, 25% of capacity. The storage facilities have been designed for seasonal load balancing and not specifically as a strategic stock to guard against supply disruptions.

Interruptible contracts make up roughly half of the industrial market, but unlike the situation in many other countries, they are not normally disrupted in winter. Their purpose is strategic - to reduce demand during a major supply interruption. Under the contract terms, supplies to interruptible customers can be disrupted for indefinite periods. The vast majority of these customers have dual-fired facilities that allow them to burn heavy fuel oil. Before renewing its interruptible sales contracts, GDF is now systematically verifying the existence of this fuel switching capability.

In the event of a disruption to one supply source the transmission grid could distribute the available gas supplies within the country. By cutting supplies to interruptible customers and using the flexibility provided by its storage facilities, France could withstand a disruption from one of its major suppliers for about a year before having to disturb firm clients.

Given a large and long-lasting disruption to supplies, GDF would, no doubt, attempt to secure extra-contractual quantities of gas from its non-disrupted suppliers. In a worst case scenario, a 1974 law on energy saving allows ministers to ration available supplies within the country and to take additional measures such as limiting the temperature to which buildings may be heated.

GERMANY

GAS POLICY

The government does not intervene heavily in the German gas sector but does supervise the supply side. All import agreements lasting over two years are subject to approval from the Ministry. The criterion under which applications for approval are considered is one of security of supply. In 1981 imports of Russian gas were limited (using the approval mechanism described above) to 30% of total gas supply. This restriction was lifted in August 1993. The government's policy remains one of supply source diversification by the gas companies.

Perhaps the most interesting recent change to the German gas industry has been the development of further competition[1] in the gas supply and transport business. Wingas, owned 65% by Wintershall and 35% by Russia's Gazprom, now claims a market share of 10% (compared to Ruhrgas' 75%) and is aiming to reach a share of 15%. Competition has been introduced by Wingas building its own transmission pipelines (it now has over 1200 kilometres of pipeline and serves more than 30 industrial and municipal customers). There is no legislation restricting companies from building transmission pipelines.

Regulatory pressure to open up the German gas industry to more competition is coming from various sources including the Federal Cartel Office (FCO). The FCO is continuing its efforts to break up the gas and electricity companies' area monopolies - although last year it suffered a setback when it failed to open up Verbundnetz Gas' pipelines to access from a third party.

The government has repeatedly declared its willingness to introduce more competition to the grid-based industries. Both the gas and electricity industries operate in a legal framework which provides exemption under areas of cartel law and allows concessions and demarcation contracts. The Federal Economics Ministry's latest draft proposals (revised to give them more chance of being accepted by the municipalities and regional gas companies) include the following elements:

- abolition of clauses exempting network-based industries from accusations of abuse of dominant market position;

- preservation of vertical demarcation contracts;

- reform of municipalities' right to refuse rights of way for pipeline laying.

---

1. The German gas industry is diverse in terms of the number of different companies operating, with 10 producers, 19 long-distance transport carriers, 151 regional gas supply companies and 478 local gas suppliers. But the sector is dominated by regional supply monopolies at each level in the supply chain and by significant cross-shareholding.

GAS DEMAND

In 1994 gas made up 18.3% of TPES. This share is expected to rise as new markets are found for gas. One important new market is eastern Germany where town gas networks are being rapidly converted to natural gas and where lignite, which has been commonly used for space heating, is being replaced by gas.

Table 1   Demand Forecast (Mtoe)

	1992	2000	2010
Total Demand	**56.8**	**71.5**	**79.5**
Industry	18.8	21.7	25.2
Electricity Generation, CHP & District Heating	12.2	17.9	20.2
Residential/Commercial	25.1	27.7	29.9
Unattributed	0.7	4.2	4.2
Gas' Share of TPES	16.7%	20.0%	22.3%

Source: Country Submission based on Prognos Institute forecasts.

The forecast demand figures show the fastest growth potential in the electricity sector. Gas sold for use in combined cycle turbines and CHP plants is subject to a reduced tax rate - although this will be phased out in 2001/2. The industry, however, is not marketing gas aggressively for power generation for fear of being perceived as the "coal killer". The forecasts show gas-fired power generation making up 15% of total generation in 2010, up from 6% in 1992.

GAS SUPPLY

In 1994 Germany's supplies came from domestic production (22.6%), Russia (35.7%), the Netherlands (25.9%), Norway (13.8%) and Denmark (2%). German gas companies have contracted for large new volumes of Troll gas over the forecast period. The general trend is one of an increasing Norwegian supply share (to 30% between 2000 and 2010), stable domestic production (in absolute terms) and stable or falling imports from the Netherlands. The balance of supply requirements will probably come from Russia and Norway and possibly the UK through the new Interconnector.

Deliveries under the Troll contract began in October 1993, with initial supplies coming from the Sleipner East field. Plateau volumes of 23 Mtoe per year should be reached by 2005.

Most of Germany's reserves are in the west of the country. Proven and probable reserves are estimated at 230 Mtoe - giving a reserves to production ratio of 17 years. Possible reserves could prolong production significantly. Nevertheless, production is forecast to be stable at 13.4 Mtoe from 1994 to 2010.

Whether the export contracts from the Netherlands to Germany which expire before 2010 will be increased will depend on new reserve discoveries. However, it seems inevitable that the

Netherlands' peak production capacity will drop as the pressure of the Groningen field falls and that supply flexibility in any new contract will be correspondingly lower.

Imports from Denmark, at 0.7 Mtoe in 1994, should reach 2.3 Mtoe/year by 1996 under a new contract between Ruhrgas and Dansk Naturgas running to 2012.

INFRASTRUCTURE DEVELOPMENT

The German gas network is well-developed and at the heart of the European grid. In addition to transporting 58.7 Mtoe for consumption within Germany in 1994, the network transported around 17 Mtoe of gas in transit to France, Italy, Switzerland and the Netherlands.

Several new pipeline projects are either planned or in development. The Europipe should be in operation in October, 1995, bringing Norwegian gas to Emden and the Netra line is being developed to transport Norwegian gas into eastern Germany. Wintershall plans to have its new Wedal pipeline through the Ruhr region in operation by 1996 and has plans for further projects into Bavaria and possibly to Switzerland.

There are plans for a large increase in storage capacity in Germany over the next 15 years, from a current level of 9.8 bcm to 21.5 bcm in 2010. This development is being driven by several factors:

- Wintershall, the new market entrant, is dependent on supplies from Russia and is building very significant storage capacity (including the 4.2 bcm aquifer at Rehden) to ensure a secure supply to its customers.

- The flexibility in supplies from the Netherlands is expected to decrease as Groningen peak production capacity drops, increasing the need for seasonal load balancing facilities within Germany.

- Demand is expected to rise by 40% between 1992 and 2010, with significant growth in the low load residential sector.

COPING WITH SHORT TERM DISRUPTIONS

Germany, as a whole, has a diversified supply portfolio, numerous storage facilities and flexibility in both supplies (from the Netherlands' swing production) and demand (through interruptible contracts). In addition the country has no critical infrastructure links. The trend is one of continued supply diversity, though with falling supply flexibility from the Netherlands which may be offset by increased storage.

Gas consumption in the new Lander of eastern Germany represented 13.8% of the German market in 1994, with 67.8% of this being met by supplies from Russia. Supply diversification there is being improved as east-west transport capacity is expanded, and volumes of Norwegian gas will be available in the autumn of 1996.

It has, however, been difficult for Wintershall to diversify its supply sources. With the exception of small deliveries from the UK Markham field, the company is dependent on Gazprom (one of its shareholders). Wintershall's attempts to buy gas from Norway's Saga have so far been thwarted by the Norwegian Gas Negociating Committee.

Reliance on voluntary agreements reached between gas companies, organised through a clearing association of companies, would be the governments initial response to a disruption. Only if this solution proved unworkable would the government invoke its legislative powers to intervene in the market and force companies to share supplies.

GREECE

The share of domestically produced natural gas in TPES was only 0.4% in 1993, down from 0.6% in 1992, due to the depletion of South Kavala, the only field producing gas in Greece. The large-scale introduction of natural gas on the Greek market remains one of the government's energy priorities, but since total gas reserves in Greece are only 9 bcm, the introduction of gas will have to be based on imports. The Government projects that the share of gas in TPES will exceed 11% by 2005.

A project aimed at importing Russian gas is progressing rapidly. A large part of the pipeline from the Bulgarian border to Athens has been built. Current plans call for deliveries of Russian gas to start in the first half of 1996 at a level of 0.73-1.40 bcm/year, subsequently increasing to 2.4 bcm per year and possibly as much as 3 bcm a year. Under a supplemental agreement reached by the Greek and Russian Governments in October 1994, a take-or-pay clause will come into effect in July 1997. In addition, as of 1998, Gazprom, the Russian gas company, will have access to DEPA's (the state gas company) grid and the right to sell gas in excess of the quantities contracted to DEPA, both in Greece and abroad via Greece, under terms to be agreed upon later. With regard to supplies of Algerian gas, an LNG plant is scheduled to start operation in 1998.

Under an agreement signed in June 1994 between PPC, the state power company, and DEPA, PPC will gradually absorb 1.3 bcm per year, starting in 1996, for use in power generation. In addition, preliminary agreements have been signed with industrial customers for the sale of 0.3 bcm a year. Plans are advancing for the construction of a low-pressure distribution grid.

IRELAND

GAS POLICY

Natural gas accounts for about 20% of TPES in Ireland, and the country is at present basically self-sufficient. Moreover, with a reserve/production ratio of only 7 years it will have to gain access to new supplies either on its own territory or as imports if it is to maintain and expand its gas market. Supplies from abroad are potentially available after the construction of the UK-Ireland Interconnector which is now operative.

The Irish Government supports the increased penetration of gas which is likely to play an important role in enabling Ireland to meet international environmental constraints. A ban on smoke-producing fuels in major cities has facilitated the penetration of gas. To keep a high level of gas self-sufficiency, the Government has taken measures to encourage exploration. Realising that the country may have to rely on external supply sources in the future, BGE took the initiative to build a pipeline to Scotland which is now operative.

GAS DEMAND

Total gas consumption in Ireland in 1994 was 2.77 bcm. According to the assumptions made for the demand forecast provided by the government for this study, demand is expected to decline somewhat up to 2000, but then to increase again before 2010. The reasons for the temporary decline are the forecast loss of industrial markets to HFO and loss of ammonia feedstock business. All incremental electricity demand is, however, to be met by gas fired power plants. The strongest gas demand growth is expected in the residential/commercial sector (total growth of 226% over the entire period). In 1993, there were more than 200.000 residential customers, and by the end of the century natural gas should be available to 40% of all Irish homes with 30% of Irish homes using natural gas as their main heating and cooking fuel.

GAS SUPPLY

At the beginning of 1995, Irish gas reserves were estimated at 20 bcm, down from 22 bcm the year before. Few gas finds have been made in recent years, and only two are producing. The major part of present production comes from the Kinsale Head field (about 245 MMcfd) while the Ballycotton satellite field produces about 15 MMcfd. In two years or so production from the Kinsale Head field will be in decline, and if new finds are not made gas will have to be imported from Scotland.

After 1986, there was a marked falloff in exploration, but in recent years the Government has taken steps to encourage exploration by more favourable terms. Legislation enacted in 1992 ended state participation and cut taxes. New licencing terms were also announced that reawakened companies' interest in exploration off Ireland. The companies are optimistic about the potential for new finds.

INFRASTRUCTURE

Kinsale Head A and B platforms, installed in 1977, can each produce 200 MMcfd of gas. The Ballycotton field is a single well, subsea satellite to the Kinsale Head B platform, connected to the mother platform by an 8 mile 10 inch pipeline and a control umbilical. The Kinsale Head A platform is linked by a single 24 inch pipeline to the Inch gas terminal southeast of Cork city. From the Inch terminal there is one transmission pipeline going northeast to Dublin and Dundalk.

An interconnector between Moffat in Scotland and Ballough, north of Dublin, was completed in December 1993 and became operational in 1994. With full compression installed, its capacity is about 5 bcm/year. It is intended to serve initially as a reserve supply source until the existing fields reach depletion, but will increasingly be used from late 1996 to meet growing demand in both the power generation and direct use market.

There are at present no storage facilities in Ireland, but there are plans to build a liquefaction plant as security backup for the interconnector pipeline linking Ireland with the UK national transmission system.

Once gas reserves from domestic fields are depleted, Ireland will again be dependent upon a single physical link for its natural gas supplies. Preliminary consideration is being given to building a pipeline linked to the Northern Ireland system, which is expected to be linked to Scotland in 1997.

COPING WITH DISRUPTIONS

In the event of a disturbance in gas supplies from domestic sources, Ireland would for the time being have two options: either interrupt supplies to electricity producers or receive backup supplies from the UK. There are at present no formally interruptible contracts in Ireland (although this possibility is being explored). There is, however, an informal arrangement with the Electricity Supply Board to cut supplies to power generation in case of need. Most gas used in electricity generation is for dual fired plants. Thus generation can be switched from natural gas to HFO at relatively short notice.

In addition, there is a "Security Gas Contract" in place between Bord Gais Eireann and the UK power generator National Power. This contract provides for emergency supplies of gas in the event of a loss of supplies from indigenous sources and will contribute to security of supply of the non-interruptible load until 1998.

ITALY

GAS POLICY

In 1992, gas constituted around 26% of TPES and accounted for 15.8% of electricity output. Historically, the government has actively promoted the "methanisation" of the Italian economy. In recent years it has introduced legislation (Law 9/1991 and Decree 6/1992) to encourage independent power producers to install gas fired production capacity by guaranteeing a fixed purchase price for the surplus power. The price has been defined on the basis of costs avoided by ENEL (the state owned electricity company), including capital, operation and fuel costs. The extra costs incurred by ENEL as a consequence of paying the specified price is recovered by an additional charge on the average electricity price paid by electricity customers. This measure has been taken to counteract a possible deficit in future electricity generation capacity.

Recently, the Italian Government has become concerned about the high level of dependence on gas, especially in the electricity sector. It is reconsidering the expansion of natural gas demand in the future, taking into account all the structural inflexibilities tied to the characteristics of natural gas (e.g., long term contracts, infrastructure for pipelines and for LNG), but no direct measures have been taken to slow down gas expansion. The Government has, however, taken some indirect measures that could reduce the rate of expansion (e.g., energy efficiency legislation, permission to burn HFO in connection with the adoption of gasification technology in power generation and burning of residues in refineries). On the other hand, no new taxes on gas are foreseen in the near future.

GAS DEMAND

The Italian government foresees strong growth in gas consumption: between 1992 and 2000, demand is expected to grow by about 19 bcm and a further 16 bcm between 2000 and 2010. More than 50% of the growth over the whole period is expected to take place in power generation. ENEL's own forecasts for gas in power generation are somewhat lower, but still imply a tripling of gas consumption over the period to 2005. ENEL forecasts a 3.5% per annum growth in electricity consumption, and reckons that in 2005 independent power producers could account for almost one-third of total electricity production. SNAM (the state owned gas company) estimates the share of independent producers in 2005 at 26%. Growth in the industrial and residential sectors is also expected to be vigourous in that total consumption will increase by 48% and 40%, respectively, over the period to 2010. The 48% growth in the industrial sector includes electricity production for own use and for sale to ENEL. Industrial consumption excluding electricity production is expected to grow by 20% from 1992 to 2010.

GAS SUPPLY

In addition to having a relatively high share of total gas supplies from indigenous production (roughly one-third in 1993), Italy has a well diversified supply pattern (in 1993: 10.9% of total supplies from the Netherlands, 27.3% from Russia and 30.5% from Algeria).

Indigenous production is expected to increase from around 19 bcm today to about 21 bcm around the year 2000, but is expected to decrease gradually to around 15 bcm by 2010. In view of the strong increase in forecast demand, import dependency is expected to increase from around 67% today to 82% in 2010.

Italy has already taken steps to further diversify its supply sources. ENEL has a contract to buy LNG from Nigeria but is dependent upon finding a solution to the problems that have arisen concerning the siting of the receiving terminal at Montalto di Castro. Import volumes from Russia and Algeria are expected to increase substantially in absolute terms, but the share of the two countries in total Italian supplies might decline somewhat in relative terms over the period to 2010. Recently a contract has been concluded with Gazprom under which Italian companies are to renovate parts of the Russian transmission pipeline system against deliveries of gas. The deliveries under this deal will reach a plateau level of 5.5 bcm in 1998/99. Recently a new contract has been concluded with Algeria for LNG deliveries into the La Spezia terminal (about 2 bcm a year). Deliveries from Algeria (including a direct contract between ENEL and Sonatrach) will increase after the doubling of the Transmed pipeline from Algeria. SNAM is also interested in receiving gas from the North Sea but so far the price required by the producers is too high, given the transportation costs to bring the gas to the market. SNAM has recently withdrawn from an LNG project in Qatar but has not abandoned the idea of taking LNG supplies from the Middle East.

ENEL has basically covered its need for gas up to 1998. In addition to the direct contract for 4 bcm with Sonatrach, it has a long term contract with SNAM for 6 bcm a year. ENEL has contracted for 3.5 bcm from Nigeria, but might increase this volume by 1 bcm. In relation to its demand forecast ENEL still needs to contract about 1.5 bcm for delivery in 2005.

INFRASTRUCTURE

In Northern Italy there is one pipeline coming in from the Netherlands and two from Russia. The sea section of the Transmed pipeline originally consisted of three parallel lines of which, if necessary in case of emergency, two were sufficient to ensure the transportation of contractual volumes. After the expansion of Transmed's capacity there will be 5 separate lines crossing the strait of Sicily. In spite of great water depths it should normally be possible to repair one of the 5 Transmed sealines within a few weeks, in the worst case within 2 to 3 months.

The gas production from the Italian continental shelf is landed at a number of different locations along the Adriatic coast. Some of the onshore terminal facilities serve several offshore fields simultaneously. Offshore production of natural gas accounts for about 75% of total production. Geographically gas production is spread out over the Italian peninsula along a North-South axis.

For the time being Italy has only one operative LNG terminal, located in La Spezia. Originally this terminal was designed to receive gas of Libyan quality, but it has now been converted to a less complex regasification plant to process LNG of standard quality, thereby increasing flexibility. Studies have been undertaken for a new LNG terminal on the Adriatic coast.

In general, the Italian domestic pipeline system is very well integrated without any major bottlenecks. The doubling of the Transmed pipeline along the whole route up to northern Italy will greatly improve transportation capacity along the north-south axis. At the same time upgrading of the main east-west pipeline in northern Italy is currently under construction.

Italy has a working gas capacity from storage of about 14 bcm, of which around 7 are used for seasonal modulation, and the rest stands as a strategic reserve. It is among the IEA countries with the highest ratio between storage capacity and annual consumption. The maximum daily send-out rate is 250 mcm/day. In total there are 8 storage facilities of which 7 are in Northern Italy. During the period to 2000, usable storage capacity is expected to increase somewhat more than demand.

COPING WITH DISRUPTIONS

According to the Italian Government there exists no special legislation concerning security of supply. General legislation, however, foresees the possibility of taking measures to restrain demand in a disruption situation. It has been left to the actors in the market to take the necessary steps to ensure security of supply. There have never been instances where firm customers have been cut off because of irregularities in supply.

In a situation where there is a shortfall in gas supplies the normal instruments would be to use flexibility under existing contracts, storage and interruptible contracts. The phasing in of the various measures would depend on the timing of the event in question. The first response to a shortfall occurring in November would probably be a drawdown of stocks. A shortfall in February would probably also be met with an interruption in interruptible supplies. Interruptible contracts only exist in the industrial sector and involve annual volumes of about 6 bcm. Contracts vary as to the duration of the interruption and as to the notification procedure to follow. Conclusion of interruptible contracts is conditional upon the customers having backup facilities. In the industrial sector 100% of interruptible customers are able to use HFO as a substitute fuel.

Deliveries to ENEL from SNAM are in principle not interruptible. Virtually 100% of the electricity production capacity that could be fired by gas also has other fuel alternatives. Of the multi-fired capacity 82% can use HFO and 18% gasoil. In a shortfall in gas supplies there would be a dialogue between SNAM and ENEL on how possible ensuing problems could be solved. In some cases flexibility in the electricity sector could be used to reduce the effects of a gas shortfall by, for example, increasing electricity imports or switching away from gas.

In the short term there seems to be considerable flexibility in domestic gas production in the sense that production could be surged for a limited period of time to counter a shortfall from other sources. The Government reckons that indigenous production could probably be increased by some 10% in a longer term but that it prefers not to tap these reserves too quickly. SNAM also considers that an increase in domestic production is possible, but it should be limited in time and could contribute only marginally to counter a serious shortfall.

Concerning security of supply in general, SNAM underlines the mutual dependence between the buyer and the seller in a gas contract. It is also of the opinion that a strong integration between partners improves security of supply. SNAM has therefore entered into a number of co-operation agreements with companies both in producer countries and in transit countries. The pipeline deal with Gazprom is a good example of this.

JAPAN

INTRODUCTION

A constant theme of this study has been the difference between the various regional gas markets. Japan's is particularly distinct. Natural gas supply comes almost entirely in the form of imported LNG, mainly from the Pacific Region, and is used predominantly for power generation at coastal sites. There is no national transmission grid; however, some 244 local distributors continue to supply natural and manufactured gas (city gas) from a variety of sources (LNG/LPG/naphta/coal) at a variety of calorific values to the residential and industrial sectors.

The special structure of the market determines the approach to security. Underground storage, interruptible contracts, pipeline links and additional approaches common in other regional markets have no significant role at present in Japan. Reliance is placed on long term contracts with stable suppliers, the modular supply and delivery systems (which limit dependence on individual facilities) and the possibilities for substitution and sharing via the electricity generation system. The arrangements have served Japan well and no security problems have been encountered.

For the future, continued attention to security issues will however be needed. Gas takes a smaller share of the energy balance in Japan than for the IEA as a whole, but gas use is projected to increase substantially and supplies are likely to come from a more diverse range of sources. Furthermore, as dependence on oil for power generation is reduced, gas may increasingly need to be used to meet peak demand, making consumption less regular and predictable while the share of dual-fired facilities is expected to decline as new plant will be mainly single-fired. Finally, deregulation will help to open up new markets for city gas. These changes will not fundamentally alter the special characteristics of Japanese gas markets, but they will have a significant impact which will need to be monitored.

GAS POLICY

The use of gas is expected to increase in Japan and - provided security is taken into account - the Government of Japan supports this trend. There are two main advantages:

i) **Diversity.** Natural gas at present takes a lower share of Japan's TPES (10.5%) than for the OECD as a whole (20.1%), while oil's share (58%) is higher than the OECD average (41.8%). In electricity generation in particular oil's share is high (30.9% vs. an OECD average of 8.6%). Increased gas use in Japan therefore potentially reduces dependence on oil and increases the diversity of Japan's energy supply.

ii) **Environment.** Japan is very conscious of the need to reconcile the three Es: energy security, the environment and economic growth. Natural gas as a clean fuel which can be used efficiently and with low environmental impact, even in an urban environment, has a potentially important contribution to make.

Japanese conditions therefore favour gas use in a number of ways. Indirectly, environmental standards may make gas the fuel of choice in many settings. Directly, MITI encourages electricity companies to decrease their reliance on oil-firing plant. The Government has also recently changed the law regulating the Japan National Oil Corporation enabling it to participate in natural gas projects via equity holdings and liability guarantees, in order to reduce the risks involved in natural gas development and liquefaction projects.

GAS DEMAND

Gas demand in Japan has grown rapidly over the past twenty years. Though future growth will be more moderate, it will still be very significant. IEA data show the following trend for Japan:

Table 1   Historical and Projected Energy Demand in Japan (Mtoe)

	1973	**1979**	**1993**	**2000**	**2010**
TPES	324.0	355.3	457.4	492.1	550.2
of which:					
Natural Gas	5.1	18.8	47.7	62.4	67.8
Gas Share (per cent)	1.6	5.3	10.4	12.7	12.3

Source: *Energy Policies of IEA Countries*, IEA, 1994.

Natural gas demand has increased nine times over the last twenty years and its share of TPES has multiplied six fold. Although the share is projected to increase only modestly over the next twenty years, with continuing growth in TPES gas use will still grow by 40% or more. Other forecasts show a higher rate of growth. For instance, the Advisory Committee for Energy projects that natural gas will account for 12.8% of energy supply in 2010.

The main use of natural gas is in power generation. About 70% of imports go to this sector, while the remaining 30% is used to make city gas. Gas-fired generation forms about 20% of electricity output. A list of gas-fired power plants is given in Table 2; about half have dual-firing facilities.

Gas use for electricity generation is projected to increase (see the discussion in Chapter 5). Central projections are that gas-fired capacity, at present around 40 GW should rise to 64.5 GW (a rise of nearly 60%) by 2003, though increasing only slightly as a proportion of total capacity. Gas's share of generation may actually fall slightly - the projections assume that coal and nuclear capacity will expand even further than gas, while oil capacity deliveries in percentage terms. Since nuclear and coal will be used for baseload, gas may move slightly up the merit order. At present gas-fired stations operate at middle order, for about 4000-5000 hours a year, i.e., for about 50% of the time, evenly spread through the year. This load factor is expected to decline slightly.

Table 2   Gas-burning Electricity Generating Plants in Japan

Generating Plants	Capacities (MW)	Dual-firing
Higashi Niigata 1-3	2290	1,2 ✓
M1.M2	700	✓
Niigata 3,4	500	✓
Kawasaki 1-6	1050	✓
Yokohama 1-6	1225	✓
Goi 1-6	1886	1-5✓
Anegasaki 1-6	1600	✓
Minami Yokohama 1-3	1150	
Sodegaura 1-4	3600	
Futu 1, 2	2000	
Higashi Ogijimal, 2	2000	
Chita 1-6	3350	1-4 ✓
Chita II 1, 2	1400	
Yokkaichi 1-4	1220	
Kawagoe 1, 2	1400	
Sakaikou 1-8	2000	✓
Osaka 1	156	✓
Nankou 1-3	1800	
Himeji II 1-6	2550	✓
Yanai 1, 2	1050	
Shin Kokura 1-5	2112	
Shin Oita 1, 2	1125	
Tobata J. V. 2-4	781	
Total (87)	**39101**	

Source: MITI.

Although growth in demand for city gas is also projected, the rate of growth is uncertain. It could be faster than growth in power generation (over 3% a year or 80% in total up to 2010) according to the Japan Gas Association (JGA), although the IEA projections show more modest growth. The JGA assumes rapid growth in demand for industrial and commercial use, primarily for cogeneration and gas cooling. This would result in a shift in the composition of demand and an improvement in its load factor. At present about 50% of city gas demand is in the household sector with only 30% in industry. City gas sales have a relatively poor load factor by comparison with gas for electricity generation, though the figure is very favourable compared with many European or North American utilities. For Tokyo Gas, for instance, the ratio of peak (January) to minimum (August) monthly send out was 1.7:1. Between peak and minimum days the ratio is higher (around 3:1).

Given the high cost of storing LNG, or providing it at low load factor, peakiness of demand can be a problem. Fortunately electricity demand has a summer peak in Japan (for air-conditioning). For those companies, like Tokyo Gas, which share terminals with electricity companies, sharing arrangements help allow contract nominations to be concentrated for both companies at their different peak periods within the context of even annual deliveries. The improving load factor of city gas demand may to some extent offset the potentially deteriorating load factor of electricity sector demand noted above.

GAS SUPPLY

Domestic natural gas production, at 2 Mtoe, covers less than 5% of natural gas demand. The remainder comes in the form of LNG imported under long-term contracts.

Table 3   LNG Supply Contracts, November 1993

Source of Supply	Date of First Delivery	Average Contract Quantity '000 tonnes/year
Alaska	11/1969	1 220
Brunei	12/1972	5 540
Abu Dhabi	5/1977	4 300
Indonesia	8/1977	8 180
Malaysia	2/1983	7 400
Indonesia	8/1983	3 650
Indonesia	1/1984	3 520
Australia	8/1989	6 820
Total		**40 630**

Source: MITI

With these contracts, plus a new Abu Dhabi contract (from April 1994) and other extensions to original contract terms, Japan's LNG needs are largely covered to the beginning of next century. New supplies will be needed for the period thereafter. Possible sources of new supply are discussed in Chapter 6. It is unlikely that there will be major difficulties in a technical sense in meeting the forecast demand levels. The supply is undoubtedly physically available. Large numbers of projects have been identified which between them would more than fill the gap. It is less clear how fast it will be possible and desirable to mobilise these potential supplies. In particular, there is as yet no agreement on the price basis for new contracts. But this uncertainty is not of itself a security issue. Any delay in signing the contracts would involve a long period of warning, given the long time scale for development of LNG sources. Gas companies, their customers and electricity companies would have time to react to a failure to conclude particular contracts, for instance by developing other sources of gas, or increasing use of alternative fuels such as oil and coal.

INFRASTRUCTURE

The terminals through which gas is imported are listed in Table 4. Many are dedicated terminals for specific power plants but a number are shared between electricity and city gas companies.

Table 4   LNG Reception Terminals

Terminal	Owner	Companies Supplied	Start-Up Date	Main Source of Supply	Deliveries in 1992 (Mt)
Negishi	Tokyo Electric Tokyo Gas	Tokyo Electric Tokyo Gas	1969	USA Brunei	2.6
Senboku I	Osaka Gas	Osaka Gas	1972	Brunei Indonesia	5.0
Senboku II	Osaka Gas	Kansai Electric Osaka Gas	1977		
Sodegaura	Tokyo Electric Tokyo Gas	Tokyo Electric Tokyo Gas	1973	Brunei Malaysia Australia	10.0
Tobata/Kitakyushu	Kitakyushu LNG shareholders: - Kyushu Electric 75% - Nippon Steel 25%	Kyushu Electric Saibu Gas Nippon Steel	1977	Indonesia	2.3
Chita Kyodo Toho Gas	Chubu Electric Toho Gas	Chubu Electric	1977	Indonesia Australia	4.5
Chita	Chita LNG shareholders: - Chubu Electric 95% - Toho Gas 5%	Chubu Electric	1983		
Himeji	Kansai Electric	Kansai Electric	1979	Indonesia Australia	3.6
	Osaka Gas	Kansai Electric Osaka Gas	1985		
Niigata	Nihonkai LNG shareholders: - Tohoku Electric 41.4% - Hokkaido Tohoku Development Bank 25% - Niigata Prefecture 16.7% - Oil Resources Development Company/Imperial Oil 16.9%	Tohoku Electric	1983	Indonesia	3.0
Higashi-Ohgishima	Tokyo Electric	Tokyo Electric	1984	Abu Dhabi Malaysia Indonesia	3.0
Futsu	Tokyo Electric	Tokyo Electric	1985	Abu Dhabi Malaysia Australia	1.9
Yokkaichi	Chubu Electric	Chubu Electric	1988	Indonesia	2.3
	Toho Gas	Toho Gas	1991		
Yanai	Chugoku Electric	Chugoku Electric	1990	Australia	0.4
Ohita	Ohita LNG shareholders: - Kyushu Electric 90% - Kyushu Oil 8% - Ohita Gas 2%	Kyushu Electric Ohita Gas	1990	Indonesia Australia	0.4

Source: MITI

Most high-pressure pipelines in Japan are short, linking LNG terminals to electricity generation plants or distribution companies in the regions around major cities.

One long pipeline exists, linking Tokyo to Niigata. The 305 kilometre line, owned by Teikoku Oil, was built in 1962 after a contract was signed between Teikoku Oil and Tokyo Gas for the sale of high-calorific natural gas produced in the region around Niigata. The initial contract level was for annual deliveries of 180 mcm over ten years. In 1965, however, Teikoku's production from this field decreased and deliveries to Tokyo Gas were reduced.

Development Plans

In October 1993, a new reception terminal was completed at Fukuoka. Storage capacity is 35,000 cubic metres (23.5 mcm regasified).

LNG import terminals under construction at Kawagoe and Kagoshima should be operational by 1996. These facilities will increase LNG storage capacity by 120 000 cubic metres (i.e., 70 mcm regasified). Other LNG import terminals under construction at Kawagoe should be operational by 1977. This facility will increase LNG storage capacity by 480 000 cubic metres (i.e., 304 mcm regasified). At the same time, storage additions to existing terminals should increase capacity by about 800 000 cubic metres (i.e., 470 mcm regasified).

An additional reception terminal under construction at Ohgishima is scheduled to be completed in 1998. Storage capacity will be 1 mcm of LNG. This facility is to be linked to the plants at Sodegaura and Negishi by high-pressure pipeline.

Storage capacity at TEPCO's Futtsu terminal is to be increased by the addition of two tanks with a total capacity of 250 000 cm (152 mcm regasified) due to be completed in 1999. Existing capacity there is 610 000 cm (370 mcm regasified). The SK pipeline linking Sendai to production at Niigata should be completed in 1996. Owned by the Japan Petroleum Exploration Company, the 250 kilometre pipeline will have a diameter of 500 mm (20 inches) and capacity of 4.5 mcm a day.

In addition, a possible pipeline connection between Tokyo and Osaka is under discussion, though its economic feasibility has yet to be demonstrated. Further LNG terminals are likely to be built on the Japan Sea side of the islands as well, because of congestion on the Pacific side, thus necessitating new pipeline connections from coast to coast.

Deregulation

Under a revision to the Gas Industry Law, companies' existing gas supplying companies will be allowed (with MITI approval) to supply gas to large users (over 2 mcm annually) whether or not they are within their "service area" and at unregulated prices. Pipeline access will be made easier but there will be no mandatory third party access. The combination of the relatively ill-developed pipeline infrastructure in Japan, the high cost of developing new LNG import facilities, and the restrictions on pipeline access are likely to mean that the implications of the new statutes will be both relatively limited and relatively slow to develop. Nonetheless, for larger consumers a greater degree of contract flexibility will result, which may lead to new approaches to security of supply - in the future this will be determined by the supply contract rather than the utility's formal obligation to supply. As regards supplying companies, it is likely that in the short term the position of the large city gas companies will be strengthened. In the future they will be able to seek customers in other companies' service areas instead of only selling gas to other gas companies outside their present area. In the longer term it is possible that such newcomers as domestic natural gas development companies or oil companies may enter the gas supply business. However, the security implications, if any, cannot be properly analysed at this early stage.

SECURITY ISSUES

Despite the absence of many security features typical of European or North American gas markets, Japan does have a series of measures providing in-depth defence against supply interruptions.

- **Supply Diversity.** As noted in Table 4, six countries supply gas to Japan. All have been dependable long-term suppliers. Individual Japanese companies generally have more than one supplier, e.g., Osaka Gas has three, under five separate contracts.

- **Long Term Contracts.** Suppliers and customers are interdependent and have a common interest in security of supply. They are linked by long term contracts which have proved a stable but flexible basis for managing the business and reconciling conflicting short term interests. Despite some disputes over price, supply has not been interrupted.

- **Modular supply systems.** Production and liquefaction systems include a number of separate trains (an average of 3 to 5 per exporting terminal); a number of separate tankers are involved in each contract (an average of 4 to 5); most importing companies - located in three major cities (Tokyo, Osaka and Nagoya) - have more than one terminal (2 or 3 on average); terminals generally have more than one jetty, etc. Thus an accident to one particular supply module has only limited impact on total supply.

- **Supply flexibility.** Most supply contracts have a certain amount of flexibility (5 to 10%) either written into the contract or on a best endeavours basis.

- **Gas supply sharing.** Although there are few pipeline connections, a number of terminals are shared between gas and electricity companies, as shown in Table 4. Furthermore there is a significant degree of standardisation of shipping capacity: extra supply available from a particular source can usually be transferred to another company which might be facing difficulties.

- **Electricity exchanges.** Japan has two frequency zones - 50 Hz and 60 Hz. Electricity interconnections exist both between companies within the zones and (to a more limited extent) between the zones. These interconnections are being expanded. For instance the present conversion capacity between the zones of 0.9 GW is planned to be expanded to 1.5 GW early next century and by 2010 could be 2 to 2.5 GW. Within the 50 Hz zone, Tokyo Electric has capacity for about 1.5 GW of exchanges. Its total exchange capacity at present amounts to around 2.4 GW.

■ **Fuel-switching.** About half of gas-fired power generating capacity is dual-fired, as listed above, with crude or fuel oil as the main alternative fuel. Fuel-switching would pose few logistical problems as the sites are all coastal and have storage and handling capacity. This flexibility will decline somewhat in future as new gas-fired generation will be single-fired. For city gas customers there is also less flexibility. There are no interruptible contracts as such, though contracts with industrial consumers contain *force majeure* clauses. Only about 20% of larger city gas consumers (accounting for a small proportion of total demand) have dual-firing, and the proportion is declining.

■ **SNG manufacture.** Considerable capacity for manufacturing substitute natural gas (SNG) from naphtha exists, estimated at around 1.4 million tonnes annually for city gas companies as a whole.

■ **Storage.** Although Japan has no underground storage, it has significant above ground capacity designed to cope with fluctuations in supply. Total storage, at 5.6 bcm, amounts to 30 to 40 days supply and most companies aim to keep around this level of stocks. New storage capacity under construction should increase capacity by a little over 1 bcm, i.e., around 20%, keeping pace with the expected growth in demand up to the turn of the century.

Taken together, these measures provide good protection against disruptions in supply, particularly technical disruptions which affect only a small proportion of supply or a larger proportion over a short period. For example, were Tokyo Electric to suffer a loss even of a large proportion (more than 50%) of supply it could cover this by a mixture of the following: oil-switching (around 50% of total demand can be switched); imports of electricity (capacity for 2.4 GW, i.e., around 30% of non-switchable demand); supply sharing (although Tokyo Electric is the largest single gas purchaser it accounts for under 30% of Japanese LNG demand, if other companies could increase production by up to 5%, as most can under their contracts, and sell it to Tokyo Electric, this would amount to a further 10 to 15% of Tokyo Electric's normal demand). Electricity purchases might be restricted at times of peak demand as Japan's reserve margins, at under 10%, are low by IEA standards. However gas storage could be used to cover peak demand if necessary. Voluntary electricity demand restraint could also be effective.

It appears that individual companies could cope with even a significant supply shortfall. In principle the above measures would enable Tokyo Electric to cope indefinitely, even with a 50% shortfall. Some companies have less flexibility than Tokyo Electric - e.g., the city gas companies do not have the ability to switch to oil and to share electricity. On the other hand many have SNG facilities and are smaller gas purchasers, thus having more flexibility to purchase from other companies, assuming only one company's supply was disrupted.

This analysis is based on the assumption that only one company is affected, or that the disruption is limited in scope. A major sustained disruption affecting more than one company (e.g., 50% of supply for the whole country for one year) would be much more difficult to cope with. It would be likely to have significant impacts on oil markets (through switching to oil in power generation and manufacture of SNG) and would lead to shortages of gas and, probably, electricity. Fortunately such an eventuality is very difficult to conceive. A disruption of this magnitude would only result from a disaster on an unprecedented scale (e.g., leading to the closure of Tokyo Bay), whose consequences would certainly extend well beyond the gas sector, or from a geopolitical development which is outside the range of current expectations.

THE NETHERLANDS

GAS POLICY

Natural gas accounted for 49% of total primary energy supply in the Netherlands in 1992, a higher market penetration than in any other OECD country.[1]

The responsibility for ensuring security of gas supplies in the Netherlands has been entrusted to Gasunie, the sole gas transmission company, which buys gas from both domestic and foreign producers as well as exporting domestically produced gas. As part of this responsibility, Gasunie produces an annual Gas Marketing Plan (described below) which sets out the current reserve situation, expected demand, imports and exports for the next 25 years.

A major growth area for gas demand has been the installation of energy efficient CHP plants. The state has been subsidising up to 17.5% of the capital costs of these plants and obliging electricity distributors to buy excess CHP-produced electricity at a price equal to their own average electricity purchase price. The program has been so successful that some of the centralised generating plant is being pushed off baseload. This has been raising the average electricity purchase price which in turn has increased the price received by the CHP producers for electricity sold to distributors. The result has been the construction of yet more of these plants. The subsidies, however, have now been stopped.

Production revolves around the operation of the huge Groningen field. Dutch policy is to encourage production from smaller fields in order to prolong the life of the Groningen field. To this end the government's take on Groningen gas (which costs very little to produce) is much higher than for other fields. In addition, by guaranteeing that it will purchase all gas produced in the Netherlands, Gasunie reduces the risk of exploring small fields.

Producers have indicated that, at current energy prices, they have little or no incentive to develop many of the small fields containing less than 3 bcm each. This assessment is reflected in the level of investment being made in offshore development. 1994/5 investment is expected to be just one third of the 1992/3 level. A 1993 report from the operator's association Nogepa made suggestions for a number of changes to Dutch production and fiscal policies, several of which have since been acted upon:

- Offtake terms should be made more flexible. Gasunie has since agreed to take gas from new fields over 10 rather than 14 years and at a load factor of 90% instead of the earlier 67%, although at a reduced price.

- The Government's take and royalties should be reduced. The government is currently considering free depreciation on fixed assets and has abolished some royalty payments for new small fields.

1. Average OECD gas share of TPES is 20%.

■ State participation should either be abolished or changed to reflect more accurately the balance of risk taken by the project partners. The level of state participation has been reduced from 50% to 40% and has been extended to exploration projects. In the past, when the government approved a gas development project, the company EBN (which holds stakes in production ventures on the state's behalf) could take either a 40% or 50% participation in the project for which it paid a corresponding share of exploration costs. This allowed the state to avoid paying costs of unsuccessful exploration.

GAS DEMAND

Currently 98% of all households are connected to the grid, leaving almost no room for increased market penetration in the domestic sector. Increased demand in this sector can only come from new construction, which is expected to increase housing stock by just over 20% between now and 2019, the end of the 25 year planning period. Large efficiency gain targets should limit actual demand growth to around 5.5% in the planning period.

So far 4 000 MW of CHP capacity has been installed, more than 25% of centralised generating capacity. Gasunie's Gas Marketing Plan foresees CHP capacity rising to 6 000 MW by the year 2000.

Between January 1, 1994, and January 1, 2019, Gasunie estimates cumulative domestic demand at 1 215 bcm.

Table 1   Forecast Gas Demand (bcm)

	1992	2000	2010
Total Consumption	**43.6**	**47.7**	**49.1**
Industry (inc. CHP)	12.4	18.1	19.0
Electricity Generation	8.0	5.1	5.4
Residential/Commercial	18.6	18.9	19
Greenhouse	4.3	5.4	5.5
Own Use	0.2	0.2	0.2

Source: Gasunie.

GAS SUPPLY

As of January 1, 1994, Gasunie estimated reserves on the mainland and on the Dutch sector continental shelf at 1 965 bcm. This reserve base is distributed among more than 275 separate areas. Of these, 185 have initial reserves estimated at under 3 bcm and 128 have yet to be brought onstream. A further 280 bcm of reserves are counted in the "yet to be discovered fields" category.[2]

---

2. Calculations of these additional reserves assume that exploration and production will be possible in environmentally sensitive areas such as the Wadden Sea and Lake Ijssel.

In 1992, Groningen accounted for 50% of Dutch production. It is currently operated below its annual capacity as a swing field, producing the balance between volumes required and volumes produced by other fields. About half of the Groningen field's initial reserves have now been extracted, and its pressure is dropping close to a level where it will no longer be able to meet the peak demand requirements placed upon it. The predicted capacity shortfall should be balanced by gas from underground storage. Storage facilities at Norg and at Grijpskerk are under construction. A further underground peak shaving storage site is planned in a gas field at Alkmaar.

The smaller fields on the Dutch mainland contributed 19% to total supplies in 1992.

It is likely that most large gas fields on the Dutch continental shelf have been already developed. The remaining reserves exist to a large extent in small fields. It is the construction of new gathering systems that will lead to economies of scale in transportation and thus allow the commercial development of some of these fields. The NOGAT gathering line, extending some 260 km into the North Sea, has been particularly important in linking developments in the northern part of the Dutch continental shelf (block F3) whose reserves could not have otherwise been economically exploited.

Table 2   Forecast Production (bcm)

1992	2000	2010
81.2	80.8	65.2

Source: Gasunie.

EXPORTS AND IMPORTS

Current exports to Germany, France, Belgium and Italy total about 40 bcm per year. Under Gasunie's export contracts, these deliveries should be maintained until 2010 and reduced thereafter. Total cumulative exports for the next 25 years are estimated at around 690 bcm.

Gasunie has contracted imports mostly from Norway, adding 175 bcm to Dutch supplies over the planning period. Small deliveries of gas directly from the offshore UK Markham field commenced in 1993.

Table 3   Forecast Trade (bcm)

	1992	2000	2010
Imports	3.0	6.5	6.8
Exports	40.6	39.6	22.9

Source: Gasunie.

The Netherlands is also a transit country. In 1992, 8.7 bcm of Norwegian gas crossed the country into Belgium and France, and deliveries of small volumes of UK gas to Germany via the Netherlands began in 1993.

SUPPLY AND DEMAND BALANCE

Table 4 shows that in 25 years, reserves equivalent to 5-10 years of domestic consumption should remain in the Netherlands.

Table 4   Reserve Depletion Forecasts (bcm)

January 1, 1994 to January 1, 2019	
Domestic Demand	1215
Exports	690
Imports	175
=> Production	1730
Situation on January 1, 1994	
Reserves in discovered fields	1965
- possible further reserves	280
Situation on January 1, 2019	
Reserves in place	235 - 515

Source: Gasunie.

INFRASTRUCTURE

The Dutch transmission system is quite complex since the calorific values of the gas produced in various parts of the country are different. Groningen gas has a significant nitrogen content and so its heat content is lower than that of gas from other parts of the country. The pipeline system consists of two networks, one carrying high calorific gas and the other low calorific gas. Blending stations in five locations allow the system operator to mix gas qualities and produce gas that meets specifications required by domestic and export markets.

Although Groningen accounts for only half of Dutch gas production, it represents the majority of Dutch production capacity. The field itself has some 220 separate wells and gas is transported in eight to nine different pipelines.

The network is designed so that it will not fail to supply normal gas deliveries more than once every 50 years. The coldest day in the last 50 years occurred on January 17, 1987, and although normal service was provided, demand on that day now serves as the reference point for future planning.

COPING WITH DISRUPTIONS

As mentioned above, the Groningen field is used as a swing producer in order to meet peak demand - both internally and to some extent in export markets. Beyond this availability of swing supplies, deliveries to power generators are routinely interrupted when temperatures drop below -5°C. As a worst case scenario, roughly one quarter of industrial demand (used by ammonia producers) could be cut for a short period of time.

With supply coming from so many separate facilities and with an important volume flexibility on both supply and demand sides, it is difficult to imagine any situation causing a serious disruption either to internal supplies or to exports.

Under the Rationing Act of 1939, local distribution companies must maintain contingency plans for dealing with supply disruptions. Emergency planning falls under the responsibility of the Queen's Commissioner in each province.

The Netherlands plays an interesting role in its neighbours' short term security. The annual export capacity is significantly higher than the normal exports of around 40 bcm per year. Back-up supply agreements with Germany and Belgium cover additional capacities of around 20 bcm per year, taking contracted annual export capacity up to 60 bcm. Physical export capacity, which is over 80 bcm per year, is limited not by production constraints but by the dimensions of the export pipelines. In time, though, falling pressure in the Groningen field will limit this export capacity if production from other fields remains stable.

Figure 1   Gas Exports from the Netherlands

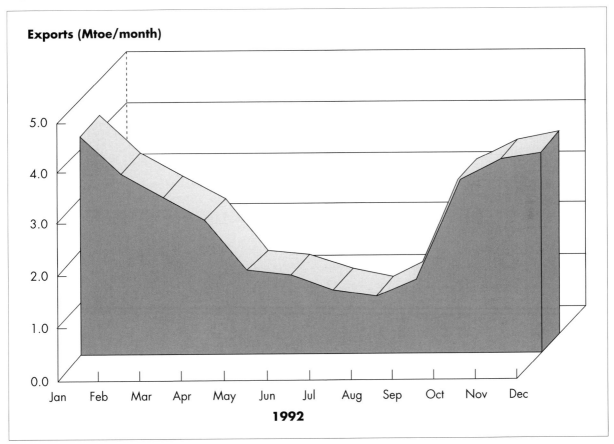

Note: 1 Mtoe is approximately equivalent to 1.27 bcm.
Source: Importing Country Statistics and IEA Secretariat Estimates.

NEW ZEALAND

GAS POLICY

New Zealand is self-sufficient in gas and does not participate in international gas trade. Gas constitutes around 30% of TPES, higher than in most OECD countries. As New Zealand has a relatively low reserve/production ratio, further gas penetration will depend on future discoveries and the development of new sources, the prospects for which are considered good.

The New Zealand gas sector has gone through a series of reforms in recent years that are part of a general policy aimed at deregulation of the entire energy sector, in particular, introduction of competition and light handed regulation of natural monopolies. Gas price controls have been removed and retail franchise areas (and the obligation to supply) were abolished by the Gas Act 1992. The gas operations of local authorities have been corporatised, under the Energy Companies Act 1992. A legal and regulatory framework has been put in place for access to transmission and distribution pipelines and interested parties are working to develop an open access policy. Given the low reserve/production ratio and the concerns about sufficient future gas supply, the Government has recently introduced legislation giving incentives for increased exploration for both oil and gas.

As a consequence of its liberal policy in the energy area the Government does not specifically promote the use of gas, but permits market forces to determine the role to be played by this fuel.

GAS DEMAND

Total gas demand in New Zealand was 4.83 bcm in 1994, up from 4.4 bcm in 1993. The structure of demand in the New Zealand gas market is unusual for an OECD country in that more than 80% of total consumption is for feedstock use: 32% goes into a synthetic gasoline plant, 10% into a chemical methanol plant, 3% into a ammonia/urea plant and 36% into power generation. The remaining 19% is distributed to industrial, residential and commercial consumers by the Natural Gas Corporation of New Zealand Ltd. which owns and operates the main high pressure pipeline system.

Gas consumption is forecast to increase up to the year 2000 but then to taper off as a consequence of supply constraints. Under a scenario where access to new gas reserves became a problem, peak consumption could reach about 6.7 bcm. After 2005 priority would be given to residential demand and high value power generation whereas feedstock use would be reduced substantially.

GAS SUPPLY

Table 1 summarises estimates of indigenous gas reserves as of December 1993.

Table 1   Gas Reserves and Production, 1993

Field/Licence	Estimated Reserves (bcm)	Proportion of Total Reserves (%)	Approximate Daily Production (MMcfd)
Maui	57.5	71.0	415.0
Kapuni	14.3	12.1	80.0
McKee	2.55	3.3	15.0
Kaimiro	0.8	1.0	0.8
Waihapa	0.4	0.5	12.6
Kupe	7.5	9.0	0
Tariki	1.5	2.1	0
Ahuroa	0.7	1.0	0
Total	**85.2**	**100**	**523.4**

Source: *Energy Supply and Demand Scenarios to 2020*, Ministry of Commerce, New Zealand Institute of Economic Research, July 1994.

The estimates represent the quantity of gas remaining in each field that is considered to be economically recoverable at foreseeable gas prices. It has been estimated that currently known reserves will be exhausted by around 2017. Therefore, in the long term, supply will have to come from new sources. The prospects for making further gas finds both onshore and offshore are good, although their magnitude may not be great and the costs of production, particularly for offshore fields, may make the development of some finds uneconomic. New Zealand's overall hydrocarbon potential is still significantly underexplored; the Taranaki basin is the only sedimentary basin to have been explored to any significant extent.

INFRASTRUCTURE

The gas infrastructure in New Zealand is uncomplicated given the supply and market structure. Only the North Island has a gas distribution system. 73% of gas production comes from the Maui field. Maui is an offshore gas/condensate field with two interconnected platforms and a single pipeline system (separate parallel lines for gas and condensate) to shore. Another 21% of the gas comes from the Kapuni field, an onshore gas/condensate field with numerous wells and one treatment facility. Both Maui and Kapuni are connected to the onshore transmission system. This system comprises a single pipeline, with loops in several places, supplying local gate stations for markets south of the production facilities (Maui and Kapuni are both located in the Taranaki area) and two pipelines serving northern markets. There is at present no gas storage facility in New Zealand.

COPING WITH DISRUPTIONS

Historically, gas supplies have been very reliable. Unforeseen interruptions have been extremely rare (none over the last five years) and have been overcome quickly without affecting supply to reticulated customers.

Flexibility in the New Zealand gas supply system to meet fluctuations in demand and interruptions is provided by the integrated control system for high pressure transmission lines, linepack and interruptible supply to large customers, including in particular the Electricity Corporation of New Zealand which can use alternative fuels in some of its gas-fired generating capacity. This multi-fired capacity amounts to 1670 MW or 22.5% of total generating capacity. An industry-agreed rationing programme is also available if necessary. For instance in the case of a breakdown in supplies from the Maui platform the synfuel plant and the methanol plant would be forced to close down. Supplies to electricity generation would be severely reduced and the ammonia/urea plant could also be affected. On the basis of present gas usage, these measures would be enough for gas to continue to be supplied to the reticulated market (comprising 22% of current total consumption).

Figure 1   Fields and Transportation Systems

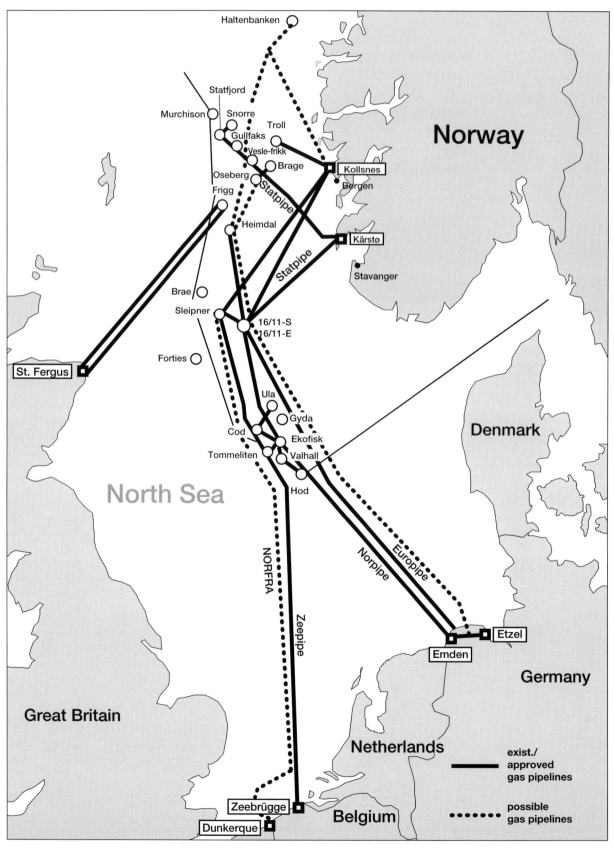

NORWAY

GAS POLICY

The principles underlying Norwegian oil and gas policy, as it is described in the Government's Long Term Programme for 1994-1997, are based on the fact that petroleum is a non-renewable national resource. As a result of this, Norwegian oil and gas resources should in the Government's view be managed with the aim of maximising value added and ensuring a high share of total petroleum revenues for the community as a whole, taking into account the needs of future generations.

The petroleum sector plays an important role in the Norwegian economy. In 1993, its share of GNP was approximately 15% and its share of export revenues 33%. Government tax revenues have varied considerably over time as a function of production and the oil price. They reached a maximum of NOK 69.2 billion (1993 NOK) in 1985, but were down to NOK 26.7 billion in 1993 with large fluctuations during the period in between. In 1993, petroleum tax revenues constituted about 12% of total government revenues from direct and indirect taxes. The wide fluctuations in revenues and the high degree of dependence on petroleum revenues for the Norwegian economy as a whole have at irregular intervals spurred a debate on the pace of the development of petroleum resources. The level of investment in the petroleum sector has fluctuated over time, contributing in some cases to an overheating of the economy. This led to the idea of smoothing the investment level by establishing a queue of projects. In practice such a policy has never been implemented and most projects have been developed as soon as they were considered mature.

Investment in the petroleum sector reached a record level of NOK 58 billion in 1993. Over the next few years a significant reduction in investments from the 1993 peak level is expected as there are fewer and smaller new oil fields to be developed. This drop in the annual investment level will be partly compensated by investments in new gas fields and gas pipelines. Based on negotiated supply contracts, annual gas exports may more than double from a 1993 level of 24.7 bcm to a peak level of 59 bcm in 2005. Potential for further increase in the annual export volumes is identified by the companies in the Gas Negotiating Committee.

Gas constituted about 18% of total petroleum production in 1993. The relative share of gas in total petroleum production and revenues will increase over time due both to increased gas sales and to an expected drop in annual oil production.

The marketing and production of natural gas are the responsibilities of the companies that are licensees on the Continental Shelf. The Norwegian State has an important stake in gas activity through the State's Direct Financial Interest (SDFI) and through Statoil. In fact the State is the largest investor on the Continental shelf. The State's average direct financial interests in the various categories of fields and pipelines in which it participates are as follows:

Fields in operation: 40.5%
Fields where development is decided: 49.6%
Fields where development is planned: 34.8%
Pipelines: 49.7%.

The state therefore plays an important role both as investor and decision maker with strong influence on policy questions concerning gas production and marketing. The SDFI in petroleum activities is managed by Statoil, and, according to the Norwegian Government, receives no special treatment compared with other licensees on the Norwegian Continental Shelf.

GAS DEMAND

Presently there is almost no onshore use of natural gas in Norway. From 1997, a methanol plant will take approximately 0.7 bcm of gas annually from the Haltenbanken area. A tiny distribution network for gas is in operation close to the Kaarstoe gas terminal. Over the past few years several proposals have been put forward to build gas based power plants but none of these has so far materialised.

There is an offshore market for gas in the sense that some producing fields buy gas from other fields for re-injection. The Oseberg field for instance buys 3.5 bcm of gas a year from the Troll field for re-injection to enhance oil recovery. The Ekofisk field consumes 4 bcm of gas a year as fuel and for injection. Re-injected gas can to a large extent be reproduced for later sales and will thus not significantly reduce potential gas sales volumes.

GAS SUPPLY

Table 1 shows the gas reserve estimates for the Norwegian Continental Shelf. Discovered resources are estimated at 2805 bcm, implying that production at the current level could be sustained for more than 100 years. The undiscovered resources are estimated at 2410 bcm. These figures mean that Norway could potentially become a much bigger gas supplier in the future. Indeed growth in output is due to take place under contracts already signed. Total plateau deliveries under contracts already signed (taking into account options under the Troll contracts) will peak at about 59 bcm in 2005, more than doubling 1993 export volumes of 24.6 bcm. Of these volumes Germany will receive 42%, France 22%, the Netherlands around 10% and Belgium about 9%. The remainder will be taken by Austria, Spain and the UK.

The first generation of Norwegian gas contracts were depletion contracts, but Troll initiated an era of supply contracts defining specific annual deliveries. Around the year 2000, deliveries under depletion contracts will amount to about 14 bcm, down from 23.2 in 1993. Deliveries under these contracts are estimated to fall to 4.5 bcm in 2005 and are expected to tail off soon after 2010. These estimates are subject to uncertainty in the sense that reserves in place may differ from current estimates.

Table 1 Resource Account for the Norwegian Continental Shelf

			OIL 10^9 Sm³ most likely	GAS 10^9 Sm³ most likely	NGL 10^6 tonnes most likely	OIL EQUIV. 10^6 tonnes most likely
Discovered Resources	Fields producing and ceased production (originally)	Current plan	2119	754	78	2598
		Improved recovery	486			405
	Fields decided developed	Current plan	264	1002	30	1251
		Improved recovery	44			36
	Fields planned developed	Current plan	128	672	24	803
		Improved recovery				
	Discoveries under evaluation		534	777	9	1238
	Fields and discoveries total		3575	3205	141	6331
Undiscovered resources			1480	2410		3670
Sold 31.12.93			Oil 1010	Gas 400	NGL 32	t.o.e 1273

☐ Reserves   ▨ Discovered Resources

The three Norwegian companies constituting the Gas Negotiating Committee expect total Norwegian gas sales to reach 70 to 80 bcm over the long term. The companies believe that it would be possible to reach a production level of 75 bcm a year by 2005 and that such volumes could be brought profitably to the market even at the gas prices reigning over the last few years. The Norwegian supply cost curve is expected to be fairly flat within production levels between 60 and 80 bcm a year. Recent work on costs from the "Forum for Drift og Utbygging" indicates that the supply cost curve might in fact be downward sloping since there is potential for reducing costs by up to 50% compared with today's level.

INFRASTRUCTURE

Today, there are three pipeline systems carrying Norwegian gas to export markets (see Figure 1):
- the Frigg pipeline to St. Fergus in the UK, having a capacity of 10.9 bcm a year of which only 4.5 bcm were used in 1993;
- the Statpipe/Norpipe system from fields in the North Sea via the Kaarstoe terminal and the Ekofisk field to Emden in Germany, having a capacity of 19.4 bcm a year;
- the Zeepipe, taking gas from the Sleipner area (in future also from the Troll field) to Zeebrugge in Belgium. Its present capacity is 11.7 bcm.

A second pipeline to Emden in Germany is under construction. This pipeline (the Europipe) starts at the 16/11 riser platform and will later be connected to the Kollsnes terminal to take Troll gas to Germany. It will be commissioned in 1995 and will have a capacity of 12.4 bcm a year, bringing total transportation capacity to Emden to 31.5 bcm a year.

As shown in Figure 1, Statpipe, Zeepipe and Europipe will be linked to each other east of the Sleipner area. Linkages between the pipelines imply that it will be possible to choose between supply sources, allowing each field to deliver gas both to Emden and to Zeebrugge.

The Ministry of Industry and Energy may decide that pipelines can be used by third parties, if it is not to the unreasonable detriment of the owner's requirements or those of another party already assured the right to use the installation. However, the Norwegian pipelines have all been tailor-made to cover transportation needs under specific gas contracts, and thus capacity utilisation will be very high except during build-up periods.

To meet obligations under contracts already concluded, there is a need for increased transportation capacity both to Germany and to Belgium and France. Integration of the transportation systems implies a greater number of options for increasing the transportation capacity to the Continent. Possibilities exist for undertaking a step-wise development and phasing in of new infrastructure ensuring cost efficient solutions matching existing and future contract obligations. Boosting the capacity in existing pipelines by adding compression and building new pipelines are both being considered. The initial decisions on new transportation infrastructure will have to be taken in 1995. In this context increased compression in Zeepipe versus a partial doubling of the pipeline is considered. The capacity of Europipe could also be increased by installing additional compression. The possibility of building a new pipeline landing in France is also being studied. As of September 1995, a decision to land a new pipeline called NORFRA in Dunkerque in France has been taken. In the long term Norway might have five pipelines landing gas on the Continent.

To link the Troll field and its export terminal at Kollsnes with the pipelines to Emden and Zeebrugge, a new pipeline is under construction to the Sleipner area. A second pipeline is planned from Kollsnes to the riser platform at 16/11, linking Troll to the Europipe pipeline. Further development of the transportation infrastructure to link fields to the export pipelines will depend on which fields will deliver under the contracts recently concluded with buyers in Germany and France and under the Troll options. Such a decision is not expected until the end of 1995.

The Ekofisk field through which Norwegian gas to Emden currently passes has often constituted a bottleneck which will be removed by diverting the gas to a new route around the Ekofisk area.

COPING WITH DISRUPTIONS

The Petroleum Act contains clauses that might be applicable in the case of shortfalls in the production of both oil and gas on the Continental Shelf. In case of war, danger of war or other extraordinary conditions, licensees may be required to make petroleum available to the Government. The Government may also apply the Supply and Contingency Measures Act to ensure supply of natural gas to domestic users.

The Norwegian Petroleum Directorate (NPD) is charged with overseeing the technical aspects of security of supply on the Norwegian Continental Shelf. One important aspect of Norwegian security philosophy is that major gas fields have been developed with a view to locating a maximum amount of equipment onshore.

NPD has studied the availability of the Norwegian gas pipelines. From 1977 to 1984, the Norpipe system had a total operational availability of 97.2%. Planned non-availability was 1.8% and unplanned non-availability 0.4%. The period 1984-1991 experienced about the same record. 1992 was an exceptional year in that unplanned non-availability was 3.1%. Since then performance has improved significantly, bringing non-planned non-availability down to less than 0.5%. With a new Ekofisk complex in operation by 1998 and a bypass connection established, the long term availability of the Ekofisk area should be considerably improved.

Strikes among personnel on offshore installations have historically caused some problems for short term gas deliveries, but more recent conflicts have been solved by compulsory arbitration before any disturbance in deliveries has occurred.

Before 1993, all gas exported to the Continent was transported through a single transportation network, Statpipe/Norpipe. The start up in 1993 of the Zeepipe pipeline to Belgium reduced this dependence.

In 1993, gas was exported from 17 different fields in the Norwegian part of the North Sea, of which the five largest ones accounted for roughly three quarters of total exports. Three of these fields, accounting for about 22% of Norwegian exports in 1993, are pure gas fields in the sense that they have no oil production. The rest of the fields produce gas associated with oil, implying that gas production will to a large extent be a function of oil production. The inflexibility that this might cause could to a certain extent be compensated for by varying the amounts of gas used for re-injection. Disturbances in gas production on the platforms could also be compensated for by using linepack, i.e., the volumes of gas stored in the export pipelines. A high capacity utilisation in the pipelines could, however, reduce this possibility.

Dependence on single facilities is relatively high in the current Norwegian transportation system. A breakdown in the Norpipe system would take away 87% of total exports to the Continent, while a breakdown in the Zeepipe would take away only 13% of the deliveries. The riser platform 16/11 is another critical point in the system given that deliveries would be reduced by 32% in case of close-down. As long as there is spare capacity in any of the pipelines, there are potential possibilities for increasing throughput where there is spare capacity and accommodating buyers by swapping between delivery points. In cases of reduction in production or in pipeline throughput, Norwegian gas sellers also have the possibility of accommodating customers by drawing on storage capacity on the Continent. This capacity is partly owned by Norwegian companies (Etzel gas storage in Northern Germany) and partly rented (access to GDF storage in France).

Generally, dependence on single facilities will decrease in the future. With five Norwegian pipelines to the Continent around 2005, the share of each in total deliveries could vary between 12 and 24%. At this time, the Troll platform, the terminal at Kollsnes and the 16/11 riser platform complex all have a large influence on the availability of Norwegian gas deliveries. The first phase of the Troll development will provide gas production capacity of 23.7 bcm. In a scenario of high deliveries from Norway this capacity could reach 30 bcm. If under such a scenario gas is also taken from Haltenbanken via Kollsnes to the Continent, a gas volume of more than 40 bcm could pass through the Kollsnes terminal, accounting for more than half of total exports. Even under a scenario with no future sales beyond those currently contracted, Troll will account for about 1/3 of total gas deliveries when the plateau is reached. From the Troll platform there will be two pipelines to shore and three trains at the landing terminal. Around 2005, around 50% of total gas exports could pass through the 16/11 riser platform complex. This throughput is, however, divided between two platforms.

Security of supply considerations play a central role in all Norwegian gas export contracts. As a consequence of the structure of the contracts, both seller and buyer have very strong incentives to keep gas flowing. Most contracts contain clauses on measures to be taken in case of shortfalls. A growing number of fields delivering gas and an increasing physical integration between transportation facilities will increase the number of measures that can be taken to ensure security of supply.

PORTUGAL

There is currently no natural gas supply in Portugal. The only area of the country supplied with town gas is in Lisbon, which has 200,000 customers and a sendout of 170-180 mcm/year.

The introduction of natural gas is planned for October 1996. Supplies are to come from Algeria through the new Maghreb-Europe pipeline that will bring Algerian gas to the Iberian peninsula. On the Spanish side the Maghreb-Europe line will join the existing network at Cordoba; the branch will run 200 km from Cordoba to the Spain/Portugal border at Badajoz and it will serve both Portugal and the areas in Spain that it crosses. Both countries are sharing construction costs - the Portuguese transmission company Transgas has acquired a 27.4% stake in Europe-Maghreb Pipeline Limited, the company responsible for the Moroccan and sub-sea sections. From Badajoz the pipeline will run to the west of Portugal where it will join a new pipeline running north-south near the coast - as far as Setubal to the south and Braga to the north. Construction work started in July 1994.

The development of natural gas supply has had a high priority in Portugal's energy policy, in line with goals of diversifying energy sources (from an oil dependence of almost 75% in 1992) and improving environmental performance.

The Ministry of Industry and Energy is forecasting gas demand at 1.6 Mtoe in 2000 (7.7% of forecast TPES) and 3.0 Mtoe in 2010. About half of the contracted volumes are covered by contracted sales for power generation. A new gas-fired combined-cycle power station with a capacity of 990 MW (two units of 450 MW each) will come on stream in Tapado do Outeiro in 1997/98.

A supply contract with Sonatrach of Algeria covers a total volume of 51.2 bcm (42.7 Mtoe) delivered over 25 years. Initial annual volumes will be 0.4 bcm (0.33 Mtoe) and will reach a plateau of 2.5 bcm (2.1 Mtoe) around 2002. There are currently no other supply contracts.

The government forecast implies a probable need for new gas between 2000 and 2010. The options considered have included:

■ Construction of an LNG reception terminal at Setubal (near Lisbon). This was in fact the original plan for bringing natural gas to Portugal before the branch to the Maghreb-Europe pipeline was chosen for economic reasons.

■ Extension from Braga (at the northern end of the pipeline being built in Portugal) to Tuy, supplying north-west Spain from Portugal, increasing Portugal's supply requirements.

■ In the longer term, there is interest in a better interconnection of the Iberian network Portugal to the European grid through Spain.

SPAIN

GAS POLICY

Spanish energy policy is guided by the National Energy Plan, last adopted by Parliament in April 1992. Features of the plan include the promotion of supply security, domestic energy resources and diversification. The development of a gas market is an important element in the diversification of energy sources. The plan is being revised to take into account recent developments in the Spanish energy sector.

The gas network is still in its early stages but is growing rapidly. Several major infrastructure projects are underway, the most important being a pipeline connection with Algeria to be completed in 1996.

The government's policy has been to promote integration within the industry: in 1991 Catalana de Gas and Gas Madrid merged to form Gas Natural which, in turn, has taken over the transmission company Enagas. The state retains a minority shareholding in Gas Natural directly through INH and indirectly through Repsol (where the state's shareholding is being reduced). There is no *de jure* monopoly over gas transportation and distribution in Spain, although in 1994 Enagas was responsible for 91% of all transmission and Gas Natural was responsible for 89% of the distribution market. There are no immediate plans to introduce competition to the gas market.

The state plays an active role in the gas market. All activities related to the supply of gas require administrative concessions (which can be granted to public and private companies) and gas prices are subject to approval by the Minister of Industry. Through INH the state will control the construction of the new pipeline crossing Morocco and the Straits of Gibraltar; after 2000 Gas Natural may buy the pipeline from the state.

Spain's gas supplies come mostly from Algeria and Libya. The government is very conscious of this dependence and has been working to improve the security position by diversifying supplies, building storage and establishing an interconnection with the French grid. The challenge for the industry is to continue the process of improving its supply diversification and increasing its flexibility while at the same time ensuring that the cost of gas to consumers remains competitive with alternative fuels. The industry is therefore pushing strongly for increased interconnection with other European gas grids to provide access to a wider range of suppliers.

GAS DEMAND

The Spanish gas market is expanding rapidly. Demand of 6.3 bcm in 1992 is expected to grow at an annual rate of 12% until 2000 before levelling off. In 1994 the electric utilities signed an agreement with Enagas to purchase 25% of Spain's annual gas imports by 2000 at a price indexed to heavy fuel oil. This should see demand for gas in power generation accounting for half the total growth in gas demand. According to the last energy plan, the gas share of TPES should increase from 6.2% in 1992 to 12.2% by 2000.

Table 1 Forecast Gas Demand (bcm)

	1992	1994	2000	2010
Total Demand	**6.3**	**7.0**	**15.4**	**17.8**
Industry	4.4	5.0	7.1	8.2
Electricity Generation (excluding CHP)	0.2	0.1	3.9	3.9
CHP	0.4	0.5	1.9	2.3
Residential/Commercial	1.3	1.4	2.5	3.4

Source: Enagas

GAS SUPPLY

In 1992 Spain's gas came from Algeria (53%), Libya (28%) and domestic production (19%). All the imported gas in 1992 came in the form of LNG. Domestic production came from the Marismas and Gaviota fields. Gaviota was exhausted in 1994 and production at Marismas is expected to last until approximately 1999. There seem to be no other prospects for production at prices below $3.50/MBtu (at this price a total of 4 bcm could become available in the Gulf of Cádiz). In 1993 deliveries began under a contract with Norway. Initial volumes of 1 bcm/year should reach a plateau of 2 bcm/year in 1998. By 1994 Algeria's and Libya's shares of total gas supply had fallen to 51% and 18% respectively. Domestic production was down but new Norwegian supplies represented 13% of total demand.

With demand growing so rapidly prior to the opening of the Algeria-Spain pipeline, Enagas has been forced to search out new gas under new arrangements. In 1993, Enagas purchased 300 mcm from Australia. The gas was swapped with Distrigaz for Algerian LNG delivered in smaller tankers that could be accommodated by Spanish terminals. In 1994 direct deliveries of Australian LNG in 70,000 cm tankers began under a short term contract covering 22 shipments. Deliveries of LNG from Abu Dhabi began in February 1995 and are expected to continue on a monthly basis (at 40 mcm/month) until March 1996. These examples show how Enagas has been able to take advantage of the flexibility offered by LNG trade.

Other European gas companies have cooperated with Enagas to provide supply flexibility. For example, Gaz de France has been reselling some of its winter LNG shipments from Algeria to Spain, helping Enagas to meet its peak demand. The volumes sold in this way in 1994 were comparatively small (135 mcm) but could grow in 1995.

Tables 1 and 2 suggest a small need for gas beyond existing contracts by 2000 (about 0.7 bcm) and a larger need by 2010 (8.8 bcm). If existing contracts were to be renewed the additional need for gas in 2010 would be only 2.1 bcm. A contract for LNG from Trinidad and Tobago is under negotiation; initial deliveries could begin around 1999 and proposed volumes are thought to be around 1.5 bcm/year.

Table 2   Supplies (bcm)

| | Delivered | | Contracted | |
	1992	1994	2000	2010
Domestic Production	1.2	0.8	-	-
Algeria	3.9	4.1	10.2	6.0
Libya	2.0	1.5	2.5	-
Norway	-	1.0	2.0	2.0
Nigeria	-	-	-	1.0
Australia	-	0.6	-	-
Other	-	0.1	-	-
Total	**7.1**	**8.1**	**14.7**	**9.0**

Source: Enagas
Note: Differences between total supply and total demand represent storage injection and losses.

The new pipeline from Norway to France could pave the way for increased deliveries of Norwegian gas to Spain. This would require some capacity expansion within France to remove bottlenecks. Increased volumes of Norwegian gas would represent a significant diversification away from dependence on Algerian supplies.

INFRASTRUCTURE

The Spanish transmission network has a single major north-south pipeline and an east-west line in the north of the country. Until very recently all imported gas was delivered into the network at one of three LNG receiving terminals in the south and east of the country.

Since 1992 there have been some major developments to the gas infrastructure, and several more are planned over the next few years.

In October 1993, a link was completed between Lacq and Calahora, joining the French and Spanish grids and allowing the delivery of new supplies under a contract with Norway. The Norwegian contract foresees maximum deliveries through the pipeline reaching 2 bcm/year. The pipeline has some spare capacity, and with the addition of compression total capacity could be raised to 6 bcm/year, though at the moment bottlenecks exist to the north in France. Further plans for interconnection with France are being contemplated.

Efforts are being made to develop underground storage. A site at Serrablo has been completed (working capacity 0.5 bcm) and another at Gaviota (with a maximum working capacity of 0.8 bcm) should be fully operational by 1998. Other storage sites are being sought and Gas Natural hopes to increase working capacity to 2.5 bcm by 2000.

A major new 9 bcm/year pipeline from Algeria to Spain via Morocco and under the Straits of Gibraltar is now under construction. It should be completed by mid 1996. The undersea section will consist of two separate 22 inch pipes in water up to 400 metres deep, making it the second deepest pipeline after the Transmed line (linking Italy to Tunisia and Algeria). Deliveries to Spain should build up to 6 bcm/year by 2000 and 2.5 bcm/year will be transported through Spain to Portugal. The transmission network in Spain is being expanded to handle the new volumes. Construction in 1995-6 will include the following new pipelines:

- **Tarifa-Córdoba** (275 km) will link the new Algerian pipeline to the Spanish grid;

- **Córdoba-Badajoz** (270 km) will transport Algerian gas to Portugal;

- **Córdoba-Granada** (173 km);

- **Valencia-Alicante** (193 km).

The LNG reception terminal at Cartagena was taken out of service for the period 1993-95. The expansion of the terminal at Huelva, to accommodate larger LNG tankers, is underway and should be completed in 1996. Expansion of the terminal at Barcelona is under investigation. Plans for a new LNG terminal at El Ferrol have been postponed because of the delay in the Nigerian project. Instead a pipeline is planned to run from the north of Portugal to bring gas to Galicia.

COPING WITH DISRUPTIONS

Spain has never faced interruptions in supply beyond weather-related effects (delaying LNG deliveries for a few days) or technical problems related to plant upgrading in Libya or Algeria. Such supply reductions have been handled without interrupting supplies to firm customers. Alternative supplies have been sought, interruptible demand cut and the limited storage drawn upon. In 1992, 25% of total demand was interruptible (down to 20% in 1994) and supplies to interruptible customers can contractually be cut for an indefinite period.

As noted above, there have been considerable changes in the Spanish gas industry since 1992 - most notably the development of storage and the construction of an interconnector with France. Both have had a positive impact on the country's short-term supply flexibility in the event of a disruption. The new Algeria-Spain pipeline will reduce the country's dependence on individual import facilities and Spain plans not to exceed a 60% dependence on Algerian supplies (compared with 51% in 1994). The new direct pipeline from Norway to France could lead to increased supplies from Norway and help Spain meet this target.

Enagas is not planning to increase the level of interruptibility in the industrial sector in line with demand growth, and of projected gas demand for power generation only 40% will be interruptible. The combined-cycle plants are to be supplied with firm gas. By 2010 interruptible demand should be less than 20% of total demand.

World LNG deliveries under spot deals have grown in the last few years to 2 bcm in 1994 as spare capacity has been exploited in exporting countries. Spain needs and intends to develop spot market possibilities in order to enhance supply flexibility.

SWEDEN

GAS POLICY

Gas accounts for less than 1.5% of TPES in Sweden. Future prospects for the Swedish gas market are thus more interesting than the current situation.

The main principle behind Swedish gas policy is that further gas penetration should be a result of gas' own ability to compete in the energy market. Gas purchases should take place on a purely commercial basis and public support for infrastructure development is not foreseen. Over the last few years the promotion of biofuels has in fact reduced the prospects for further natural gas penetration in Sweden. Recent changes in the energy taxation system have also worked in that direction.

If Sweden decides to phase out all or parts of its nuclear power capacity, natural gas fired power generation is one of the few alternatives available. Such a decision will therefore be of paramount importance for future gas consumption.

GAS DEMAND

Present annual gas consumption is about 0.75 bcm, of which about 40% goes into industry, about 40% into power generation and district heating and the remainder into the residential/commercial sector. The long term potential for gas penetration, however, is considerable. According to a recent study for the Nordic Ministerial Council on the prospects for gas in the Nordic countries and the Baltic states, the total market potential for natural gas in Sweden is estimated at 8.4 bcm by 2010. This estimate is broken down as follows:

Consumption in areas already covered by the natural gas network   1.3 bcm

Market potential in other areas   1.9 bcm

Electricity production independent of nuclear phaseout   1.3 bcm

Replacement of 30% of nuclear capacity by natural gas   3.9 bcm.

GAS SUPPLY

Sweden has no domestic gas reserves and imports all of its gas from Denmark. Vattenfall Naturgas AB, a subsidiary of Vattenfall, the leading power producer in Sweden, has a contract with Dansk Naturgas a/s for deliveries of 20 bcm over the period 1985 to 2010 implying annual deliveries of 1.1 bcm at a plateau level up to 2002. Larger volumes could in principle be taken from Denmark when there is a need (the pipeline to Sweden has a capacity of 2 bcm even without extra compression), but realisation of the market potential mentioned above will necessitate at least one more supply source. The supply solution closest at hand is probably gas from the Norwegian North Sea, either through Denmark, through a pipeline along the Norwegian coast into the Gothenburg area or through an onshore pipeline through Norway into Sweden. A bigger market for natural gas in Sweden could facilitate a Nordic gas grid which in due course could also include the Baltic countries.

INFRASTRUCTURE

The Swedish gas infrastructure is uncomplicated; it consists of one transmission line from the southern tip of Sweden up along the west coast to Gothenburg with some branches in the southern part of Sweden. Plans exist for a link between Gothenburg and Stockholm, though these plans are not progressing at present. There are no storage facilities in Sweden, but until recently Vattenfall Naturgas had an agreement for the rent of storage capacity in Denmark. This contract has now terminated.

COPING WITH DISRUPTIONS

In spite of the fact that Sweden has no storage facilities and there are no interruptible contracts as such, the country should be able to cope with an interruption in supplies from Denmark without too many problems, because most industrial gas consumers have kept their oil boilers. District heating plants using gas also normally have multi-firing possibilities. In two major cities LPG-air facilities have been installed to cater to residential customers in the event of a cut in supplies. In the contract with Denmark there are rules for the allocation of available gas from storage when there is a breakdown in offshore supplies from Denmark.

SWITZERLAND

ENERGY AND GAS POLICY

The "Action Programme Energy 2000", which came into effect in 1991 as a response to the referenda, is Switzerland's most important policy initiative to date. It attempts to reconcile the nuclear moratorium and environmental concerns with considerations such as the high and potentially growing dependence on imports, particularly in the electricity sector. The strategy is based on energy efficiency, but also on increasing the contribution of renewable energies and existing nuclear power stations. In particular, it aims to:

■ stabilise fossil energy consumption and CO_2 emissions at 1990 levels by 2000, with subsequent unspecified reductions;

■ slow electricity demand growth by 2000 and stabilise consumption thereafter;

■ increase the contribution of non-hydro renewables to electricity generation by an additional 0.5% and expand their share of heat production by an additional 3% from 1990 levels by 2000;

■ raise hydroelectric generation as compared to 1990 by 5% until 2000, by upgrading and optimising hydro capacity and constructing new plants;

■ upgrade the capacity of existing nuclear power plans by 10% by 2000.

Current policy debate centres around the proposal for a CO_2 levy which the Government has issued in order to follow up its "Energy 2000" programme and a number of provisions in the draft Energy Law. Both proposals went through a nationwide consultation process in 1994. In 1995 the Government decided upon further steps, the major elements of which are:

■ to revise the proposed energy law in order to allow for more responsibilities for cantons and industry;

■ to prepare a CO_2 reduction law which will set targets and a timetable for a reduction of CO_2 emissions. A CO_2 levy, for which the legal basis would be provided by this law, shall only be implemented if the targets are not reached with other measures. The proposed levy could favour gas at the expense of heating oil.

One of the key energy questions in Switzerland concerns future electricity generating capacity. A moratorium on the construction of nuclear power plants was enacted in 1990 and will remain in force until 2000. For nuclear power the outlook beyond 2010 is unclear. One solution, among others currently under investigation, is the replacement by gas-fired generation of the oldest nuclear power plant (Mühleberg, 335 MWe) on the expiration of its operation permit in 2002. The Government is of the opinion that electricity production should remain nearly free from CO_2 emissions, which means that if more gas is to be used, compensation measures (promotion of energy efficiency, heat pumps, utilisation of waste heat) will have to be taken. In 1992, nuclear power accounted for about 40% of total electricity generation.

GAS DEMAND

At present gas is used almost exclusively for heating. The heating market represented 56% of total Swiss final energy consumption in 1994; the market share of gas in this segment was nearly 21%.

Gas consumption was 2.0 Mtoe in 1994. The gas industry is expecting gas demand to rise to about 2.5 Mtoe in 2000 and 3.2 Mtoe in 2010.

GAS SUPPLY

There is currently no gas production in Switzerland. Between 1985 and 1994 there was minor production in a field near Lucerne. Extensive exploration has revealed only small deposits not economically recoverable at current prices.

In 1994, gas supplies to Switzerland were as follows: 47.8% Germany; 22.6% the Netherlands; 15.6% Russia; 12.5% France; 1.4% Italy and 0.1% indigenous production.

There are only local gas storage facilities in Switzerland. To supply the heating market it is therefore important to have supply contracts with a low load factor (around 0.5). In addition, the regional gas company GAZNAT has an agreement with Gaz de France to withdraw up to 2.1 mcm per day (up to a total of 75 mcm per year) from the French storage facility of Etrez (northwest of Geneva).

The existing import contracts fully cover the anticipated demand for the next decade. Depending on future market developments, additional supplies may be needed after 2005.

INFRASTRUCTURE

There are ten delivery points around the country for gas imports. The Swiss gas distribution network totals nearly 13 000 km of which 1 823 km are major transmission lines.

A significant extension programme is to be implemented by 1997. It will lead to a transportation capacity of 12 GW and allow for the future growth in sales at least until 2005.

COPING WITH DISRUPTIONS

Interruptible gas sales to industry make up approximately 80% of the total industrial gas market. For more than 95% of these interruptible customers the alternative fuel is gasoil; the remainder use coal. For all interruptible customers (more than 40% of total sales) the gas industry holds special stocks of oil and coal reaching up to six months of gas consumption; these stocks could be used in case of an emergency on a decision of the Federal Government. The conditions attached to interruptible contracts vary among the four regional companies. For instance, GAZNAT, which serves the west of the country, generally maintains deliveries to all interruptible customers until the temperature drops below -10°C. Other companies may begin cutting supplies to interruptible customers when the temperature is around 0°C. In general, interruption is used only in peak periods; the duration of interruptions is usually short (less than three weeks per winter).

In response to potential supply disturbances, the Swiss gas industry relies on a wide range of precautionary measures comprising in particular: the high degree of flexibility of widely diversified import contracts, special back-up agreements with suppliers, ten delivery points for gas imports, access to the French storage facility in Etrez, the strongly interconnected transmission system in the country and contracts for interruptible gas deliveries.

TURKEY

GAS POLICY

Along with economic growth of around 6% per year, Turkey's energy demand is growing rapidly. The country's dependence on imported energy sources is also increasing. Two fundamental themes of Turkey's energy policy are thus diversification (of both the sources of primary energy and the number of supplying countries) and protection of the environment.

The development of gas in the energy balance is an important part of this policy. Gas currently makes up 7% of TPES; it is intended that this penetration be increased to 20%.

Although both lignite and coal are used extensively for residential heating in Turkey, in Ankara and Bursa lignite and high sulphur coal or fuel oil are banned. The VAT on gas is only 8%, compared with 15% for all other fuels. Further encouragement for natural gas use is given through interest rate credits on installations in Istanbul and subsidised installations in Bursa.

The rapidly growing use of gas implies a significant requirement for new supplies. Rather than being in competition with the rest of Europe for new supplies from Russia and Algeria, Turkey very much views itself as a bridge between the gas rich countries of Turkmenistan and Iran to the east and the rest of Europe to the west, generating, in the medium to long term, new sources of supply for Europe.

GAS DEMAND

Consumption of just 700 mcm in 1987 grew to 5 bcm by 1993, as gas use spread to two combined-cycle power plants, two fertilizer plants, numerous industrial zones and commercial and residential use in the cities of Ankara, Istanbul and Bursa. This growth is set to accelerate as the gas transport network is expanded. Current projections indicate that annual demand will grow by 20% each year until 2000 (reaching 20 bcm) and will rise to over 30 bcm by 2010.

Table 1   Forecast Gas Demand (bcm)

	1992	**2000**	**2010**
Total Demand	**4.6**	**20.0**	**30.6**
Industry	1.6	9.6	12.6
Electricity Generation	2.6	7.7	14.2
Residential/Commercial	0.4	2.7	3.8

Source: Ministry for Energy and Natural Resources.

Annual growth in demand for electricity is now around 10%. The share of gas-fired generating capacity is expected to rise from 13% of total capacity in 1993 to over 20% in 2010 with the construction of 14 combined cycle plants (total capacity 9 500 MW).

GAS SUPPLY

In 1993 almost all of Turkey's gas came from Russia by pipeline via the Ukraine, Romania and Bulgaria. A very small volume (200 mcm) was produced domestically. In 1994 a new LNG terminal at Marmara Ereğlisi (near Istanbul) began taking deliveries from Algeria.

At the end of 1994, Turkey had contracted for annual deliveries of 6 bcm from Russia and 2 bcm from Algeria. Given that domestic production is not expected to increase beyond its current level, there will be a significant gap between potential demand and existing supply provisions well before the turn of the century.

Several options for increasing supplies are under either development or active consideration:

■ **Russia** has agreed to supply an additional 4.5 bcm/year.

■ **Qatar** has signed a cooperation agreement for the delivery of 2 million tonnes per year of LNG (2.8 bcm) by 1998.

■ A further 0.5 bcm/year is being sought from **Algeria**.

■ An agreement is under discussion with **Georgia** and **Russia** for the transit of 8 bcm/year of gas from **Turkmenistan**. This project would require the construction of a north-south pipeline along which the new gas would be marketed. It could be completed within 3-5 years.

If all of the above-mentioned projects materialise before the turn of the century, they will add annual volumes of 11-14 bcm to existing contracts covering 8 bcm, bringing total supply more or less into line with demand projections.

A major new pipeline bringing gas from Turkmenistan through Iran into Turkey and then on to Europe is a longer term project. The proposal is for a 40 bcm/year pipeline, of which around 10 bcm would be consumed in Turkey, with the rest going to Europe. The project is not expected to be undertaken until 2005 at the very earliest.

In 1992, the Turkish gas industry received virtually all of its gas supplies from Russia. By 2010, Turkey clearly aims to have added significant diversity to its supply base, with four separate suppliers.

INFRASTRUCTURE

Existing gas infrastructure in Turkey is limited, with a main transmission line running from the Bulgarian border past Istanbul and the LNG import terminal to Ankara. Distribution networks exist in only three cities. There are, however, plans for development. The new supply projects described above call for the construction of major new pipelines. The cost of the Turkmenistan-Iran-Turkey-Europe pipeline, for example, is estimated at some US$ 10 billion. The capacity of the Marmara LNG reception terminal can be expanded by 5-6 bcm/year, although the construction of a new terminal in the west or south of the country is under investigation.

The demand figures presented above are based on a rapid extension of the internal gas transport grid. Construction of 400 km of new transmission lines in northern Anatolia and in the west of the country is underway. A further 1 200 km serving southern Anatolia is planned.

As the share of gas consumed in the residential and commercial sectors increases, so will the need for load balancing facilities. There are plans to develop salt cavern storage of about 1 bcm in central Anatolia. Other flexibility may be obtained through more interruptible sales.

COPING WITH DISRUPTIONS

During the winter of early 1994 some difficulties were experienced with deliveries of Russian gas, with daily supplies being reduced, at times, by almost 50%.

Top priority for supplies was given to residential consumers. In early March the two gas-fired power plants switched the majority of their inputs to fuel oil and two state-run fertilizer plants, in the west of the country, were put on standby because of an interruption in their supplies. Reductions in Russian deliveries have not yet reached durations of a month. The two dual-fired power plants (only one of which buys formally interruptible gas) together with interruptible industry users made up over 75% of total consumption in 1992.

The opening of the LNG terminal in August 1994, shortly after the March 1994 supply problems, has not only diversified supplies but its storage facility has also brought a degree of short term flexibility. The terminal has three 85,000 cm LNG tanks which can hold the equivalent of 150 mcm regasified (about 12 days of average 1992 consumption).

There is no formal legislation concerning the rationing of gas in the event of a disruption. Therefore, in a longer, more significant disruption, there is little the pipeline company, Botas, can do other than cut most supplies to power plants and industry consumers.

Diversification of supply sources will reduce the impact of a disruption to any single source. This gain from diversification may, however, be partially offset by the large volumes of gas to be used for baseload power generation in the new single-fired plants.

UNITED KINGDOM

GAS POLICY

The aim of the Government's energy policy is to ensure secure, diverse and sustainable supplies of energy in the forms that people and businesses want, and at competitive prices. The Government firmly believes that its aim will be achieved most fully through the mechanisms of the market. Even security and diversity of supply are best achieved through the operation of competitive and open markets. One of the key elements of the Government's policy has been and will remain to encourage competition among producers and choice for consumers - the best guarantee that energy will be produced and supplied efficiently and securely to the benefit of consumers and users - and to establish a legal and regulatory framework to enable market forces to work well.

The British Government may be said not to have a specific gas policy in the sense that it is not actively supporting further gas penetration in the energy market. There is no doubt, however, that by establishing and enforcing a legal and institutional framework for the gas industry the Government plays an important role as far as gas is concerned. For instance, its consistent policy has been to encourage the development of gas to gas competition in the UK market. An exception to the "hands off" policy generally adopted by the Government is the promotion of CHP capacity as a part of the UK climate change programme. The measures taken in this context will no doubt imply an increase in gas use for CHP purposes.

In 1993, UKCS (UK Continental Shelf) oil and gas production accounted for about 1.4% of UK GNP at factor costs. During the period 1987-1993 the contributions from this sector have varied between 2.3% and 1.1%. Total proceeds from the sale of gas are estimated to have been GBP 3.6 billion in 1993, that is 29% of the total proceeds from oil and gas combined.

Expenditure on the construction and installation of platforms and associated equipment and on related pipelines and terminals was estimated in 1993 to amount to GBP 3.229 billion for the development of oil fields and GBP 1.340 million for the development of gas fields. For gas this represents a fall of around 15% on the previous year. The gross capital investment in the mineral oil and natural gas extraction industry as a whole, including that of drilling contractors was estimated to be about GBP 4.7 billion in 1993, constituting about 20% of total UK production industrial investment and 5% of gross domestic fixed capital investment in 1993, among the highest shares realised after 1987. In real terms, investment in 1993 and 1992 was at the same level as in the early eighties. These investments are not negligible in a national context and there should be no reason why investments in oil and gas fields should be limited by Government intervention, thereby potentially reducing gas production in the longer run.

By world standards the UKCS, with some exceptions, is an area of high-cost development. There are always rival claims on gas companies' exploration and development funds. The UK has recently tried to enhance its position by abolishing the Petroleum Revenue Tax (PRT) for new fields and reducing the PRT rate for existing fields. The Government pursues an active policy to promote exploration and development. The 14th Round of offshore licensing was completed in June 1993. This was the largest Round in terms of the number of blocks on offer since 1972. The 15th and the 16th Rounds were announced by the Minister for Energy in April 1994. The 15th Round offers acreage in the gas-prone established areas of the Central and Southern North Sea. The Department of Trade and Industry (DTI) has recently launched a new set of guidelines for operators preparing UKCS development plans. This will lead to shorter approval times and significant savings for operating companies. The DTI also works with industry to identify ways to improve the competitiveness of the UKCS. This has culminated in the Cost Reduction Initiative for the New Era (CRINE) which aims to reduce capital costs by at least 30% in 2 to 3 years. Savings of this order has already been achieved on some projects.

GAS DEMAND

The Government does not attempt to prepare forecasts of energy demand, but released new energy demand projections in 1995. Reference here is made to IEA secretariat estimates of future UK energy consumption. According to the IEA 1994 *Energy Policy Review*, gas consumption in the UK is expected to grow from 50.2 Mtoe in 1992 to 61.0 Mtoe in 2000 and 85.5 Mtoe in 2010. The strongest growth in demand will take place in the power generation sector.

GAS SUPPLY

The share of gas in TPES has increased from 15.7% in 1980 to 26.7% in 1993. So far 918 bcm of gas have been produced on the UKCS. Table 1 shows the estimated potential of initially recoverable reserves.

Table 1   Estimates of Total UK Gas Resources
(already discovered and possibly to be discovered) (bcm)

Discovered recoverable	
Cumulative production end 1993	918
Remaining reserves	
Proven	630
Probable	805
Possible	480
Range of total remaining reserves	630 - 1,915
Possibly to-be-discovered	
Potential additional reserves	125 - 280
"Undiscovered"	300 - 1,295
Total UK resources	**1,975 - 4,410**

1993 saw a slight increase in the lower and upper limits of the estimates for undiscovered gas. Gross gas production in 1993 was 65.5 bcm which means that the present reserves could last at least 24 years at the present pace of production. The 1993 production came from more than 50 fields, of which 11 supplied more than 1.8 bcm, 9 between 1.0 bcm and 1.7 bcm and the remainder less than 1 bcm. Since 1989, production has increased by 46%. According to the "Energy Report', Volume 2 (corresponding to what was earlier the Brown Book) gas production may develop as follows over the next few years:

> 1994: 65-75 bcm
>
> 1995: 65-85 bcm
>
> 1996: 70-90 bcm
>
> 1997: 70-90 bcm
>
> 1998: 70-100 bcm.

The UK still has significant gas reserves in the southern part of the North Sea that can be developed relatively cheaply. Combining this with the efforts to cut costs mentioned above, it seems that the gas supply cost curve should be relatively flat over the interval relevant for the production volumes expected.

In 1993, around 30% of total gas production was associated gas. The share in 1991 was around 20%. Since 1981 this share has varied between 4.5% and 28%.

The UK is basically self-sufficient in gas but still imports gas under depletion contracts from Norway through the Frigg pipeline. In 1993, imports from Norway were 4.5 bcm, down from around 11 bcm only four years earlier. British Gas is buyer under these contracts.

Over the past few years contracts between Norwegian gas sellers and companies in the UK, power producers in particular, have been negotiated but remain conditional upon the conclusion of the jurisdiction negotiations between British and Norwegian authorities concerning the Frigg pipeline. This pipeline has a capacity of more than 10 bcm.

The UK has the possibility of importing natural gas as LNG through the LNG terminal at Canvey Island. The terminal has a storage capacity of 57000 cum of LNG and a regasification capacity of 5 mcm per day, but no imports took place in 1993.

Recently, the UK has become a gas exporter. In 1994, 0.6 bcm of gas from the Markham field was exported to the Netherlands .

In December 1994, a decision was taken to build an Interconnector between the UK and the Continent with a capacity of 20 bcm a year. Initially, this pipeline will probably convey gas to the Continent, but in a longer term it could enable the UK to take gas from the Continent, for instance Russian gas or LNG landed in Belgium.

No gas export forecast is available from the British Government, but an estimate of future export capacity gives an indication. Table 2 gives the Government's best estimate of such capacity:

Table 2   Future export capacity (bcm)

	1994	1995	1998	2000
Markham	0.6	0.6	0.6	0.6
Ireland	9.0	9.0	9.0	9.0
Interconnector	-	-	5.0	20.0
Total	**9.6**	**9.6**	**14.6**	**29.6**

INFRASTRUCTURE

There are about fifty offshore fields producing gas in the UK. These fields are served by a comprehensive system of offshore pipelines conveying the gas to shore. Most of the terminals receive gas from more than one pipeline. There are 10 operational gas terminals in the UK: the Southern Basin gas fields are serviced by 7 terminals: 3 at Bacton, one at Dimlington, 2 at Easington and one at Theddlethorpe. On the west coast, a terminal at Westfield Point serves the Morecambe South field. On the east coast of Scotland, 2 terminals at St. Fergus take supplies from the twin Frigg pipelines, and the FLAGS, Fulmar and Miller pipelines. A third terminal takes supplies from the Scottish Area Gas Evacuation (SAGE) pipeline. The Central Area Transmission System (CATS), a pipeline to a landfall and an onshore receiving terminal at Teesside, was opened in 1993.

The gas volumes landed in the UK are fairly well spread out on the different terminals, all of them taking less than 30% of the total volumes. The most important landing areas like St. Fergus (29% of total volumes in 1993) and the Bacton area (23% of total volumes in 1993) have more than one terminal. The other terminals received between 2 and 15% of total volumes in 1993.

Compared to most other gas consuming countries, storage capacity in the UK is modest. In 1993, working capacity of all storage facilities was around 3.5 bcm. The effective duration of this capacity (available storage volume divided by peak output capacity) is about 25 days.

This relatively low figure reflects a limited need for ordinary storage because the need for swing in gas supplies is provided for in other ways, especially through the high flexibility in British Gas' (BG) purchase contracts. The following example gives an impression of how gas could be supplied on a cold winter day (the figures date from 1991, but should still give a good indication of the present situation):

The flexibility in the gas supply contracts to a large extent explains the modest need for storage in the UK. One might say that the producing fields themselves provide part of the storage capacity. Minimum contract nominations from producing field amount to only 20% of the total gas needed on a cold winter day. The flexibility in beach supplies, however, varies somewhat: it is much higher in the Southern basin than in the Northern basin. The maximum daily sendout on the BG system in 1993 was 317 mcm, whereas the average daily sendout was 168 mcm. Minimum daily sendout in 1993 was around 66 mcm.

Table 3 Gas Supply on a Cold Winter Day (mcm/day)

Beach supplies	
Minimum contract nominations	72
Beach flexibility from swing in contracts	136
⇨ Maximum contract supplies	208
Supplies from Morecambe and Sean (offshore field)	49
Total beach supplies	**257**
Storage	
Rough storage field	38.1
Hornsea salt cavities	39.5
LNG	50.3
Total storage	**127.9**
Total of beach and seasonal supplies	**385**

The 5600 km long National Transmission System brings the gas out to the 12 BG gas regions. Each of the regions has at least 8 offtake points where gas is brought on to the Regional Transmission System which has a total length of 12,300 km. The BG operational activities are undertaken through the 12 regions and 90 BG districts managed by the regions. From Hinckley in the Midlands gas from offshore fields, offshore and onshore storage facilities is dispatched to serve the finely knit gas distribution pipeline network (more than 243,000 km long) conveying gas to Britain's more than 18 million customers. In addition to the storage capacities mentioned above the there exists a diurnal storage capacity capable of supplying some 57 mcm/day from low-pressure gas holders, line-pack, diurnal storage in the National Transmission System, etc. In general the whole gas distribution system is very well integrated, reducing the risk of protracted shortfalls in any part of the system .

COPING WITH DISRUPTIONS

The Energy Act 1976 provide a legislative framework within which emergency action in the case of gas supply interruptions can be undertaken. When an Order in Council under this act already exists the Secretary of State for Trade and Industry may make orders and directions governing the use of gas. Fairly detailed guidelines exist for how emergency situations should be dealt with.

The UK has well defined criteria for security of supply in the rules according to which BG is operating. Although competition is being introduced, there is no reason to believe that the security of supply criteria presently used will be substantially changed. The discussion around security of supply criteria which has recently taken place in the UK in context of the consultation procedures leading up to the reforms in the gas market is dealt with in other parts of the study. Here, only an outline of the criteria presently applied will be given.

There is a probabilistic element in planning gas supply. Daily gas demand depends on a number of factors, including weather conditions. Gas supply is also uncertain: for instance, fields and transmission lines may break down introducing a random supply component into the gas balance. From a planning point of view it is necessary to balance expected demands and expected supplies to an extent depending on the probabilistic degree of security desired. Many other operational and planning decisions require a view of the extent of security of supply (degree of risk) which is acceptable. This will reflect the relative value users place on secure supplies compared with the costs to BG should supplies fail. It has to be recognized that absolute security of supply is impossible.

Different groups of users might desire different degrees of security. On a network system, however, this may be impossible as a common standard of security will apply. Interruptible users do contract for a lower security of supply and operating arrangements have to accommodate additional control of their use. Generally the higher the degree of security the higher the level of stand-by capacity and thus cost.

For planning purposes BG judges security in probability terms, usually expressed as the acceptable 1-in-N risk of failure, where N refers to the expected number of years between failures. Once such a risk level is agreed, it is possible for planning purposes for BG to construct the hypothetical load duration curve that may be expected for any particular 1-in-N risk.

BG's current standards of security of supply are based on the following criteria:

- 1-in-20 peak day: the risk of failure to meet peak demand in the 1-in-20 peak day, that is the day's demand that in a long series of winters, with connected load held at the levels appropriate to the winter in question, would be exceeded in 1 out of 20 winters. This is principally a standard for the transmission system, being applied only to the National and Regional Transmission systems.

- 1-in-50 winter period: the risk of failure to meet peak demand over a winter period defined by the 1-in-50 load duration curve. This is principally a standard for the annual availability of gas and the adequacy of seasonal storage. The 1-in-50 load duration curve is that curve which, in a long series of years, with connected load held at the levels appropriate to the year in question, would be such that the volume of demand above any threshold would be exceeded in 1 out of 50 years. Meeting the winter peak demand depends on both beach and stored gas. If these are planned correctly the supply should fail only in winters with severity greater than 1-in-50.

- 1-in-50 annual supply/demand matching: the risk of failure to meet annual demand due to weather variations and forecasting errors. This is used to determine how close sales should be allowed to approach the volume of supply.

BG is a public gas supplier as defined in the Gas Act. In evaluating the above criteria it takes into account its Gas Act obligations as a public gas supplier to develop and maintain an efficient, co-ordinate and economical system and, in respect of those it is obliged to supply, to give and continue to give a supply of gas to any premises. It is its responsibility to translate the requirements of he Gas Act into small but acceptable levels of risk for the various aspects of the system giving due regard to the requirements to provide an economical supply.

In the event that BG anticipates being unable to meet firm demand, procedures would be put into effect by which demand would be curtailed. This would only be undertaken when beach supplies were at maximum level, all interruptible load was disconnected, stocks of peak and seasonal storage were approaching depletion and the prevailing extreme weather conditions were expected to continue. The first action to be taken would be to appeal to the public for economies in the use of gas. If this did not resolve the problem then the need to disconnect firm customers would arise. In that case Department of Trade and Industry officials, acting on behalf of the Secretary of State, can order customers to stop using gas; BG will act as an agent of the Department and send Letters of Direction from the Department to the relevant gas customers. There are priority group of customers who would not be ordered to stop using gas in an emergency.

In addition to use of the significant flexibility in beach gas supply contracts the use of interruptible contract is a normal way both of load balancing and of meeting extraordinary shortfalls in supply. BG offers a series of different types of interruptible contracts with durations from 6 months to 15 years with annual maximum cut-off periods from 55 to 90 days. The required advance notice varies, but most customers can be notified one day that their gas supplies will be interrupted at 6 a.m. the day after. In some countries, interruptible customers are very rarely interrupted. In the UK interruptions are more common. During the 1980s up to 1986/87, interruptions occurred between 3 and 51 days every year. During the 1987 to 1989 period, there were no interruptions whereas in the 1990/1991 and 1991/92 gas years interruptions occurred 12 and 4 days. BG has around 1200 interruptible customers. The volumes sold under interruptible contracts varied between 8.0 bcm and 10.8 bcm between 1985 and 1993. In 1993 this accounted for about 15% of the total gas volumes supplied to the UK market. BG is losing market shares in some segments of the gas market, but this has not been the case in the interruptible market so far. BG expects the interruptible market to grow somewhat over the next few years but also expects to lose shares in that market.

Interruptible gas users will normally have an alternative fuel available. The principal alternative is HFO.

Historically, there have been no significant loss of supply to the system as a result of production problems. Although there have been a number of small scale industrial actions in the industry since 1973, none of these have had a major effect on the bulk of gas as they occurred at times of low gas demand.

UNITED STATES

NATURAL GAS POLICY

US natural gas policy has evolved over many years beginning with the enactment of the Natural Gas Act (NGA) in 1938. The NGA established the institutional framework for the federal regulatory process that shaped the industry over the next forty years. The regulatory process at both the federal and state level controlled all aspects of the industry from the wellhead to the burner tip. By the early seventies natural gas shortages began to appear. It was generally perceived that an over abundance of regulations (in particular wellhead price controls) were stymieing the exploration and development of new natural gas reserves. In 1978, in response to a natural gas crisis, Congress passed the Natural Gas Policy Act (NGPA). Its primary objective was to phase in a gradual decontrol of wellhead prices. The initial impact of the NGPA was to create an immediate surge in drilling activity that moved the industry from shortages to a surplus in a few years and also resulted in a precipitous decline in wellhead prices. However, it was not until 1989 that the Well Decontrol Act lifted all price ceilings on producer sales of natural gas.

The decontrol of wellhead prices was only the first phase in the development or more accurately redirection of US natural gas policy to one that relies more on market forces and less on regulation. The next phase of natural gas policy development began with the issuance of Order 436 by the Federal Energy Regulatory Commission (FERC) in 1986. Order 436 allowed interstate pipelines (as opposed to intrastate pipelines) to become voluntary "open access" transporters for gas bought directly from producers. This was the first in a series of FERC actions that was intended to loosen the power wielded by interstate pipelines in controlling access to natural gas markets. The final phase was completed on November 1, 1993 when Order 636 was put into effect.

FERC Order 636, often titled Unbundling of Pipeline Services or Restructuring, finalized the process begun in 1986. It required pipelines to separate their merchant function from their transportation service. Order 636 has had the effect of taking interstate pipelines out of the business of selling gas and making them transporters of gas without owning it. End users and distributors must now buy gas directly from producers, aggregators or marketers. The impact of wellhead price decontrol and Order 636 has been to greatly increase the level of competition for most industry participants. The policy of promoting competition in an industry, which heretofore had been highly regulated and monopolistic in its structure, has been supported by successive administrations since 1978.

US natural gas policy was further defined in December 1993 with the release of The Domestic Gas and Oil Initiative. The policy for natural gas as outlined in the Initiative is based on three strategic activities:

i) Increase domestic natural gas production and environmental protection by advancing and disseminating new exploration and production technologies.

ii) Stimulate markets for natural gas and natural-gas-derived products, including their use as substitutes for imported oil where feasible.

iii) Insure cost effective environmental protection by streamlining and improving government communication, decision making and regulation.

The primary thrust of US natural gas policy can be found in activity (ii). It calls for the stimulation of markets for increased use of natural gas in electricity generation and transportation. The policy of increased natural gas use will be accomplished by addressing issues regarding limitations in the present infrastructure including gathering, transporting, storing and distributing natural gas. Other areas that are also essential to the policy of increasing gas use are found in regulatory reform at the federal and state level. The reforms are intended to strengthen gas deliverability by expediting construction of new facilities and reducing impediments to innovative gas use such as in natural gas vehicles.

Natural gas production is regulated by state organizations such as the Texas Railroad Commission. Permits to drill for gas and the establishment of production levels are regulated by each producing state. Pipelines that transport gas from producing regions to consuming areas across state borders (interstate pipelines) are regulated by the Federal Energy Regulatory Commission (FERC). They are primarily responsible for regulating pipeline transportation rates, pipeline siting and construction of new pipelines and facilities. Natural gas is transported by interstate pipelines to local distribution companies. Local distribution companies are regulated by state public utility commissions in regard to rates and most other matters involving their operations.

Natural gas usage has benefitted from favourable environmental policies that have encouraged its use because of the benign nature of gas use as compared with other energy sources. These policies will continue to foster natural gas at the expense of other fuels. Conversely, future natural gas exploration may be hampered by environmental concerns. There is strong public sentiment against offshore drilling on the Atlantic and Pacific coast lines where extensive potential gas reserves are believed to exist. Growing environmental concern about drilling for oil or gas in environmentally sensitive wetlands regions may inhibit development in these areas.

Approximately 89% of US natural gas supply comes from indigenous production with the remainder from imported sources, primarily Canada. In certain regions of the US, Canadian supplies account for up to 30% of total supply. Natural gas imports were reviewed by the Department of Energy pursuant to the Natural Gas Act to see if these imports were deemed in the "public interest". However with the passage of the Energy Policy Act of 1992 (EPACT) the importation of natural gas with any nation that has a free trade agreement with the US is deemed to be in the "public interest". In retrospect, this has never been a major consideration since Canada has always been a very reliable supplier of natural gas to the US

US policy regarding LNG imports is the same for pipeline imports as previously noted. There are no restrictions on LNG imports regardless of the country of origin. Market forces will determine when and where these imports will be made.

NATURAL GAS DEMAND

The demand for natural gas in 1995 is expected to grow by 1.9% to 21.53 trillion cubic feet (Tcf). The growth rate for 1995 is below that for 1994 due to a resumption of more normal winter temperatures. The industrial sector demand will increase by 4.3% in 1995 due to rising industrial output. Electric utility generation gas demand is projected to rise by 3.1 per cent to 3 Tcf in 1995. Table 1 indicates US gas demand by sector.

Table 1 Natural Gas Demand by Sector (trillion cubic feet)

	Commercial	Utility	Residential	Industrial
1993	2.9	2.7	5.0	7.8
1994	3.0	2.9	5.1	8.2
1995	2.9	3.0	5.1	8.6

Source: *Annual Energy Outlook 1994*, DOE/EIA.

Regulatory policies that increased competition in natural gas markets, advances in gas-fired technology, and a growing emphasis on a cleaner environment contribute to an increase that is forecast to reach 24.1 Tcf in 2010. Much of this increase is in electricity generation in the electric utility and industrial sectors (Table 2). In addition to increased gas use in existing generation facilities, a significant part of this increase is for cogenerators, small power producers, independent power producers, and exempt wholesale generators.

Table 2 Forecast Gas Consumption by Sector (Quadrillion Btu per year)

	Residential	Commercial	Industrial	Transportation*	Electricity
1990	4.52	2.70	8.50	0.68	2.88
2000	5.00	2.88	9.61	0.82	4.36
2010	4.99	3.01	10.69	1.10	5.10

Source: *Annual Energy Outlook 1994*, DOE/EIA, Table A2.   * Includes pipeline fuel natural gas and compressed natural gas.
Note: For 1993, the thermal conversion factor was 1.027 Btu per cubic ft.

The DOE's Energy Information Administration forecasts the industrial sector to increase its natural gas use by 1.2 per cent a year until 2010. Increased gas use resulting from the greater competition in natural gas markets is partially offset by technological advances in industrial processes and the use of more efficient equipment. A further dampening effect on future demand will be the result of the US industrial base continuing to shift away from energy intensive industries, such as iron and steel, to less energy intensive such as electronics and pharmaceuticals.

Natural gas will continue to gain in dominance as the primary fuel for new housing and conversions at the expense of electricity and oil, but improved efficiency of replacement furnaces and new installations will have a moderating effect on residential and commercial growth. Residential demand is projected to increase 10 per cent by 2010 while commercial demand should increase by 12 per cent. Transportation uses for natural gas will increase significantly in percentage terms but quantities of actual gas consumed is estimated to be only 0.4 Tcf by 2010.

GAS SUPPLY

The surge in drilling activity that occurred after the enactment of the NGPA in 1978 and ended in the early eighties left the industry with a long term excess supply capability. The surplus productive capacity has depressed prices and conversely has discouraged drilling. By 1993 much of the excess production capability had been worked off bringing the industry closer to a supply demand balance. It is now generally perceived that the industry is in balance. With the recovery in prices, gas drilling activity has been rising. By the middle of 1994 the number of gas wells drilled was 25 per cent higher than in 1993.

One of the key elements to improved drilling activity has been the improvement in natural gas prices and the perception that prices will continue to improve. Technological innovations have reduced the cost of finding and developing gas reserves that have helped to sustain a level of drilling activity even at very low wellhead prices that was formerly thought to be unrealistic. However, increasing domestic production to insure sufficient supplies will be available by 2010 will depend on prices that will encourage further increases in drilling activity. In this regard there is much uncertainty.

DOE's *Annual Energy Outlook* contains forecasts for prices and production levels by five different organizations (Table 3). There is almost a 30 per cent difference between the AEO94 reference case and the highest price ($3.88). The variations are due to several facts including the outlook for oil prices, different perceptions of the impact of technology and the composition of the recoverable resource base. Tentative conclusions can be drawn from the comparisons that show higher gas prices correspond to higher oil prices.

Table 3   Comparative Forecasts for Natural Gas, 2010

Forecast	AEO94	DRI	GRI	AGA	NPC
World Oil Price (1992 dollars per barrel)	28.16	30.03	27.27	24.47	29.72
Average wellhead price, lower 48 states (1992 dollars per thousand cubic feet)	3.47	3.88	3.22	2.89	3.77
US natural gas production (trillion cubic feet)	20.2	21.8	21.6	21.9	20.5
US natural gas consumption (trillion cubic feet)	24.1	24.8	25.3	25.4	24.0

Source: *Annual Energy Outlook* 1994, DOE/EIA.

The US has a vast natural gas resource base to support growing natural gas demand. The technically recoverable resource base is the level of proved reserves (gas that can be readily produced) plus the amount of gas that can be found and developed under current prices and technology. At the end of 1992, proved reserves in the United States (including Alaska) equalled 165 trillion cubic feet, equivalent to 10 years of production at current rates. In its 1992 study, *The*

Potential for Natural Gas in the United States: Source and Supply, the National Petroleum Council (NPC) estimated a technically recoverable gas resource base for the lower 48 States of 1065 Tcf, sufficient to meet US demand at current levels for about 60 years. The NPC estimates of a technically recoverable resource base do not consider price as a factor. Their range of estimates for North America are as follows: in Alaska, 152 Tcf of natural resources of which 10 Tcf is proved; in Canada; 621 Tcf of which 70 Tcf is proved; in the Lower 48, 1065 Tcf of which 155 Tcf is proved; and in Mexico 252 Tcf of which 72 Tcf is proved.

Natural gas imports from Canada represent an important source of supply to the United States. In 1993 the US imported 2.35 Tcf of natural gas from Canada or about 11 per cent of total supply. Natural gas imports from Canada are predicted to rise to 3.9 Tcf in 2010 in response to readily available supplies and a significant increase in pipeline capacity between the US and Canada. With the exception of California, Canadian imports have a greater regional impact on supply by nature of proximity to the Canadian border. In New York State and California, Canadian imports account for 25 per cent and 40 per cent of total supply respectively. During the January 1994 cold spell, Canadian gas accounted for almost a third of the natural gas supplied to consumers in the New England area. The reliability of Canadian supplies was severely tested during this period and many delivery records were established by TransCanada Pipeline.

Natural gas imports from Canada are considered very secure and not subject to the uncertainties of international oil. Furthermore, in light of the Free Trade Agreement and the North American Free Trade Agreement there appears to be few restraints to the flow of gas from Canada to the US On the other hand, this does not guarantee that future reserves of Canadian gas will be developed for exports to the US With over half of Canadian production exported to the US, there is growing public sentiment in Canada that additional production for export will have an adverse environmental impact. It is unlikely that the environmental movement will impact near term exports but, upper limits on exports could be impacted in the more distant future.

Small quantities of gas were exported by Mexico to the U.S in late 1993 and early 1994 but they have since ceased. The long term future for Mexican gas deliveries to the US does not appear promising. Significant imports from Mexico are only expected to resume in 2006, rising to 0.2 Tcf in 2010. Mexico has significant quantities of natural gas that is associated with oil production. There is much internal debate within Mexico about this resource base as to whether it should be sold for export or husbanded for future internal use. In order to become a major factor in the US gas market, Mexico would need to make major investments into its infrastructure. This would require major foreign investments in capital and technology. Pemex, the state owned oil company, has consistently resisted such moves but indications are that Mexico's political climate is changing in a direction towards seeking accommodation with non-Pemex investors, albeit very slowly.

Venezuela, with extensive gas reserves and very limited demand, has proposed to construct a pipeline to the border with Mexico. Natural gas would be transported to the US by existing pipelines in Mexico. This is only a proposal and significant obstacles to such a costly and complex project would need to be overcome.

Finally, LNG at current natural gas prices is not considered as a major supply source in the near term. However, by the year 2010 proposed LNG projects in Trinidad and Tobago could vie for US markets.

INFRASTRUCTURE

The US natural gas infrastructure has evolved from the need to transport gas from producing regions to distant consuming areas. Natural gas is produced over a wide ranging area of the United States. More than 20 states produce commercial quantities of natural gas. A closer examination reveals that production is highly concentrated in three states, Texas, Louisiana and Oklahoma account for about 70 per cent of all production. Slightly over 25 per cent of indigenous production is produced offshore in the Gulf of Mexico. Within this producing area is a highly developed and complex gathering, processing, storage and transmission system that is capable of supplying markets in the eastern third of the US, even during extreme winter weather conditions. Significant quantities of this gas are also sent westward to California. The remaining infrastructure is designed to supply gas from Canada or to transport gas from smaller pools to the nearest markets. The natural gas system in its entirety (gathering, transmission and distribution) was comprised of 1,263,500 miles of pipeline as of 1993.

Consumers typically purchase their gas from a local distribution company (LDC) although large industrial consumers and power plants often purchase natural gas directly from a pipeline company. Gas distribution companies are either private corporations or as in many states they are municipal or publicly owned companies. They are regulated by the states in which they conduct their operations. The key link between distribution companies and producers is the interstate network of 52 pipelines. These pipelines are unique from all other systems because they cross state borders and are therefore subject to federal regulation in terms of siting, interconnections and transportation rates.

The interstate pipeline network is completely integrated such that natural gas from Southwest producing regions is capable of moving just about anywhere in the network. Furthermore, the interstate pipeline network is also the key link between LDCs and storage fields. Increasingly, storage has become a vital component in the exemplary performance of the US natural gas industry's deliverability record. The importance of storage was demonstrated in the January 1994 severe cold spell that required record withdrawals from storage. Estimates indicate that 37 per cent of the gas supplied during a one week period in January 1994 was from storage.

The US has approximately 7.3 Tcf of underground storage capacity. Less than half of this gas is available for withdrawal (working gas) while the remainder serves as base gas and is not considered available for use. Most of the gas is stored in depleted gas wells. Storage sites are spread over a wide geographic area but tend to be located close to markets with large winter heating demand such as Michigan and Pennsylvania. The maximum daily output of all underground storage when full is 52 Bcf.

There are presently four LNG import terminals in the US. Their combined capability to receive and regasify the LNG is about 1 trillion cubic feet per year or about 5% of US demand. At present only one of the terminals is operating. The terminal is located in Everett Massachusetts and receives its supplies from Algeria. Current domestic US natural gas prices are at a low enough level that Algerian or other sources of imported LNG cannot be successfully marketed in most regions of the US.

A recent development in the US natural gas infrastructure has been the addition of market centres (trading hubs). There are about 25 existing market centres with several more in development stages (Figure 1). The centres are designed to offer a variety of physical services including storage, parking, wheeling, pooling, balancing and peaking. Financial or transactional services such as title transfers, capacity release, electronic trading, risk management and credit are also being offered. The Electronic Bulletin Board services throughout the centres will provide information on pricing, weather and other important news related to gas industry operations.

COPING WITH SUPPLY DISRUPTIONS

Section 302 of the Natural Gas Policy Act of 1978 contains authorities for the federal government to act in a major natural gas emergency. The use of this authority requires the President to declare a natural gas emergency. The Department of Energy would then be remanded with the responsibility of implementing Section 302. The authorities contained in Section 302 give the Department wide latitude in actions such as allocating gas to pipelines and requiring large industrial users to cease consuming gas. These authorities were written in 1978, a time when the industry was very different from today. The authorities under section 302 may need to be revised to reflect current industry structure.

The implementation of Order 636 has not only changed the way the natural gas industry conducts its usual business, but it has fundamentally changed the way it can respond to a supply emergency (or demand emergency). Prior to Order 636 pipelines assumed the risk of assuring that gas supplies would be available even on the coldest days because of their combined role as transporter and merchant. Order 636 has ended the pipeline merchant function thus abrogating pipelines from supply liability. Supply risk has now moved closer to the consumer because LDCs are required to assume the risk of managing supply access and availability that was formerly part of the pipeline merchant function. The brief but record breaking cold spell that gripped the eastern third of the US in January 1994 severely tested the ability of the gas industry to respond to a demand crisis (supply was not a problem).

The ability of the natural gas industry to meet the challenge of record breaking gas demand is an excellent illustration of the ability of the US gas industry to cope with a severe system stress. In a post-freeze study conducted by the Department of Energy it was found that communications played a major role in assuring that firm supply commitments were met. Pipeline electronic bulletin boards instantaneously relayed to LDCs critical operational information that aided in making quick decisions. A spirit of cooperation and open lines of communication between producers, pipelines, storage operators and LDCs that was initiated by Order 636 moved gas to where it was needed most.

Figure 1   Major Market Centres

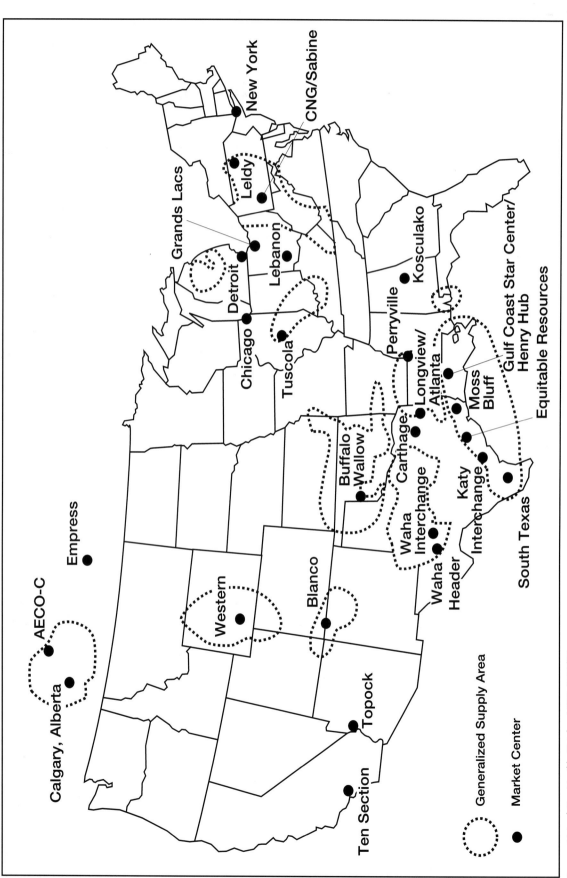

The scope of natural gas storage as part of the US infrastructure has been previously noted but the importance during January, 1994 can not be overly emphasized. Pipelines ran at 95 per cent capacity which is considered the maximum sustainable limit. Withdrawals from storage both upstream and downstream locations made up any deficits. LDCs called upon their peak shaving facilities (propane air, LNG) to meet critical needle peaks caused by unexpected low temperatures that were as much as 8 degrees below prior record lows.

Demand side management played an important role in assuring the integrity of supply to high priority consumers. Invoking the terms of interruptible contracts enabled pipelines and LDCs to meet all firm commitments. Pipeline customers with interruptible transportation agreements were asked (or told) that their capacity was needed to meet the requirements of other transporters with more urgent needs and to switch to an alternate energy source. For at least a portion of January, 1994 all 22 interstate pipelines serving the eastern third of the US had to interrupt service to their non-firm transportation customers. Most of the freed up capacity was used by LDCs to exercise supply options that enabled them to get more gas. In turn, LDCs exercised their interruptible supply contracts that insured all priority consumers would get all the gas needed.

The use of interruptible contracts as a demand management tool is standard practice for pipelines and LDCs with industrial or electric utility loads. There are now a significant number of large institutions such as hospitals and apartment complexes that purchase their gas under the terms of an interruptible contract. A purchaser of interruptible gas (or transportation) must be able to switch on short notice to an alternate fuel. Fuel switching can serve as a natural gas emergency management tool. But, the question of how much gas could be switched to oil in a natural gas disruption has not been successfully answered.

Recent experience has revealed that many interruptible consumers have limited stocks of fuel, making switching out of gas a very limited option, even though the data indicate dual-fuel capability. Annual data show that in 1993 electric generation accounted for 13 per cent of natural gas consumed in the US, nearly all of which was switchable to oil. However, the data show that on a seasonal basis electric utility gas consumption in August is twice the January consumption, therefore the volume of switchable gas is only about 6 per cent of consumption in the months when a gas emergency would have major significance. What all this illustrates is that any attempt to determine the volume of gas switchable to oil is likely to be so unreliable as to make any estimates nearly meaningless. Such factors as season, length of switching period and availability of alternate fuels would have to be factored into the determination.

Pipelines issue operational flow orders to correct or prevent system imbalances. These directives typically require a pipeline customer to inject more gas into the system to meet their contractually agreed upon terms. Operational flow orders assist pipelines in balancing their loads during periods of extremely high demand when takes may exceed inputs.

The fact that the natural gas industry was able to deal with a level of gas demand of crisis proportions with almost no government intervention must not be overlooked. Industry executives realize that as the balance between supply and demand gets tighter the probability for spot shortages may increase. To prevent or mitigate such occurrences, the industry has formed the Natural Gas Reliability Council. Its mission will be to identify issues that may affect gas deliverability and to help facilitate coordination of industry operations personnel during emergencies to insure reliable gas service.

The natural gas industry has shown that it is able to respond to extraordinary situations. However, in the event that government intervention is deemed necessary, state and federal legal authorities are available. Every state has emergency regulations that would allow some form of response in the event of a supply shortfall. In most cases state emergency responses usually require action by the governor and are limited to entities within their state. Emergency actions regarding interstate pipelines would be outside their purview. Governors usually have a wide latitude in dealing with emergencies affecting the citizens of their respective state.

A disruption in pipeline supplies has normally been dealt with through curtailment plans that enable pipelines to cease service to their customers in accordance with a pre-approved plan. Gas would then be diverted to higher priority customers. The curtailment plans are based on the premise that the curtailed gas is owned by the pipeline. Now that pipelines own little of the gas in their systems, this authority has greatly limited curtailment plans as an emergency response measure.

BELARUS

INTRODUCTION

Belarus is currently a relatively minor transit country for Russian gas. The country plays host to a segment of Gazprom's Northern Lights export pipeline system. In 1993 the Russian company shipped some 21 bcm via Belarus to Ukraine, Poland, Lithuania and Latvia. Transited volumes apparently declined by one quarter between 1990 and 1993.

Belarus' importance as a transit country may increase considerably towards the end of the 1990s, or after the turn of the century, if Gazprom plans to construct a new export pipeline system to the west via Belarus and Poland with a design capacity of 67 bcm are realised. Apart from this project, which may take longer to materialise than foreseen, depending on market and funding constraint developments, the Belarusian gas industry and Gazprom plan to undertake investments that would increase Belarus' capacity to transit Russian gas by up to 30 bcm a year.

THE BELARUSIAN ECONOMY

Until World War II Belarus was a predominantly rural society, but the 1950s, 1960s and 1970s saw a massive movement of people and resources to the cities, and in 1992 industry accounted for 47 per cent, and agriculture and forestry for 24 per cent, of net material product. Belarus was strongly integrated in the FSU economy, exporting some 50 per cent of GDP, mainly agricultural machinery, transportation equipment, military hardware and chemicals, and depending on imports for a high share of its energy and fuel supplies. The break-up of the FSU, the withering away of markets in the other FSU republics and the jump in prices of Russian oil and gas therefore hit the Belarusian economy very hard. Preliminary figures suggest that GDP fell by another 12 per cent in the first quarter of 1995 compared with the same period of 1994.

Table 1   Macroeconomic Developments

	1990	1991	1992	1993	1994
GDP growth (%)	-6.9	-2	-9.6	-11	-22
Consumer price inflation (%)	5.5	98.6	1070	1290	2130
Trade balance (mill. US$)	-1645	-1598	-8612	-4471	-2491

Source: PlanEcon, The Economist Intelligence Unit.

Belarus has proceeded much more hesitantly with economic reform than Russia and, recently, Ukraine. The Government envisages a "third way" between socialism and capitalism, inspired by the Chinese model and characterised by a private sector emerging alongside an invigorated state sector. Only in 1993 did the Government start taking advice from the International Monetary Fund and similar institutions, and the unwillingness to adopt painful policies seems to have lingered. It is estimated that in 1994 nearly 70 per cent of the Government's expenditures went to subsidise consumer goods and state enterprises.

Foreign advisors criticise the Belarusian Government's monetary policies for being too loose, and its fiscal policies for being too lax. In 1994 price liberalisation led first to increased inflation and then to a doubling of nominal minimum wages. The 1995 budget envisages a deficit equal to 4 per cent of projected GDP; but since it is premised on a decline in inflation to 2 per cent a month by the end of the year, which is considered highly unrealistic, observers expect actual spending to exceed budgeted spending.

ENERGY BALANCE DEVELOPMENTS

In 1993 Belarus' primary energy production corresponded to about 12 per cent of TPES. The country produced some 2 million tonnes of crude oil, equal to 14 per cent of net crude supply, and 225 million cubic metres of associated gas, equal to about 1.5 per cent of domestic gas use. Primary (hydro) electricity production was only 19 GWh, all public power and heat plants are oil and/or gas based, but domestically produced peat and wood accounted for some 5 per cent of TPES.

An opening of the Belarusian petroleum industry for foreign investment could lead to increases in oil and gas production, but new discoveries would probably be small; the republic's dependence on imported fuels seems destined to increase.

Belarus' domestic energy use peaked in 1990-91 at about 45 Mtoe. According to World Bank calculations, 1992 and 1993 saw declines of around 15 per cent per annum, and PlanEcon estimates that TPES in 1994 fell by another 11-12 per cent.

According to World Bank estimates, energy consumption per unit of GDP is several times higher in Belarus than in the most developed countries, and some 40 per cent higher than might be expected given Belarus' level of development as measured by GDP per capita. The main reasons for this appear to be:

■ the dominant role of industry in total production;

■ the high share of heavy industry within the industrial sector;

■ the technologies and management practices in use in the industrial sector;

■ the energy price structure.

As GDP dropped by about 21 per cent from 1990 to 1993, the energy intensity of the Belarusian economy apparently declined by some 10 per cent between 1990 and 1993. According to PlanEcon's TPES and GDP estimates for 1994, however, energy use per unit of GDP bounced back by 10-11 per cent that year.

The long term energy programme submitted in 1992 emphasises energy efficiency improvement, and identifies a technical energy savings potential of 12.6 Mtoe, equal to about one third of TPES as of that year. The households/commercial/public services sector could according to the programme cut its annual energy use by 3.8 Mtoe, the chemical and petrochemical industry had a savings potential of 2.5 Mtoe and the power industry could reduce its fuel consumption by 1.7 Mtoe.

Belarus' energy use is heavily weighted towards petroleum. In 1993 the oil and gas shares of TPES were 48.9 per cent and 39.2 per cent respectively. Net imports of electricity accounted for 4.7 per cent, coal for 2.1 per cent and peat and wood for 5 per cent. The main trend since 1985 has been a massive substitution of gas for oil, the share of the former fuel has increased by 21.5 percentage points while the share of oil has declined by almost exactly as much.

Belarus' 22 public power plants are all thermal. In 1990 electricity industry fuel consumption was 8.2 Mtoe of fuel oil and 5.7 Mtoe of gas. In 1993 power plant fuel use amounted to about 3.9 Mtoe of fuel oil and 7.4 Mtoe of gas, implying a drop in the oil share from almost 59 per cent to 35 per cent, and an increase in the gas share from 41 per cent to 65 per cent, over only three years.

On the basis of 1992 data, it is estimated that industry accounts for about 35 per cent, the transport sector about 15 per cent and other sectors some 40 per cent of total final consumption of energy. The balance of TFC is feedstock for the chemical industry and other non-energy fuel use.

THE GAS SECTOR

Gas Balance Developments

Domestic gas use increased by an average of about 10 per cent a year between 1985 and 1992, but fell by some 8 per cent in 1993 and, according to PlanEcon estimates, by another 12-13 per cent in 1994, primarily as a result of economic contraction.

Since the mid 1980s substitution to gas within the electricity sector has been the main driving force behind the growth in total gas consumption. Today, gas fired power plants account for more than half of Belarus' gas use. Industrial gas consumption increased throughout the 1980s, but stagnated around 1990 and dropped by some 20 per cent last year. Within the industrial sector, the chemical and petrochemical industries are the biggest gas consumers. The housing and municipal sector's gas use has increased more or less in parallel with total gas consumption, but continued to grow in 1993 when most other sectors' gas use declined.

Table 2   Gas Balance Developments (bcm)

	1990	1991	1992	1993
Production	0.30	0.29	0.29	0.23
Imports (incl. transit)	42.33	42.08	37.19	36.62
Total Supply	**42.63**	**42.37**	**37.48**	**36.8**
Transit	**27.62**	**27.15**	**20.82**	**20.62**
Industry	3.63	3.66	3.43	2.70
Public power and heat	7.06	7.41	9.72	9.18
Transportation	0.09	0.09	0.10	0.10
Construction	0.19	0.20	0.21	0.20
Agriculture	1.04	1.15	1.25	1.25
Residential	0.70	0.77	0.85	0.89
Other	1.79	1.91	1.88	1.60
Distribution losses	0.11	0.11	0.10	0.13
Use for transmission compressor fuel	0.17	0.15	0.12	0.14
Transmission losses	0.05	0.05	0.04	0.05
Total Domestic Consumption	**14.82**	**15.50**	**17.69**	**16.23**
Stock change (incl. storage in Latvia)	0.29	-0.16	-1.23	0.00
Unaccounted for	0.48	-0.11	0.20	0.00

Source: World Bank.

Belarus seems bent on increasing the gas share of its TPES further. The burning of heavy fuel oil in power plants and in the industrial sector causes environmental problems, and needs to be reduced because of constraints on the supply of oil. The residential market is also expected to continue to grow.

Imports

Belarus imports gas exclusively from Russia. Imports (net of volumes in transit) increased by about 9 per cent from 1990 to 1992, but declined in 1993, by 2 per cent judging by World Bank figures, but by some 9 per cent according to PlanEcon. The latter source estimates that imports dropped by another 13 per cent in 1994. If so, actual deliveries fell 11 per cent short of contracted deliveries. The two countries have contracted for deliveries of 16 bcm in 1995, which is as much as Belarus had agreed to buy in 1994. PlanEcon reports that deliveries during 1st quarter 1995 amounted to 4.2 bcm.

Recently, both demand and supply side factors have worked to dampen Belarus' gas consumption and imports. The steep falls in GDP and TPES in 1993 and 1994 have been mentioned. On the supply side, Russia's Gazprom is getting increasingly reluctant to fulfil delivery contracts with other FSU republics that do not pay their bills. By June 1995, Belarus reportedly owed Russia US$ 410 million for gas received in 1994, and another US$ 100 million for gas received during 1st quarter 1995. Belarus is Russia's second biggest debtor among the FSU republics, owing almost as much as the other republics, apart from Ukraine, combined.

Under a payment-in-kind deal for 1995, Belarus is supposed to ship engineering plant, tractors and assorted consumer appliances to Russia to pay towards its energy bill. Moscow is reportedly unwilling to accept the goods, however, arguing that there are no suitable wholesalers in Russia.

Belarus' location does not lend itself well to a diversification of imports. Belarusian authorities have held discussions with representatives of gas producing republics and regions within the Russian Federation on importing Russian gas outside the agreements between Minsk and Moscow, but volumes acquired this way would probably be small. They have also visited Turkmenistan to learn about the possibilities of importing Turkmen gas, but costs might be high. Ukrainian authorities have talked about importing Iranian gas, and if this plan gets off the ground, Belarus could be one of the takers of Ukrainian re-exports, but a pipeline would have to be built, meaning that currently insoluble funding problems would have to be solved. Finally, pipelines through the Baltics and/or Poland could move North Sea gas to Belarus, but again, this would be a costly alternative.

Belarusian worries about their dependence on Russian gas have so far fed into their overall strategy of supporting Russian positions and accommodating Russian policies. Striving to secure favourable treatment from Russia arguably makes sense from an energy supply perspective as Belarus may remain dependent on Russian gas supplies for the foreseeable future.

Transit

Belarus transits Russian gas to Ukraine, Poland, Lithuania and Latvia. Transited volumes dropped from 27-28 bcm a year in 1990-91 to 20-21 bcm a year in 1992-93.

Belarus' importance as transit country for Russian gas exports to the West looks set to increase. Russia wants to reduce its dependence on Ukraine for its gas exports. Moreover, pipelines from central Russia to the German border via Belarus and Poland would be 260 km shorter than the lines through the Ukraine and the Czech and Slovak Republics. Russia therefore intends to construct a pipeline system westwards through Belarus (see below).

Organization of the Gas Industry

The Belarusian energy sector consists of various state concerns or state committees controlling individual sub-sectors and reporting directly to the cabinet. These entities have the dual function of government agencies and holding companies, and their powers to decide on strategies and formulate long term policies for themselves result in losses of efficiency and make formulation and implementation of an overall energy policy difficult. The Belarusian Government has therefore requested Parliamentary approval for establishing a Ministry of Energy with the tasks of setting prices, formulating and coordinating energy policies and handling intra-governmental energy issues and Belarus' energy trade and cooperation with other countries, and exercising ownership and management of the above mentioned entities.

One such entity, Beltransgaz, is charged with importing gas from Russia, running the transmission gas pipeline system and the compressor stations and operating the republic's underground gas storage facilities. The concern is also involved on the distribution and retailing side of the gas business through its sales of CNG to motorists. Beltransgaz has seven regional divisions, one for each oblast and one for Minsk city, operating the pipelines, compressor stations and CNG stations in their respective areas.

Beltransgaz has only one customer for its natural gas: Beltopgaz which buys the gas at distribution stations where pipeline pressure levels are lowered, and distributes and sells it to end users of all kinds, factories, institutions and households. Beltopgaz is also a state concern with seven regional divisions operating as autonomous cost centres. These divisions are furthermore subdivided into 117 service enterprises. Beltopgaz also runs departments for building and construction, research, training etc.

Beltopgaz buys domestically produced gas directly from Belarusneft, the state enterprise in charge of oil and associated gas production.

Gas Price Developments

Most domestic energy prices are controlled, the exceptions being coal prices for industrial users and certain oil product prices. Proposals to change gas prices are prepared by the Committee of Oil and Chemistry, the Ministry of Resources, Beltransgaz, Beltopgaz and the Ministry of Housing and Communal Services, and submitted to the Ministry of Economy for approval.

The import price of gas is set through intergovernmental agreements between Belarus and Russia. During 1993 the border price increased from 2,500 rubles to 88,750 Russian rubles (equal to about 71 US$ using the official end-1993 exchange rate) per 1000 cubic metres (tcm); in February, 1995 it was reported at US$ 55/tcm. Thus, Russia has not yet introduced "world level" prices for its gas exports to other FSU republics; doing so would presumably only add to Gazprom's problems with non-payment for deliveries. The producer price for (associated) gas in November 1993 was only 4,350 Belarusian rubles, i.e., less than a dollar, per tcm.

Beltransgaz charges Beltopgaz the border price plus a transmission margin intended (but in practice failing) to cover operation, maintenance and depreciation costs and to include a 20 per cent gross profit margin. This margin was in late 1993 6,000 Russian rubles/tcm. Beltopgaz adds a distribution margin which, amounting in late 1993 to 1,200 (Belarusian or Russian, depending on consumer group) rubles/tcm, is just as inadequate in the light of that enterprise's costs.

By November 1993, Beltopgaz demanded 366,000 Belarusian rubles/tcm from its industrial customers, i.e., at an exchange rate of 4.2 Belarusian ruble to one Russian ruble, almost the same as Beltransgaz paid at the border for imported gas. Gas used for food and other agricultural production was priced at 77,550 Belarusian rubles/tcm. Households were charged between 10,000 and 15,000 Belarusian rubles, equal to US$ 1-1.50, per tcm. According to World Bank calculations, full economic costs of supplying gas to industry and households were US$ 70/tcm and US$ 85/tcm respectively. Industrial consumers thus paid cost covering prices, while residential consumers only covered a small fraction of the costs of their supplies.

The household sector's energy use has been financed mostly through cross-subsidisation, industry has been charged higher than cost covering prices for electricity and heat.

In the spring of 1995 the Belarusian Government ordered a fivefold increase in gas prices to 412,500 Belarusian rubles/tcm for households and 912,000 Belarusian rubles/tcm for industrial consumers. Using the official exchange rate for non-cash transactions which at the end of March was 11,600 Belarusian rubles to the dollar, these prices translate into US$ 36/tcm for households and US$ 79/tcm for industry. It appears that the gap between household supply costs and the household gas price is narrowing. To what extent the higher prices will translate into higher revenues for Beltopgaz remains to be seen. They could conceivably only add to the enterprise's problems with non-paying customers.

Non-payment for deliveries is a major problem for Beltopgaz, and in 1993 the enterprise adopted a policy of cutting off non-paying customers. As of December that year, 29 industrial gas users had been cut off, and another 41 had had their supplies reduced. However, deliveries continued to non-paying customers whose services were considered essential, e.g. power plants.

GAS INFRASTRUCTURE

Beltransgaz operates approximately 2,800 km of transmission pipelines with a diameter of 720 mm or more, and a number of smaller lateral lines to city gate stations. Pressure is maintained by means of six mainline compressor stations with 146 turbo-compressor units having a total nameplate capacity of 706 MW.

Table 3   Large Diameter Gas Pipelines

Inlet-Outlet	Length (km)	Diameter (mm)	Built (year)	Purpose
Torzhok-Ivatsevichi I	454	1220	1975	Transit to Ukraine
Torzhok-Ivatsevichi II	454	1220	1978	Transit to Ukraine
Torzhok-Ivatsevichi III	454	1220	1982	Transit to Ukraine
Ivatsevichi-Dolina I	146	1220	1977	Transit to Ukraine
Ivatsevichi-Dolina II	146	1220	1981	Transit to Ukraine
Minsk-Vilnius	196	1220	1988	Transit to Lithuania
Kobrin-Poland	88	1020	1985	Transit to Poland
Minsk-Gomel	315	720	1984	Local delivery
Ivatsevichi-Grodno	175	720	1989	Local delivery
Torzhok-Dolina	364	1420	Constr.	Transit to Ukraine

Source: World Bank.

The three Torzhok-Ivatsevichi pipelines are part of the Russian Northern Lights export pipeline system. All deliveries of Russian gas to Belarus take place via these lines. They enter Belarus from the north-east and run to Minsk from where one lateral moves gas to the Gomel area in south-east Belarus, and another runs to Lithuania and Latvia. The three lines continue south-westwards to Ivatsevichi in the Brest oblast where the system forks into one smaller pipeline running north-westwards to Grodno in Belarus and onwards to Lithuania, and two 1220 mm lines continuing south-westwards to Kobrin. There the system forks again into one pipeline running westwards to Brest and Poland, and two running southwards to Ukraine.

Construction of a 1440 mm pipeline from Torzhok in Russia via eastern Belarus to Dolina in Ukraine started in the mid 1980s, but the project was put on ice due to contamination problems following the Chernobyl accident. The Belarusian portion of the line was completed in 1993, but there is a need for more compressor stations, and on the Russian side of the border, the Smolensk-Belarusian border link is not yet operable.

All transmission pipelines have cathodic protection. About 80 per cent of the network is equipped with remote control systems. Some valves may need to be repaired or replaced and the cathodic protection and the control systems may need to be improved; however, the World Bank does not see an immediate need for a major pipeline rehabilitation programme.

Beltransgaz runs one storage field located at Osipovichi between Minsk and Bobruysk. The field is an aquifer-type reservoir with a working gas capacity of 420 million cubic metres and a buffer gas volume of 380 million cubic metres and is used mainly to ensure gas deliveries to Minsk in the winter. It is already inadequate, however, to meet peak demand. The field is equipped with six gas engine driven reciprocating compressors with a capacity of 4.4 MW.

The domestic gas distribution network includes about 12,000 km of pipelines and covers 62 cities. A relatively high share of Belarus' urban population, but few villages and rural areas, have access to gas. The World Bank characterises the gas distribution control and dispatch system as obsolete and inadequate. There are also 1580 km of pipelines distributing LPG from central reservoirs.

Planned New Infrastructure

Beltransgas' investment programme for 1995-2000 includes replacing 16 compressor station units with a nameplate capacity of about 100 MW, developing another storage field, at Pribug near Brest, with a working capacity of 1.3 bcm and a buffer gas volume of 1.5 bcm, and constructing various new lateral lines and city gate stations. The company also intends to increase the number of compressed natural gas (CNG) vehicle fuelling stations.

Not included in the five year investment programme, but under consideration, is a project to complete the Belarusian segment of the Torzhok-Dolina pipeline. Changes in the routing of the pipeline and natural decrease in radiation have reduced the risk of putting the missing compressor stations in place to levels deemed acceptable. When these stations are operable and the delayed investments on the Russian side of the border are undertaken, Belarus' capacity to transit Russian gas to Ukraine will increase by some 20 bcm a year.

Another project is to add a pipeline to the system moving gas from Minsk to the Belarusian-Polish border near Brest. There is about 10 bcm of spare capacity in the transmission pipelines upstream of Minsk that cannot be utilised because of bottlenecks downstream of Minsk. Building another 1420 mm pipeline from Minsk to Poland would increase Belarus' capacity to transit gas to Poland by 7-10 bcm a year.

A third project relates to Russia's plans to construct new export pipelines from fields in the Yamburg-Urengoy-Medvezhye area, and later in the 1990s from the Yamal peninsula, to European Russia and Europe. As noted, Gazprom intends to route these pipelines through

Belarus and Poland. The plans call for building two new parallel 1420 mm pipelines with five compressor stations and a combined capacity of 64 bcm a year across Belarus in the 1995-2002 period. Belarus has reportedly suggested to settle its gas debts to Russia through contributing to the project.

Although agreements have been signed and companies set up to implement the project, it could be delayed by factors such as funding difficulties, unpromising market developments in Europe, changes in gas availability due to declines in domestic Russian, Ukrainian and Belarusian demand and, conceivably, changes in Russian-Ukrainian relations.

With respect to the gas distribution system, Beltopgaz has prepared a five year investment programme including expansion of the distribution network by 1,500 km a year, installation of a Supervisory Control and Data Acquisition (SCADA) system, installation of 50,000 meters for commercial and residential customers annually and replacement of inaccurate low pressure industrial meters.

CONCLUSIONS

The Belarusian economy keeps contracting, and the domestic political climate, marked by disagreement on the importance of political independence and of building democratic institutions, and on where to look for economic development models, appears inconducive to engineering a turnaround and renewed growth. These features of Belarus' situation could be seen as worrying if the republic were to play host to pipelines moving large volumes of gas towards Europe. Moreover, the high and increasing share of gas in Belarus TPES, the republic's total dependence on imported Russian gas and its difficulties in honoring its debts to Gazprom could conceivably lead Belarus to try to meet supply reductions by siphoning off gas meant for customers further down the pipelines.

However, Belarus is a relatively small country with little political clout, and most Belarusians, including the more nationalistically inclined, seem to agree on the importance of continued co-operation with Russia, indicating that the Government would have to be very hard pressed to challenge Moscow on something as important as Russian gas in transit, be it through stealing gas off the lines or by charging exorbitant transit fees. At the same time, the Russian Government has displayed a readiness to continue supporting Belarus that has been absent in its dealings with Ukraine. The possibility of Belarus wilfully disturbing Russian gas exports to Europe may therefore be more hypotethical than real.

As for the probability of technical transit breakdowns, existing transmission pipelines are reportedly in acceptable shape, and the planned new pipeline system would presumably be state-of-the-art and not represent abnormal risks to buyers.

BULGARIA

INTRODUCTION

The Bulgarian economy is closely tied to the former Soviet Union and, before its break-up, Bulgaria received all of its gas and around three-quarters of its oil from the FSU. The economic collapse in Bulgaria was arguably the most severe of the former countries of Eastern Europe. This collapse has been exacerbated by the requirement to pay hard currency for energy imports from the FSU and the breakdown of trade within the CMEA.

Total gas demand declined 30% from 1990 to 1994 and will continue to decline as the economy restructures and various heavy industries reduce their gas consumption. The Bulgarian government plans to have natural gas available to domestic and commercial users in 60 cities as an alternative to centralised heat supply and electric heating. Financial constraints will likely prevent this goal from being realised in the near future. Given the problems facing the nuclear industry in Bulgaria, it is possible that gas may increase its share in power generation. Even if Bulgaria does increase its gas use for electricity generation (which may be justifiable on both economic and environmental grounds), total gas demand will still be at least one-third lower in 2000 than in 1989.

The FSU is the only source of natural gas to Bulgaria and will most likely remain so through 2000. A proposed pipeline through Ukraine and Romania carrying gas from Turkmenistan is projected to diversify imports in the period post-2000.

GAS POLICY

Bulgargaz, the state-owned gas transmission and distribution company, built and operates the gas transmission system. A government-owned export-import organisation, Chemimport, is responsible for gas import contracts. Bulgargaz reports to the Ministry of Industry and Trade. The Government currently has no plans to restructure the gas industry or privatize Bulgargaz.

Bulgargaz holds *de facto* monopoly rights to transmit and distribute natural gas. The Government has yet to develop a regulatory framework for the gas industry. Administrative oversight of the downstream gas industry is exercised by the Ministry of Industry (the Committee on Geology is responsible for oil and gas exploration and production, which does not involve Bulgargaz).

GAS DEMAND

Gas demand accounts for just 7% of current TPES in Bulgaria. Almost no gas is used directly by the household sector. With the exception of a small pilot project in Samakov, outside Sofia, no cities have gas distribution grids for households and commercial buildings. Households use gas indirectly in the form of hot water produced by gas-fired district heating systems or electricity produced from gas. Only about one-fifth of the population, however, is connected to district heating systems.

In the future, the Bulgarian government aims to convert households from heating with electricity to heating with gas. According to the World Bank, the electricity savings from converting an additional 550,000 households to gas by the year 2010, bringing the total to around 1 million households or about 30% of the population, are estimated around 1.5 TWh. The financing for such a conversion is subject to considerable uncertainty, particularly if major reconstruction of buildings to accommodate new pipes was required.

The main consumers of gas in Bulgaria have been the chemicals (i.e., fertiliser) and oil industries, ferrous metallurgy, the cement industry and the power sector. These four sectors currently account for over 90% of total gas demand. Natural gas demand in the power sector is highest in the summer as it is primarily used to counterbalance seasonal variation in electricity demand. All of the consumers of natural gas in Bulgaria are state-owned companies.

Table 1 — Gas Consumption and Production

	1990	1991	1992	1993	1994
Total Gas Consumption (bcm)	**6.79**	**5.80**	**5.2**	**4.87**	**5.06**
Share of TPES	18%	20%	20%	-	-
of which:					
District Heat/Power Plants	2.88	2.81	2.85	-	-
Industry	3.68	2.83	2.25	-	-
Households	0.00	0.00	0.00	-	-
Other	0.23	0.16	0.10	-	-
Indigenous Production (bcm)	**0.01**	**0.00**	**0.01**	**0.07**	**0.06**
Imports	6.83	5.16	5.20	4.80	5.00
Exports	0.00	0.00	0.00	0.00	0.00
Transit (to Turkey)	3.26	4.04	4.44	-	-
Storage Capacity (bcm)	**0.9**	**0.9**	**0.9**	**-**	**-**
Maximum Send-Out Rate (mcm/day)	280	256	220	-	-
Storage Capacity as % of Consumption	13%	17%	16%	-	-

Source: 1990-1992 from World Bank; 1993 and 1994 from Cedigaz, *Natural Gas in the World: 1995 Survey.*

GAS SUPPLY

Bulgaria has low proved natural gas reserves, 7 bcm in 1994. Natural gas production is currently negligible. This may change, however, as foreign companies have recently stepped up exploration efforts both onshore and offshore in the Black Sea. Texaco discovered gas in the Black Sea 12 km southeast of Varna in 1993. Further drilling will be required to determine whether the discovery becomes commercial.

Bulgaria has two contracts for the delivery of Russian gas. The first is from 1974 to 1998 for 2.8 bcm per year, while the second runs from 1989 to 1998 for 3.75 bcm per year. The gas is delivered through a 40 inch pipeline across eastern Romania.

INFRASTRUCTURE AND TRANSIT

Bulgaria's gas transmission and distribution system includes some 2 000 km of pipelines, consisting of 720 to 1000 mm (28 to 40 inch) lines for transmission and 100 to 500 mm (4 to 20 inch) lines for distribution to industry. The two main domestic transmission lines, 720 mm, run through the Danubian plain to the north of the Balkan Mountains and through the Thracian plain to the south, joining in the east near Varna and in the west in the vicinity of Sofia. The system supplies gas to major industries throughout the country (including the Sofia, Plovdiv, Burgas and Varna areas) but cannot supply industries in more isolated locations away from the two main lines.

Bulgargaz is building a 1000 mm (40 inch) pipeline parallel to the south leg of its existing transmission system to deliver Russian gas to Greece (and, it hopes, ultimately to former Yugoslavia). From Ihtiman, southeast of Sofia on the Bulgarian transmission ring, a new 720 mm (28 inch) pipeline west to Stanke Dimitrov and then south to the border with Greece has been completed. Initially gas may be transported to Greece using excess capacity in the existing pipeline to Ihtiman. Gas in transit to Greece will initially total about 1.5 bcm a year, but the new pipeline will be able to take much larger volumes. Construction on the new pipeline to deliver Russian gas to Greece, however, is behind schedule; the pipeline should be completed by the first half of 1996, at the earliest. Current total transit capacity is 10 bcm per year. Half this capacity is unused, but current plans call for all transit capacity to be used in eight to ten years time.

Three related possibilities for expanded gas use could affect transmission capacity: construction of gas-fired power plants, development of distribution to households, and offshore and onshore exploration.

Gazprom of Russia has shown interest in using storage capacity in Bulgaria for transit to other countries. Russian crews are conducting geophysical surveys at the depleted Chiren gas field and helping Bulgargaz maintain the wells.

Bulgargaz transports Russian gas from the Romanian border to Turkey via a 260 km pipeline, which Bulgargaz owns. The pipeline 1200/1000 mm (48/40 inches) can nominally operate at 55 bar but the pressure at the Romanian-Bulgarian border is now only 35-40 bar because of compressor problems in Ukraine.

GAS STORAGE

Storage capacity at the Chiren gas field close to Sofia is barely adequate to meet peak demand. Despite the lack of direct household sales, Bulgaria's gas demand is winter peaking, since a substantial portion is used to produce hot water for district heating systems. It may be necessary to increase storage capacity at Chiren, especially if gas-fired power plants are built.

Bulgaria's only underground storage facility is a depleted gas field at Chiren, about 100 km north of Sofia. Working capacity is around 0.2 bcm, with peak output of 3.6 mcm per day. Of its 12 ten-cylinder reciprocating compressor units for gas injection, eight are in operation. The Russian-made compressors have small nominal capacity (1500 HP), low efficiency and inadequate control systems. The need for modernisation and rehabilitation appears urgent.

SECURITY OF SUPPLY

Many methods are used to alleviate variations in gas demand. Certain customers, primarily power plants, can meet temporary interruptions if they have the capacity to substitute other fuels for gas. Linepack can be used to some extent but this possibility is extremely slight given the low pressure in the pipeline network.

Bulgaria plans to build a second storage facility in salt cavities and to double Chiren capacity by 2000. This expansion will presumably be funded by transit fees received for transporting Russian gas to Turkey and Greece.

An active exploration program in Bulgaria by international oil companies may find commercial quantities of gas. Meanwhile, Russia is the sole source of gas for Bulgaria, with the pipeline route crossing Ukraine, Moldova and Romania. The long-run price of gas from Russia and the quantities available are uncertain. Gas is likely to be available at a long-run price of about US$ 2.50 per Mbtu or around US$ 80 per thousand cubic metres at the Bulgarian-Romanian border. Given the turmoil in parts of the region, Bulgaria is reluctant to increase its reliance on gas until it has more than one supplier.

The risk of an interruption in Russian gas supplies cannot entirely be avoided. However, it can be mitigated by encouraging the development of transit agreements such as those with Turkey and Greece and by increasing the current level of gas storage.

A recent development in the Bulgarian gas industry may also increase Bulgaria's importance as a major distribution center in the Balkans. The private Bulgarian gas firm Overgas, half owned by Gazprom, has said it will invest over US$ 500 million over the next five years to construct new transit pipelines and to widen existing ones. Gazprom's experience and guaranteed reserve base will help Overgas develop Bulgaria's gas market. Overgas expects parliament to adopt a concession law soon, enabling foreign investors to supplement the state's currently limited investment funds.

GAS PRICES

A transit fee equal to a percentage of the throughput is paid in gas to Bulgargaz for the transit of gas to Turkey, amounting in 1991 to about 0.3 bcm. Bulgargaz is also to be paid in kind for carrying gas to Greece.

Import prices for Russian gas are adjusted every three months, using a base price of US$ 90 per thousand cubic metres indexed to the prices of residual fuel oil with 1% sulphur content, residual fuel oil with 3.5% sulphur content and gas oil. Using this formula, the price for the fourth quarter of 1992 was just slightly above the base.

Over half of the gas imported from Russia is not actually paid for, but is obtained either as debt repayment for Bulgarian assistance in the construction of the Yamburg pipeline or as a transit fee for gas going to Turkey. The remaining gas is paid for by barter.

Payments between Bulgargaz and Chemimport are made in Bulgarian leva as part of a bilateral arrangement with Russia. Bulgargaz pays Chemimport, the government-owned import-export organization, for gas in leva at the dollar clearing rate, and Chemimport settles its accounts with Russia by exporting products, compensated by the leva from Bulgargaz. Changes in the leva/dollar clearing rate in late 1991 resulted in the price of Russian gas supplied to Bulgaria being set below world market prices, producing significant distortions in Bulgarian domestic gas prices.

The gas Bulgargaz receives as debt settlement is a repayment for the civil engineering and construction work performed by Bulgarian companies on the Yamburg gas pipeline delivering Russian gas to western Europe. Bulgargaz organised and financed participation (with funds provided by the Bulgarian Government). In 1991, Bulgargaz received about 2.9 bcm of gas to service this debt. The payments increased to 3.75 bcm per year in 1992, and the debt is expected to be repaid by the end of 1996, depending on the price of gas.

Natural gas prices in 1991 were not controlled directly by the Government, though they were subject to oversight by the Bulgarian Commission on Prices. Gas prices were set by Bulgargaz, based on the price it pays for imported gas plus a small margin to cover the company's costs as well as transit fees for moving Russian gas across Romania. Movements in end-use prices (expressed in leva) have been large since 1990 due to indexation of Russian gas prices (denominated in dollars) to world oil product prices, and changes in the leva/dollar exchange rate.

Since the beginning of 1992 prices have been pegged to the price of heavy fuel oil. Bulgargaz is required by the Government to sell gas at 70% of the price of 3.5% sulphur heavy fuel oil on a heat equivalent basis. The gas price resulting from this formula is fairly close to the cost of imported gas but does not cover Bulgargaz's costs.

CZECH REPUBLIC

GAS POLICY

The Czech Republic has a very large gas transmission system and a comparatively smaller but well developed distribution network. The country is located on the main transit pipeline system transporting Russian gas to Germany and France. In 1993 gas in transit through the Czech Republic accounted for about 16% of total primary gas supply in OECD Europe. Development of the gas industry began in 1847 with the production of gas from coal in Prague. Natural gas first began to be distributed in the second half of the 1960s. By calorific value, 73% of gas supply in 1992 was natural gas and 27% manufactured gas. Manufactured gas, coke oven gas, blast furnace gas and town gas is gradually being replaced by natural gas. Natural gas accounted for 14% of TPES in 1992.

In general security of gas supply is addressed at a strategic level through diversification in sources of gas supply and at an operational level through storage capacity, flexibility in supply contract off-take conditions and through reducing deliveries to consumers with interruptible contracts. The Czech Republic relies on the NIS, mainly Russia, for 98% of its gas supplies, and these are all delivered through pipelines in Ukraine and Slovakia. Scope for diversification is limited: the only supply source likely to prove competitive with Russia in the near term is Kazakhstan and deliveries of Kazakh gas will depend on the same pipelines as Russian supplies. Connection to the planned Europol pipeline to deliver Russian gas via Belarus and Poland could diversify supply routes though not the source of gas. The government accepts that the country will remain dependent on Russia for the majority of its supplies in the foreseeable future, although it shares the goal of IEA member government's to limit dependence on any single import source.

The main focus of government policy on gas is restructuring and partial privatisation of the industry. Transgas, the gas transmission company, generates higher profits than any other Czech industry and redefining the relationship between the company and the state to ensure both continued profitability and secure revenues for the Treasury is central to the debate on restructuring. Meanwhile gas distribution has been separated from transmission prior to partial privatisation, and pricing and other regulatory arrangements require urgent attention.

GAS DEMAND

Total gas consumption was roughly 6.4 bcm in 1993, slightly up on 1992 and virtually the same as in 1991. Demand is concentrated in the industrial and heat generation sectors. In 1993 industry accounted for 38% of gas consumption, the transformation sectors - mainly heat generation for 22%, households for 22% and the commerce and service sectors for 16%.

Natural gas competes with coal rather than oil products in the Czech industrial market due to the relative prices of different fuels. In 1992 gas accounted for 19% of the industrial energy market, coal 30% and heat 31%. In the household market gas accounted for 20% of the market, coal 36% and heat 20%. There is no market for domestic heating oil in Czech Republic due to its high relative price.

Table 1   Forecast Gas Demand, 1993-2005 (bcm)

	1992	1993	1995	2000	2005	1993-2005 (% change)
Heat Generation and Other Transformation	1.27	1.33	1.50	1.96	3.72	180%
Industry	2.94	2.85	2.90	3.44	3.80	33%
Households	1.24	1.47	1.70	1.90	2.10	43%
Commerce and Agriculture	0.98	1.10	1.60	2.70	3.19	190%
Total	**6.43**	**6.75**	**7.70**	**10.0**	**12.81**	**90%**

Source: CPP, Transgas Marketing Department.

In the household market gas is subsidised, making it the cheapest fuel available for heating. Gas distribution companies earn no profit on sales to households as controlled prices only allow for the subsidy to be recovered. They have no incentive to expand sales to this market and the rate of connection of new households to distribution networks is determined by the ability of potential new consumers to finance connection themselves. Demand for new connections greatly exceeds the rate at which new connections are made.

Transgas' 1994 projections of gas demand for the Czech Republic as a whole are summarised in Table 1. They show total gas demand almost doubling between 1993 and 2005. The heat and power generation and the commercial sectors are expected to account for most of the increase with consumption almost tripling in both sectors. More modest growth in industrial and household sector consumption is forecast at 33% and 43% respectively. These projections are based on a number of considerations in addition to extrapolation of current trends including allowance for more aggressive marketing of gas as the gas industry becomes more commercially orientated.[1]

Much of the substantial growth expected in the transformation sector is attributable to conversion of heating plants in industry and to municipal district heating from lignite. Gas is only likely to be a competitive alternative if such heat is produced in combined heat and power plants. These require a market for the electricity produced, at an economic price. Given major overcapacity in the Czech power system, prices offered for production by electricity companies will be low, suggesting that a significant part of the envisaged conversions are unlikely to prove economic. Environmental considerations will drive the conversion of lignite power plants to gas, but CEZ, the association of Czech power companies, also plans major investments in post and in-combustion SO_x controls at existing plants. Thus Transgas' projected gas demand in the transformation sector may be overstated.

---

1   Transgas used a dis-aggregated model for forecast demand.

GAS SUPPLY

Indigenous production of natural gas is small, about 100 mcm in 1992 and accounting for only 2% of Czech gas supply. CPP, the Czech gas supply company, expects this level of natural gas production to remain stable. Coal bed methane may contribute to future gas supplies, depending on the outcome of test drilling and fracturing underway to assess the economics of production. If successful, coal bed methane could contribute as much as 300 mcm to gas supply in 2000 and perhaps 1 bcm in 2005, according to Transgas projections.

Table 2   Forecast Gas Supply, 1993-2005 (bcm)

	1992	**1993**	**1995**	**2000**	**2005**
Total Production	0.1	0.1	0.1	0.4	0.6
Transgas Imports	6.0	6.9	7.6	9.8	11.4
Third Party Imports	0	0	0	0	0.3
TOTAL	**6.1**	**7.0**	**7.7**	**10.0**	**12.3**

Source: CPP, Transgas Marketing Department.
Note: Gas storage accounts for the difference between demand and supply in Tables 1 and 2.

Imports now account for 98% of gas supply. Russian gas is imported under 3 types of contractual arrangement: as payment of transit fees; as payment for construction and engineering work by Czech and Slovak companies in the former USSR; and under normal supply contract. The exact volume and price of deliveries under these arrangements were traditionally negotiated annually in common with the practice for exports of NIS gas to other states in central and eastern Europe. In December 1992 Metalimex negotiated a three year contract to cover deliveries in 1993 through 1995. Russian gas supply contracts for the Czech and Slovak Republics as a whole for 1994 as agreed under the contract of December 1992 are as follows:

■ **Payment of transit fees, 5.7 bcm.** Under an inter-governmental agreement between the former USSR and CSFR, gas is received as payment in return for guaranteeing the availability of 53 bcm per year of transit capacity to Baumgarten (via Slovakia only), Waidhaus and Hora St Kateriny. Prices are calculated in hard currency, gas is priced at its market value and transit fees are reported to be close to a European average. Gas deliveries are calculated to balance transit fees exactly.

■ **"Yamburg contract", 4.9 bcm.** Gas is supplied in payment for Czech and Slovak construction and engineering services (provided mainly by Transgas), related primarily to development of Russian gas fields, especially the Yamburg field (the origins of the gas delivered are various). Services include construction of pipelines, gas treatment facilities, schools and housing developments. Due to difficulties in recalculating the value of debts accrued in relation to these services, roubles continue to be used as the accounting basis for valuing the gas to be delivered in exchange. The volume of gas to be delivered each year is fixed and its value invoiced against outstanding debts until these are cancelled out. Re-payments are expected to be complete sometime between the end of 1994 and mid 1995. Further deliveries to meet the fixed volume agreed will be paid for in hard currency at the same border price as under the "Orenburg contract" to the end of 1995.

■ **Orenburg contract", 2.8 bcm.** Remaining gas deliveries are supplied under a normal supply contract for hard currency. This category of deliveries is known locally by the name of the field from which the bulk of supplies have come in the past - Orenburg. Though smaller in volume than the other two contracts this is significant as it is the only source of hard currency earnings for the supplier under these arrangements. The gas is paid for in cash and through barter trade. The price for the gas is negotiated quarterly with escalation based on Rotterdam prices for heavy fuel oil and light fuel oil.

The border prices for gas under the Orenburg and Transit contracts were equal on 1 January, 1993 when the existing contracts entered into force. Since then, however, prices under the Orenburg contract have fallen. Prices under the Transit contract have remained constant, since the price paid for gas is effectively linked to the transit fee and the volume of gas to be delivered in return for transit is fixed.

The overall cost of imported gas will increase in 1995 when repayments under the Yamburg contract are completed and this portion of gas imports is priced in hard currency at a normal border price rate rather than according to the Rouble account carried over from arrangements made under the COMECON trading system.

Some of the factors determining the prices negotiated for supply contracts in the past by Metalimex will continue to influence future contracts. Though the Czech Republic is entirely dependent on the NIS for imports of gas and on Ukraine and Slovakia for transit of this gas, Russia is dependent on the Czech Republic for transit of a significant part of its exports. The Ukraine and Slovakia are similarly dependent on Czech pipelines for the transit of gas from which they derive transit fees. Czech border prices for Russian imports are reported to be somewhat lower than border prices charged to companies further west even allowing for differences in transport distances. This also reflects the fact that, although priced in relation to crude oil and heavy fuel oil prices on the Rotterdam market, gas competes mainly with coal rather than oil products in the Czech market and coal prices (both for domestic production and imports) are lower than oil prices on a delivered heat basis.

New, probably long term, supply contracts will be negotiated by Transgas to take effect from the beginning of 1996. Gas provided in payment for transit fees will continue to be the largest element in gas imports. Transgas will seek supplies of gas in return for further construction and engineering services for example in development of the Yamal field in Russia. It will also tender for work in the pipeline planned to bring Russian gas to Europe via Poland.

New gas from Kazakhstan may be the first significant non-Russian source for gas imports, though delivery would continue to depend on pipelines in Russia. Gas produced from the field being developed in Kazakhstan by British gas and Agip is likely to be priced competitively and, should either of these companies acquire shares in Czech distribution companies in the forthcoming privatisation, they would be particularly interested in marketing this gas in the Czech Republic.

The government and Transgas have held discussions with potential Norwegian gas suppliers. Possibilities have been examined for import of gas from the British North Sea via the proposed UK-Europe Interconnector pipeline or the proposed Polpipe from the Britannia field via Denmark. Transgas also participates in the consortium examining construction of an LNG gasification plant at Krk Island in Croatia and in the Iran Gas Europe economic interest group studying production and transportation of Iranian gas to Europe. However, NIS gas will remain the most competitive source of imports available to the Czech Republic for the foreseeable future.

It appears likely for strategic reasons (by-passing Ukraine will diversify Russia's routes for export of gas) that the proposed Polish/Russian Europol project to build a pipeline to deliver Russian gas to Europe via Poland will proceed, even though new pipelines added to the Transgas system could deliver gas more economically to the same markets using existing facilities and rights of way. Lines could in future be added to the Europol pipeline to bring Yamal gas south as far as Austria and Italy, crossing from Poland to Baumgarten via the eastern part of the Czech Republic. This could provide a measure of increased security of supply by offering an alternative route of supply to the existing Ukraine/Slovak route. Though normal supply contracts would probably be more expensive than through the existing supply route, small quantities of gas could be provided as payment of transit fees.

INFRASTRUCTURE

There is one international pipeline system that transports gas across the Czech Republic, the multi-line Transgas system. (The older Brotherhood pipeline delivers gas to Bratislava in Slovakia and was extended to Velke Nemcice near Brno and to Austria). The total volume of gas transported through the former Czech and Slovak Federal Republic, including both transit gas and supply to the domestic market, was 68 bcm in 1991 and 71 bcm in 1992. The transgas pipeline system's working capacity was 73.064 bcm in 1993 for the Czech and Slovak Republics combined. The capacity of the Czech part of the system alone was approximately 46 bcm.

Slovtransgas currently operates four transit lines through Slovakia as far as the delivery station near Plavecky Peter (north of Bratislava). Four branch lines lead to Baumgarten in Austria. From Plavecky Peter, five principal pipelines cross the Czech Republic, two to the north passing close to Prague and three to the south along the Austrian border and on to Waidhaus. The total nominal capacity of the Czech and Slovak system together is 75 bcm/year with a maximum operating capacity of 73 bcm in 1993. The system was constructed in four stages.

Transgas I delivered its first gas to Austria in 1972. Beyond Plavecky Peter, where the branch to Austria is connected, the pipeline continues to Prague and on to the (former east) German border at Litvinov/Hora Sv. Kateriny. A branch was added from near Prague to take gas southwest to the (former west) German border at Waidhaus. The pipeline diameter is 1200 mm to Plavecky Peter, then 900 mm to Prague and for the two German branches, and 900 mm for the Austrian branch. Operating pressure is 75 bar to Plavecky Peter and 61 bar beyond. The nominal capacity of Transgas I was 28 bcm/year.

Transgas II was constructed between 1976 and 1978 along the same route as Transgas I as far as Brno, and from there direct to Waidhaus, for a total length of 850 km. The diameter is 1000 mm to the compressor station at Breclav near Brno, then 800 mm to Waidhaus with an operating pressure of 75 bar throughout. Transgas II brought the nominal capacity of the Transgas system to 37 bcm/year.

Transgas III was designed as an extension to the Soyuz pipeline from Orenburg to deliver gas to eastern European countries collaborating in the project. However, spare capacity is used to transport additional volumes of gas to other countries. The line follows the route of Transgas II with a diameter of 1200 mm to Breclav then 1000 mm to Waidhaus. It also has a branch to Austria (700 mm). The operating pressure is 75 bar. At the same time the existing line from Plavecky Peter north via Prague was doubled with a second 900 mm line extending almost to the northwest Czech/German border. Transgas III brought the nominal capacity of the Transgas system up to 53 bcm/year.

Transgas IV was designed as an extension to the Urengoy pipeline and was constructed between 1983 and 1988. The line follows the route of Transgas II and has a diameter of 1400 mm for its entire length to Waidhaus, with a branch to Austria of 1200 mm diameter. An extension has been added from Veseli to Prague (capacity 2.9 bcm/year). Operating pressure is 75 bar. Transgas IV brought nominal system capacity to 75 bcm/year.

A new pipeline is under construction to provide an additional 11.2 bcm/yr capacity to meet the requirements of contracts entered into with Wintershall and VNG. It will run from the Czech border with Slovakia to Hora Sv. Kateriny along the route of Transgas I. Additional compressors will be added to existing compressor stations for this pipeline, with an additional 23 MW machine at Breclav and two new 14 MW units at each of the Kralice and Kourim stations. The date for completion of this work and related control systems is 1999.

The Transgas system is supplied by a number of pipelines from Russia. These are interconnected and all lead to a delivery point near Uzhgorod at the western tip of Ukraine. Gas from the various lines can be mixed, providing flexibility in the case of pipeline failures, but occasinaly resulting in variable gas quality and pressure.

Though there is some spare capacity in the Transgas system on an annual basis, in winter peak demand periods almost all capacity is utilised. The next steps in expansion of the transmission system include:

■ looping of the northern branch of the transit system through construction of a 1000 mm pipeline of 75 bar from the Malesovice stop-valve near Brno to the Hora St Kateriny border crossing station;

■ five new compressors, one 23 MW set at Breclav near the border with Slovakia, and two 14 MW sets at Kralice and Kourim compression stations;

■ and a new control centre in Prague, in operation since the end of 1994.

Total capacity of the Transgas transmission system is planned to increase from 46 bcm in 1993 to 55 bcm by 1999.

Underground gas storage capacity in the Czech Republic totals 1,600 mcm with an additional 500 mcm leased in Slovakia at a site close to the border. CPP owns and operates the larger part of gas storage facilities in the Republic with four sites at Hrusky, Dunajovice, Lobodice and Stramberk. CPP also leases storage capacity at Zukov in Moravia and 0.5 bcm capacity from the Slovakian oil company Nafta Gbely at its site in Láb just across the Border.

The withdrawal rate from existing storage capacity is insufficient to manage maximum winter peak demand and CPP/Transgas has contracts with western companies to import small volumes of gas to meet winter peaks in case of need. Such imports began in the winter of 1993/94 but have only been made so far on a test basis as peak demand did not exceed available supplies. Construction of a new rock cavern underground storage at Pribram near Prague is under way, scheduled for completion in 1997. Preparations for new storage sites at Zukov and Uhrice have begun. The town gas aquifer storage facility at Lobodice is to be converted to the storage of natural gas. The shortage of storage capacity for the domestic market rules out the use of storage in relation to transit contracts and potential sites for new storage development are limited.

Table 3 Underground Storage

Location	Status in 1993		Planned Capacity in 2000	
	Storage Capacity (mcm)	Maximum Withdrawal Rate (mcm/day)	Storage Capacity (mcm)	Maximum Withdrawal Rate (mcm/day)
Hrusky	400	5.0	440	6.9
Dunajovice	700	7.0	700	8.8
Lobodice	100	1.5	105	2.0
Stramberk	350	3.3	420	6.0
Zukov	50	0.2	240	4.5
Pribram	-	-	125	6.0
Uhrice	-	-	270	6.0
Total	**1600**	**17.0**	**2300**	**40.2**
Lab, Slovakia (leased)	+ 500		+ 700	

Source: CPP.

COPING WITH DISRUPTIONS

A draft Energy Law before parliament in 1994 will introduce emergency powers through which the Ministry of Industry and Trade would be able to cut supplies to selected consumers in cases of interruption of gas supplies. Such powers are necessary as a last resort and for special purposes such as responding to serious air pollution episodes. However, the development of interruptible contracts (currently not available), managed solely by the distribution companies, would be a more efficient means of response to supply emergencies, and at least for relatively short lived emergencies would make intervention by government unnecessary.

In general, security of gas supply is addressed at a strategic level through diversification of sources and at an operational level through storage capacity, flexibility in supply contract off-take conditions and reducing deliveries to consumers with interruptible contracts. Scope for diversification is limited: the only supply source likely to prove competitive with Russia in the near term is Kazakhstan and deliveries of Kazakh gas will depend on the same pipelines as Russian supplies, i.e., through Ukraine and Slovakia. Connection to the planned Europol pipeline to deliver Russian gas via Belarus and Poland could diversify supply routes though not sources of gas.

The Czech government accepts that the country will remain dependent on Russia for the majority of its supplies for the foreseeable future. Estimation of the likely price differences between potential future deliveries of Russian and other gas supplies is complicated by the fact that Russian supply contracts will be re-negotiated in 1995. Some observations can, however, give a rough indication of potential price differences. The price of Norwegian gas landed at Emden differs relatively little from the border price of Russian gas delivered to the Czech Republic. The cost of transporting gas from Emden to the Czech border via German transmission systems would probably add over 20% to the price, based on present tariffs for transit. Assuming border prices for Russian gas do not significantly change, they should serve as a minimum price premium for potential deliveries of Norwegian gas to the Czech Republic (new supplies of Norwegian gas will also have higher costs than existing supplies). Costs of other potential import supplies are even more uncertain as they would depend on new supply routes, e.g., the proposed Polpipe from the North Sea via Denmark or a pipeline from an LNG terminal on the Croatian coast. Imports to the Czech Republic via either of these projects would require a regional buying consortium to achieve economies of scale that could reduce prices. A 20% premium for improved supply security is probably an unacceptable burden to impose on Czech industrial and especially household consumers particularly at a time when other factors are already pushing up gas prices.

Storage capacity within the country represented 24% of gas consumption in 1993, 31% included storage facilities leased in Slovakia. Annual average consumption of gas was 18.5 mcm/day in 1993 with a maximum withdrawal rate from storage of 17 mcm/day. These figures indicate that while gas from storage could cover around three months of average consumption, storage alone would be insufficient to cover peak winter gas demand.

Transgas has negotiated a contract for supplies of small quantities of gas to meet winter peak requirements in case of a shortfall in supplies, including in cases of emergency, from Ruhrgas in Germany. A few thousand cubic metres of gas were imported in the winter of 1993/94 under this contract on a test basis.

Interruptible supply contracts are not available to industry from the gas distribution companies. According to reports from distribution companies, the government-regulated maximum industrial tariffs preclude them from offering interruptible tariffs at attractive prices as reduced revenues from interruptible sales could not be recouped through higher tariffs elsewhere. At the same time there is a stigma attached to the concept of interruptible tariffs as a result of interruptions to deliveries imposed on industries in the past to meet the arbitrary requirements of fulfilling production targets of the central planning system. Much dual-firing capacity and many oil storage tanks in industry are currently idle as a result. Commercial interruptible contracts have a valuable role to play in improving gas supply security and typically account for 15-50% of total industrial sales in EC countries.

Table 4   Security of Supply Indicators (mcm/day unless otherwise indicated)

	1993	*Share of demand*	**2000**	*Share of demand*
Storage capacity*/annual average daily deman	86 days		84 days	
Storage capacity/January average daily demand	48 days		51 days	
Storage capacity/annual average daily imports	70 days		100 days	
Storage capacity/January average imports	70 days		100 days	
Annual average daily demand	18.5	100%	27.4	100%
Annual average daily production	0.4	2%	0.4	1%
January average demand	18.5	100%	27.4	100%
January production	9.0	49%	9.0	33%
Maximum storage output	17.0	92%	40.2	147%
Shares of January demand:				
Firm contracts			100%	100%
Interruptible contracts			0%	0%

* Excluding capacity leased in Slovakia.
Source: IEA Secretariat; Transgas.

HUNGARY

GAS POLICY

Manufactured town gas was first distributed in Budapest in 1865, but gas distribution began to develop as a major industry in the 1960s with the discovery of significant indigenous reserves of natural gas. In 1993, natural gas accounted for 32% of primary energy supply and was available to 51% of households. Gas is currently distributed to almost all parts of the country.

The main focus of government gas policy is supply security. In response, the national integrated oil and gas company, MOL, is investing in expanded gas storage capacity at a rate faster than the increase in gas demand. Diversification of gas supplies is sought in the long term but the government recognises that new supply sources and routes will bear significantly higher costs than existing imports from Russia, the sole supplier. A new trunk pipeline link is under construction between Győr in the west of Hungary and Vienna, with the Hungarian section being financed by MOL with government guarantees.

Gas prices do not cover costs, and profits from indigenous gas production effectively subsidise imports. Cross-subsidies between industry and households have also been significant. Cross-subsidies are to be eliminated and prices are to fully reflect costs by 1 January, 1997, according to the 1995 Gas Law and assurances made to the IMF and World Bank.

Government energy policy provides no special incentives for gas though some government money may be directed at accelerating the conversion from coal to gas use in the residential sector. Gas is gradually displacing coal in both household and district heating markets. In electricity generation a number of combined and open cycle gas fired CHP units are planned as a flexible means to expanding power generating capacity and in some cases retrofitting district heating plant which were formerly supplied by heat-only boilers.

GAS DEMAND

Total gas demand is expected to increase in the medium term. MOL forecasts 13 bcm in 2000, nearly 25% up on 1994 (an average growth of 2.5-3% per year). From 2000 to 2010 demand is expected to grow at less than 1% per annum. Over the last two years MOL's forecasts of the growth in demand have been revised to envisage a later but stronger growth in gas demand, delaying the expected period of steep growth from 1992-95 to 1995-98, but with a higher level of consumption reached from 1998 onwards.

Recent trends in the shift in demand structure away from heavy industry and towards commercial and residential sector demand are expected to continue in the near term. The residential sector is expected to show the greatest increase in consumption. Forthcoming price rises are expected to slow, but not halt, growth in demand in this sector. Some further contraction in industrial consumption is possible. There are plans for expanded power and heat generation from gas: gas turbine units with heat recovery steam generators and combined cycle cogeneration units with a total capacity of 750-950 MW; and an additional combined cycle power plant to be built near a small gas field in the south of the country. However, the Hungarian Power Companies, MVM Rt, expect almost all of the increased gas consumption in planned new power plants to be offset by a reduction in gas firing at existing dual fuelled plants, although this is subject to the availability of fuel oil since the dual-fired plants in question are equipped to burn heavy fuel oil or gas in boilers.

Table 1   Gas Supply and Demand Outlook

	1992	1993	1995	2000	2005	2010
Total Primary Energy Supply (Mtoe)	**25.6**	**23.4**	**28.3**	**29.6**	-	**32.8**
of which: Natural Gas	30%	32%	34%	34%	-	34%
Gas Demand (bcm)	**10**	**10.7**	**10.9**	**13**	**13.6**	**13.7**
Domestic Production	4.7	4.9	4.7	3.6	3.2	2.5
Imports	5.1	5.8	6.2	9.4	10.4	11.2
Import Dependency	53%	54%	57%	72%	76%	82%
Structure of Consumption (bcm):						
Households	2.5	2.5	2.5	3.0	3.4	3.7
Commercial	0.9	0.9	0.9	1.1	1.2	1.2
District Heating	1.9	2.0	2.0	2.2	2.3	2.4
Small Industry	1.2	1.5	1.8	1.9	1.9	2.0
Power Stations	2.1	2.1	2.2	2.9	2.9	2.5
Large Industry	1.1	1.1	1.2	1.4	1.4	1.4
Other	0.3	0.4	0.3	0.5	0.5	0.5

Source: Gas Demand - MOL, September 1994;
Structure of Consumption and TPES - MOL, *Development and Prospects of the Gas Industry in Hungary in the Years 2000-2010*, presented at ECE conference in Istanbul, October 1993;
IEA database for 1992/93.

Note: 1 Mtoe is approximately equivalent to 1.27 bcm.

The main industrial markets for gas are: power stations and cement where consumption is stable, chemicals where demand is currently depressed, metallurgy where the market has declined sharply and is not expected to recover and fertiliser production which is currently idle. Lower price interruptible contracts are widely used in industry and dual firing facilities are widespread. Industrial gas tariffs continue to be significantly lower than the price of heavy fuel oil though this will change in the forthcoming price increases. Beyond 1996, when gas will lose its subsidised competitive advantage over oil products, industry and power sectors will present the largest long-term potential for growth in gas sales.

The residential and commercial sectors have shown strong growth in demand over the last few years. Further expansion of distribution networks to service these customers is expected to be at a generally reduced rate as connections to households approach saturation levels. Nationwide there were 2.1 million small gas consumers in 1994. This number is expected to rise to around 3 million by 2005 when the market will near saturation with 75% of all apartments and houses connected to distribution networks. There is further scope for increasing natural gas sales to this sector through conversion to gas space heating systems. Gas is presently only used for cooking and hot water. Natural gas prices have been far below domestic heating oil (and LPG) prices and will remain so until the price increases anticipated between now and 1996 are completed. Uneconomic parts of the country's 300 district heating systems are likely to be replaced with boilers in each apartment block, some gas-fired. Existing gas use in low rent apartment buildings is generally inefficient, and future gains in equipment efficiency could completely off-set increased consumption through conversion to gas fired central heating systems in the half million flats concerned.

The outlook for gas markets varies markedly from region to region with many local factors providing particular opportunities for growth. Gas markets are particularly well developed in Budapest and in areas surrounding producing gas fields. Markets in the west of the country tend to be more mature than in the east, with a higher density of residential connections, a larger commercial sector and a more diverse industrial base that has weathered the post-1989 industrial recession. There are, however, some areas in the west as yet remote from gas distribution lines, for example the new Gyor-Baumgarten link will provide an opportunity to connect large numbers of new consumers along its path. In the east of the country many industrial gas consumers have reduced or halted production in the crisis resulting from the breakdown of trade in the former Council for Mutual Economic Assistance (CMEA) area. Industrial restructuring and local development initiatives may, however, result in new opportunities for gas sales.

GAS SUPPLY

On an annual basis nearly half of the total demand for gas is covered by indigenous production. The remainder is imported from Russia under two government-to-government contracts (totalling 4.8 bcm/yr) and through spot purchases of Russian gas (1.0 bcm in 1993). Storage capacity is significant and 78% of peak winter demand is met from indigenous production and storage. Indigenous reserves are large enough to provide cushion gas to manage peaks in demand. Gas supply is thus reasonably secure. However, indigenous production is expected to decline continuously in the future, and is forecast to cover little more than a third of demand by 2000.

The seasonality of gas demand has increased markedly with the contraction in industrial demand and expansion of residential sector demand. As a result some gas fields are only operated in the winter. In 1994 maximum gas production capacity was 20-21 mcm/day and maximum output from storage 24 mcm/day. The difference in winter demand is made up from imports.

Over recent years 50-57% of gas supplies have been imported from Russia (5.8 bcm in 1993). Imports are expected to expand in the future and may double by the early years of the next century. The major part of Russian gas delivered to Hungary is supplied under two contracts: one for gas from the Yamburg field, 2.0 bcm/year contracted from 1992 to 1998 with an option to extend to 2008; the other for gas from the Orenburg field (paid for on a barter basis), 2.8 bcm/year from 1991 to 1997.

Table 2 Forecast Sources and Disposal of Natural Gas (bcm at 15°C)

	1994	**1995**	**2000**	**2005**	**2010**
Production from proven reserves	4.83	4.72	3.08	1.86	0.86
Production from new reserves	-	-	0.52	1.14	1.64
Imports	5.52	6.18	9.40	10.40	11.20
Discharge from storage	1.87	1.90	2.85	3.20	3.60
Storage charge	1.70	1.90	2.85	3.20	3.60
Budapest Gas Distribution Company	2.13	2.27	2.59	2.62	2.65
Other Distribution Companies	4.60	4.81	5.82	6.42	6.92
Power stations from high pressure grid	2.25	2.25	2.90	2.90	2.50
Large industry from high pressure grid	1.20	1.22	1.38	1.40	1.40
MOL own use and losses	0.34	0.35	0.28	0.25	0.18
Total Demand	**10.52**	**10.9**	**12.97**	**13.59**	**13.65**

Source: MOL, September 1994.

The two supply contracts differ somewhat from the contractual arrangements typical in OECD countries. Until the collapse of the CMEA in 1990, the contracts were part of a framework of economic cooperation plans based on inter-governmental agreements. Exact volumes and prices under the agreements were negotiated annually giving flexibility but little security to either the buyer or the seller. Since 1990, the contracts have functioned reasonably smoothly (with only minor disruptions in supply resulting from disputes between Ukraine and Russia on transit arrangements).

In Russia, the balance of gas supply and local demand appear to provide for increased exports in the short and medium term. Except for minor bottlenecks, pipeline capacity to the border and in Hungary will be sufficient to satisfy imports which are forecast to increase from 5.8 in 1995 to 7.7 bcm or more by 2000.

INFRASTRUCTURE

For imports of Russian gas an 820 mm pipeline runs from the Hungarian compressor station at Beregdaroc on the border with the Ukraine to Zsámbok just east of Budapest. From there 600 mm (24") branches run west to Gyór, southwest towards lake Balaton and south to Szeged near the Serbian border. During periods of peak winter demand (at -8°C), though there is scope for transporting additional volumes over some sections of the transmission network (including Beregdaroc to Zsámbok), there would be no spare capacity in the system overall were it not for the collapse of transit to former Yugoslav republics.

The total volume of gas transported through Hungary, including imports, gas in transit and indigenous production was 13.5 bcm in 1991, and has been between 13.4 and 16 bcm/year since 1985. Capacity constructed for imports from Russia totals around 7 bcm/year with an additional 6 bcm/year constructed for transit of gas to the republics of former Yugoslavia. In 1991, 6.1 bcm of gas was imported from Russian with an additional 2.4 bcm transported to the former Yugoslavia. In 1994 Russian imports were 5.6 bcm and transit volumes (for Bosnia Herzegovina) were 0.2 bcm.

The new pipeline to link Györ with Baumgarten in Austria was approved in 1992 as part of plans to diversify sources and supply routes for gas imports. The 700 mm, 114 km line will have a capacity of 4.5 bcm per year. Construction began on the Austrian section in September 1994 and will begin on the Hungarian section in 1995, with completion scheduled for 1996. No new compressors will be needed for the link. The most likely use of the pipeline for transit on a day-to-day basis will be to transport Russian gas to Austria, and perhaps beyond, under future supply contracts.

Gas storage totalled 2.16 bcm in mid-1994, located at 3 depleted gas fields with a maximum withdrawal rate of 25.5 mcm/day. Capacity is being expanded at the Kardoskút site and at Zsana, where, to keep pace with expected increases in peak demand, 8 mcm/day capacity is planned by 1996 and 16 mcm/day by 2000. Completion of Zsana will bring total storage capacity to 3 bcm. In the period post-2000 MOL plans for storage capacity to rise to 4 bcm. Potential new sites have been identified and a feasibility study for developing further new storage at Zsana is underway.

Sufficient storage capacity can be provided for the foreseeable future with an additional potential to offer storage facilities to third parities associated with possible new transit contracts.

Table 3 Gas Storage Facilities in mid 1994

Location	Capacity (bcm)	Withdrawal Rate (mcm/day)
Hajdúszoboszló	1.59	19.2
Kardoskút	0.24	3.4
Pusztaederics	0.33	2.9
Zsana	(planned)	—
Total	**2.16**	**25.5**

Source: MOL.

COPING WITH DISRUPTIONS

The government is developing demand restraint plans to cope with major gas supply disruption. The plans are to restrain non-essential industrial processes first and residential sector consumption last. MOL already has such plans to schedule outages in industrial consumption. Though the Ministry of Industry and Trade bears responsibility for supply security, MOL bears the burden of guaranteeing supply. Gas distribution licences confer an obligation on the distribution companies to guarantee supply. MOL is obliged under the terms of its own licence to enter into contracts with the distribution companies that pass the obligation to supply entirely to MOL. MOL honours this obligation through its gas production, import contracts with Mineralimpex, spot purchases and through the control of all of Hungary's storage facilities which are all linked to producing wells. There have never been instances where firm customers have been cut off because of irregularities in supply.

Ruhrgas and MOL have entered into an agreement to the effect that, in case of interruption to Hungary's imports of gas from Russia, up to 4.8 mcm/day emergency gas supplies will be made available for delivery via the Györ-Baumgarten pipeline link once this is complete. Apart from payments for any gas delivered, there will be no charge for this facility.

Underground gas storage capacity represented 67 days of average supply in 1993 or 40 days of average consumption in January, the peak consumption period. Planned increases in storage capacity will bring the annual average to 83 days in 2000 or 50 days of projected average January consumption. In planning increased storage capacity MOL intends to more than compensate for the forecast decline in production and the increased peakiness of the annual load curve.

Interruptible contracts also provide a potential response to any unexpected gas supply shortfalls. By invoking interruptible contracts and through fuel switching in electricity generation, January demand in 1993 could have been reduced 25% (three quarters of this with immediate effect). Fuel switching capacity is widespread in industry and almost all companies that have it buy gas on interruptible contract terms representing 3 to 4 mcm/day consumption. Fuel switching capacity in electricity generation represents 8.5 mcm/day.

Table 4 Security of Supply Indicators (mcm/day unless otherwise indicated)

	1993	*Share of demand*	**2000**	*Share of demand*
Storage capacity/annual average daily demand	67 days		83 days	
Storage capacity/January average daily demand	40 days		50 days	
Storage capacity/annual average daily imports	143 days		117 days	
Storage capacity/January average imports	112 days			
Annual average daily demand	29	100%	36	100%
Annual average daily production	13	45%	9	28%
January average demand	48	100%	63	100%
January production	21	44%	13	24%
Maximum storage output	26	54%	41.4	68%
Potential emergency supplies from Ruhrgas	0	0%	4.8	8%
Shares of January demand:				
Firm contracts	36	75%	50	80%
Interruptible contracts for power	4	8%	3	4%
Alternative interruptible contracts	8.5	18%	10	16%

Source: MOL.

There is no spare capacity available for supply from the most competitive new source for Hungary, Algeria. The next most economical options are Iranian gas via pipelines through Turkey, Bulgaria and Romania, possibly involving swaps with Russian and or Kazakh gas, and LNG supplied from Algeria or Libya to a re-gasification terminal in the northern Adriatic. Both these potential supply routes depend on infrastructure that has not passed the feasibility study stage and depend on extensive regional cooperation with areas of potentially disruptive ethnic tensions along the route. The focus of efforts to maintain and improve gas supply security will remain on developing underground storage to keep pace with the increasing share of imports and the use of interruptible supply contracts in industry.

KAZAKHSTAN

INTRODUCTION

At present, Kazakhstan's importance to OECD Europe's security of gas supply is limited, and it is not clear whether this situation will change. The republic's aspirations and hopes are geared more towards becoming a major oil producer and exporter than developing into a major player in the Eurasian gas market. Kazakhstan is and may remain a net gas importer, at least in the medium term; although its gas production is forecast to increase, its gas use may grow even more.

Kazakhstan serves as transit country for Turkmenistan's gas exports outside Central Asia, which, although destined mainly for other FSU republics, affect Russia's ability to direct its own gas exports to Europe. However, Kazakhstan's importance as transit country could decline rather than increase. Pressing ahead with large-scale gas field development and pipeline construction plans in the face of a shrinking or at best stagnant domestic gas market, Russia may become increasingly able both to accommodate growth in the European gas market and to make up for eventual drops in the supply of Turkmen gas. Meanwhile, Turkmenistan, which sees itself as becoming one of the world's major gas exporters, envisages building its own export pipelines bypassing Russia and consequently Kazakhstan.

This being said, Kazakhstan *may* become a net gas exporter, particularly if exploration for petroleum in the Kazakh sector of the Caspian Sea is successful. Russia's gas balance *may* also develop so as to increase the importance of Central Asian gas in the total supply picture, particularly if Yamal is not developed on schedule and domestic demand rebounds. Moreover, Turkmenistan's pipeline plans *may* not be realised in the foreseeable future; as of today, funding and political problems abound. There are thus plausible longer term scenarios in which Kazakhstan's importance in a European security of gas supply context could increase considerably.

ECONOMIC DEVELOPMENTS

According to official figures, GNP declined by 13 per cent in 1992 and another 13 per cent in 1993. Production plummeted in 1994; preliminary data suggest a drop in GNP of 25 per cent as a number of enterprises closed down or reduced operations. One problem is that Russia restricts Kazakhstan's oil exports forcing the Kazakhs to shut in production, depriving the state of export and tax revenues and reducing the Government's possibilities to support other parts of the economy. Other problems are declines in domestic and foreign demand for Kazakh industrial and agricultural goods, cash shortages, increasing inter-enterprise debts and a widespread lack of inputs and spare parts. Consumer price inflation ran at some 1,500 per cent a year in 1992 and 1993. Inflation received a boost from the Russian monetary reform in July 1993; old FSU roubles made worthless in Russia poured into Kazakhstan and the other FSU republics where they were still legal tender. Prices rose at 2,000-3,000 per cent in annualised terms through the first half of 1994, but inflation slowed somewhat during the autumn as a result of tighter monetary policies and expenditure cuts.

In February 1994 the Government launched a stabilisation and liberalisation programme encompassing, among other things, further price reform and rapid privatisation. However, implementation problems led first to the dismissal of most members of the Government and then to the dissolution of Parliament.

Gas sold to industrial users was priced at about US$ 28 per 1,000 cubic metres in February, 1994; in March 1995, however, the price was reported at US$ 74 per 1,000 cubic metres. The Anti-Monopoly Committee of the Kazakh Government offers the following information on energy and fuel prices to industry as of early 1995:

Table 1   Fuel and energy prices in Kazakhstan, early 1995

	Kazakh Price in Tenge	Kazakh Price in US$	Estimated World Price in US$	Kazakh Price as % of World Price
LPG (tonne)	29,100	481	136	354
Diesel (tonne)	12,020	199	145	137
Natural gas (1000 cm)	3,750	62	80	77
Gasoline (tonne)	7,570	125	169	73
Coal (tonne)	1,015	17	26	65
Electricity (kWh)	1.48	0.0245	0.05	60
Crude oil (tonne)	3,150	52	114	46

Source: British Gas, quoting the Anti-Monopoly Committee, Government of Kazakhstan.

Only a few big state enterprises have been transferred to the private sector. Privatising major energy producing or distributing companies is not on the agenda. The Oil and Gas Minister appointed in October, 1994 has stated that if privatised now, the energy companies would be easy prey for "criminal structures". Instead he has suggested reestablishing the national oil company Kazakhstanmunaygaz as a holding company for three fully integrated oil companies each consisting of about a third of the republic's oil producing associations and one of its three refineries.

ENERGY BALANCE

Kazakhstan's energy statistics are often unreliable. One consultant suggests the following estimates for the republic's energy production, trade and TPES in 1992 and 1993:

Table 2   Energy Balance, 1992-1993 (Mtoe)

		Oil	Natural Gas	Coal	Primary Electricity	Total
1992	Production	25.8	6.5	55.7	1.6	89.6
	Imports	16.1	11.5	1.9	7.1	36.3
	Exports	-25.1	-3.1	-19.1	-3.2	-50.5
	Net supply	16.8	14.9	38.5	5.5	75.7
1993	Production	23.0	5.4	49.5	1.6	79.5
	Imports		9.5	0.9	6.8	17.2
	Exports	net -1.5	-2.8	-15.0	-3.1	-22.4
	Net supply	21.5	12.1	35.4	5.3	74.3

Source: Energy Data Associates.

According to these estimates, in 1993 coal accounted for 48 per cent of TPES, oil 29 per cent, natural gas 16 per cent and primary electricity 7 per cent. The gas share has increased steadily from less than 8 per cent in 1970.

Energy use has not declined as much as GNP, implying an increase since 1990 in the energy intensity of the republic's economy, which was high even by Soviet standards at the time of the break-up of the union.

Most foreign analysts expect further declines in TPES as energy use adjusts to the smaller size of the Kazakh economy, and only moderate growth thereafter as structural change gets underway and old, energy inefficient technology is replaced by modern technology. The World Bank projected in 1993 that energy consumption would fall by some 28 per cent from that year to 1996 before levelling out and rebounding by some 10 per cent from 1997 to 2000.

According to the World Bank, industry accounts for nearly 40 per cent of total final energy consumption, with the steel industry being the largest single consumer. Another source suggests that gas consumption in 1993 was made up of 83 per cent power plant and industrial use, 10 per cent household use and 7 per cent other sectors' use.

Kazakhstan is a net exporter of coal and crude oil, but a net importer of refined oil products, natural gas and electricity. The republic's energy trade surplus in calorific terms declined from 14.2 Mtoe in 1992 to 5.2 Mtoe in 1993. Its energy trade generated a surplus of 13.9 billion roubles during January-June 1992, up 17 per cent — nominally — from the first half of 1991. However, Kazakhstan reportedly ran into debts of some US$ 200 million during 1993 related to its imports of oil products, gas and electricity from Russia, Turkmenistan, Uzbekistan and Kyrgyzstan.

Through 1993, Kazakh policymakers promoted an extremely ambitious gasification plan. They envisaged a growth in gas use from about 17.5 bcm in 1992 to more than 50 bcm in 2000 and to some 90 bcm a year some time into the 21st century as a consequence of rapid growth in electricity production, further substitution to gas in the power sector and expansion of the gas transmission and distribution pipeline network to cover most of Kazakhstan's cities, town and villages; currently, only seven of the republic's 19 oblasts are connected to the system.

During 1994 the Government shelved these ideas, realising that it would not be possible in the foreseeable future to finance the necessary gas trunk lines and storage and distribution facilities. Security of gas supply considerations would also seem to caution against increasing Kazakhstan's dependence on imported gas from 10 to 60-80 bcm a year. Kazakhgas' current forecasts for domestic gas use are in Table 3. Assuming a rapid and strong recovery in industrial gas use, even this projection may be too high.

Table 3   Gas Consumption Forecast (bcm)

	1995	**2000**	**2005**	**2010**
Power generation	6.5	8.2	9.5	10.5
Industry	7.4	17.4	19.1	19.2
Agriculture	1.1	1.2	1.9	1.9
Households,services	2.9	3.5	4.8	4.8
Total	**17.9**	**30.3**	**35.3**	**36.4**

Source: Kazakhgas.

GAS RESERVES

Kazakhstan's "total recoverable" gas reserves are officially reported at some 1.9 trillion cubic metres. This estimate is of the same order of magnitude as the estimates of Norway's and the Netherlands' proved gas reserves, and puts Kazakhstan's reserves at about 70 per cent of Turkmenistan's reserves (as reported by most western sources; the Turkmens themselves are much more optimistic with regard to their gas wealth) and 4 per cent of Russia's reserves.

The accuracy of the Kazakh figure is debatable, and comparing estimates is difficult, as FSU definitions and reserves classification criteria differ from those used in the west. The FSU figures may err in both directions, however, reflecting a disregard for field development, production and transportation economics, but also under-exploitation of large areas on- and offshore and use of primitive (by present western standards) exploitation technology and methods. US Geological Survey estimates Kazakhstan's identified gas reserves (defined as "approximately economically recoverable proved, probable and possible reserves in an American sense, and hence incorporating significantly more resources than commonly reported proved reserves") at 2.4 trillion cubic metres, and the republic's undiscovered gas resources at between 1.9 trillion cubic metres (with a probability of only 5 per cent that they are below this level) and 6.2 trillion cubic metres (with a probability of only 5 per cent that they are even higher).

Kazakhstan's known gas reserves are distributed between 19 dry gas fields and some 50 fields containing gas, condensate and oil in varying proportions. The giant Karachaganak gas condensate field located in northwest Kazakhstan, just south of the border between Kazakhstan and Russia and southwest of the Russian Orenburg field (Karachaganak was viewed by Soviet planners as an appendage of the Orenburg operation), is estimated to account for more than 70 per cent of the total.

GAS INFRASTRUCTURE

Kazakhstan's gas transmission pipeline network is not very extensive, consisting in 1993 of about 2,050 km of pipelines.

The main cities in south Kazakhstan, Chimkent, Dzhambul and Almaty, receive gas from fields around Bukhara in Uzbekistan on a pipeline system whose capacity varies along the way, but whose upper limit is reported at 26 bcm a year.

Two systems carrying Turkmen and Uzbek gas enter Kazakhstan from Uzbekistan. The largest, with two to four strings whose diameters range from 1020 mm to 1420 mm, crosses the Uzbek-Kazakh border southeast of Beyneu between the Caspian Sea and the Aral Sea, runs northwest past the Caspian Sea and forks at Makat near the northern tip of the Caspian with the bulk of the system continuing north to the Kazakh-Russian border to link up with the Soyuz export pipeline system at Alexandrov Gay, while one line with a diameter of 1420 mm runs west around the Caspian to the Trans-caucasian republics. From the Uzbek-Kazakh border to Makat the system has a capacity of 63 bcm a year. Onwards to Alexandrov Gay it can move about 35 bcm a year, whereas the capacity of the line to Transcaucasia is reported at 28 bcm a year.

The other, much smaller, system enters Kazakhstan just west of the Aral Sea, runs northeast, crosses the Kazakh-Russian border south of Orsk and continues to Chelyabinsk where it joins pipelines coming from west Siberia. Its two to three strings, each with a diameter of 1020 mm, can transport up to 3.2 bcm a year.

Another system runs north along the Turkmen Caspian coast, enters Kazakhstan north of the Kara Gulf and links up with the pipelines described above at the Beyneau compressor station in southern Kazakhstan. Its strings vary in size from 720 to 1220 mm and its total capacity is reported at 1.6 bcm a year. Finally, the Soyuz export pipeline system originating at Orenburg in Russia, consisting of a number of strings and with a design capacity of 75 bcm a year, transits northern Kazakhstan on its way eastwards.

Gas is produced mainly in the republic's northwestern provinces. In 1993 Karachaganak alone accounted for some two thirds of total output. However, the republic's gas consumption centres —Chimkent, Dhzambul and Almaty — are situated close to its southern border. Because of the distance, there are no pipelines connecting the two areas.

The problem of making domestically produced gas available to southern Kazakhstan is being addressed with plans for a pipeline linking Chelkar in the Aktyubinsk area with Chimkent. Kazakh authorities have also considered various options for supplying Karachaganak gas to the central and eastern parts of the republic. One proposed scheme involves building a 1,020 mm pipeline from Karachaganak across the north of the country via Aktyubinsk in the west to Ust-Kamenogorsk in the east.

To supply the eastern provinces with Karachaganak gas would, however, be very costly. The Government has therefore proposed to make Russian gas available to central and eastern Kazakhstan, and to the areas in the north not within reach of the pipeline between Orenburg and Alexandrov Gay, by constructing two spurs from the Russian Novosibirsk-Omsk pipeline.

One is to run southeast from Omsk to Pavlodar, Semipalatinsk and Ust-Kamenogorsk. With a length of 1300 km and a capacity of about 6 bcm per year, it would cost an estimated US$ 1 billion. Western companies have reportedly been invited to contribute US$ 300 million. The other is to run southwards from Ishim in southern Tyumen to Kokchetav and Karaganda in Kazhakstan. This line would be 1,100 km long, with a capacity of about 6 bcm per year, and cost about US$ 1 billion.

According to Kazakhgas the republic has two underground gas storage facilities: Akir-Tobe with an active capacity of 0.6 bcm, and Bozoi with a capacity of 3.6 bcm. No further details are available.

GAS EXPLORATION, PRODUCTION AND DISPOSAL

The Kazakh Ministry of Oil and Gas supervises all oil and gas field development and production activities, particularly the activities of the national oil company Kazakhstanmunaygaz and the national gas company Kazakhgaz, established in 1991. The latter company administers all Kazakhstan's gas fields. Fields are developed and production is carried out by seven production associations organised along regional lines. Besides these associations, various joint ventures with state and foreign company participation (the most famous of which are Tengizchevroil and Karachaganakgaz), some trading companies and a few small, independent producers are producing oil and/or gas.

The Ministry of Geology is responsible for most exploration activities. As of early 1995, complete exploratory/appraisal drilling statistics for 1993 had not yet been made available.

The most widely publicised exploration effort in progress is not carried out by one of the Ministry's drilling units, but by a consortium of six international oil and gas companies and a state owned company, Kazakhstankaspiyshelf, set up by the Government to oversee offshore activities. The consortium has started implementing a three year programme involving seismic studies and maybe some exploratory drilling on a 100,000 square kilometre area in the northeast Caspian Sea. After three years, the consortium will be dissolved and the area partitioned into sectors and, provided the exploration has been successful, developed individually or jointly by consortium members.

Kazakhgas projects gas production to increase to about 28 bcm a year by 2000. Thus, the company expects Kazakhstan's net gas imports to decline to about 2 bcm a year by the turn of the century.

Kazakhstan now disposes of most of its gas by exporting it to Russia for processing at the Orenburg processing plant and distribution to Russian consumers, and supplies most of its own consumers by importing gas from other FSU republics, i.e., Turkmenistan, Uzbekistan and Russia. This situation makes Kazakhstan's gas industry vulnerable to developments in gas supply and demand in Russia. Recently, Gazprom has had little need for Kazakh gas, and Kazakhgaz has had to reduce production accordingly.

The Karachaganak field was discovered in 1979 and started to yield gas and condensate in 1984. Proven reserves are estimated at 1.3 trillion cubic metres of gas, 189 million tonnes of crude oil and 644 million tonnes of condensate. Soviet engineers ran into technical problems developing the field, and as consequence of that and the Nazarbayev administration's desire to build new infrastructure and become independent of the Orenburg plant and the Russian pipeline system, the Kazakh Government offered the field for tender in early 1992. A preliminary agreement between Kazakhstan, British Gas and Agip was signed in June 1992 giving the two companies exclusive rights to negotiate a field development plan and a production sharing agreement with the Government.

Discussions have gone on much longer than foreseen. The deal will involve foreign investment of at least US$ 6 billion with output levels of about 25 bcm of gas and 10-13 million tonnes of liquids a year early in the next century. However, there are still questions regarding the disposal of the output from the field. At present, Karachaganak liquids are sent via Orenburg to Russian refineries while the gas, which as yet does not meet export quality standards, is distributed from Orenburg to local users. Russia wants Karachaganak gas for its Orenburg plant, which has idle capacity. Kazakh authorities would like some of the gas to be marketed domestically. British Gas and Agip want to export the gas as well as the liquids outside the FSU.

In the short to medium term, the latter alternative may be realised only if the Karachaganak developers gain access to Russian export pipelines. Liquids could be sent on a branch line to the Druzhba pipeline system while gas could be sent via Orenburg to the Soyuz pipeline system. But Russia is not interested in making its pipelines unconditionally available to its petroleum producing neighbours. Thus, Moscow has insisted on Gazprom being taken on board as a partner in the development of the field. In late 1994 Kazakh authorities acceded to this request, and in March 1995 an "interim production sharing principles agreement" giving British Gas a 42.5 per cent stake, Agip a similar stake and Gazprom 15 per cent in the project was signed.

This agreement which will be in force for 2 to 4 years, provides for a restoration of gas and liquids production to their 1991 levels and for securing the field which has deteriorated severely since 1992. In the meantime, the parties will work out final development, production sharing and transportation agreements under a 40 year production license. Whether the deal will involve a Russian guarantee of access to Gazprom's transmission pipelines all the way to Europe, for all the gas that the Karachaganak developers may want to export outside the FSU, remains to be seen.

In the longer term, the developers of Karachaganak may join forces with the Caspian Pipeline Consortium in building a pipeline system which could handle the liquids from Karachaganak as well as the oil from Tengiz. The possibility of building a new gas export pipeline westwards, or a link to the planned system from Turkmenistan through Iran and Azerbaijan to Turkey, has also been mentioned. These, however, are highly uncertain prospects.

GAS SECURITY OF SUPPLY CONSIDERATIONS

Kazakhstan's Own Security of Supply

Kazakhstan is currently a minor gas producer, forced to cover the bulk of its needs by imports. The republic's security of gas supply is linked to the ability and willingness of its suppliers, i.e., Turkmenistan, Uzbekistan and Russia, to deliver, to the capacity and state of the pipelines used and to Kazakhstan's ability to pay.

Gas consumption in the republics supplying Kazakhstan is declining and will according to most forecasts continue to decline for some time before bottoming out. Their gas exports outside the FSU will remain constrained by pipeline capacities for several years to come, and perhaps also by slower than anticipated growth in export demand. At least in the short to medium term there should be little danger of domestic and export demand starting to outstrip supply capacities, forcing some kind of rationing of exports, especially as the republics in question intend to base their economic recoveries on oil and gas output growth.

Kazakhstan's ability to pay world level prices for its gas and other energy imports will depend on the Government's pursuing economic reform policies and its success in finding solutions to its oil and gas export problems. Cuts in supply related to payment delays have occurred, and may occur again.

Little is known about the technical state of the pipelines carrying gas to Kazakhstan. However, in November 1994 deliveries of Turkmen gas to Russia and various other FSU republics were suspended for a short period after a leak in the Uzbek section of an export pipeline. The possibility of future technically related cuts in supply cannot be ruled out.

Kazakhstan and Gas Importing Countries' Security of Supply

For the time being, Kazakhstan serves as transit country for Turkmenistan's and Uzbekistan's gas exports. Turkmenistan's use of these pipelines has dropped because of declines in demand from other FSU republics, non-payment for earlier deliveries to these republics and cuts in Turkmenistan's quota of FSU gas exports to the West. Meanwhile, Uzbekistan's exports outside the region have become negligible. At present, pipeline capacity is not a limiting factor on Kazakhstan's ability to transit Turkmen and Uzbek gas. Turkmenistan intends to increase its exports outside the FSU considerably, but this intention appears linked to various schemes for acquiring independent export pipelines, bypassing Russia and consequently Kazakhstan. If none of these plans are realised and Russia lifts the restrictions on Turkmenistan's access to Russian export pipelines, the capacity of the pipelines transiting gas across Kazakhstan could become an effective constraint on exports of central Asian gas.

Kazakhstan also plays host to segments of the Soyuz pipeline system moving gas from western Siberia to Europe. This system accounts for a relatively small share of Russia's gas exports to Europe, however, indicating that supplies could probably be re-routed in case of transit breakdowns.

Conceivably, Kazakhstan could siphon off gas in transit to ensure its own supply, as the Ukraine has done on occasions. However, the present Kazakh leadership's emphasis on reintegration and cultivation of links with Russia as well as with its Central Asian neighbours, and the location of consumption centres relative to the location of transit pipelines, make such a possibility appear unlikely.

POLAND

GENERAL

Poland adopted radical reform policies in 1990 and entered a period of severe economic contraction; GDP declined by some 18 per cent from 1989 to 1991. However, 1992 saw a turnaround and in 1994 the economy expanded by about 4 per cent. For 1995-96 the OECD projects growth of 5 per cent a year. Inflation came down from 550 per cent in 1990 to about 30 per cent in 1994. Unemployment, however, shot up during the first years of economic stabilisation and levelled out only in late 1994, at about 16.5 per cent. During the last months it has fallen by about one percentage point.

Although most domestic prices were liberalised in 1990, energy prices are with a few exceptions still subject to Government control and below their cost-covering levels, implying a continued need for subsidisation. Rapid growth in the number of private companies has led to the private sector now accounting for more than half of GDP and almost 60 per cent of total employment; however, the privatisation of large, state-owned enterprises has proceeded at a slower pace than foreseen. Regarding the energy sector, some restructuring has taken place and some state-owned enterprises have been turned into Treasury owned joint stock companies, but little actual privatisation has taken place.

There is much tension within the coalition of parties presently in power and between the Sejm (Parliament) and the President, and the upcoming presidential election looks set to accentuate old, as well as reveal new, schisms in Polish politics. However, the rules of the game of democracy seem firmly entrenched, and the outlook for some political skirmishes has not occasioned observers to change their projections for the economy.

GAS POLICY

Gas prices to end-users which in 1989 covered only a fraction of supply costs, have increased considerably. However, adjusting for inflation reveals that the process of aligning prices with economic costs has proceeded at a very uneven pace. Households paid 13 times more in real terms for their gas supplies in September 1994 than at the outset of the transformation process. However, the entire adjustment took place in 1990-91; between January 1992 and September 1994 CPI-deflated prices declined by about 7 per cent. Industry paid only about 13 per cent more in real terms in September 1994 than in December 1989; an initial doubling of the real price level was almost wiped out during 1990-93 by inflation.

Table 1   Gas Prices (Index: December 1989 = 100)

	Households Nominal		Households Real		Industry Nominal		Industry Real	
	without SH	*with SH*	*without SH*	*with SH*	*Small*	*Large*	*Small*	*Large*
Jan 1990	499	501	277	279	350	350	195	195
Jan 1991	1822	1830	522	524	561	562	160	161
Jan 1992	6876	7887	1228	1408	771	773	137	138
Jan 1993	9245	10732	1143	1327	739	744	91	92
Jan 1994	10907	12660	980	1137	916	922	82	83
June 1994	13436	15598	1093	1266	1040	1047	84	85
Sept 1994	14830	17117	1118	1291	1080	1147	81	87

Notes: SH = space heating; real price = nominal price deflated by the Polish consumer price index
Source: Ministry of Industry and Trade

In late 1994, prices — which are set by the Ministry of Finance in a process of trading the need for the gas industry to cover its costs against the social problems entailed by price increases — were estimated at somewhere between 50 per cent (residential) and 80 per cent (industrial) of their proper levels. They now broadly cover operating costs but do not generate funds for replacement of capital or system expansion.

Unlike the situation in other energy sub-sectors, most gas use is metered, about 6 out of 7 consumers, including all industrial consumers and residential heating customers, have the necessary equipment. meters. On the other hand, non-payment for supplies, particularly by industrial customers, is a significant problem.

The Polish Oil and Gas Company (POGC) is as yet the country's sole producer of natural gas as well as monopolising importation, transmission, storage and distribution both to industrial and to residential customers. At present the company includes some 23 separate affiliates operating with their own budgets. It enjoyed a formal monopoly of oil and gas exploration and production until 1991, when licensing was opened to both domestic and foreign companies.

POGC is widely seen as needing substantial restructuring to be able to function in a free market economy. The company is large and unwieldy, embraces too many different activities, allows internal cross-subsidization, fails to distinguish clearly between monopoly activities requiring regulation and activities which should be exposed to competitive markets, and leaves responsibilities blurred, particularly as between Government and company.

The Ministry of Industry and Trade has developed a restructuring plan aimed at achieving:

■ separation of core and ancillary activities;

■ transparency of accounting between upstream and downstream activities;

■ improved cost control;

■ precise division of authority and responsibility between the individual units within POGC.

The plan was originally to be implemented in stages:

i) Initially, originally by April 1994, technical support functions, e.g.,equipment and vehicle repair works and design functions, were to be commercialized and part privatized, i.e., set up as separate companies with a POGC shareholding of less than 50 per cent;

ii) then — by April 1995 — the upstream exploration companies would be subject to the same reform;

iii) the next stage (no target yet) would amount to separating out the upstream production companies;

iv) finally the downstream gas business would be unbundled into a transmission company and distribution companies.

In practice this timetable has not been met. There is still disagreement on the desirability of spinning off ancillary activities before commercialisation of the whole company.

A new energy law, reportedly about to be submitted to the Sejm, sets up a potentially effective framework for regulation of the gas industry and the other grid based energy industries. It provides for licensing of energy suppliers by an independent regulatory authority which will also set quality standards, access to the grids, unbundling of accounts, pricing principles relating prices to suppliers' costs, protection of consumers' interests and discrimination between consumer groups solely on cost grounds.

However, this framework has been qualified both within the draft law and by prior decisions. The mandate of the regulatory agency will be limited. The Minister of Industry and Trade is to establish detailed terms of tariff-setting for gas, although the regulatory authority must be consulted, and another Ministry has been given tasks which appear to override and overlap both with regulatory authority functions and with tasks which should be performed by the industry itself. Furthermore, the independence of the regulatory authority may prove to be limited as its President will have little security of tenure.

GAS DEMAND

Gas plays a relatively small part in Poland's energy balance, in 1993 the gas share of the country's total primary energy supply (TPES) was only a little over 8 per cent compared with an OECD Europe average (in 1992) of 17 per cent. Furthermore, consumption has declined, whereas in 1989 Poland used 12.1 billion cubic metres (bcm) of natural gas (including 0.1 bcm, in high methane natural gas terms, of town gas), in 1993 consumption was 9.7 bcm. Gas also has a narrower range of uses than is typical in OECD countries: primarily industrial processes and residential cooking. Gas based residential heating is relatively uncommon in Poland, and gas is not yet used for power generation.

Although gas demand has declined in recent years, this masks two different underlying trends — a substantial fall in industrial demand and relative stability in the residential/commercial market.

Table 2 Gas Consumption Developments since 1980 (bcm)

	Industry	Households		Industry	Households
1980	8.60	2.91	1989	7.62	4.46
1982	7.69	3.22	1990	6.40	4.78
1984	8.05	3.50	1991	4.76	5.52
1986	8.34	3.90	1992	4.19	5.40
1988	8.04	4.34	1993	4.19	5.49

Source: Polish Oil and Gas Company (POGC).

Industrial demand is concentrated in a few energy intensive sectors, fertilizer production, glass and iron account for around two thirds of industrial demand. By the end of 1993 there were 2,270 industrial users.

The number of households using gas is currently growing at around 200,000, i.e., at more than 3 per cent per year. However, of POGC's 6.23 million household customers in 1993, only around 730,000, 11.7 per cent, used gas for space heating, due to the prevalence of district heating systems in Poland and restrictions (in the form of requirements for formal approval) previously in force on the use of gas for heating. The 11.7 per cent is nonetheless over twice the figure, 5.4 per cent, for 1988. These factors and the willingness of consumers to pay for new connections suggest that there is probably some pent-up demand for gas in the Polish residential sector.

Another market with growth potential is district heating, at present almost entirely coal-fired. For environmental and convenience reasons a number of municipalities are likely to wish to convert to gas. This has happened, to cite just one example, in a number of cases in the former Eastern Länder of Germany.

Gas will play a more important role in Poland's energy balance if the plans of the Government and the Polish Oil and Gas Company (POGC) are realized:

Table 3 Gas Consumption Forecast (bcm)

	Low			**High**		
	Industry	Households, other	Power generation	Industry	Households, other	Power generation
1993	4.2	5.5	-	4.2	5.5	-
1995	4.8	5.8	-	5.0	6.0	-
2000	6.7	8.0	-	8.3	9.0	3.5
2005	8.5	9.5	5.0	9.6	12.0	7.5
2010	9.0	11.0	7.0	10.0	15.0	10.0

Source: POGC.

In addition to growth in the buildings sector's demand, the forecasts also show substantial growth in industrial consumption, from the present 4.2 bcm to 6.7-8.3 bcm in 2000 and 9-10 bcm in 2010. This could be seen as optimistic; on the other hand, industrial demand at the end of the period is projected to be only a little higher than it was in the second half of the 1980s.

Similar uncertainty surrounds power generation demand. From zero today, gas use is projected to rise to as much as 25-30 per cent of gas demand in 2010, i.e., to a level exceeding total current gas demand. The POGC assumes that gas will be used for baseload because of "anticipated shortage of fuels for power generation". Again this could be seen as fairly optimistic. Gas fired power plants will face hard competition from the larger coal and especially lignite-fired plants for baseload. Developments will to a large extent depend on how strictly Poland's rigorous new environmental rules are applied.

GAS SUPPLY

Current supply is made up of about 40 per cent indigenous production and 60 per cent imports, all from Russia. Imports will have to increase if projected demand is to be met.

Four types of gas are produced in Poland:

- Indigenous high methane natural gas coming from conventional deposits in southeast Poland, in the form of coal bed methane and from processing low methane natural gas (see below), i.e., from removing the nitrogen.

- Low methane natural gas produced from 48 fields in western Poland, with a high nitrogen content and correspondingly low calorific value, i.e., about 2/3 of that of the high methane gas.

- Coke oven gas produced as a by-product from coke manufacturing and distributed in parts of Silesia. The calorific value is also lower again, about half that of high methane natural gas.

- Manufactured (town) gas produced and distributed locally from the gasification of coal.

In addition, some districts use an LPG/air mixture for local distribution.

In 1993 indigenous natural gas production was as follows:

high methane		1.8 bcm
coal bed methane		0.3 bcm
low methane	2.8 bcm =	1.9 bcm in high methane equivalent terms
Total		4.0 bcm

Both coke oven gas (0.6 bcm in 1993, equivalent to 0.3 bcm high methane gas) and town gas are being replaced by natural gas. Coke oven gas is due to be phased out by 1996; on present assumptions town gas will be largely superseded by 1997.

Indigenous production of natural gas is projected to increase moderately, to 5.4 bcm, by 2000 before falling back to 4.9 bcm by 2010. However, even this modest increase will depend on the success of current and future exploration efforts.

Since 1991 two licensing rounds have been held. Foreign companies have found the terms acceptable; several, including Exxon, Shell, British Gas and Amoco, have participated. Although price controls on gas distributed in Poland still exist and although license holders are obliged to offer the right of first refusal to the Government for the purchase of any gas discovered, this is not considered a major disincentive for exploration. The Government undertakes to offer export parity prices, and any gas it does not purchase can be exported.

POGC did not participate in these rounds as such although the company was granted licenses in the most prospective of the areas in question, where some exploration has already been undertaken.

In spite of the interest in acquiring licenses on Polish territory, the country is not regarded as a highly attractive prospect by international companies. There seem to be two main reasons for this. First, Poland is apparently not very well endowed with natural gas resources. A recent estimate of onshore resources puts them at only 158 bcm which is much lower than pre-reform assumptions. Offshore resources and coal bed methane (see below) would add to this figure, but hardly change the order of magnitude. Poland is fairly well explored, and relatively little territory is available for licensing, given POGC's ownership of most the prospective acreage. Second, tax exemptions, particularly for imported equipment, are thought necessary by many foreign companies to make exploration viable, and there has been some dissatisfaction with the Polish Government's offers in this area.

Poland has large reserves of coal bed methane of high quality. Some estimates are as high as 1 trillion cubic meters or more. Although production costs are relatively high and the full economic potential of this resource remains to be assessed, the coal bed methane issue has generated considerable foreign interest. Several international and Polish companies have obtained concessions and started exploration and development activities in the Silesian coal field region.

The scale of Poland's future coal bed methane production remains very uncertain, but an output of 1 to 1.5 bcm a year by 2000 and perhaps twice that by 2010 seems feasible. This would make a useful contribution to Poland's gas balance, but not change it radically.

The projected growth in gas demand therefore points to a need for substantial increases in imports, to 10-15 bcm in 2000 and conceivably 20-30 bcm in 2010. Poland would then be dependent on imports for up to 85 per cent of its gas supply. POGC is interested in diversification of its sources of supply and has looked at a number of options. For the period to 2010, Algerian and Iranian gas would be too expensive and the lead times would be too long, leaving the Poles with only two options:

- increased imports of Russian gas through the existing network or the proposed new transit pipeline.
- imports of North Sea gas from the UK or Norwegian sectors, by dedicated pipeline or through the main European system;

The second option has been discussed in the context of various projects, the most concrete of which was the so-called "POLPIPE" project. In its original form, this would have taken gas from the Britannia field on the UK Continental Shelf across Denmark and via the Baltic area to Poland to avoid the complications of transit through the main European network. However, several options for the Britannia field — e.g., landing in the UK — were discussed, and the means of financing a dedicated pipe for Poland, even with the participation of other Central European countries, were unclear. As for deliveries from the Norwegian sector, discussions have not so far reached the project stage.

Russia is therefore likely to remain the main source of imports. The present arrangements date from the days of the Council for Mutual Economic Assistance (CMEA). Supplies are provided to Poland via the Brotherhood pipeline from the Orenburg (2.8 bcm in 1993) and Yamburg (2.5 bcm) fields in payment for services supplied during the construction of pipelines for these fields. The Orenburg arrangement runs from 1974 to 1998, the Yamburg agreement from 1989 to 2008.

It would be misleading to describe these agreements as contracts. The former practice was to trade within the framework of economic cooperation plans and agreements and negotiate exact volumes and prices annually. While this gave considerable flexibility, for instance in adjusting to demand changes, it also gave, and still gives, little security to either side, whether on volume or on price. Since the collapse of the CMEA arrangements, import prices have moved to European levels, roughly speaking, but formal long-term supply contracts remain to be negotiated.

Although there have been short term disruptions in transit through the Ukraine, under present circumstances neither Poland's import capacity nor Russia's supply situation represent constraints on deliveries. However, the longer term expansion plans of POGC call for new contractual arrangements which most likely will require firm commitments on POGC's part, e.g., include take-or-pay clauses typical in European gas supply contracts.

If the Europol Gaz project (see below) is implemented to the extent forecast, Poland will have the capacity to import around 20 bcm a year from Russia. Doing so would probably be more economic than securing supplies from other sources. The Government may therefore have to face some hard decisions in terms of the trade-off between diversification of sources of supply and minimising costs.

INFRASTRUCTURE

The main Polish gas transmission system is constructed for transmission of high methane gas. Smaller systems transmit low methane gas or coke oven gas but are being adapted for high methane gas, the norm in OECD Europe. There are 16,400 km of transmission lines. Pressure is maintained by means of 27 compressor stations with a total capacity of 102 MW. (There are another 5 stations with a total capacity of 15 MW on gas fields.) Relatively low working pressure in the transmission pipelines, 55 bar, is an impediment to upgrading.

Two small interconnections with the German system have recently been built. In the North, at Swinoujscie, some gas is exported to Germany. Volumes are small, less than 20 mcm/year, but the capacity of the link allows for growth to 60 mcm/year. In the south at Zgorzelec, the intention is to enable imports of 1-1.5 bcm/year of natural gas to replace the coke oven gas used at present in this part of the country, though current exchanges are also less than 20 mc/year.

The main natural gas import capacity is, however, in central Poland where Russian gas is received through a lateral to the Russian Northern Lights pipeline system, and in the southeast of the country where Russian gas is received via the Ukraine through the Brotherhood line. There is capacity to increase imports on these pipelines to almost 10 bcm/year of which 60 per cent would be imported into central Poland and 40 per cent in the southeast.

Capacity expansion projects are ambitious. POGC plans to build some 16,000 km of transmission lines in the period to 2010, in addition to a pipeline to be constructed for transmission of Russian gas to Poland itself and onwards to Western Europe. The company, Europol Gaz, has been set up with POGC and Gazprom as main shareholders to build the Polish segment of this pipeline. It would enter Poland east of Bialystock and follow a more or less straight route across Poland to the German border near Frankfurt an der Oder. Europol Gaz' task would be to design, construct and manage the pipeline, i.e., it would not be responsible for the gas supplies as such. The gas in the pipeline would belong to the Russian company Gazprom. The long term function of the pipeline would be to deliver gas from the Yamal field to Central and Western Europe, but until that field is developed other Russian gas would be transmitted.

The eventual aim is to build 665 km of pipeline (2 x 1,420 mm) with 5 compressor stations of 50-100 MW each, capable of carrying some 67 bcm/year of which Poland would have an option on 14 bcm. Investment costs would be shared 85/15 between Gazprom and POGC, reflecting their shares of gas transported. Total investments required (within Poland) for the whole project is put at about US $2.5 billion.

At present, it is not clear when or whether the project will reach the final stage. The pace of implementation will depend mainly on factors outside Poland's control such as demand developments in western Europe and Gazprom's ability to raise finance. However, a first stage designed mainly to meet Polish requirements is at an advanced stage of planning. This stage, with costs estimated at about US$ 135 million, would be financed mainly by POGC and would allow for transportation of about 500 mcm/year.

Around 68,000 km of distribution lines serve 2,800 localities and over 6 million customers, slightly over half the households in Poland. The system has grown by over a third since 1990, and currently some 200,000 new customers are connected each year, despite economic recession and recent consumer price increases. POGC plans to construct some 45,000-60,000 km of distribution pipelines in the period to 2010.

One reason for the rapid growth to date, which has been especially marked at distribution system level, is the unusual method of financing new developments. Normal practice in Poland is for new consumers to finance infrastructure development themselves via upfront payment for connection or through regional development grants, although ownership of the new infrastructure and responsibility for its maintenance passes to POGC.

There are four underground storage facilities with a total working capacity of 620 mcm and a combined withdrawal capacity of 6.5 mcm/day. All are situated in depleted natural gas fields in Southeast Poland. This is operational rather than strategic storage, designed to cope with seasonal demand variations. Poland has a relatively favourable load factor compared with some West European countries due to its high industrial load (which is not weather sensitive) and relatively low residential heating sales. The ratio of winter peak demand to summer demand is around 2.5:1 compared with 4:1 or more in some West European countries. Despite this, storage is inadequate to ensure that peak winter demand is covered — residential sector demand is about 20 mcm/day higher at winter peak than in summer. Short term supply disruptions in gas transiting the Ukraine have therefore led to supply shortages, and in some cases major industrial users have been cut off.

The projected growth in gas demand, including a significant growth in residential demand as gas fired residential heating becomes widespread, will inevitably lead to a deterioration in the load factor of demand. Gas fired power generation could further exacerbate this trend if, as some expect, gas will be used first for middle order and peaking plant. Poland therefore needs both to construct new gas storage and to look at other ways of matching supply and peak demand, e.g., introducing flexibility in purchase contracts and the use of interruptible contracts. At present, formally interruptible contracts have been proposed, but the relatively low level of general prices and the fact that security cannot in any event be guaranteed have rendered them unattractive.

POGC plans to develop 800 mcm of salt cavity storage — one facility is already under construction — with finance from the World Bank and other sources. Poland is very well endowed with depleted natural gas fields, and POGC plans to build 4.5-5.5 bcm of storage, with withdrawal capacity of 80-100 mcm/day, in the period to 2010. This would expand existing capacity tenfold. The French company Sofregaz is helping POGC to assess the required volume of storage.

POGC's two demand scenarios would require very substantial investment, including significant investment in storage. Table 4 shows the estimates, in billions of Zlotys. Total investment over the next 15 years would be some US$ 7-8 billion, or around US$ 500 million per annum.

Table 4   Investment Needs for Gas, 1994-2010 (billion zlotys)

	Low Demand Scenario	**High Demand Scenario**
Upstream	40,800	40,800
Transmission	25,998	35,418
Storage	23,870	25,790
Distribution	53,931	70,118
Total	**144,599**	**172,126**

Source: POGC.

SECURITY OF SUPPLY

As will be apparent from the description above, Poland has some difficult issues to resolve in relation to the security of its gas supplies. The country is already heavily dependent on imports and this dependence is expected to increase. Furthermore, at present Poland only has one external supplier for its imports, accounting for around 60 per cent of supplies. Increased dependence on imports appears inevitable. This is not in itself a reason for worry, but it calls for certain measures.

IEA countries normally seek to diversify their imports so that no single source accounts for more than 30 per cent or so of supply. Where this is not practicable — for example in Austria which, like Poland, is on pipeline routes from Russia — flexibility is sought in other ways, for instance by using storage (of which Austria has three times as much as Poland, despite lower consumption, with firm plans for expansion) and interruptible supplies. Poland has little flexibility in its system — inadequate storage, no interruptible supplies and limited interconnection capacity apart from the main supply route, i.e., the Brotherhood line.

These deficiencies have been recognised in principle. Some useful progress has been made including the development of interconnections with Germany, and some first steps towards constructing additional storage. There are plans to improve security further. It is essential that these plans are properly costed, that an optimum mix of measures is identified and that the framework conditions are in place for them to be implemented. The latest draft version of the new energy law requires electric generators to maintain fuel stocks. Apparently there is no equivalent provision for gas, and it is not clear how the stocking requirement would apply to gas-fired power generation or what level of storage, interruptibility, etc. should be aimed for in gas supply.

Polish authorities appear to rest a lot of faith on the transit pipeline proposal, the argument being that the existence of major customers further down the pipeline will reduce the risk of disruption to Poland's supplies. That argument has some validity, and a further interconnection with Germany —already part of Poland's strategy — will in any event serve to increase the flexibility of Poland's gas supply system. However, as the case of Austria shows, this would not normally be considered a sufficient answer to the problem of gas security.

The other means of promoting gas security referred to by Polish authorities are: intensifying gas exploration, increasing coal bed methane production, building more storage capacity and diversifying import sources. The right mix of measures remains to be calculated, however, and it is not evident that it will prove adequate. Gas exploration and coal bed methane production are as noted unlikely to change the overall supply picture substantially. Poland's gas storage capacity needs to be expanded, but this will be expensive and it will take a major effort only to keep pace with projected growth in demand and deteriorating load factors. Diversification is worth pursuing, but would have to be costed carefully, and it appears unlikely, for geographic and economic reasons, that eventual new external suppliers would take sufficiently large shares of the market to put an end to Russia's dominance.

ROMANIA

GAS POLICY

Romania has a large, well developed gas transmission and distribution system. The country's location gives it a significant strategic role in transporting gas from the NIS to southeastern Europe. Development of the gas industry began at the turn of the century, and the industry experienced rapid growth in the 1970s and 1980s based first on large indigenous discoveries made in the 1960s and later on imports from Russia. The gas transmission and distribution business is run by ROMGAZ from its headquarters in Medias near the Transylvanian gas fields.

Government policy is primarily concerned with providing the conditions for adequate financing of investment within the gas industry. Raising prices to levels that cover the full costs of supply is the key element of this policy. Though prices have been raised in several large steps in nominal terms, inflation and repeated devaluation of the national currency mean further large increases in real terms are required. ROMGAZ has been commercialised through improved accounting procedures and separation of business units, but the company is not expected to be split up in the medium term.

To improve supply security and strengthen the gas grid in the northwest of Romania, ROMGAZ is seeking interconnection with gas pipelines running through Uzgorod in Ukraine. Possible construction of an LNG terminal on the Black Sea coast is under study, but unlikely to prove economic in the medium term.

GAS DEMAND

Although natural gas accounted for almost 60% of TPES in the 1960s, its share has been only around 40% in recent years. Total annual gas demand averaged about 40 bcm between 1979 and 1989 but decreased to about 29 bcm by 1991. Demand has been concentrated in the industrial and power generation sectors. In 1991 industry accounted for 49% of the total, power generation 35% and households 11%.

The chemical industry accounts for the largest part of industrial gas consumption, with fertilizer production accounting for the largest share at about 2.3 bcm in 1991 and 2.0 bcm in 1992 (including supplies from WIEH, a joint venture between Wintershall and Gazprom). Though natural gas contributes more to power generation than any other fuel, the decline in gas production has resulted in a progressive decrease in its share of electricity generation, from 57% in 1970 to 37% in 1991. The replacement of gas by other fuels, encouraged by the Government, has been carried out in power plants originally designed to burn gas. In 1992, to further reduce gas consumption, the Government obliged the electric utility RENEL to promote the use of fuel oil instead of gas in power generation. It is uncertain whether this programme of fuel substitution will be implemented because of the time scale and cost involved.

Table 1 Gas Consumption by Sector, 1986-2000 (bcm at 15°C)

	1986	1987	1988	1989	1990	1991	1992	1995	2000
ROMGAZ Supply[1]									
Industry	24.1	23.8	24.7	23.7	20.1	14.1	12.7	12.2	10.6
of which chemicals	*12.8*	*12.7*	*13.1*	*12.8*	*9.6*	*5.5*	*6.0*	*n.a.*	*n.a.*
Power generation	12.8	12.2	11.9	11.8	10.8	10.0	8.5	6.7	4.6
Households	2.8	2.8	2.6	2.7	2.7	3.1	3.2	6.4	9.6
Other	2.1	1.8	1.6	1.8	1.7	1.6	1.8	2.0	3.1
Total	**41.8**	**40.6**	**40.8**	**40.0**	**35.3**	**28.8**	**26.2**	**27.3**	**28.0**
Third party imports[2]	-	-	-	-	-	0.8	2.0	4.0	5.0
Shares of ROMGAZ supplies[3]:									
Industry	58%	59%	60%	59%	57%	49%	48%	44%	38%
Power generation	31%	30%	29%	29%	31%	35%	32%	24%	16%
Households	7%	7%	6%	7%	8%	11%	12%	23%	34%

1. Excluding direct deliveries by PETROM, and deliveries from third parties, such as WIEH, via the ROMGAZ grid.
2. Such as those arranged by WIEH.
3. Excluding third party imports, which go mainly to industry and power generation.
Note: Gas storage accounts for the difference in demand and supply in Tables 1 and 2.
Source: ROMGAZ.

Demand for natural gas, as forecast in ROMGAZ's minimum scenario, is expected to remain roughly at the 1991 level of 29 bcm to 2000, with steep declines in the industrial and power sectors compensated by growth in the household and commercial sectors, where a trebling of consumption to over 30% of demand is foreseen. The expected decline in industry and power generation gas demand is a result of industry restructuring, fuel switching in power generation and price reform. In the longer term, however, this decline may not continue. After the transitional period, there is a strong possibility that gas demand in these sectors will recover and increase, especially for power generation. RENEL forecasts higher gas consumption than envisaged by ROMGAZ for electricity generation (9 bcm in 1995, 10 bcm in 2000), partly to meet its environmental protection objectives.

GAS SUPPLY

Romania produced large quantities of natural gas in the 1970s and 1980s, peaking at nearly 35 bcm per annum. Production declined 23% between 1988 and 1990 to 28 bcm. By 1990, one-fourth of gas supply was imported, even though the gas requirements could not be readily satisfied because of a severe shortage of foreign exchange.

Gas production appears to have stabilised, as a result of improved organisation, financing and equipment in producing fields, and was expected to total 21.4 bcm in 1993. Questions surrounding reserve estimates result in large uncertainties concerning production projections. ROMGAZ and the oil producer PETROM estimate marketed gas production in 2000 at around 13 bcm. This would bring import dependency to 60% according to ROMGAZ projections of demand and supply (see table).

Table 2 Evolution and Forecast of Gas Supply Minimum Scenario, 1986-2000 (bcm at 15°C)

	1986	1987	1988	1989	1990	1991	1992	1993[1]	1995	2000
ROMGAZ production	26.8	25.3	25.2	22.2	19.2	17.2	15.1	14.8	12.6	9.0
PETROM deliveries[2]	12.5	12.1	11.7	10.5	8.9	7.5	6.9	6.6	5.7	4.0
Total Production	**39.3**	**37.4**	**36.9**	**32.7**	**28.1**	**24.7**	**22.0**	**21.4**	**18.3**	**13.0**
ROMGAZ imports	2.5	3.2	3.9	7.3	7.2	4.5	2.5	na	9.0	15.0
Third party imports[3]	-	-	-	-	-	0.8	2.0	na	4.0	5.0
Total Imports	**2.5**	**3.2**	**3.9**	**7.3**	**7.2**	**5.3**	**4.5**	**na**	**13.0**	**20.0**
TOTAL	**41.8**	**40.6**	**40.8**	**40.0**	**35.3**	**30.0**	**26.5**	**na**	**31.3**	**33.0**

1. Estimate.
2. Deliveries to ROMGAZ; a small part of production is supplied directly by PETROM to end-users.
3. WIEH.
Source: ROMGAZ.

Romania has imported natural gas from the former Soviet Union since 1979. Import pipeline capacity is 25 million cubic metres a day with expansion possible to 35 million cubic metres a day if compressor capacity is increased. In 1992, total gas imports had fallen to 4.6 bcm, not so much because of lower demand but because of a shortage of foreign exchange.1 Purchases of imported gas are by hard currency or barter trades. Prices are generally negotiated every quarter, mainly using a formula based on prices for crude oil, heavy fuel oil and diesel.

There are five different types of arrangement for gas imports:

■ ROMGAZ imports from Gazprom through the trader ROMPETROL. Gas is supplied as payment for work in the development of Russian gas fields contracted to ROMPETROL. Gas comes primarily from Orenburg as well as some other fields. The approximate volume in this category was 1.8 bcm in 1993. The existing contract is for 25 years, beginning in 1974 and ending in 1998, at an annual volume of 1.5 bcm. There are no strict off-take conditions, however. Prices are negotiated quarterly, mainly under a formula using prices in the Mediterranean basin for crude oil, heavy fuel oil and diesel.

■ Barter trade contracts are negotiated between the Romanian Government and NIS governments. Purchase transactions are concluded by ROMPETROL. Payment is made through exports of goods such as machine tools, pipes and furniture. Under the latest agreement, this pattern of barter trade is allowed up to a limit of 45% of the total volume of gas trade. The volume in this category was about 0.7-0.8 bcm/year for 1992 and 1993.

---

1. Imports of Russian gas averaged less than 15 million cubic metres a day in 1992.

■ Since 1991, WIEH has negotiated barter trade contracts with Romanian fertilizer companies. Payment is made in products through third party traders. The approximate volume of this category of trade was 2 bcm in 1992. An additional small supply contract between RENEL and WIEH based on barter trade was arranged in 1992. WIEH delivers gas to the border and ROMGAZ provides transport to the customer.

■ ROMGAZ receives gas as a fee for the transit of gas to Turkey (and recently for transit to Bulgaria, although Bulgaria normally pays in cash). The volume of supply to ROMGAZ in this category is generally less than 0.35 bcm.

■ A very small amount of trade with Gazprom, for temporary balancing of supplies, is paid for in US dollars.

Through barter trade ROMGAZ received gas for less than US$ 5 per tcm (US$ 0.13 per MBtu) in 1992. Gas buyers have to pay cash for other supplies. In 1992 the border price for ROMGAZ's imports, excluding barter, averaged about US$ 2.50 per MBtu. The border price paid by third party importers (WIEH) was about US$ 2.60 per MBtu[2].

With declining domestic production, ROMGAZ forecasts that its own imports will treble from 4.5 bcm in 1991 to 15 bcm in 2000. In addition it expects third party trade to increase from 0.8 bcm in 1991 to 5 bcm in 2000. Existing gas import contracts are only part of expected imports. The long term contract between ROMGAZ and Gazprom expires in 1998. There is an urgent need to develop new long term contracts. The main barrier to increased imports is a lack of hard currency.

Table 3   Imports of Natural Gas (bcm at 20°C)

	1990	1991	1992
Bulgarian transit fees[1]	0	0	0.152
Turkish transit fees	0.240	0.227	0.253
Orenburg contract: - cash payment	n.a.	2.473	0.434
- barter payment	n.a.	1.537	0.708
Payment for ROMPETROL and Arcom services in Turkmenistan	n.a.	0.300	0.200
Payment for Arcom services in Astrakhan and Maloiaroslavets	n.a.	0	0.800
Third party processing (Wintershall) contracts	0	0.833	2.010
Total	**7.240**	**5.370**	**4.557**

1. Bulgaria normally pays for transit in US dollars, but in 1992 was unable to do so.
Source: ROMGAZ.

ROMGAZ is considering several potential options in addition to new supply contracts with NIS countries based on the existing infrastructure. Projects under consideration include:

■ A link to the Transgas system via a 60 km pipeline from the transit gas pipeline (serving western Europe via Slovakia) from Uzhgorod in Ukraine to the Romanian transmission system in the northwest of the country. The rationale for such a link is twofold: it would be an alternative to the Shebelinka-Izmail pipeline that crosses the troubled Trans-Dniester area in the Republic of

2.   N. Pavlovschi, *Romania, the Natural Gas Industry*, ROMGAZ, 1992.

Moldova, providing increased flexibility in import routes for gas supplied by NIS countries; this new route would be useful in strengthening supply to the gas distribution network in northwestern Romania. The cost of such a pipeline link would be of the order of US$ 50 million. The cost of gas supplied via Uzhgorod would be somewhat greater than for deliveries via Izmail because the route is longer.

An economic evaluation of this proposal is required. A full appraisal of investments necessary to enhance the national transmission and storage network to accommodate the new supply route would also be required before investments in such a pipeline could be committed.

■ Building an LNG terminal at Constanta. Such a terminal would offer additional supply flexibility, but the cost of LNG supply would greatly exceed that of incremental Russian gas supplied via existing pipelines. Firm long term demand forecasts taking account of price will be required as the basis for decisions on the economics and strategic value of an LNG terminal. The Governments of Romania, Bulgaria, Serbia and Hungary have agreed to undertake a market survey, to be followed by a feasibility study if the results are positive. An accord agreed by MoI envisages a joint venture between ROMGAZ and ROMPETROL together with a foreign engineering company, to carry out these studies. A preliminary call for tender resulted in two companies being selected as candidates. Grant funding is being sought.

LNG imports may only prove economic for high load factor, high value uses such as electricity generation using combined cycle gas turbines and are unlikely to be competitive with Russian gas supplied by pipeline. RENEL's forecasts point to increased consumption of gas in power generation, driven partly by its strategy to improve environmental protection, but ROMGAZ forecasts suggest a decline in power sector consumption. Supply contracts and financing arrangements would have to be negotiated before any commitment of investment funds.

■ Iranian gas supply by a new pipeline via Turkmenistan or Turkey. Sofregaz of France is undertaking a feasibility study for deliveries via either route.

■ Gas from Kazakhstan or Turkmenistan delivered by pipeline via Iran and Turkey.

Romania is well placed to exploit a potential for providing gas storage facilities in depleted wells to support any plans to deliver gas from Central Asia or the Middle East by pipeline to Europe via Turkey. Possibilities for further regional co-operation should be fully explored, including the potential participation of neighbouring countries in the proposed Constanta terminal, access to supplies of Algerian LNG through Turkey (where a terminal linked to existing international pipelines is under construction), and participation in the consortium examining construction of an LNG plant at Krk Island in Croatia.

INFRASTRUCTURE

Gas is transported to Romania from Russia via the Shebelinka to Izmail pipeline in the Ukraine. The pipeline which entered service in 1974, is sometimes known as the "Friendship" gas line (not to be confused with the Friendship oil pipeline to Hungary and Slovakia). It is a 40 inch (1,020 mm) pipeline nominally operating at 55 bar (currently operating at 35 bar). The pipeline extends 660 km across southern Ukraine and the southeastern part of the Republic of Moldova from its origin in the now depleted Shebelinka gas field in eastern Ukraine. It links up with the Soyuz (Union) pipeline that exports gas from the Orenburg field in Russia, just west of the Urals, to eastern Europe via Uzhgorod, Ukraine.

The transmission pipeline network has been developed from the centre of the country radially, linking gas fields including the associated gas production areas. The total length of pipeline is about 12,000 km and the diameters range from 250 to 1,000 mm. The transmission grid can be divided into nine subsystems, each with two pipelines installed in parallel and interlinked. The capacity of the system is about 135 million cubic metres a day or 40 bcm/year. The maximum working pressure of the pipeline is 50 bar, though average working pressure is now 20 bar because of shortage of gas supply. The compressor stations work in two stages with a capacity of 10 million cubic metres per day for each station. There are 17 turbo compressors with total installed capacity of about 70,000 horsepower.

Romania has three underground storage facilities using depleted gas fields near Bucharest to provide a buffer against supply fluctuations. Total storage capacity is 0.7 bcm with total maximum output of 4.65 million cubic metres a day. Gas is injected in summer and discharged under its own pressure during peaks in winter demand. Maximum working pressure is in the range of 60 to 80 bar.

Table 4   Gas Storage Capacity

	1993	**Planned for 2000**
Storage capacity (bcm)	0.7	2.1
Maximum withdrawal rate (mcm/day)	4.65	14

Source: ROMGAZ.

Three parts of the distribution network suffer from a drop in supply pressure during the winter peak: in the northwestern and northeastern parts of the country and in Bucharest. The reason for the low pressure in Bucharest is that it is supplied only from small gas fields. Gas consumption in Bucharest in winter peak periods is about 14-15 million cubic metres a day, against the maximum output from storage of 4.65 million cubic metres per day. Thus storage capacity is inadequate at current demand levels. ROMGAZ plans to triple storage capacity by 2000 using depleted gas fields and aquifers. Further storage could be developed should the plan to transport Iranian gas through Romania materialise.

COPING WITH DISRUPTIONS

Inter-enterprise debts and a shortage of hard currency in the banking system have limited imports of gas over recent years and the Government has operated a rationing system allocating available supplies first to households and then to selected industries. The allocation system was ended in 1993 but the mechanisms for rationing in case of need are available within ROMGAZ and the Ministry of Industry.

Though underground storage facilities are inadequate, indigenous gas production limits vulnerability to supply interruptions. Storage capacity currently represents 57 days of net gas imports. Plans to increase storage capacity by 2000 are not, however, adequate to maintain this level of security. Projections of gas demand suggest that storage will only cover 38 days of imports in 2000.

Table 5   Security of Supply Indicators (mcm/day unless otherwise indicated)

	1992	*Share of demand*	**2000**	*Share of demand*
Storage capacity/annual average daily demand	9 days	23 days		
Storage capacity/annual average daily imports	57 days	38 days		
Annual average daily demand	77	*100%*	90	*100%*
Annual average daily production	61	*79%*	36	*40%*
Maximum storage output	4.7	14		

1. Imports of Russian gas averaged less than 15 million cubic metres a day in 1992.
2. N. Pavlovschi, *Romania, the Natural Gas Industry*, ROMGAZ, 1992.
Source: ROMGAZ.

RUSSIA

GAS POLICY

In 1994, gas accounted for about 50% of TPES in Russia. The demand for and supply of gas has declined much less than those for oil and coal since the break-up of the former USSR. For instance, gas production fell by 2.6% during the first nine months of 1994 relative to the first nine months of the year before, but this decline is minor compared with the general decline in economic activity. This strong resistance to recent upheavals in the Russian economy is the result of the high priority given to the gas industry by the Russian Government and a policy of strong vertical integration, low gas prices, the physical state of the industry and a will to substitute gas for other fuels.

The priority given to gas is clearly reflected in the recently published Russian Energy Strategy. The main aim of the Energy Strategy is to "establish ways and means of creating the conditions for the most effective use of energy resources and productive potential of the fuel and energy sector for improving the living standards of the population and socio-economic regeneration of the country".[1] Two central elements in the Energy Strategy are to halt the decline in gas production and to increase the level of gasification, particularly in rural areas. Higher gasification has a very high social priority and special measures like preferential gas tariffs and privileged credit terms will be used to achieve this.

The new Energy Strategy signals a different attitude to supply and demand issues: instead of focusing on large scale increases in the production of energy resources, a greater priority is given to increased energy efficiency and energy savings. The Government clearly recognises that realisation of the enormous energy saving potential requires price reforms. Gas prices are regulated both at end- user and wholesale levels. The general objective of the Government in this area seems to be upward adjustment of prices to world market levels for energy in general. In the gas sector this would ultimately mean alignment of domestic prices at a level corresponding to export prices at the Russian border. In spite of the price rises over the last few years, gas prices are still far below market levels. Even industrial gas prices, which are more than 30 times higher than residential gas prices, do not correspond to more than 20-25% of export prices to Western Europe. Although the Government aims to do something about the distorted price structure, it is a sensitive political issue. Future pricing policy will of course have an important bearing on future demand as higher prices will certainly give an incentive (at present lacking for many reasons) to control or reduce demand.

The Energy Strategy seems to give a higher priority to coverage of domestic demand for gas than to export markets. This priority is reflected in the demand forecasts made in the context of the

1. Ministry of Fuel and Energy: *The Energy Strategy of Russia*, Moscow 1994.

Energy Strategy. The Strategy announces a new feature in Russian export policy: a drive to break into wholesale and retail gas markets in countries of the former Soviet Union and other importing countries. The practical consequences of this new policy can already be observed in Germany where RAO Gazprom, the dominating entity in the Russian gas industry, has entered into a joint venture with Wintershall, a German company. The Energy Strategy also announces a change in attitude to export projects implying a replacement of "the formerly practised approach of getting the currency by any means" by a more detailed economic evaluation of every project.[2] Perhaps the most serious problem in the Russian gas sector today is the non-payment problem. An example given by Gazprom in November, 1994, eloquently illustrates its seriousness: so far that year the company had only received payment for half the volumes dispatched. One of the effects is lack of investment resources. This is one reason why the Russian Government is trying to establish a more stable legal framework for foreign investment. Gazprom itself, however, seems to have mixed feelings about involvement by foreign companies in the gas sector. It clearly wants access to Western capital (it is for instance willing to let foreign companies acquire up to 9% of its shares) but is more reticent when it comes to letting foreign companies participate in production, let alone opening up its transportation system to foreign companies.

Gazprom's monopoly position is under political pressure. Recent draft legislation on natural monopolies and on oil and gas activities in general contain clauses that could potentially reduce Gazprom's dominance. It still remains to be seen whether this legislation will be adopted and in what form.

In the present situation of decline in economic activity, unemployment is a growing problem. This is one of the reasons why both Gazprom and the Russian authorities in some contexts are strongly promoting the idea that large scale new grassroots projects like the Yamal project are necessary in the near future.

Russia has recently signed the European Energy Charter Treaty, which may be useful in solving some of the difficult transit problems that Russia currently faces.

GAS DEMAND

Over the last two decades of the former USSR's existence, gas demand grew by more than 5% annually. Historically, demand has been defined as apparent consumption, i.e., total production minus net exports. This reflects the very strong emphasis on production; at the low prices paid, the market would take almost any volumes of gas. Even today, it is not clear that the demand concept is relevant as long as only half of internal consumption is paid for. As long as prices are as low as current levels, it is of course extremely difficult to forecast what will happen to demand if prices are raised toward international levels. As Russia's future gas exports, undoubtedly very important for the European gas market, are dependent both on future production and future demand, some discussion of demand is necessary. This will be done by reference to official Russian material supplemented by some alternative suggestions.

2. Ministry of Fuel and Energy, *The Energy Strategy of Russia*, Moscow 1994.

Table 1 shows a complete gas balance for Russia between 1990 and 2010 produced jointly by the Ministry of Fuel and Energy and the Ministry of Economy.

Table 1 Natural Gas Balance in the Russian Federation (bcm)

	1990	**1991**	**1992**	**1993**	**1994**	**1995**	**2000**	**2005**	**2010**
Total gas extraction	640.3	643	640	618	610	620	700	760	820
Storage injection	26.9	29.1	30	27.8	32.2	32.2	40	45	50
Other receipts	2.4	2.2	2.2	1.9	1.6	1.6	2.2	2.2	3
Imports	31.1	19	19.8	15.2	4	4	—	—	—
Gas resources available	700.8	693	692	663	648	658	742	807	873
Internal demand total	461.1	464	455	443	444	444	500	540	580
Internal consumption (of which):	**450.4**	**457**	**447**	**435**	**436**	**436**	**491**	**531**	**571.2**
Conversion *of which:*	275	279	273	277	271	271	313	345	369
Power stations	191	198	190	194	189	189	215	238	254.6
Boilers	84	81	83.2	83	82	82	98.5	108	114.4
Other consumption (of which):	**175.4**	**177**	**174**	**158**	**165**	**165**	**178**	**186**	**202.2**
Industry	55.8	54.2	52.3	46	43	43	56.8	60.4	63.7
Construction	0.3	0.3	0.3	0.3	0.3	0.3	0.3	0.3	0.3
Transport	59	59.4	59.4	54.4	57.5	57.5	59.4	60	65
Agriculture	1.2	1.4	1.4	1.8	1.8	1.8	1.9	2.3	2.9
Public	28.2	29.8	30.3	31	34	34	34.8	37.4	43.4
Raw material and Non-fuel needs	28.7	24.2	22.4	22	21	21	22	22.8	23.7
Other	2.2	8	8	2.6	7.3	7.3	3.2	3.2	3.2
Losses	10.7	7.6	8	8	8	8	8.6	8.6	8.8
Export	212.0	197.0	206.0	179.0	172	182	197	217	243
Storage withdrawal	27.6	31.6	31.1	37.9	32	32	45	50	50

Source: Ministry of Economy/Ministry of Fuel and Energy: *Demand for energy resources and their supply: the situation and prospects,* Symposium on the energy strategy of Russia, Tokyo, October 4-8, 1994.

Concerning the historical figures the following observations can be made:

■ the recent decline in production has taken place due to falling demand. Some 20 to 30 bcm of production has been shut in because of insufficient demand. This is a new experience in Russia;

■ relative to the decline in GDP (by some estimates to be around 40% between 1990 and 1994), the decline in gas demand is very small. Gas is a relatively inexpensive fuel and has too large extent substituted for oil and coal;

■ two salient features of the Russian gas demand structure are the very high share of gas in power generation (43.9% of total internal demand in 1993) and the low share of residential/commercial demand (14% in 1993, although this does not appear directly from Table 1);

■ the item called "transport" in Table 1, includes natural gas as a vehicle fuel but the overwhelming part of it is pipeline fuels (volumes roughly corresponding to total gas consumption in Italy);

■ losses are estimated at 1.8% of total internal demand;

■ from 1990 to 1993 total export demand fell from 212 bcm to 179 bcm, with most of the decline taking place in exports to former republics of the USSR. The decline in exports to these countries can be attributed to the downturn in economic activity, the non-payment problem and transit problems. By 1994, imports, most of which were destined for re-export, had almost come to a halt.

In 1990, the share of gas in what is called boiler and stove fuel (comprising all bulk fuel uses) was 54%. The forecast in Table 1 implies an increase of the gas share to 67% by the year 2000 which reflects the fact that Russian authorities are very ambitious about further gas penetration, high in most regions but low in the East and in the North.

According to the forecast in Table 1, total internal gas demand is expected to increase by almost 137 bcm between 1993 and 2010. Demand will bottom out around the 1993-95 period but will increase beyond the 1990 level well before 2000. About two thirds of total demand growth between 1993 and 2010 is expected to take place in the production of electricity and heat, where natural gas will be used as a substitute for fuel oil and coal. The remainder of the growth will take place in agriculture and the residential/commercial sector.

The assumptions underlying the forecast in Table 1 have not been stated in great detail, but the major assumptions seem to be:

■ energy prices will approach international levels over the period, but gas prices will remain regulated;

■ steps will be taken to realise some of the potential for energy savings present in the gas sector. In its Energy Strategy document the government has estimated the potential for gas savings at 100 to 110 bcm of which 45 to 60 bcm is in the energy sector itself and 34 to 42 bcm in industry. The Government recognises that it has to rely on administrative measures to realise this potential before prices have reached a level where they give consumers an economic incentive to save gas. It has not been specified, however, what share of the total potential will be realised by the year 2010.

Economic activity in Russia is still declining: industrial output fell by 22.4% in the January-October, 1994 period compared with the same period in 1993. Gas production fell by around 13 bcm over the same period. In general, there are many indications that the forecast presented in Table 1 is too optimistic. Recent figures seem to underpin this: the volume of marketed gas in Russia (at the outlets of Gazprom) dropped from 405 bcm in 1990 to 382 bcm in 1993 and to 350 bcm in 1994. It is beyond the scope of this annex to go into detail on demand issues, but some alternative arguments that could justify deviation from the official forecasts will be put forward.

As long as non-payment is allowed to continue to any significant extent, all calculations of "demand" are fatally flawed. Demand is a concept which presupposes that those to whom gas is being delivered are paying an agreed price, and that if they fail to pay then they will not be supplied. In the present situation, Russian gas demand is what Gazprom and the Government decide it to be. Until it becomes clear how many customers cannot pay (i.e., are bankrupt), as opposed to how many are finding it convenient not to pay, thereby using gas suppliers as a cheap source of credit, it will be impossible to understand levels of real demand at current prices.

Figure 1 summarises some of the forces that are shaping future Russian gas demand under the assumption that the country continues on its path towards economic reform. The arrows in the chart indicate the forces that are at play, their most likely time sequence and how their effects might offset each other.

The first stage, on which the country is well-advanced, is macro economic decline, but the decline in total energy demand is to a large extent offset by substitution of gas for other fuels: oil in industry, and coal and nuclear power in power production. The next stage, which Russia is now in, prices are being raised to levels which start to reflect costs, but enterprises fail to pay their bills — or do not pay the full amount of the new prices — and run up massive debt to the gas and electricity industries. In the next stage, many loss-making enterprises will be closed down through bankruptcy, but economic recovery in these and other sectors may begin to push up energy demand. Finally, the full introduction of cost-based pricing will lead to major conservation and efficiency measures along with the replacement of old equipment with new energy efficient plant. It is likely that new plant will be more efficient than that which it replaces and that the vast majority of it will be gas-fired.

Figure 1   Forces Shaping Russian Gas Demand

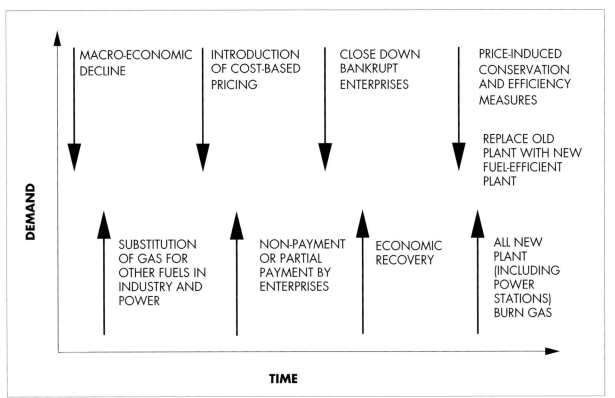

Source: Jonathan Stern, "Russian Natural Gas Exports Availability to 2010: the Gas Bubble and Its Impact on European Gas Markets", RIIA, 1995.

The official forecast cited above predicts a gas demand in 2000 which is considerably higher than the level in 1990. Gazprom has, however, presented scenarios where gas demand in 2000 is around the same as in 1990, which probably reflects a growing recognition of the fact that an increase in demand over the next five years is unrealistic. This trend has been corroborated by external analysts who have identified the possibility of a gas bubble by

2000.[3] One of these analyses, based on estimates of the possible production decline in the various sectors followed by calculations of the effects on gas demand, points out that gas demand in 2000 could be 66-96 bcm lower than in 1990 and 43-83 bcm lower than in 1993. The major trends identified are a reduction of gas demand in power generation and industry with a significant increase in demand for residential and heating purposes.

Demand beyond 2000 will depend heavily on the future development of the industrial structure in Russia, particularly in terms of the balance of energy-intensive industry against light industry and services. Another important factor is the actual potential for energy saving. It is not very likely that a high share of the actual potential (which by three different sources has been estimated at around 100 bcm of gas) will be realised before 2000. Given a price structure with incentives to save energy, it could therefore take a long time for gas demand to reach the level of 1990.

GAS SUPPLY

At the beginning of 1994, Russia had a proven reserve base of 48-49 tcm, which accounted for around 35% of world proven reserves. Around three quarters of proven reserves are located in North Western Siberia in some 20 fields located on and around the Taz and Yamal peninsulas (See Map 1). The potential resource base is colossal; according to Gazprom's definition it is around 212 tcm.

Table 2 provides an overview of Russian gas production over the last few years. The following features are noteworthy:

- The heavy reliance on production in West Siberia (close to 87% in 1993), implying transportation over long distances to take the gas to markets.

- The very low share of associated gas which means that gas production is basically independent of oil production.

- The dominant position of Gazprom (accounting for more than 93.5% of total production in 1993).

Gazprom is the direct descendant of the Soviet Ministry of the Gas Industry. It controls almost the entire Russian gas industry as far as the "city gate", owns the high pressure transmission grid and increasingly also sells gas to big end-users. The importance of gas as a domestic fuel and an export commodity, combined with its evident success at maintaining its position during a period when the entire Russian industrial sector has been in decline, has made Gazprom a very powerful organisation in the new Russia. The corporate culture of the company has been heavily oriented towards the development of multi-trillion cubic metre fields with multiple large diameter pipelines over thousands of kilometres, and it has not, in the past, been too much concerned about markets and prices to be obtained for the gas. After (Russian style) privatisation of the company, this is changing, as Gazprom is now required to provide all the capital investment from its own resources or to attract foreign investment.

---

3. Jonathan Stern: *Russian Natural Gas Exports Availability to 2010: the "Gas Bubble" and Its Impact on European Gas Markets.* RIIA 1995.

Map 1 Major Natural Gas Producing and Perspective Regions and Pipelines

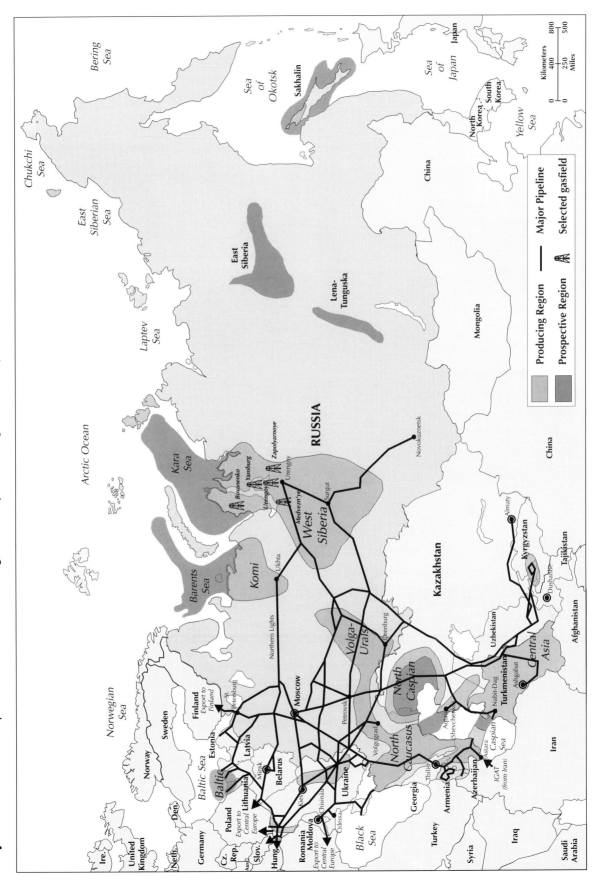

Table 2   Natural Gas Production in the Former Soviet Union* (billion cubic metres)

	1988	1991	1992	1993
Russia	589.7	642.9	640.4	617.6
Gazprom Production	546.7	601.6	602.7	577.7
West Siberia				
of which:	**475.4**	**533.3**	**549.8**	**535.5**
Nadymgazprom	73.3	68.9	69.1	68
Yamburggazodobycha	84.5	166.8	178.2	173
Urengoygazprom	298.8	282.8	287.6	281
Surgutgazprom	18.8	14.8	14.9	14
East Siberia	5.1	4.9	5.0	5.2
Outside Siberia				
of which:	**66.2**	**63.4**	**47.9**	**37.0**
Orenburggazprom	45.9	48.0	36.4	27.1
Astrakhangazprom	4.8	3.3	2.9	2.6
Severgazprom	8.3	5.2	4.9	4.4
Non-Gazprom Production				
Gas from oil production including:	43.1	41.3	37.7	39.9
associated gas	37.9	35.1	32.0	—
non-associated gas	5.2	6.2	5.7	—

* Totals may not add due to rounding.

Sources: David Wilson, "CIS and East European Energy Databook", *Eastern Block Research*, 1994, "Table 33; Gas in the Former Soviet Union", *Petroleum Economist Special Report*, September 1994, p.8.

Table 2 shows the trends in production from the major gas fields since 1988. Medvezhe (represented by Nadymgazprom in the table) came on stream in 1972 and is in the decline phase. The Yamburg field, which came on stream in 1986, has a nameplate capacity of 205 bcm annually, but produced only 173 bcm in 1993. Given sufficient investment, production could be increased to nameplate capacity and kept there for 7 to 10 years by drilling new wells and installing new compressor capacity. The Urengoy field (on stream in 1978) reached peak production of around 300 bcm in the mid 1980s. Although its production has fallen by 10% since that time, it appears to have been used as the "swing" field. A rough computation reveals that since the start of production, some 3,200 bcm of gas has been produced from Urengoy, or just over 40% of proven reserves. Although, in terms of numerical reserves, the field should be able to continue production at 250-300 bcm per year for some time, there have been indications that overly rapid production may have significantly reduced ultimate recovery at the field.

A possible sudden decline in Urengoy production might indicate an immediate need to develop fields on the Yamal Peninsula. However, there are 67 smaller fields located relatively close to existing infrastructure (4 are within 100 km of Medvezhe, 23 within 150 km of Urengoy and 15 are within 150 km of Yamburg). Given the will to develop them, it would be surprising if these fields were not able to compensate for declines in production from existing fields for at least 10 years into the future. Table 3 shows the likely production of some of the new Siberian fields.

Table 3   Siberian satellite field development

Field	Likely production level* (bcm)
Komsomolskoye**	25
Yubilyeynoye**	15
Yamsovey	25
Kharvutinskoye	30
West Tarkalinskoye	20
Zapolyarnoye	100

*   forecast annual plateau production for 5-7 years
**   in production

In addition to the above mentioned category of fields (which in any other country would be characterised as huge), there are around 600 smaller deposits spread over Russia, having average reserves of 10 bcm each. Little attention has so far been paid to these fields, but this attitude is now changing.

For a long time the so-called Yamal project has been presented as the next major gas development in Siberia. The majority of the proven Yamal reserves are contained in four big fields: the Bovanenko/Kharasevey/Kruzenshtern cluster and Novoport. Gazprom maintains production from Yamal could reach 170 bcm a year. As the need for these volumes over the next 10 years may be questionable, it seems that the Yamal project is presently being promoted primarily because the Russian construction industry is underemployed. Although there are still a number of technological and ecological problems to be solved before the project can take off, there is no doubt that over the long term the area could play a very important role in European gas supply.

The huge Shtokcmanovskoye, Rusanaovskoye and Leningradskoye fields in the Barents Sea with reserves at up to 8 tcm provide an alternative production option to the Yamal development. The Shtockmanovskoye field alone is able to produce 50-100 bcm per year for 25 years.

COST OF PRODUCTION AND TRANSPORTATION

An assessment of present and future production and transmission costs is crucial to any evaluation of Russia as a future gas exporter. Any such assessment is, however, fraught with a number of problems arising from the fact that market economic calculations are not yet fully relevant for existing and imminent projects. It is for instance very difficult to determine what the production and transmission costs for gas from the West Siberian fields are since the calculation of costs critically depends on what assumptions are used. A technical cost based on market principles of costing and depreciation could be used, but the result would probably be of little interest since Gazprom could treat the facilities in question as a dowry from the Government incurring very low capital and operating costs; the calculations would therefore be very robust to downward movement in international gas prices. A detailed discussion of such issues is beyond the scope of this annex but a few general observations on costs will be made.

A notional supply cost curve for Russia could have the following features:

■ it would be upward sloping but remain fairly flat as long as new gas is taken from Western Siberian fields close to existing infrastructure. Production costs will increase somewhat, however, since the new fields coming on stream are smaller than the existing ones and therefore will benefit less from economies of scale;

■ as soon as gas from new smaller fields triggers the need for new transmission capacity, costs will increase rapidly as transmission cost in Russia will always be high given the long distance from production centres to markets. Since there is quite a lot of spare capacity in some parts of the system, new volumes from these fields are not likely to necessitate construction of completely new pipelines but rather occasional looping;

■ new projects on the Yamal peninsula and in the Barents Sea would make the supply cost curve rise steeply to a new level because of the very harsh climatic conditions and new technologies needed to exploit these reserves. Both these projects would also need new transportation infrastructure, constituting the major increase in costs. Development on the Yamal peninsula is expected to be 50% more costly than development of the giant fields producing in Siberia today, although even higher figures have also been quoted;

■ the lower part of the supply cost curve could probably be extended substantially for the export market by improvements in energy efficiency leading to gas savings. It could also be extended by simply switching gas volumes previously supplied to domestic users to the export market because domestic users would be less inclined to pay the higher prices that will inevitably have to be charged;

■ the potential for cost reductions in production and transmission in Russia is probably at least as large as in most other major producing countries, but will take a longer time to be realised because the mentality of the communist era is still present and because limited need for investments in new projects will limit the turnover of capital stock.

For illustrative purposes the following tables indicate ranges for the cost of Russian gas. Table 4 shows an estimate of production and transportation cost elements in 1993 Russian gas prices.

Table 4   Production and Transport Cost Elements in 1993 Russian Gas Prices to Domestic and Export Markets (US cents per Mbtu)

	Domestic	**FSU**	**Europe**
Exploration and Production Costs (of which):	—	**7.3**	—
Exploration	—	1.8	—
Operating Costs	—	3.6	—
Depreciation	—	1.8	—
Transportation Costs (of which):	**70.7**	**84.2**	**84.2**
Operating Costs	3.4	4.3	4.3
Depreciation	67.3	79.9	79.9
Total Costs	**78.0**	**91.5**	**91.5**

Source: International Energy Agency, *Russian Energy Prices, Taxes and Costs*, Paris: OECD/IEA, 1994, Tables 8a, 8b 8c, pp. 56-58.

These figures give a reasonably good impression of the cost structure for present gas production in Russia, but the calculations raise a number of questions concerning the level of costs, especially the depreciation cost. Another source claims that the cost of "old" gas is around US$ 2/Mbtu delivered at Western European border. Which figure is correct probably to a large extent depends on what assumptions are taken about the degree of depreciation of the present transmission system. What is important here is not to know exactly where the gas supply curve starts, but to be aware that at today's gas price levels significant volumes of gas could be delivered profitably from Russia.

Table 5 presents an estimate of gas supply costs for gas from Yamal which probably indicates the higher end of the supply cost curve. Under the assumptions taken, the figures indicate a delivered cost of some 3.4 US$ per Mbtu (transportation cost US$ 2.40 per Mbtu plus an implied wellhead cost of US$ 1 per Mbtu). This estimate is not very different from other known estimates.

The protagonists of the Shtockmanovskoye project believe that gas carried by a single pipeline having a capacity of 30 bcm a year could be brought to Europe at a cost of US$ 3 per Mbtu. Roughly speaking, it can probably be assumed that a large part of the Russian supply cost curve is below US$ 3 per Mbtu.

Table 5   Transport Costs of Gas from the Yamal Peninsula to Export Borders
(US$ per Mbtu)

	Belarus/Poland	**Ukraine**
Length (km)	6000	6500
Third country crossing	1600	2100
Technical cost*	1.8-2.0	2.0-2.2
Transit fees**		
A	0.3	0.45
B	0.5	0.60
Total Transport Cost**		
A	2.20	2.50
B	2.40	2.75

Source: "Observatoire Méditerranéen de l'Energie" cited in: *Natural Gas Transportation: Organisation and Regulation*, Paris: OECD/IEA, 1994, Table 3, p. 141

*   Total technical cost per unit of transportation including "normal profit".

**   In variant A, third countries take 5% of the gas which flows through their territories; in variant B third countries charge 3 cents per Mbtu per 100 km.

PRODUCTION PROJECTIONS

In the light of the above discussion one might legitimately question the purpose of making long-term forecasts of Russian gas production. It is still interesting, however, to study the views of the Russian Government, Gazprom and other institutions, since such views hopefully will at least give an indication of what level of production is physically possible. Table 6 gives an overview of recent forecast of Russian gas production up to 2010.

Table 6   Russian Gas Production Projections, 1995-2010

	1995	**1997**	**2000**	**2005**	**2010**
Vniigas: [1] **Production (of which):**	**680**	**705**	**735-755**	**785-820**	**820-860**
W. Siberia	593	640	642-658	691-722	723-760
Yamal	—	—	0-10	20-45	93-135
Gazprom: [2]	680	—	735-755	—	900-1000
mid-1993	655-675	—	720-745	—	910-960
late 1993	655	—	735	—	—
Ministry of Fuels and Energy: [3]	650-655	—	715-730	—	785-820
Ministry of Fuels and Energy, Ministry of Economy:	620	—	700	760	820

Source: [1] Data from Vniigas, cited in: *Cedigaz, Natural Gas in the World, 1994 Survey*, Table 40, p.96

[2] Ministry of Economy/Ministry of Fuel and Energy: *Demand for energy resources and their supply: the situation and prosects* Symposium on the energy strategy of Russia, Tokyo, October 4-8, 1994.

[3] Jonathan Stern: *Russian Natural Gas Exports Availability to 2010: the "Gas Bubble" and Its Impact on European Gas Markets.* RIIA 1995.

PAST AND FUTURE EXPORTS

Historically exports of Russian gas have been closely related to the development of fields like Orenburg, Urengoy and Yamburg. Central and Eastern European countries received gas under long term government-to-government agreements as repayment for their involvement in the construction of gas facilities within the USSR. They also purchased gas under agreements where prices and volumes were renegotiated annually. All gas trade was conducted on a transferable rouble or barter basis. Countries in OECD Europe purchased gas on long term contracts with high take-or-pay levels. Many contracts included a significant element of counter-trade. By the close of the Soviet era, hard currency earnings from gas exports had become a substantial item in Soviet foreign trade.

The breakup of the Soviet Union created a set of trading relationships between newly emerging sovereign states, which had formerly treated these relationships as internal transfers of gas without financial significance. The problems of gas trade between the former Soviet republics and in particularly the triangular relationship between Russia, Turkmenistan and Ukraine, not only affect Russian relations with the other republics, but are crucial to the continuing relationship with Europe. Table 7 shows figures for gas trade between the republics in the former USSR.

Table 7 does not show the pattern and extent of inter-republican gas trade during the Soviet period. Of importance here is that Russia primarily supplied Ukraine (which also received some volumes from Turkmenistan), Moldova and Belarus. This is important because all Russian gas exports to Europe pass through these three republics. The break-up of the USSR caused

Table 7   Russian Natural Gas Exports to former Soviet Republics, 1990-93

	1990	1991	1992	1993
Ukraine	60.8	60.7	77.3	54.9
Belarus	14.1	14.3	17.6	16.4
Moldova	2.3	2.5	3.4	3.2
Lithuania	6.1	6.0	3.2	1.9
Latvia	3.4	3.2	1.6	1.0
Estonia	1.7	1.9	0.9	0.4
Kazakhstan	-	-	1.7	1.1
Total*	**92.0**	**90.0**	**106.4**	**78.6**

* Totals may not sum due to rounding.
Source: *CIS and East European Energy Databook 1994, "European Gas Markets".*

immediate and continuing problems in gas trade between all of the republics. The essence of these problems has been the requirement that gas and transit tariffs be paid for at prices and in currencies which none of the recipients can afford. The relationship to Ukraine is particularly important because it takes very high volumes of gas (up to 77 bcm a year) and, because of non-payment has an influence on Russian revenues. In addition, Ukraine transports 90% of the Russian exports to Europe and has occasionally "siphoned" off gas intended for Europe in situations where Russia has tried to cut deliveries to Ukraine because of non-payment. This latter practice has jeopardised Russia's image as a reliable supplier of gas to Europe. The high reliance on transit through Ukraine has spurred Russian plans for a new pipeline through Belarus and Poland which will avoid transit through Ukraine. Belarus transits gas to Poland whereas Moldova transits gas to Romania, Turkey and Bulgaria. Over the past few years gas exports to former republics have fallen and may continue to do so, depending upon settlement of transit issues and the prospects for economic growth in these countries. A continued decline in these exports could free additional volumes for exports elsewhere.

Table 8 shows the development in Russian (and Turkmen) gas exports to Europe over the past few years.

Total exports have fallen somewhat since 1990, mainly due to the economic recession in Central and Eastern Europe. Exports to OECD have increased slightly, but less than exports from Algeria, the Netherlands and Norway over this period.

Over the past five years Gazprom has developed a new strategy towards selling gas in Europe. The traditional method of sales in the Soviet era was to sell at the border of the importing country, with Gazprom having no involvement in the transportation or marketing of the gas. In 1990 Gazprom entered the downstream part of the gas chain in Germany through a joint marketing venture with Wintershall. Since then, Gazprom has created a number of similar ventures in other European countries. The possibilities for expansion in this area may be particularly good in Central and Eastern Europe as virtually all the existing contracts will expire by 1998, by which time the entire basis of the trade will have to be renegotiated.

Table 8   CIS Gas Exports to Europe 1990-93
(billion cubic metres)

	1990	1991	1992	1993
EXPORTS FROM:				
Russia	96.0	89.6	87.9	90.3
Turkmenistan	13.0	15.6	11.2	10.6
TO:				
Former Yugoslavia	4.5	4.5	3.0	2.7
Romania	7.3	5.4	4.4	4.6
Bulgaria	6.8	5.7	5.3	4.8
Hungary	6.4	5.9	4.8	4.8
Poland	8.4	7.1	6.7	5.8
Czech/Slovak Republics	12.6	13.7	12.8	13.2
Total: Central/Eastern Europe	**46.0**	**42.3**	**37.0**	**35.9**
Turkey	3.3	4.1	4.5	5.0
Finland	2.7	2.9	3.0	3.1
Austria	5.1	5.2	5.1	5.3
Switzerland	0.3	0.4	0.4	0.4
France	10.6	11.4	12.1	11.6
Italy	14.3	14.5	14.1	13.8
Germany	26.6	24.4	22.9	25.8
Total: OECD	**63.0**	**62.9**	**62.1**	**65.0**
GRAND TOTAL	**109.0**	**105.2**	**99.1**	**100.9**

Source: Gazexport.

Table 9 reproduces a forecast of the difference between government projections of production and domestic demand, i.e., the potential for future exports.

Table 9   Future Russian Gas Exports (bcm)

	1993	1994	1995	2000	2005	2010
Gas available	622	616	626	697	757	823
Internal demand	443	444	444	500	540	580
Exports (of which to):	**179**	**172**	**182**	**197**	**217**	**243**
States of the former USSR	77	66	66	72.2	87.2	98
Foreign states	102	106	116	125	130	145

Source: Ministry of Economy/Ministry of Fuel and Energy: *Demand for energy resources and their supply: the situation and prospects,* Symposium on the energy strategy of Russia, Tokyo, October 4-8, 1994.

The potential export figures in Table 9 are logical consequence of the fact that satisfaction of domestic demand has priority over exports and that future demand is still expected to be high in relation to expected production. It might be said at the outset that the export forecast is inconsistent with existing plans to expand export pipeline capacity from 116 bcm today up to 200 bcm over the next few years (see below). Additionally, the following comments can be made:

■ there is already shut-in production capacity of some 40 bcm. As pointed out above, a decline in demand of around 60 bcm relative to the demand figure in Table 9 may not be unrealistic. This implies a gas bubble of some 100 bcm around 2000;

■ after 2000, a fair share of the gas savings potential of around 100 bcm could probably be realised given less distorted prices and access to finance;

■ the forecast assumes a relatively quick upturn in deliveries to the "near abroad". These volumes will depend critically on transit problems being sorted out and on the general economic development in the countries concerned. The forecast seems optimistic and implies a potential for taking some of these volumes to other countries;

■ adding the indicated bubble and the savings potential to the export figures in Table 9 give a potential volume for export which could cover a very high share of unaccounted for European gas demand by 2010;

■ even in a scenario of very high exports, it will be possible to find relatively low cost gas from existing fields to cover this demand without tapping sources like Yamal and Shtockmanovskoye;

■ infrastructure exists to bring Central Asian gas supplies into Russia at a relatively low cost. The infrastructure which brought around 40 bcm of Turkmen gas to Russia and the Ukraine in 1990 is currently underutilised, and until 2000 will probably remain underutilised by around 20 bcm a year. The Karachaganak gas field lies less than 300 km from the existing Orenburg pipeline which, with the depletion of the Orenburg field, could eventually allow up to 30 bcm of Kazakh gas to be brought to Europe after 2000.

As far as the prospects for exports are concerned the conclusion is that gas availability is less of a problem than transportation capacity and market access.

INFRASTRUCTURE

In total, there are some 368 gas fields in Russia, of which 132 are in operation and 45 have been developed but are not yet in operation. The 20 biggest fields account for more than 90% of total production. The gas produced is treated in 114 complex gas treatment plans. The gas transmission system (pressure above 55 bar) is around 140,000 km long and is owned and operated by Gazprom. The medium and low pressure gas distribution network is around 257,000 km long, serves about 80% of the population and is owned by the regions and the local distribution companies. Gas is pumped through the transmission system by 233 compressor stations having 650 compressor units with a total effect of some 38 GW.

Some of these pipelines are illustrated in Map 2.

Daily and seasonal load balancing is taken care of by use of 20 storage facilities having a usable capacity of 40 bcm. Russia lost about 40% of its storage capacity when the Ukraine became

Map 2

Russian Gas Deliveries to Europe

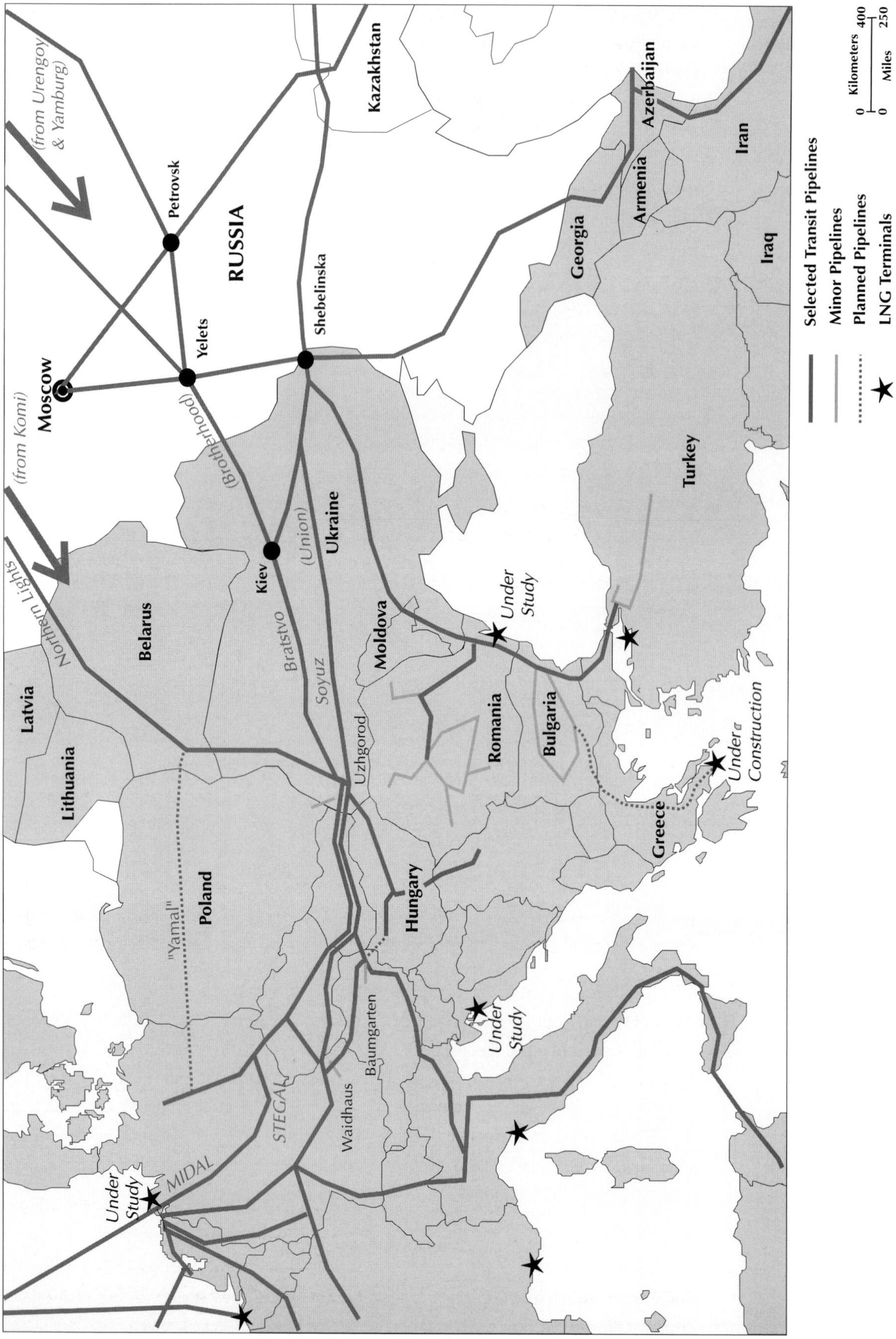

Kazakhstan

(from Urengoy & Yamburg)

Petrovsk

RUSSIA

Yelets

Shebelinska

Moscow

(from Komi)

(Brotherhood)

Azerbaijan

Armenia

Iran

Georgia

Iraq

(Union)

Ukraine

Kiev

Turkey

Bratstvo

Soyuz

Moldova

Under Study

Belarus

Northern Lights

Latvia

Lithuania

Uzhgorod

Romania

Bulgaria

Under Construction

"Yamal"

Poland

Hungary

Greece

Baumgarten

Under Study

STEGAL

Waidhaus

MIDAL

Under Study

Selected Transit Pipelines

Minor Pipelines

Planned Pipelines

★ LNG Terminals

Kilometers 0   400
Miles   0   250

independent. The maximum daily output from storage today is around 500 mcm. Plans exist to expand usable storage capacity to 80 bcm by 2000. Current storage capacity constitutes 9% of annual domestic gas consumption, which means 33 days of consumption. Seasonal swing in Russia is much lower than in Western Europe, the ratio between the month with the highest average consumption and the one with the lowest average consumption being only two, whereas four to five is quite common in Europe. Gazprom is trying to increase access to storage capacity by entering into storage agreements with companies in Europe.

Possibly the biggest immediate challenge for the Russian gas industry lies with the refurbishment of the current gas trunkline system including both pipelines and compressor stations. While it is not easy to briefly summarise the condition of such a large system, available evidence suggests that it is generally satisfactory, and that the more dramatic foreign commentaries describing a system on the verge of breakdown, are wide of the mark. This is not to deny that replacement of both aging pipes and compressors are essential for the continued safe and efficient operation of the network. Gazprom is very well aware of what is required and has already begun the necessary work. The system has begun to show signs of age. Out of 140,000 km of trunk pipeline, only 7.5 % was built in the past decade; 42% is 10-20 years old; 17.5% is 30-40 years old; and 2.5% is more than 40 years old. 15% of compressor capacity is more than 20 years old and needs modernisation or replacement. According to Gazprom plans, 4,320 km of pipe and 7.4 GW of compressor capacity will be replaced over the next five years.

Gazprom statistics show accidents per thousand kilometres of pipeline steadily declining over a 20 year period from 1.1 in 1973 to 0.215 in 1993. 23% of accidents arise from poor construction work which in the past was carried out by the Ministry of Oil and Gas Construction, giving Gazprom (and its predecessors) little or no control over the work. A further 16% of accidents are caused by external corrosion of pipe, principally linked to poor insulation, and this is being improved using on-site insulation facilities. It may be more difficult to find a solution for the 13% of accidents caused by stress corrosion. The remainder of the accidents are due to mechanical damage (16%) and natural disasters (13%).

The expansion of gas exports to Europe will depend on the creation of new transmission capacity. The current situation in terms of availability of existing pipeline export capacity is extremely complicated. Table 10 shows an estimate of the current capacity of gas export pipelines in Russia/Ukraine/Belarus and the capacity at the export points.

With the present pipeline capacity, exports could be increased by about 15 bcm relative to 1993 exports of some 100 bcm. Plans already exist, however, to increase capacity substantially: there is a clear intention to increase capacity through the Ukraine by around 30 bcm over the next decade. To reduce Russian dependence on the Ukraine for transit, a new corridor through Belarus and Poland will be built roughly over the same period with a capacity of 50 to 60 bcm. This pipeline is also part of what is called "the Yamal project" because it is ultimately intended to carry gas from the Yamal fields. What will happen in reality is that the pipeline will be built from the market to join fields in Western Siberia. This matches well with the fact that a new line from Punga to Ukhta with a capacity of 50 to 60 bcm is being built and will be commissioned in 1996. This line will enable more Western Siberian gas to join the northernmost of the export pipelines.

Table 10   Approximate Nameplate Capacity of CIS Gas Export Lines to Europe (billion cubic metres)

1. Pipelines commencing in Russia and CIS, 1993

Name of line	Point of Export	Route	Capacity to CIS Border
Bratstvo	Uzhgorod	Czech/Slovak Republic, Hungary	3.5
Shebelinka/Ismail	Ismail	Romania, Bulgaria, Turkey	20
Northern Lights	Uzhgorod*	Finland, Poland	22
Soyuz (Orenburg)	Uzhgorod	Eastern/Western Europe	27
Urengoy	Uzhgorod	Western Europe	27
Progress (Yamburg)	Uzhgorod	Eastern Europe	27

2. Pipelines outside CIS, 1993

Name of line	Point of Export	Route	Exit Capacity
Northern Lights	Imatra	Finland	4.0
Northern Lights	Brest Kobrin	Poland	3.8
Shebelinka/Ismail	Ismail	Romania, Bulgaria, Turkey	20.0
Transgas (4 lines)	Velke Kapusany	Slovak/Czech Republic	75.0
TOTAL			**102.8**

Sources: Marie Françoise Chabrelie, "European Natural Gas Trade by Pipelines", *Cedigaz*, July 1993, Table 10, p. 6. "PH Energy Analysis", *Petroleum Economist*, Special Supplement, September 1993, p.40

COPING WITH DISRUPTIONS

For the time being it is hard to trace legislation dealing explicitly with the responsibility for security of supply and action to be taken in case of supply problems. Draft legislation will, however, be quite specific on these issues. Both in the draft "Law on oil and gas" and in a new supply code under elaboration there will be clauses dealing with security issues. Gazprom officials, however, clearly consider security of supply to be part of their mandate. The company takes security of supply very seriously and makes the point that consumers are rarely, if ever, inconvenienced by pipeline and compressor breakdown or accident. Pipelines are looped and circles are created in order that different regions and cities can be supplied by different routes if a problem develops on a particular line or a particular system. There are points on the corridors which carry several parallel pipelines at which, if a breakage occurs, gas can be transferred from one line to another. At compressor stations, reserve capacity has been installed in order to cope with breakdowns. The margin of reserve capacity depends on the particular station. At the 25 MW stations, the policy is to have two units operating and one in reserve (with a margin of 50%). However, in smaller capacity stations using 6 MW units, the reserve is only around 20%. The average reserve capacity at compressor stations is around 30%. Foreign pipes and equipment tend to be used at the critical points in the system and Russian pipe at the less critical points.

One weakness in the Russian way of thinking about security of supply is the lack of economic comparison between different measures to meet peaks and deal with emergency shortfalls. In the past there has been a lack of economic incentive to think in this way, but this situation is likely to change in the future.

An example of the ability of the system to deal with emergencies occurred in June 1993 when a fracture at the measuring unit at the Torbeyevo compressor station caused an explosion. Six parallel pipelines supplying 500 mcm per day to the Central region of the country needed to be shut down for the three days needed to repair the damage. No consumers were inconvenienced, and even had the accident occurred during the winter months, when production runs around one third higher than in summer to cope with greater demand, there is confidence that the system would have been able to deal with the problem by using gas from storage.

Despite this confidence, there are certainly vulnerable points in the system. The most vulnerable are the major pipeline crossovers in the Nadym-Punga corridor where fifteen 56 inch pipelines carry nearly 90% of gas production with only a 10-15 metre gap between the lines. Although these then divide into a northern and southern route, Gazprom is quite aware of the potential problem which could be caused by an accident or sabotage in this corridor.

The transmission and distribution system in Russia appears to have been designed to maintain supplies under even the most extreme weather conditions, although no design criteria, defined in terms of frequency and duration of extreme weather conditions, appear to exist. There is, however, an expectation that the industry should be able to cope whatever the severity of the weather conditions. Emergencies which arise because of prolonged periods of severe weather conditions are managed jointly by Gazprom, the distributions companies and the local political authorities. For example in Moscow, Mostransgaz (the local Gazprom transportation subsidiary), Mosgas (the Moscow distribution company) and the City council would jointly decide which customers to curtail if supplies began to run low during a severe winter.

Interruptible customers exist but their extent and responsiveness is uncertain. The nature of interruptibility is administrative rather than contractual or commercial. The estimate of 60 mcm per day of interruptibility would require a large number of telephone calls and persuasion to achieve. According to some accounts, all consumers which have plant in continuous operation are required to keep stocks of alternative fuels (principally fuel oil), equivalent to three days of supply, available for use during severe winter periods. Gazprom has arrangements with industrial customers under which such stocks must be kept. However, it is not clear how many actually keep such stocks, nor whether there are any financial incentives to make such provisions. Given the regulation of the industrial gas price at a uniform level, there would appear to be a positive disincentive to maintain alternative fuel stocks, particularly when these are likely to be more expensive than gas and unlikely to be called upon very often.

As regards total flexibility in the gas delivery system, the following can be observed:

■ shut-in production capacity amounts to about 40 bcm today, i.e., some 110 mcm/day. This volume could presumably substitute for volumes that are normally on stream, in the event of production problems. The shut-in volume will probably increase over the next few years;

■ maximum output from storage is 500 mcm/day. This volume will increase considerably over the next few years;

■ interruptible volumes constitute some 60 mcm/day. Given the right economic incentives, these volumes could probably be increased;

■ linepack in the transmission system is some 7 bcm, but there are of course limits as to how much these volumes can exploited before pressure in the lines drops too much.

In case of shortfalls in supply, priority rules exist for the allocation of gas. They are not published but it appears that exports have a high priority, an impression which is supported by the track record of Russian deliveries and the efforts made in the few cases where there have been problems. Historically, Gazprom has, on occasion, made up for shortfall in deliveries from other gas exporters in favour of gas importers in Western Europe; in fact, there are provisions for such measures in most export contracts.

SLOVAKIA

INTRODUCTION

The Slovak gas industry is a highly profitable state-owned monopoly. Despite a near 100% dependence on Russian gas supplies, Slovakia serves as the gateway to Western European gas markets, creating a mutually dependent relationship between supplier and purchaser. The main commercial question is how long the Slovak gas transit system can remain competitive with new pipelines that will be built to carry Russian gas through Slovakia's northern and southern neighbours.

GAS POLICY

The Slovak government's policy on natural gas is focused on replacing coal in industrial power and heat generation. The current 25% share of gas in total fuel consumption is thus expected to rise to 28.5% by the year 2000. By 2005, natural gas may hold a third of the Slovak energy market. In addition to the use of gas in combined cycle and co-generation power units, about 200,000 households will be connected to gas by 2010.

The Slovak gas company, SPP, has the sole right to purchase, distribute and sell natural gas in Slovakia. Since the government's policy is to expand gas sales and eventually deregulate prices, SPP has the potential to generate high profits on its domestic services. This would be especially true if gas demand increases according to government forecasts.

The expected growth in gas demand could entice new private investors, independent power producers and co-generators into the domestic market. Such an evolving gas structure must be capable of supplying gas efficiently and competitively. SPP has carried out a plan to turn itself into a joint stock company, thus allowing certain parts of its business to be sold or divested according to the needs of the market and private investors. The future direction of these changes, and the influence of regulation in ensuring that the industry operates within a competitive framework, is vital to the long term health of the Slovak gas industry.

GAS MARKET

The gas market in Slovakia is somewhat different from gas markets in Western Europe; it has fewer household sales and a higher concentration of sales to heavy industry, resulting in high-average consumption per customer. SPP sold a total of 5.9 bcm in 1993, a 4.2% increase from 1992. All of this gas was sold on the domestic market since re-export of gas is prohibited under the contracts signed with Russian gas supplier Gazprom.

The industrial sector represents 75% of total gas demand.[1] Industrial sales totalled 4.7 bcm in 1993, a 2.5% increase over 1992. This increase is mainly the result of gas sales to the Lab 4 underground storage site under construction. Sales to heavy industry and the agricultural sector are still declining. Supplies to the chemicals sector, a large gas consumer, have sharply decreased from 802 mcm in 1990 to 271 mcm in 1993. However, gas demand is growing in the power and heat generation sector.

SPP provided gas to 56% of Slovak households in 1993. Average household use runs around 1 mcm per year, considerably below the OECD Europe average. The share of household gas in 1993 accounted for 16.4% of total gas demand, compared with 13.3% in 1990. Czechs and Slovaks face similar situations in that more households want to be hooked up to gas than the distribution companies are willing to connect. Artificially low gas prices continue to discourage distributors from expanding service, despite growing demand.

In addition, Slovak gas distribution companies face chronic difficulties in processing and collecting payments. Meter reading is still carried out by hand, resulting in extensive lag times between metering and billing. Distribution companies are hoping new investment in automated meter-reading will improve billing, although collecting payments from gas customers remains problematic.

Table 1 Gas Supply and Demand Outlook

	1992	1995	2000	2005
Primary Energy Supply (Mtoe)	**19.5**	**n.a.**	**n.a.**	**n.a.**
Natural gas as % share	26%	n.a.	n.a.	n.a.
Gas Supply (bcm)	**6.08**	**n.a.**	**n.a.**	**n.a.**
Domestic Production	.20	n.a.	n.a.	n.a.
Imports	5.88	n.a.	n.a.	n.a.
(from Brotherhood line)	(3.93)	n.a.	n.a.	n.a.
(from transit line)	(1.95)	n.a.	n.a.	n.a.
Import dependence	97%	n.a.	n.a.	n.a.
Gas Consumption (bcm)	**5.928**	**6.25**	**9.10**	**10.00**
Households	.856	.930	1.19	1.50
Commercial	.225	.270	.325	.395
Industrial	4.576	4.825	7.245	7.720
(of which: heavy industry)	(3.211)	(3.335)	(3.725)	(4.00)
Power and Heat	.200	.200	2.100	2.200
Chemical Processing	.408	.500	.550	.550
Agriculture	.502	.510	.520	.530
Construction	.222	.230	.250	.290
Transportation	.033	.050	.100	.100
Losses/Other	.272	.240	.340	.385

Source: SPP. Note: SPP and the Slovak Ministry of Economy differ with respect to the gas forecast to the year 2005. SPP expects a more rapid substitution of natural gas for nuclear energy and thus has a higher gas demand estimate.
Note: 1 Mtoe is approximately equivalent to 1.27 bcm.

---

1.   However, this percentage includes what the IEA classifies as commercial users — schools, hospitals, etc.

GAS SUPPLY

Slovakia is dependent on gas imports from Russia via Ukraine for 96% of its domestic consumption. The remaining 4% is supplied through domestic gas production from underground reserves owned by the Slovak company Nafta Gbely. About 4.2 bcm per year of Russian gas is carried to Slovakia through the Brotherhood pipeline (IGP-1). The Slovtransgas transit system provides another 1.5 bcm per year to meet Slovakia's import needs.

Underground storage is the key to maintaining gas supply during periods of peak demand. Russian gas is received at level rates throughout the year (i.e., there is no seasonal adjustment in deliveries based on peak gas use). The maximum daily withdrawal rate of about 24 mcm is sufficient to meet current peak gas demand, which is around 130% of average daily demand. Existing gas storage capacity of 1.6 bcm is being expanded to add another 21 mcm over the next ten years, which should meet projected peak demand.

In late 1994, a new gas transmission station opened on the Czech-Slovak border, allowing the Slovak company Slovtransgas to take over responsibility (from Czech company Transgas) for managing international gas transmission. Slovtrangas is suddenly a major player in the European natural gas market. The Transgas pipeline crossing Slovakia generates an estimated $500 million per year in transit fees, which are expected to grow.

Gas supplies are delivered under three contractual arrangements negotiated by Slovtransgas. The largest share of imports is provided by Russia to pay gas transit fees. The second largest share provides Slovakia with relatively cheap gas under the so-called "Yamburg" agreement, which reimburses Slovak state enterprises for their help in installing equipment at the Yamburg gas field in Siberia. Russia's debt to Slovakia under this contract will be paid off by the end of 1995 and the Russian company Gazprom has suggested that Slovakia will have to pay the world gas price of $80 per tcm (or $2.10 per GJ).

The Slovaks have been negotiating to renew the Yamburg deal's terms by investing in the construction of the Schwechat pipeline link that would carry Russian gas from the Friendship line across Slovakia to Austria and Italy. This new line is expected to be completed by the end of 1996 or early 1997. Slovakia will also be able to receive additional transit fees from Gazprom either in hard currency or available gas. The third and smallest share of Russian gas is paid in hard currency under a conventional supply contract.

INFRASTRUCTURE

IGP-1, the connecting distribution lines to cities and towns, and the supply and withdrawal lines serving the Lab underground gas storage site are all operated by SPP. IGP-1, which has a diameter of 700 mm (28 inches) and an operating pressure of 55 bar, starts at the Ukrainian border and extends 422 km to the town of Jablonica, where it then divides into two branches. One line travels south 53 km to the Lab gas storage site northwest of Bratislava. The other line continues 35 km to the Mokry Haj metering station where it connects with the Czech Republic. Three compressor stations are along the route.

SPP's secondary lines range in size from 150-700 mm and have a total length of 4,681 km. SPP's distribution system serves over 900,000 customers and includes 8,682 km of local pipe networks.

COPING WITH DISRUPTIONS

It is unlikely that Slovakia will experience prolonged disruptions or curtailments in gas shipments from Russia, simply because Slovakia is an essential conduit for the 68 bcm per year of gas flowing to Western Europe. Until such time as alternative supply lines are built to create more competition for the Brotherhood line, Slovakia will be in an enviable bargaining position with its Russian supplier.

Gas transit agreements appear stable enough to avoid extended disputes during negotiations which could have an effect on gas availability in Western Europe. Slovakia and Russia are currently on good political terms and both sides for the moment have a strong incentive to keep the maximum amount of gas flowing West.

Slovakia's domestic gas demand is also not likely to increase dramatically over the next ten years, and nearly half of the country's gas needs can be obtained through delivery of gas as transit fee payment.

There are a number of gas supply diversification strategies that are being considered to meet SPP's forecasted gas demand. Among these are:

LNG. Slovakia is considering the import of LNG from at least three sources: Algeria, Libya and Venezuela. LNG would be supplied through either a new regasification terminal on the Adriatic Sea or through existing North Sea terminals. A new LNG terminal on the Adriatic involves carrying gas through either Slovenia and/or Croatia, Austria, and into Slovakia. LNG from North Sea terminals would be delivered through exchange arrangements with European gas distributors, thus reducing transportation costs to Slovakia. Algerian gas is already linked to Western Europe through the Trans-Med pipeline, crossing Tunisia, the Mediterranean, Sicily and into Italy. Algeria also exports LNG to several Western European buyers.

North Sea. Another gas supply diversification option is to import gas from either the British or Norwegian sectors of the North Sea. The three most discussed projects are 1) the Polpipe project, which would transport UK gas through Germany or Denmark, then through Poland and into Slovakia; 2) the Zeepipe project, which would bring gas from Troll/Sleipner fields through Belgium; and 3) the Europipe extension tying Slovakia into the European network (i.e., the Midal or Stegal systems) at Emden, Germany.

Iran. Despite the long distances involved in transporting Iranian gas to Europe and thus the need to carry large volumes (around 20 bcm per year) to keep a pipeline competitive with other gas sources, talk continues about Iranian gas entering the Central and Eastern European market either through Turkey and Bulgaria or through Ukraine.

It remains difficult to estimate the costs of bringing natural gas from various non-Russian sources to Slovakia. Moreover, the costs of gas delivery may be quite different from the price of gas negotiated between buyer and seller. The Slovaks suggest that they should be paying about US $40/mcm for Russian gas and would have to pay as much as US $140/mcm for North Sea gas. Algerian LNG and Iranian gas apparently come somewhere in the middle at a delivered cost of US $70-110/mcm.

Underground Gas Storage - Lab Field. Slovakia's current gas storage capacity is 1.65 bcm, with a maximum withdrawal rate of 24.8 mcm/day. Six gas-driven compressors, each with 4,500 kW capacity, compress incoming gas from about 45 bars to a maximum of 90 bars. The compressed gas is then carried about 15 km through 350-450 mm pipes and injected into individual wells.

Slovakia is expanding the lab site to add another 780 mcm of active storage capacity and boost withdrawal/injection rates another 8.5 mcm/day to a maximum of 33.3 mcm/day. Drilling of new injection wells would begin in 1996 and reach full capacity by 2002.

TURKMENISTAN

POLITICAL AND ECONOMIC BACKGROUND

The Republic of Turkmenistan is situated in the far south of the FSU, bordering Kazakhstan in the north, Uzbekistan in the north and the east, Iran and Afghanistan in the south and the Caspian Sea in the west. 90 per cent of the country's area of 488,000 square kilometres is desert, which is why the Turkmen population numbers only 3.9 million.

Shortly after the failed coup in Moscow in August 1991, the Parliament in Askhabad declared Turkmenistan an independent republic. In December the same year the Communist Party dissolved itself, but only to reemerge as the Democratic Party of Turkmenistan. In May 1992 a new constitution was adopted by referendum, and Sapurmurad Niyazov, since 1985, the Chairman of Turkmenistan's Supreme Soviet and First Secretary of the Communist Party and, since 1990, the President of the republic, was reelected for 10 years.

The Turkmen economy is based on agriculture (especially cotton cultivation) and extractive industries (especially petroleum production). Since the break-up of the FSU it ,has contracted less than most other FSU republics' economies, but GNP dropped by some 5 per cent in 1992, and the downturn continued in 1993. Emphasising the highly preliminary character of its results, the World Bank estimates Turkmenistan's GNP per capita at US$ 1,230 (1992).[1]

Gas accounts for about 80 per cent of Turkmenistan's exports to other CIS republics and a little over 60 per cent of its exports outside the CIS, i.e., for about three fourths of its total exports. The republic's balance of trade swung from a deficit of nearly one billion Roubles in 1990 to a surplus of the same size in 1991, reflecting steps to correct the distorted commodity price structure of the FSU. However, the country no longer receives transfers from Moscow, and its actual export incomes may differ significantly from its imputed incomes because of non-payment for gas deliveries.

The Turkmen Government is not among the leaders in the FSU either in terms of economic stabilisation efforts or in terms of reforms with the aim of transforming the country to a market economy. Consumer prices may have increased by as much as 3,000 per cent in 1993. A policy of granting wage increases and bonuses and subsidising consumer prices to soften the impacts of inflation on living standards, combined with a habit of overestimating the state's energy revenues, have led to explosive growth in the budget deficit. Although some liberalisation has taken place, prices and foreign trade transactions are still by and large subject to controls. Privatisation had by mid 1994 been negligible. The energy sector is specifically exempted from privatisation targets and schemes.

---

1. This and the following figures are based on the official Rouble rate; use of purchasing power parity rates would have resulted in higher estimates.

GAS PRODUCTION AND EXPORT DEVELOPMENTS

Although oil was discovered in Turkmenistan in 1876, FSU geologists started to look systematically for hydrocarbons there only in the 1950s. Turkmenistan's gas production took off two decades later, growing from about 13 bcm in 1970, to 52 bcm in 1975 and to 70.5 bcm in 1980. It peaked in 1989 at nearly 90 bcm; since then, disputes with foreign customers over prices, non-payment for deliveries and a shortage of funds and equipment have forced Turkmen gas authorities to shut in capacity.

Table 1 Turkmenistan's Natural Gas Balance, 1985-94 (bcm)

	1985	1987	1989	1991	1992	1993	1994
Production	83.2	88.1	89.9	84.3	60.1	65.2	35.6
Exports	68.4	73.2	74.3	70.0	46.9	55.7	26.5
Imports	0.0	0.0	0.0	0.0	0.0	0.0	0.0
Apparent consumption*	14.8	14.9	15.6	14.3	13.2	9.5	9.1

* including pipeline use.
Source: PlanEcon.

The Turkmen economy is very gas intensive. PlanEcon estimates that the gas share of the country's TPES increased from about 40 per cent in 1970 to 66 per cent in 1980 and to around 90 per cent in 1990 before declining to some 75 per cent in 1993.

Nearly all of Turkmenistan's electricity generation capacity is based on gas, and the power sector's share of domestic gas consumption net of pipeline use has recently been over 50 per cent. Some fertilizer and other chemical industry, commerce and households in Askhabad and district heating enterprises account for more or less equal portions of the remaining 40-45 per cent of domestic gas use. The late 1980s and early 1990s have seen declines in the industrial sector's gas use in absolute as well as relative terms.

In recent years, 85 to 90 per cent of Turkmenistan's gas output has been exported, with 80-85 percent of this share going to other FSU republics and the balance going to European countries. In 1992, the Turkmen Government started negotiating its own gas sales with FSU and European buyers, including swapping and transportation contracts with Russia's Gazprom on the basis of the Turkmens' and the Russians' shares of total FSU gas supplies to these markets in 1991. Gazprom absorbs certain amounts of Turkmen gas into its supply system and credits Turkmenistan for similar amounts of Russian gas sold to the other FSU republics and to the West.

Turkmenistan's gas exports plummeted in 1992 mainly because of a fall in shipments to the Ukraine. An agreement to deliver 28 bcm broke down in March as a result of a disagreement on terms. Unlike Russia, Turkmenistan tried to introduce world level prices and convertible currency payments in its gas sales to other FSU republics at one stroke. Shipments were only restarted in October.

Table 2   Turkmenistan's Gas Exports 1992-94 (bcm)

	1992	**1993**	**1994**
Total	**51.8**	**55.6**	**26.5**
FSU	40.6	47.4	26.5
Ukraine	12.5	25.5	12.0
Uzbekistan	1.8	5.9	1.9
Kazakhstan	9.7	6.1	4.7
Georgia	4.9	3.7	2.6
Azerbaijan	3.8	2.3	2.4
Armenia	1.9	0.8	0.9
Kyrgyzstan	1.7	0.0	1.6
Tajikistan	1.4	0.0	0.2
Russia	3.1	3.1	0.3
Non-FSU	11.2	8.2	0.0

* contracted volumes.
Source: PlanEcon.

The Turkmens regained most of their former share of the Ukrainian gas market in 1993, as trading was switched from a monetary base to a clearing (essentially barter) base. This switch which affected 87 per cent of contracted deliveries in 1993, probably implied a considerable fall in effective prices below notional prices. However, it did not prevent the problem of non-payment for deliveries from worsening by the month.

Turkmenistan also ran into difficulties with its exports to Europe. Russia abrogated the inter-governmental agreement providing for Turkmen exports outside of the FSU, arguing that the republic's export quota should reflect the decline in Turkmenistan's gas production.

Turkmenistan's gas output plummeted in 1994 as a result of new payment related cuts in deliveries to Ukraine and Russia's decision not to sell more gas to Europe on the Turkmen's behalf. As for 1995, data for January through March indicate a further drop of 15-20% from the 1994 level.

Meanwhile Turkmenistan is facing increased gas transit fees. In late 1993, Uzbekistan and Kazakhstan started to charge the Turkmens US$ 3 per 1000 cubic metres per 100 kilometres, representing a 15-fold hike over the old rate of 225 R/1000 cm/100 km. When Turkmenistan refused, Uzbekistan cut its neighbour's gas shipments across its territory by 40 per cent. After several rounds of negotiations, the two countries reportedly reached an agreement in late 1994 on a rate of US$ 1.50/1000 cm/100 km.

In November 1994, Turkmenistan's gas exports were reportedly curtailed for some days because of a leak in the Uzbek section of a pipeline moving Turkmen gas to Russia and other FSU republics.

THE ORGANISATION OF THE TURKMEN GAS INDUSTRY

In November 1993 a new long term program for Turkmenistan's oil and gas sector was officially adopted, and at the same time the sector was reorganised. By presidential decree the independent structures or concerns which had emerged in 1992 from the former Soviet organisations were liquidated, i.e., split into smaller entities which report to an Oil and Gas Ministry. The industry now consists of four regionally based gas and oil producing operators, Balkannebitgazsenagat, Akhalneftegazdobycha, Lebapneftegazdobycha and Maryneftegazdobycha, the gas transport company Turkmentransgaz and various units carrying out exploration.

The Government welcomes foreign investment in the gas and oil sector. Three tenders organised so far have attracted some interest. However, the major international oil companies are wary of committing themselves in Turkmenistan. Only in the third round did one major company, Occidental Petroleum Corporporation, bid for, and win, exploration and development rights on a block in West Turkmenistan. Terms have included submitting a work program, paying an US$ 20-40 million signature bonus and setting up a joint venture (percentages have varied) with Balkanneftekhimprom, a state-owned entity responsible for oil production and some exploration in the area where the blocks offered to foreigners are situated. Contracts are for 25 years. Apart from the tenders, Elf Aquitaine has reportedly been granted the right of first refusal for prospecting, exploration and development rights over some 40,000 square kilometres of the Turkmen continental shelf.

TURKMENISTAN'S POTENTIAL AS A GAS PRODUCER AND EXPORTER

Reflecting differences between Western and former Soviet definitions and concepts, and possibly also political considerations, estimates of Turkmenistan's natural gas resources and reserves vary:

■ At the time of the break-up of the FSU, the Moscow-based State Geology Committee operated on the assumption that Turkmenistan's remaining proven gas reserves amounted to 2.7 trillion cubic metres (tcm);

■ The World Bank seems to have adopted this estimate, reporting total indicative resources at 14 (tcm), total identified reserves at 4.0 tcm, remaining identified reserves at 2.7 tcm, and remaining proven and probable reserves which can be produced economically under current market and technical conditions at 1.3 tcm;

■ Turkmen authorities, however, claim that reserves that can be recovered economically amount to at least 21 tcm.

Combining the World Bank's figures on remaining identified reserves with the level of production in 1993 yields a reserves to production ratio of between 20 and 40 years, depending on one's price and cost assumptions, whereas Wavetech's figures indicate that Turkmenistan could go on producing 60-70 bcm/year for more than 300 years.

Most of the country's gas reserves are located in the Amu Darya basin in south-eastern Turkmenistan, and in the South Caspian basin. The former basin extends into Uzbekistan; U.S. Geological Survey estimates that three fourths of its petroleum contents are on the Turkmen side of the border with the balance on the Uzbek side. The latter basin includes Azerbaijan's offshore oil and gas reserves; on the same source's estimates its contents are shared 40-60 between the Turkmens and the Azeris.

There are 25 producing fields, five of which account for over 50 per cent of current production and about half of total remaining reserves (as estimated by the World Bank). The balance of the reserves is distributed among 122 relatively small fields.

From 1986 to 1990, cumulative production exceeded additions to identified reserves by about 0.2 bcm. This reserves replacement ratio reflects an end to the period of easy gas discoveries. The industry is moving into areas with complex geological conditions with neither the experience nor the equipment to operate effectively.

Turkmen authorities are nonetheless very optimistic about their country's potential as a gas producer and exporter. The most recent long term program for the Turkmen oil and gas sector envisages a growth in gas output to 130 bcm by 2000, 200 bcm by 2004 and 230 bcm sometime in the decade 2010-2020. It is assumed that this growth will follow from three phases of expansion: the first covering the period 1993-98, the second extending through 2004 and the third running to 2020. During the first phase, the gas industry is to decide on and start implementing pipeline projects to gain access to Europe, the Mediterranean and the Persian Gulf. During the second phase the focus will be on identifying fields off-shore and developing fields in central and eastern Turkmenistan. The third phase should include opening new fields in central and eastern Turkmenistan and exploring for large gas fields in the western as well as the central and eastern portion of the country.

Given Turkmenistan's small population and limited industrial base, most of the incremental gas production would have to be sold abroad.

Analysts generally consider the government's plan too optimistic. Granting that the resource base may be considerable, they cannot see markets growing at the assumed rates and believe that the Turkmens underestimate the competition they will face in the markets that will develop. Moreover, they cannot envisage sources for the funding of the field and infrastructure development projects in the plan.

GAS EXPORT PIPELINES

Gas produced from fields in the Amu Darya basin is collected and transported in pipelines running northwards to Khiva near the Turkmen-Uzbek border where it joins the pipelines moving Uzbek gas northwest. Southwest of the Aral Sea this aggregate of lines forks into two systems — one running northwards through Kazakhstan to Chelyabinsk in Russia where it links up with the southernmost of the pipeline systems moving gas from Siberia to Europe, the other running northwest via Kazakhstan to Alexandrov Gay in Russia and further on to Moscow.

The annual flow capacity of the pipeline strings moving Turkmen and Uzbek gas northwest to Kungrad near the forking point is reported at 63 bcm.

Gas produced from fields in the South Caspian basin is transported northwards in a pipeline which links up with the western leg of the system described above, i.e., with the pipelines running to Alexandrov Gay, via Beyneu in Kazakhstan. The annual flow capacity of the Turkmen part of this pipeline is reported at 1.6 bcm.

Turkmenistan's gas exports to FSU and European markets travel via Gazprom pipelines moving Russian gas westwards. Turkmenistan is thus totally dependent on Gazprom's and Russia's dispositions for its gas sales to foreign customers. Because of their weak position, the Turkmens were forced to accept a particular, and for Turkmenistan rather unfavourable, key for the calculation of a Turkmen quota of FSU's total gas exports. Since late 1993 Russia has refused to credit Turkmenistan for any exports to the West. Additionally, Turkmenistan depends on Uzbekistan's willingness to transit Turkmen gas to the Uzbek-Kazakh border, and Kazakhstan's willingness to transit the gas further to the Kazakh-Russian border.

The Niyazov Government intends for defensive as well as offensive reasons to construct several new export pipeline systems to Europe, to the Arabian Sea and to the Far East. The European markets are to be accessed via a pipeline running southwards along the eastern shore of the Caspian Sea into Iran and further on to Turkey and Western Europe. A pipeline from Turkmenistan to the Iranian-Turkish border would be 1260 km long, and with a capacity of 28 bcm per year it would cost US\$ 3.5-4 billion.

Preparations have so far included forming an Interstate Council to oversee the project. As Turkmenistan will need access to Gazprom's export pipelines for several years to come even under the best of circumstances, Russia is represented in this Council together with Turkmenistan, Iran, Turkey and Kazakhstan. Efforts to put together a consortium of companies to plan, finance and undertake the project have so far met with limited sucess.

The West and South Asian markets are to be accessed via a pipeline running from the Sovietabad gas field in Turkmenistan via Afghanistan and Pakistan to the Arabian Sea. With a length of about 2000 km, a diameter of 1,420 mm and a capacity of 20 bcm/year, such a pipeline would cost some US\$ 4 billion.

Finally, the Turkmens are promoting the construction of a pipeline to the Far East. The plan involves laying a 1,420 mm, 28 bcm/year pipeline through Kazakhstan and China either to a 10 million tonnes/year liquefaction plant on the shores of the Yellow Sea, or all the way to Japan. In the former case the pipeline would measure about 6,000 km; a subsea extension to Japan would give it a total length of nearly 7,000 km. The Turkmen Government has reportedly managed to interest the Mitsubishi Corporation as well as the China National Petroleum Corporation — which is looking for transport solutions for its own Tarim basin gas fields — in the project. A feasibility study is scheduled for completion by the end of 1994. Construction would take a minimum of five years. Total costs of the project including three LNG ships are preliminarily estimated at US\$ 10-12 billion.

The main problem with all of these projects is that their financing is uncertain and that, at least for the time being, they appear too risky, from a political as well as from a commercial point of view, for most potential investors. Western governments (especially the US Government) do not look favourably upon projects involving Iran or Afghanistan, and the scope of the Far East project is too vast for many lending institutions and companies to consider it seriously.

However, the presence of Turkmen and Iranian gas reserves requires transport solutions, and the last months have seen much political activity on the Turkmenistan-Iran-Turkey pipeline project. Difficult as it may be to distinguish between symbolic gestures and real movement in cases like this, the possibility that the pipeline constraint on Turkmenistan's gas exports to Europe may start to weaken in not too many years, should not be discounted.

CONCLUSIONS

Under most of the competing estimates of Turkmenistan's gas resources and reserves, the country appears to have enough gas to become an important supplier to Europe. In the absence of independent export pipelines, however, the republic's exports will remain a function of the ratio between the West's demand for gas from the FSU and Russia's capacity to deliver. As this capacity looks set to grow in the years to come, Turkmenistan may remain a fringe gas supplier of only indirect and limited interest to the OECD.

On the other hand, Turkmenistan may, together with Iran and Turkey, manage to establish its own export pipelines to the West, implying that from the turn of the century the country's importance as a supplier could start developing towards its reserves based potential.

The danger of intended supply cut-offs, i.e., governmental use of the supply cut-off weapon to achieve some political target, appears small. Turkmenistan's cuts in its gas supplies to Ukraine and the Transcaucasian republics in 1992-94 were provoked by the latter countries' inability to pay economic prices and growing gas related debts. The political situation in Turkmenistan appears comparatively stable, with low levels of ethnic and/or religions tension, and although the Government's authoritarianism and apparent distaste for economic and political reform may undermine stability in the long run, any future leadership would have to take the country's dependence on gas exports for its hard currency revenues into account.

There is, however, a danger of unintended supply cut-offs, i.e., drops in deliveries as a consequence of domestic unrest, transit country action and/or technical breakdowns. The technical state of the Central Asian gas transit pipelines is not fully satisfactory, reflecting low levels of maintenance over a number of years.

UKRAINE

GAS POLICY

The current 56% share of gas in total fuel consumption makes Ukraine one of the most gas-intensive economies in the world. Gas is used for power production, industrial processes and residential heating and cooking. Natural gas demand is not expected to rise until the economy recovers, but the need to maintain a balanced energy mix, especially in power generation, is likely to keep natural gas an important part of the energy economy.

The Ukrainian gas company Ukrgazprom has a monopoly on the purchase, distribution and sale of natural gas in Ukraine. The government's policy is to expand gas sales, especially to the residential sector, and to deregulate prices so that gas distributors will have more incentive to offer service to new customers. A significant current preoccupation is simply finding a way to pay for Russian and Turkmen gas.

GAS MARKET

Partly because household gas prices remain heavily subsidized, the share of natural gas in total fuel consumption has increased from 48.5% in 1990 to 54.4% in 1994. Gas consumption, like all other fuel use in Ukraine since 1990, has declined, from 115 bcm in 1990 to 92.4 bcm in 1994, although not as dramatically as coal and oil. Higher gas use in proportion to other fuels may be better for the environment (reducing the current rate of coal-related emissions) but it has helped worsen Ukraine's imported fuel bill.

The industrial sector now consumes about one-third of total gas used, a substantial decline brought about both by the decline in heavy industry and by households' inability to control their consumption. Gas use in power generation has also declined, forcing the country to rely more heavily on base load nuclear plants. Compared to OECD countries, however, the share of gas use in power generation is still high and the share of gas in the residential sector is low.

GAS SUPPLIES

Ukraine relies heavily on gas imports to meet its domestic energy needs and has accumulated huge arrears to Russia and Turkmenistan. Ukraine's natural gas bill (for 57 bcm of gas from Russia and 12 bcm from Turkmenistan) came to US$3.5 billion in 1994. Russian gas deliveries in

1994 continued at 1993 levels despite Ukraine's inability to pay. However, gas imports from Turkmenistan (about 15% of total imports) have experienced serious interruptions due to non-payment. Imported gas purchases are expected to increase in 1995 to 67.4 bcm.

Table 1   Natural Gas Balance for Ukraine (bcm)

	1990	1991	1992	1993	1994
Imports	-	-	-	79.8	69.1
from Russia	-	-	-	54.3	57.1
from Turkmenistan	-	-	-	25.5	12.0
Imports (including transit)	204.4	203.4	212.0	198.3	203.1
Production	**25.5**	**22.0**	**20.9**	**19.2**	**18.3**
Ukrgasprom	23.6	20.1	19.5	17.7	15.1
Other	1.9	1.9	1.4	1.5	3.2
Storage Out	20.0	21.3	20.6	21.3	19.5
Total Supply	**249.9**	**246.7**	**253.5**	**238.8**	**240.9**
Transit					
CIS	12.9	14.2	30.0	30.0	32.0
non-CIS	104.2	99.7	92.9	95.2	102.0
Total Transit	117.1	113.9	122.9	125.2	134.0
Total Domestic Use	**115.1**	**113.6**	**114.1**	**96.2**	**92.4**
Industrial	55.0	51.5	53.5	39.9	31.0
Power	33.9	30.8	25.4	19.3	19.7
Res/Comm	19.8	24.4	26.5	26.6	30.5
Comp. Fuel	5.4	5.4	6.4	7.4	7.5
Losses/Unaccounted	1.0	1.5	2.3	3.0	3.7
Storage In	**17.7**	**19.2**	**16.5**	**17.4**	**14.4**
Total Demand	**249.9**	**246.7**	**253.5**	**238.8**	**240.8**

* Preliminary data for 1994.
** Storage in and Storage out refer to gas that has been withdrawn or added to underground gas storage facilities.
Source: State Committee for Oil, Gas and Oil Refining Industries, Ukrgazprom.

Natural Gas Debt with Russia. Arrears for gas supplied to Ukraine by Gazprom in 1994 totalled US$1.48 billion. Arrears for first three months of 1995 amounted to around US$450 million. In January 1995, Russia and Ukraine agreed to restructure Ukraine's gas debt arrears and to smooth the delivery of Russian gas to Ukraine in the future. According to an agreement reached between the Russian company Gazprom and Ukrgazprom, 30% of arrears would be paid through the delivery of Ukrainian goods and products, and the remaining 70% would be paid in convertible currency.

As part of the deal, Ukraine will be required to 1) supply housing and social services in Russia; 2) deliver Ukrainian industrial and technical goods to Russian plants; and 3) offer shares in newly-privatized Ukrainian enterprises to RAO Gazprom. Since then, however, Ukraine has insisted on increasing the barter share of the payment, arguing that it cannot pay such sums (about US$1.05 billion) in hard currency and that Russia has underestimated Russian companies' interest in Ukrainian goods.

Natural Gas Debt with Turkmenistan. Ukraine and Turkmenistan have had trouble agreeing to the future delivery of natural gas. A January 1995 agreement holds Ukraine to providing hard currency payment for 40% of the cost of actual delivered volumes of natural gas, with the remaining 60% paid for in goods and commodities. However, deliveries of Turkmen gas have been very small this year and as of June 1995 supplies have completely stopped. Ukraine's debt for Turkmen gas has risen to US$245 million and despite the earlier agreement, the organization of delivery of Ukrainian goods and commodities to pay for these gas imports has been plagued with delay and accusations of corruption.

In an effort to improve the current system of payments, the state-owned joint-stock company "Ukrresursy" is now the sole purchaser of gas imported to Ukraine. Ukraine will need considerable capital inflows, combined with a comprehensive restructuring program, to avoid a further squeeze on fuel imports. Several options have been recommended by the World Bank to handle the payments problem, including the adoption of long-term supply agreements, conversion of accumulated arrears into commercial debt, and debt-equity swaps. Active promotion of exports, a move away from energy-intensive industries, and improved energy efficiency are also part of the solution.

Domestic Production. Domestic natural gas production has declined (peaking in 1975 at 68.7 bcm) mainly due to depletion of existing reserves without any significant new discoveries. Recent seismic surveys performed by Western contractors show gas reserves holding steady at 680 bcm through 2010 at current production rates (about 50 mcm per day), with 436 bcm from onshore wells and 243.9 bcm from Black Sea and Azov Sea offshore wells. By the end of 1994, however, about 75-84% of proven gas reserves had been depleted.

In 1994, total gas production was only 18.3 bcm. In 1995, Ukraine expects to produce 18 bcm of natural gas, 1.6 bcm of which is produced offshore. The drop in natural gas production is linked to poor technology and extraction methods but also to the fact that prospective reserves are smaller in volume and located in geologically-complex areas.

The Crimean Oil Company has been set up for developing oil and gas on the Black Sea Shelf, with a 55% share going to the State Oil Enterprise "Chernomorneftegas" and 45% share held by a British company. The State Committee for Geology issued exploration licenses to carry out work at the "Dolphin" platforms, and drilling is planned to begin in mid-1995. The company is also planning to build a gas processing plant near the Shtormovyi region.

A general cooperation agreement has also been signed with British Gas, which will lead to granting a license to explore prospective areas in the vicinity of the Kerch peninsula. British Gas is prepared to conduct seismic studies and drill wells up to depths of 5000 meters.

INFRASTRUCTURE

Ukrgazprom operates 34,500 km of gas transmission lines, of which about 10,000 km are high-pressure pipelines with diameters of over 1000 mm operating at pressures ranging from 55-75 bar. Ukrgazprom also operates 12 underground storage facilities with an active volume of 35.5 bcm. Ukraine has 66 compressor stations, with 847 compressor units rated at 5600 MW each. Gas turbines with capacities between 2.6-25 MW power roughly two-thirds of the compressors, while electric motors power the remainder.

The high pressure pipelines are in good condition, despite reports to the contrary. Based on a total gas throughput of about 220 bcm in 1994, gas losses were less than 0.5% — as good if not better than gas operations in Europe and North America. On the other hand, many compressor units are approaching or have surpassed their normal operating life and there is a severe shortage of parts and materials to keep equipment running. Safety precautions (e.g., gas detectors, water flooding systems, fire walls) are also nonexistent at older compressor stations.

Ukraine's gas distribution network includes 60,000 km of small diameter pipe operating at maximum pressures of 12 bar. Nearly all of the pipes are cathodically protected and have been installed within the last 30 years. The gas distribution company Ukrgaz distributes gas to 6 million customers, with 70% delivered to urban areas. Residential gas use is not metered, except by bulk measurement, making it impossible to determine gas distribution losses accurately.

Huge volumes of Russian and Turkmen gas, about 120 bcm per year, pass through the Ukraine on their way to markets in Slovakia, the Czech Republic, Hungary, Bulgaria, Romania, Germany, Italy, France, Austria, Switzerland and Turkey. Six major lines with a total length of 8600 km enter Ukraine at Sumy and Novopskov and exit to Slovakia at Uzhgorod.

The issues raised by transit of gas from Russia through Ukraine are discussed in the OME study for the IEA entitled *Future Natural Gas Supply for Europe, the Role of Transit Countries and Security of Supply*. A summary of this study is included as Annex 2 of this book.

NATURAL GAS PRICES

Wholesale prices for natural gas increased considerably by the end of 1994 and have continued upward in 1995, although inflation has whittled down these increases in real terms. A single wholesale price for natural gas amounting to US$80 per tcm has been set since February 1995 for all consumers.

In October 1994, the retail gas price was set at 380,000 KBV (US$2.53 at 150,000 KBV/US$) per tcm, a substantial rise from the earlier rate of 49,000 KBV (US$0.33) per tcm, but still a level which covered only 5% of the actual cost. In February 1995, retail gas prices were increased to 3.6 million KBV (US$24) per tcm, or roughly one third of the cost of gas. In July, gas price rose another 10% for customers who have gas meters and thus can adjust their consumption levels. Gas subsidies for households cost the government about 75 trillion KBV (US$500 million) per year.

COPING WITH DISRUPTIONS

Ukraine's gas import dependence, roughly 80% of the gas it consumes, heightens the importance of negotiating stable, long-term gas import agreements with Russia and Turkmenistan. The pipeline infrastructure to import large volumes of gas from other countries simply does not exist. Even if it were built, no other gas supply source will easily be priced competitively with these two sources. On the other hand, Ukraine is Gazprom's largest foreign customer in terms of volumes of gas sold, and Russia depends on Ukraine as a transit country, so long-term supply arrangements are in both countries' interest.

The issue is thus how to pay for future gas supplies in a way which offers meaningful revenue to Gazprom but does not put the clamps on Ukraine's potential economic recovery or threaten the country's national sovereignty. At least in the short term, Ukraine does not seem able to pay in convertible currency.

Ukraine also must take steps to strengthen communication between Ukrgazprom and European gas buyers and to improve its contingency plans for coping with sudden cutbacks in gas deliveries from Russia. Although there has been no recent incident like that in October 1992, when sharp curtailments did not allow Ukrgazprom sufficient time to draw down from storage and Western European gas companies were forced to impose emergency plans to maintain deliveries to their customers, a better understanding of the measures Ukraine would take to ensure the reliability of the supply network is needed. This would presumably include an idea whether Ukraine will be able to release a portion of its contract gas in order to maintain delivery at Western border stations.

MEXICO

POLITICAL AND ECONOMIC BACKGROUND

Former President Carlos Salinas de Gortari instituted significant market-oriented structural economic reforms during his 1988-1994 Presidency. These included bringing Government expenditures into balance, lowering inflation significantly, reducing the size of the public sector, including many privatisations, opening most of Mexico's economy (but not the energy sector) to foreign trade and investment and encouraging export growth. The single most notable development during his presidency was Mexico's entry into the North American Free Trade Agreement (NAFTA). The new President, Ernesto Zedillo Ponce de Leon, who assumed power in early December 1994 and who played a significant role in the Salinas' reform effort, has indicated he will continue the liberalization process instituted by his predecessor.

Table 1   Basic Economic Indicators, Mexico, 1993

Population (million)	86.2
% Population Growth (from previous year)	1.6
GDP (billion $US 1980)	222.9
Per Capita GDP ($US 1980)	2,587.1
% GDP Growth	1.0
Final Energy Consumption (million BEP)	640.3
Energy Intensity BEP/GDP (thousand US$ 1980)	2.9

Source: OLADE Energy-Economic Information System, December 1994.

Mexican and foreign businessmen responded well to the reform initiatives. Growth averaged nearly three percent during the reform period, compared with almost no growth during 1982-1988. Although growth in 1993 was only 0.6 percent due to stringent fiscal measures, the economy recovered strongly in 1994 until late December when a sudden economic crisis, precipitated by Mexico's very large current account deficit, led to a major devaluation of the Mexican Peso and flight of foreign investor capital. In response, a US $50 billion international rescue package was assembled and the new Mexican Administration instituted very severe domestic austerity measures to counter inflation and restore confidence in the Mexican economy. In the very short term, Mexico faces economic stagnation and much higher inflation.

Political developments in 1994, notably the assassination of several prominent Mexican leaders and the unresolved rebel uprising in the Chiapas, contributed to a general climate of increasing political and economic tension.

ENERGY SECTOR BACKGROUND AND POLICY

Mexico averaged 2.67 million barrels per day (mbd) in oil production in 1993 with exports at 1.36 mbd. While the almost decade long decline in oil Mexico's reserves came to an end in 1992 (proven/probable reserves in 1993 were at 50.8 billion barrels), this level is still significantly lower than the historic high of 57.1 billion barrels in 1984.

Article 27 of Mexico's Constitution provides the legal framework for the Mexican energy sector and essentially reserves oil and gas related activities to the Mexican state. PEMEX, Mexico's national energy company, assumes this monopoly role for the Government. There are five principles which provide the framework for Mexico's nationalistic energy policy. These are:

- Mexico shall retain full sovereignty and direct domain on oil;

- only the Mexican state shall be empowered to market oil, gas, refined products and basic petrochemicals directly;

- PEMEX shall not enter into risk agreements;

- no obligation to guarantee oil supply shall be contracted; and

- there cannot be foreign owned gas stations in Mexico.

PEMEX was created in 1938 by transforming private companies operating in Mexico into a state enterprise. With the discovery of large quantities of petroleum in 1976, PEMEX became an energy exporter and a major player in world energy affairs. It is now one of the world's 10 largest oil corporations. It also ranks ninth in natural gas reserves and sixth in natural gas production. For Mexicans, PEMEX traditionally has been a symbol of pride, nationalism and economic independence. It contributes roughly 30 percent of both foreign exchange earnings and public sector income.

PEMEX has undergone significant reform in recent years, including substantial staff cuts, and in 1993 was restructured into four separate operating units, each of which is autonomous and acts as a separate profit centre. One of these, PEMEX Gas & Basic Petrochemicals, is responsible for the supply and marketing of LPG, natural gas and basic petrochemicals. It owns and operates PEMEX's gas plants, LPG pipelines and distribution terminals, natural gas transmission facilities and basic petrochemicals plants. In early 1995 PEMEX reinitiated an effort to privatise its secondary petrochemical production. Most likely further reform of PEMEX will occur, but the breadth and pace of this change is uncertain.

Under NAFTA, which came into force on January 1, 1994, Mexico granted US and Canadian companies greater access to certain portions of its energy sector. Most notably, NAFTA opens Mexico's petrochemical market, lifting restrictions on 14 of the 19 "basic" petrochemicals, permits investment in electricity co-generation, production for own use and independent power production (IPP) and allows US and Canadian natural gas suppliers to negotiate direct sales of natural gas to industries, utilities and other Mexican customers. However, PEMEX still retains the responsibility for setting gas prices and must approve any contract. NAFTA also pressures PEMEX to pay greater attention to environmental concerns and to providing better gas service to Mexican industry; in particular near the US border.

Since 1985, Mexico has been an importer of gas from the United States with flows reaching a record 250 million cubic feet per day (mcf/d) in 1992. However, reflecting the 1993 economic turndown in Mexico, gas imports fell dramatically in that year to 97 mcf/d, and even lower in early 1994. Most gas imports are to meet demand increases in the northern part of Mexico, particularly the border areas and around the industrialized Monterrey area. Mexican natural gas exports in 1993 amounted to 5 mcf/d.

Mexico still has not developed natural gas regulations similar to those already developed for the electric power sector. They are a requisite if Mexico is to attract investment financing for gas sector expansion. Currently, PEMEX functions as both a supplier and a de facto regulating agency in the gas sector.

GAS RESERVES, PRODUCTION AND CONSUMPTION

Mexico's reserves of natural gas, at 1880 billion cubic metres (bcm), are the ninth largest in the world and second largest in Latin America (after Venezuela). Current reserves amount to more that 50 years at current production levels (see Table 2) and undiscovered potential could amount to over 200 tcf.

Table 2   Reserves/Production, Mexico

Year	Reserves (bcm)	Production (mcm)	Reserves/Production (Year)
1970	340	21824	15.6
1971	326	21025	15.5
1972	326	22055	14.8
1973	326	22606	14.4
1974	425	25123	16.9
1975	340	26810	12.7
1976	340	21854	15.5
1977	850	21149	40.2
1978	906	26175	34.2
1979	1671	30144	55.4
1980	1826	36772	49.7
1981	1935	41973	46.1
1982	2134	43243	49.3
1983	2134	40947	52.1
1984	2181	37605	58.0
1985	2172	35883	60.5
1986	2168	34219	63.3
1987	2147	34954	61.4
1988	2119	34626	61.2
1989	2060	35457	58.1
1990	2025	35254	57.4
1991	2010	34726	57.9
1992	1972	34204	57.7
1993	1880	35818	55.0

Source: OLADE Energy-Economic Information System (SIEE) - December 1994.

Mexico is Latin America's largest producer and marketer of gas. The major associated gas reserves and gas production areas are Chiapas-Tabasco and the offshore Campeche Sound (see map). In 1993 the former produced 53 percent of total output and the latter 35 percent. The remainder was produced from the Burgos Basin in the north. Currently around 85 percent of natural gas produced is associated gas. The only significant non-associated gas deposits are located in northern Mexico.

Table 3   Gas Profile, Mexico, 1993 (bcm)

Production	35.8
Imports	0
Exports	0
Unused	1.2
Total Supply	**34.7**
Power Plants	0
Self Producers	0
Gas Treatment Plant	31.8
Own Consumption	0.8
Losses	0
Total Transformation	**32.5**
Industry	2.0
Residential/Commercial Sector, Service, Public	0.15
Non-Energy Consumption	0
Total Consumption	**2.1**

Source: OLADE Energy-Economic Information System, December 1994.

Natural gas production increased in parallel with the large increases in Mexican oil production in the early 1980s. Production peaked in 1982 and since then has declined by around 15 percent. However, the domestic demand for natural gas over this same period has increased around nine percent annually. Beginning in 1988 demand began on a sporadic basis to exceed supply and imports of natural gas began to grow rapidly.

Currently natural gas provides for 20 percent of Mexico's primary energy requirements. There is a relatively high degree of concentration in terms of Mexican gas consumption. There are four principal consumers: PEMEX, the Federal Power Commission (CFE), and the industrial and household sectors. Table 4 provides a breakdown in consumption by these four sectors for the period 1980-1992. PEMEX and the Mexican industrial sector consistently have been by far the largest consumers of natural gas. However, the future consumption profile is likely to change somewhat with power generation and the industrial sector expected to be the high growth areas.

Rapid economic growth in the medium and long term are expected to substantially increase electric power and industrial sector demand for natural gas. Furthermore, in late 1992 Mexican electricity legislation was amended to allow private sector generation and sale of electricity. Plans are to increase electric power gas generation 5 to 6 per cent annually between 1994 and 2005. There are estimates that, along the US-Mexican border, 10,000 MW of new electric generation capacity will be needed by the year 2,000 to supply industrial zones and maquilladora facilities.

Table 4   Natural Gas Consumption by Sectors (mcf/d)

	1980	1981	1982	1983	1984	1985	1986	1987	1988	1989	1990	1991	1992
Pemex	801	899	1 034	1 108	1 054	1 096	1 046	1 093	1 132	1 137	1 099	1 106	1 041
CFE	316	290	315	263	211	227	284	302	289	288	366	431	442
Industrial	927	987	982	955	923	912	804	786	772	774	774	821	932
Household	58	59	73	78	82	85	85	89	90	92	90	98	101

Source: Pemex, Gas y Petroquimica Basica
Note: 1 bcm = 0.0353147 tcf.

Mexican authorities anticipate that much of this new demand will be satisfied by private capital investment in IPP. This should result in the construction of new gas-fired electric generating plants. Forecasts indicate that virtually all new thermal power plants will be natural gas fired combined cycle because of the high efficiency of combined cycle technology and increasingly demanding environmental considerations. Environmental concerns are also likely to lead to conversion of some of the current oil-fired plants to natural gas.

As regards industrial sector demand for natural gas, the Salinas Administration announced plans to practically reverse the current industrial fuel consumption profile, in which 55 percent of industrial energy needs are satisfied through fuel oil and 32 percent by gas, to one where in 2005 fuel oil only accounts for 35 percent of consumption and natural gas 53 percent. This policy shift implies an additional supply of some 1,760 mcf/d of natural gas.

Mexico's overall demand for natural gas, spurred by Mexican attempts to reduce pollution by substituting gas for oil and coal, as well as rising electricity demand, is predicted to soar to 213 bcf/y by 1997, even without new co-generation projects coming on stream, and some reports foresee gas demand doubling between 1994 and 2005. There are reports that if "dry" gas reserves in northern Mexico are not developed, Pemex would have to boost oil exploration by 55 percent to produce the amount of associated gas required, a clearly unrealistic scenario. Since it is unlikely that financially-strapped PEMEX will be able to satisfy rising gas demand in the short or medium term, imports from the US and Canada are expected to take up the slack.

However, estimates of a major shift from fuel oil to gas for power generation assume that recent Government policy pronouncements regarding the restructuring of the sector are implemented. Given Mexico's current economic and political difficulties, this cannot be considered certain.

A variable affecting the development of Mexican gas production is the level of investment in the refining system to upgrade fuel oil to produce alternative products. PEMEX must either have a ready market for its high sulphur fuel oil or invest heavily in coking and desulphurization capacity to produce lighter products which could be sold abroad. It is quite possible that if refinery upgrading efforts, intended to provide an alternative use for fuel oil, do not expand sufficiently, the continued large-scale production of fuel oil will prove to be a barrier to natural gas assuming its potential major role in the Mexican power generation sector. A PEMEX/Shell joint venture project, involving Shell's Deer Park refinery in Texas, whereby heavy Maya crude is used as feedstock to produce light products, offers a possible approach to resolve this issue. However, many more such collaborative ventures would be required. Also, PEMEX's continued complete control of the gas pipeline system could slow gas' penetration into the power generation sector.

INFRASTRUCTURE

Mexico's current gas infrastructure primarily serves Mexico City and Monterrey. Infrastructure is inadequate in most other parts of the country. The basic infrastructure problem constraining gas development is a insufficiently extensive pipeline network. Most of the gas production takes place in the southeast of the country, while consumption, other than for direct PEMEX use, takes place in the rapidly growing north. There is only one trunk line to carry gas from south to north (see map). Consequently, to meet incremental demand it has often been cheaper for PEMEX to import natural gas for the border region than to add pipeline capacity from the Gulf of Campeche. Mexico-US cross-border transmission capacity totalled 959 mcf/d at the end of 1992, but imports peaked that same year at only 300-350 mcf/d. There are currently eleven gas processing plants in Mexico.

Mexican Government officials have indicated that Mexico will need at least US $2 billion in pipeline grid investment by the end of the century to meet projected industrial demand. Other reports state that a US $5 billion expansion is being considered which would consist of US $2 billion to expand Mexico's northern grid, US $2 billion to develop sizeable offshore reserves in the Mazatlan basin and connect them to the market and US $1 billion to fully interconnect Mexico's grid with the US grid at the border.

GAS PRICES

Consistent with Mexico's market-oriented liberalization, by early 1994 PEMEX had eliminated energy subsidies, the last one being on LPG, Mexican homes' main fuel. Nevertheless, final prices of energy products continue to be determined in most cases by Mexican authorities. Two pricing systems prevail. One sets administered prices for LPG, mogas and diesel fuel. The other is a market related mechanism for sales of all other oil and petrochemical products, including natural gas.

OUTLOOK FOR MEXICAN NATURAL GAS EXPORTS

In theory Mexico, with its large proven and potential reserves and proximity to the US, could become a major exporter of gas within a decade. However, this appears increasingly unlikely, given Mexico's severe adjustment process and the economic downturn in response to the December currency crisis, unless these recent developments generate rapid, major Mexican Government policy changes in the energy sector.

The consensus seems to be that any additions to gas production in the current major producing areas, located in southeastern Mexico, will have to be aimed at reducing pollution in the Mexico City area. However, northern Mexico, by far the fastest growing area economically, also needs gas to sustain its economic growth and to meet increasingly stringent environmental requirements. Consequently (assuming no change in Article 27) Mexico will either: a) have to increase its imports from the US and Canada in the medium and long term; b) fund exploration and development efforts in northern Mexico or c) further develop its infrastructure, connecting the north with the south.

It seems likely Mexico will opt for option (a) and be a net importer of natural gas from the US until early into the 21st century. However, given its current financial difficulties, imports may be at a lower level than earlier anticipated. Some analysts had expected that Mexico would treble its 1992 (250 mcf/d) import volume by the year 2000. As of mid 1994, PEMEX's strategy regarding natural gas was to import relatively large quantities up to the year 2000, while simultaneously developing its own internal reserves, so as to be able to eventually satisfy most of its domestic demand internally and perhaps export some gas to the US, should the US "gas bubble" disappear.

However, PEMEX's traditional focus has been on oil exploration and it is unlikely to devote increasingly scarce funding to non-associated gas development in northern Mexico. To bring its gas reserves fully on line Mexico will need a great deal of money and many years. Some analysts expect that Mexico will become a net exporter to the US around 2010. While Mexico's objective of having more than 50% of Mexico's total energy consumption satisfied by natural gas by 2005 may be overly ambitious, Mexico's natural gas demand is expected to soar.

The financial situation of Mexico's dominant energy companies, CFE (Comision Federal de Electricidad) and PEMEX, and the degree of private sector participation which will be permitted in the energy sector are major variables. PEMEX faced serious financial constraints due to rising demand for investment in the upstream and downstream sectors even before the current economic crisis. Without additional resources, which most likely would have to come from the private sector, it will be difficult for Mexico to upgrade the refining system, further develop its oil and gas reserves and improve the gas infrastructure simultaneously. An obvious solution would be to open up the upstream oil sector significantly which could lead to substantially increased oil production and presumably associated gas production. But this may not be politically achievable, at least in the short term.

Nevertheless, Mexico's continued economic growth in the medium and long term and expanding international economic linkages, particularly to the US and Canada, will promote change in the Mexican energy sector. While Mexico's prospects for exporting gas would appear to be marginal at best until early in the next millennium, by 2010 Mexico could be a consistent net exporter of gas to the US. However, it is likely that even then, given the rapidly increasing Mexican domestic demand for natural gas, the quantities involved will be small, relative to the size of the US market.

TRINIDAD AND TOBAGO

POLITICAL AND ECONOMIC BACKGROUND

Trinidad and Tobago's economy has traditionally been heavily based on exploitation and exportation of energy resources. After a sustained period of petroleum based-growth during the 1970s, the economy began a prolonged slump in 1983 during which GDP actually declined up to 1990. In recent years the Government has adopted a strategy of structural adjustment. This has entailed a shift toward a much more market-oriented economic approach with increased emphasis on fiscal and monetary discipline, private sector involvement and export-led growth. Investment in the energy sector, the largest and most dynamic sector of the economy is encouraged. The country's economic direction now seems to have been reversed, with most non-oil sectors of the economy showing growth. Recently, a tight monetary policy and a depressed oil sector, in part due to low oil prices, have been the major overall growth constraints. Despite its economic problems since the early 1980's, Trinidad and Tobago in 1993 still had the second highest per capita GDP in Latin America and the Caribbean (US $3,780).

Table 1   Basic Economic Indicators, Trinidad and Tobago, 1993

Population (million)	1.3
% Population Growth (from previous year)	0.6
GDP (billion $US 1980)	4.7
Per Capita GDP ($US 1980)	3,780.4
% GDP Growth	-1.0
Final Energy Consumption (million BEP)	20.7
Energy Intensity BEP/GDP (thousand US$ 1980)	4.4

Source: OLADE Energy-Economic Information System, December 1994.

Since independence, except for the period 1986 through 1991, the country has been governed by the Peoples National Movement (PNM). During the 1986-91 period the National Alliance for Reconstruction (NAR), a coalition of traditional opposition parties, governed the country. The current Prime Minister is Mr. Patrick Manning, with the United National Congress party leading the opposition. Parliamentary elections will next occur in 1996. Trinidad & Tobago has traditionally had a strong trade union movement.

ENERGY SECTOR BACKGROUND AND POLICY

Trinidad and Tobago is one of the oldest gas and oil producing countries in the world, with petroleum exploration, production and refinery activities dating back to 1908. Commercial gas production began in 1974. Current petroleum reserves are just under 500 million barrels and are not expected to increase. Oil production, traditionally the mainstay of the country's economy, has been declining since 1978. Recognizing and responding to this decline, the Government has invested in and promoted a number of gas-based activities designed to utilize gas reserves discovered during the aggressive oil exploration period of the late 1960's and 1970's. These include ammonia production plants (TRINGEN and TERTRIN), a methanol company (TTMC) and iron carbide plants. As part of this effort, the country's first gas-based industrial estate at Point Lisas on the East-Central Coast of Trinidad was established. State-owned companies, TRINTOC and TRINTOPEC, were merged into a new oil firm, PETROTRIN in early 1994. The new entity is expected to boost efficiency, open up new oil fields for drilling and facilitate privatization of some parts of the company. Currently the petroleum industry comprises 26 percent of the domestic economy.

In 1992 the Government identified the natural gas sector as the engine of growth in the economy and as a key component in its strategy to reverse economic decline. It also specified the state-owned National Gas Company (NGC) as the prime mover in gas based development. NGC was established in 1975 to purchase, sell and distribute natural gas in Trinidad & Tobago. It is the owner of the gas transmission system and the designated transporter of natural gas. While a proposed LNG project (see discussion below) makes an exception to this rule, and NGC's role as sole purchaser and distributor of natural gas may change, the Government has indicated that NGC will continue to play a significant role in the energy sector. One indication of this has been that NGC has been assigned the task of developing the nation's second gas-based industrial estate at La Brea. The proposed LNG facility would likely be located at La Brea, as well as contemplated ammonia and methanol plants. Formal authorization of the US$1.1-1.7 billion, 425 mcf/d LNG project, expected in mid 1995, would signal that natural gas has supplanted petroleum as Trinidad and Tobago's key generator of economic activity.

Plans are now well underway to sell 49 percent of the power generation facilities of the state-owned Trinidad and Tobago Electricity Commission (T&TEC) to foreign investors. T&TEC is the only authorized entity in the country for the generation, transmission, distribution and sales of electricity. However, a number of industry entities also generate energy for their own needs with T&TEC providing additional energy requirements. T&TEC uses gas to generate almost all of its electric power.

PROPOSED LNG PROJECT

An LNG project was first considered almost 25 years ago. Now NGC, together with AMOCO, British Gas and Cabot LNG Corporation, have developed a LNG project which would export gas to the U.S. market (probably New England) and possibly European markets. It would likely be constructed on the Brighton/La Brea industrial estate in Southwestern Trinidad Island. This effort would be the country's largest ever project. Tentatively British Gas and AMOCO would each have 37.5 percent shares in the project, with NGC holding a ten percent share and a Cabot Corporation subsidiary 15 per cent.

An overall design contract, covering the LNG plant and marine terminal, was signed in late 1994, as was a contract for the detailed design of the liquefaction process for the LNG facility. Accords have also been reached concerning on-shore geo-technical site investigations, marine soil testing and initial site preparation. Final project authorization and awarding of the main engineering, procurement and construction projects are expected in the third quarter of 1995. First deliveries of gas to the U.S. market are planned for October 1998.

Project prospects have received an additional boost from AMOCO's two additional discoveries in its South East Galeota and East Mayoro fields in mid 1994. The first of these finds, off the southeastern coast of Trinidad, exceeds one trillion cubic feet and reportedly brings AMOCO's proven reserves to, at a minimum, somewhere between 2.5 tcf and 3 tcf. The other gas supplier to this project is British Gas which, in a joint venture with Texaco in 1993, signed a TT$ 1.7 billion 20-year gas production/sharing contract with the Government to develop the Dolphin gas field. This field, located some 50 miles offshore Trinidad's East coast, reportedly contains gas reserves estimated at 2 tcf. The Dolphin Field is expected to come on stream in 1995 or 1996 and while gas volumes ranging from 150 to 275 mcf/d are committed to NGC, surpluses will be available to the LNG project. In addition, British Gas/Texaco will be drilling exploratory wells in the Marlin Field which adjoins the Dolphin field with the aim of proving up additional reserves for the LNG project.

While the broad ownership structure of the project is agreed to in principle, final ownership arrangements and revenue split between the several component parts of the project - gas supply, gas transmission, liquefaction, LNG transport and re-gasification and distribution in the U.S. and possibly in other markets - are still under negotiation.

Reportedly around 50 percent of the LNG produced will be marketed in the US New England market using Cabot's US Everett terminal. Nevertheless, other markets must be secured for the project to be viable. Other potential markets reportedly include France, Germany and Spain. In August, 1995 a contract with Spain was reported imminent. Several Caribbean markets, including Puerto Rico and Jamaica, also have been identified, but the project's feasibility really rests on New England and European gas markets since these markets are larger and have the expensive re-gasification facilities already in place. Used LNG tankers would be employed to ship the gas to export markets. Both Cabot and British Gas own LNG carriers.

The Brighton/La Brea site has a good natural harbour, some 15 miles wide with water depths around 42 feet. Given the sheltered nature of the site, no expensive breakwaters would be required and the terminal can be constructed around an extended pier. Natural gas would be brought to the estate by a 30" pipeline extending some 57 miles from the East Coast offshore gas fields. The project involves the construction of the world's first LNG plant with a single liquefaction process train capable of producing approximately 430 million cubic-feet per day (mcf/d) (2.7 million tons of LNG per annum). Originally, planned capacity was 300 mcf/d but the additional 1994 AMOCO discoveries now permit the higher figure. If necessary, a second train could subsequently be added, should additional gains in reserves justify it.

Cost estimate ranges for the project are as follows:

LNG liquefaction plant:	US $600 million to $1 billion
Upstream costs:	US $300 to 500 million
Pipeline costs:	US $100 million
Downstream/Terminal Costs:	US $100 million
Total:	US $1.1 billion to 1.7 billion

Estimated component costs of the T&T project per (Mbtu), assuming shipment to the U.S. New England market, are as follows:

Well head cost:	US $1.00
Liquefaction:	US $1.30
Shipping:	US $1.00
Re-gasification:	US $0.20
Total:	US $3.50

Assuming the above estimates are correct, the landed cost for shipment to the European market would probably be around U.S. $4.00 per (Mbtu).

The project has the Government's complete support. The Government's interest in concluding negotiations and initiating the project as soon as possible is understandable given upcoming 1996 national elections.

Pricing is an important unresolved issue. Low world gas prices and, in particular, a US gas price of less than $2.00 per million btu, are a disincentive to rapid movement on the project, although its capital costs are considerably lower than most other LNG projects under consideration. Nevertheless, a final commitment to proceed is expected by late 1995 with project completion expected in late 1998.

GAS PRODUCTION, CONSUMPTION AND RESERVES

Growth in natural gas production and utilization in Trinidad and Tobago has accelerated markedly since the mid-1970s. Gas generates a significant portion of electric power and is a feedstock for the country's petrochemical industries. Gas currently comprises 75 per cent of primary energy consumption, the highest percentage in Latin America.

Virtually all of Trinidad and Tobago's gas reserves are non-associated. Two-thirds of the reserves are located off the south East Coast of the island of Trinidad with the remainder in the less developed North Coast Marine Area. The East Coast fields were largely discovered during the 1960s and 1970s. The deeper North Coast fields were discovered in the mid 1970s and 1980s. These gas fields are located at depths ranging from 180 to 550 feet and at distances of 25 to 50 miles offshore. If recent LNG reserves identified by AMOCO are included, Trinidad and Tobago's total proven reserves amount to 10.4 tcf. The LNG project is expected to consume some 3 tcf, assuming a standard 20-year contract. Hence, even given other anticipated demand amounting to some 4 tcf over the next 20 years, and excluding the likely possibility of further significant discoveries, Trinidad and Tobago appears to have ample reserves to satisfy anticipated demand well into the 21st century.

With the inclusion of possible and probable gas reserves, the current reserves to production ratio of forty years could be increased to over 75 years. The fact that there are currently several suppliers and several fields from which natural gas can be drawn, enhances the security and reliability of gas supplies.

Table 2   Reserves/Production, Trinidad & Tobago

Year	Reserves (bcm)	Production (mcm)	Reserves/Production (Year)
1970	142	2761	51.3
1971	142	2504	56.6
1972	165	2380	69.2
1973	167	2736	61.1
1974	170	2926	58.1
1975	113	2884	39.3
1976	197	3146	62.7
1977	241	3412	70.5
1978	227	3602	62.9
1979	227	3871	58.5
1980	335	4511	74.3
1981	330	4463	73.9
1982	324	4652	69.7
1983	319	5032	63.3
1984	312	5757	54.2
1985	305	5970	51.1
1986	297	6106	48.7
1987	289	6192	46.7
1988	282	7438	37.9
1989	269	7233	37.1
1990	261	6651	39.2
1991	247	7405	33.3
1992	239	7462	32.1
1993	221	6513	33.9

Source: OLADE - Energy Economic Information System (SIEE) - December 1994.

Natural gas production has traditionally come largely from the East Coast Teak and Cassia fields. In 1988 Trintomar's Pelican field was developed. However, production in this field peaked at 130 mcf/d in 1991 and since then has declined precipitously. In 1993 production commenced in three new East Coast fields, the Flamboyant, the Kiskadee and the Immortelle and production from the East Coast Dolphin field is expected to commence in 1996.

Due in part to anticipated modest economic growth and greater efficiencies in converting natural gas to electricity, domestic use of gas for power generation is expected to grow by only 1 to 2 per cent per annum up to the year 2000. However, heavy industry's natural gas demand is expected to increase somewhat, given newly-initiated iron carbide production and an on-going refinery upgrading. An 8 to 10 per cent annual expansion in natural gas usage is anticipated for the petrochemical sector, given increased methanol production, possible increased ammonia production and a general development strategy focusing on downstream petrochemical expansion.

Table 3   Gas Profile, Trinidad and Tobago, 1993 (mcm)

Production	6,513
Imports	0
Exports	0
Unused	1,330
Total Supply	**5,183**
Power Plants	1,352
Self Producers	64
Gas Treatment Plant	0
Own Consumption	452
Losses	17
Total Transformation	**1,885**
Industry	2,220
Residential/Commercial Sector, Service, Public	0
Non-Energy Consumption	1,078
Total Consumption	**3,298**

Source: OLADE Energy-Economic Information System, December 1994.

INFRASTRUCTURE

Trinidad and Tobago's main gas transmission network currently consists of two major sub-sea and sub-terrain pipelines of 24" and 30" diameter. The pipeline system has a throughput capacity of 800 mcf/d and transports gas at an inlet pressure of 900 psi from East Coast fields to the natural gas liquid recovery plants in Point Lisas and then on to domestic customers.

GAS PRICES

To encourage the domestic market the NGC since 1988 has moved away from a fixed price regime and introduced the concept of product related gas pricing to major petrochemical companies that utilize natural gas as a feedstock. Over the medium term it is the Government's stated intent to have gas prices move in line with well head prices.

VENEZUELA

POLITICAL AND ECONOMIC BACKGROUND

In 1993 Venezuela had the third highest per capita income in Latin America (US$ 3604.3). However, following three years of substantial economic growth, the economy went into recession in 1993, declining by one per cent. GDP reportedly fell by 3.3 per cent in 1994 and marginal economic growth, at best, is expected for 1995. Nevertheless, the Government expects the oil sector to grow five per cent in 1995.

The country's most important economic activity by far is petroleum production. The petroleum sector accounts for around 25 per cent of GDP. Petroleum exports have traditionally accounted for a very substantial portion of export revenues, some 75 per cent in 1993. Likewise, Petroleos de Venezuela S.A. (PDVSA), the state-owned oil company which enjoys a monopoly status in the hydrocarbons sector, generates some 60 per cent or more of the Government's tax revenue. For a number of years the Government has attached considerable importance to reducing Venezuela's dependence on the petroleum sector, but these efforts have enjoyed only mixed success. It is likely that Venezuela's heavy fiscal and foreign exchange dependence on oil exports will continue for the foreseeable future. Given this high dependence, the sustained drop in world oil prices since the Gulf conflict has had a significant adverse impact on the economy.

Table 1   Basic Economic Indicators, Venezuela, 1993

Population (million)	20.8
% Population Growth (from previous year)	2.4
GDP (billion $US 1980)	74.9
Per Capita GDP ($US 1980)	3,604.3
% GDP Growth	- 1.0
Final Energy Consumption (million BEP)	244.7
Energy Intensity - 1993 BEP/GDP (thousand $US 1980)	3.3

Source: OLADE Energy-Economic Information System, December 1994.

Under former President Carlos Andres Perez, Venezuela undertook significant economic reform measures, including efforts to encourage to a limited degree foreign investment in energy-related joint ventures. His administration also embarked on an ambitious privatization plan, which included electricity generation and distribution facilities, much of which now has stalled. A total restructuring of the national electrical system was also contemplated. In June 1994 the Caldera Administration, which assumed power in February 1994, reacting in particular to a early 1994 banking crisis and its spillover effects on other parts of the economy, imposed foreign exchange and price controls and suspended a number of constitutional guarantees. For the short term, at least, the previous Administration's trend toward economic liberalisation has been reversed.

ENERGY SECTOR BACKGROUND AND POLICY

Venezuela has enormous petroleum resources with proven oil reserves of 63.3 billion barrels, the sixth largest in the world and the largest outside the Middle East. Venezuela also has the largest reserves of extra-heavy crude in the world (267 billion potentially recoverable barrels in the Orinoco heavy oil belt). Oil production peaked at 3.7 million barrels per day (mbd) in 1970 and gradually declined until 1985. This trend has been reversed and production in 1993 averaged just under 2.4 mbd. Venezuela is currently the world's seventh largest oil producer and Latin America's second largest. It is also Latin America's largest oil exporter.

Venezuela also has enormous proven gas reserves of 3,636 billion cubic meters. Annual production is 42,365 million cubic meters. Venezuela's proven gas reserves and domestic production of gas have increased steadily over the years (see Table 2). Corpoven is Venezuela's principal gas producer, as well as its main gas transmission and distribution company. In 1992 it supplied 77 per cent of the domestic market for gas. It is the Venezuelan Government's long-standing policy to use natural gas to back out residential and diesel oil consumption in electric power generation and industry, so as to have more oil available for export within Venezuela's OPEC production quota. Venezuela also hopes to export substantial quantities of gas.

PROPOSED LNG PROJECT

In January, 1994 Lagoven signed with Shell, EXXON and Mitsubishi an "Association Agreement" to pursue the US$5.6 billion Cristobal Colon LNG project. This undertaking, the largest single project in Venezuela's history, has been under consideration for some 15 years. It aims to produce gas from offshore gas fields, bring it onshore to a liquefaction plant and then ship all production to markets in the US, and possibly Western Europe.

The gas fields were discovered by Lagoven in 1978 during the course of offshore oil exploration. Potential customers in Italy, Spain, France, the United Kingdom, Germany and the US reportedly have been approached. Presumably, the joint venture partners' own marketing systems would also be brought into play. Between 4 and 8 offshore platforms would be constructed in the 4 non-associated gas fields selected - Mejillones, Patao, Dragon and Rio Caribe, all located off Venezuela's North East Paria Peninsula. The two-train liquefaction plant would be built near Mapire on the southern shore of the Paria Peninsula and would process 5.9 million tonnes per year of LNG for the 960 million cubic feet per day plant. A 45-kilometre pipeline would transport the extracted gas to the liquefaction plant. A second, 32-kilometre pipeline would be built to bring condensate from the Rio Caribe field to the liquefaction facility. Up to 6 tankers would be purchased for shipping the LNG. Project investment reportedly would be broken down as follows:

Production costs:	US $1.4 billion
Construction of liquefaction plant:	US $2.1 billion
Purchase of transportation vessels:	US $1.5 billion.

Table 2   Reserves/Production, Venezuela

Year	Reserves (bcm)	Production (mcm)	Reserves/Production (Year)
1970	928	28316	32.8
1971	1088	26593	40.9
1972	1099	25506	43.1
1973	1972	27643	71.3
1974	1170	23340	50.1
1975	1173	17040	68.8
1976	1179	16635	70.9
1977	1185	17656	67.1
1978	1193	17021	70.1
1979	1247	18625	67.0
1980	1262	18915	66.7
1981	1365	18562	73.5
1982	1471	19402	75.8
1983	1562	18901	82.6
1984	1666	20515	81.2
1985	1734	20568	84.3
1986	2622	24235	108.2
1987	2839	24870	114.1
1988	2856	25518	111.9
1989	2993	24493	122.2
1990	3428	28521	120.2
1991	3536	31518	112.2
1992	3636	32432	112.1
1993	3630	42365	85.8

Source: OLADE - Energy-Economic Information System (SIEE) - December 1994.

Revenues have been estimated at US $84 billion over the 30 year life of the project, with the Venezuelan Government expected to receive some US $13 billion in taxes and royalties. Income would commence in 2000.

Lagoven estimates the project will have an investment return range of between 15 and 23 per cent, if gas prices rise to somewhere between US $3.20 and 4.20 per million Mbtu in the United States and to US $3.60 in Europe by the year 2010. The first LNG could be delivered in 1999. Under the January 1994 "Association Agreement", some US $200 million will be spent by the consortium over a two year period in firming up gas reserves, defining the exploration plan and on selection of key long-term customers, engineering contractors, sea transport options, etc., after which final investment decisions will be taken. A final decision on whether to proceed with the project is supposed to be made by the end of 1996. However, the project does have a history of delays.

Venezuela's proximity to its most important potential natural gas market, the United States, and its location within easy shipping distance of other important potential markets, make the project attractive. The primary market would appear to be the US East Coast, given that the shipping distance is short, in some cases less than for US produced gas. Also, well depth in the Venezuelan fields will be less than for some US produced gas, further enhancing competitiveness. Given its traditionally higher natural gas prices, the European market also appears attractive, despite higher shipment costs.

While PDVSA and the executive branch of the Venezuelan Government have strongly supported the project for a number of years and it has received a Congressional go-ahead, some Venezuelans, including some Congressmen, continue to have concerns about the project. These concerns focus on: a) the project's economic viability given current low natural gas prices, particularly in the US market, and b) whether the joint venture is legally permitted under the Venezuelan Constitution, since Lagoven only holds a 33 per cent share, not a majority equity stake, in the venture. For their part, PDVSA and Government officials state the Agreement's provisions still give Lagoven control of the joint venture, but that "the concept of control is more a type of administrative control than of proportional share participation".

Projected natural gas prices in the United States and Europe will play a crucial role in determining whether this project ultimately is given the go-ahead. At the current US gas price of under US $2.00 per Mbtu, the project does not seem likely to generate a sufficiently high rate of return to justify moving ahead. At least one report indicates the project would not be viable under US $2.60 per Mbtu. There also appears to be some concern that even should the current supply bubble in the US gas market disappear, the subsequent price rise may not be sustained for very long, given that a higher price will encourage greater US production.

NATURAL GAS RESERVES, PRODUCTION AND CONSUMPTION

Venezuela has the world's seventh largest proven natural gas deposits (3,636 billion cubic meters) and the largest in Latin America. It is likely that this figure will increase as hydrocarbon exploration efforts continue. Over 90 per cent of the proven reserves are associated gas. In addition, Venezuela has made large non-associated gas discoveries onshore in the Venezuelan states of Guarico and Anzoategui, as well as in the area off the Paria Peninsula.

Natural gas production, which increased quite rapidly in the late 1980s, amounted to 42.36 bcm in 1993. Over the next several years output of associated natural gas is expected to increase substantially, particularly in eastern Venezuela with increased crude oil production. Given this likely increase and Venezuela's long-standing policy of maximizing gas utilization, PDVSA is looking to increase Venezuela's already relatively heavy domestic consumption of gas. Venezuela currently ranks second in the use of gas in Latin America (after Mexico).

Efforts are under way to use more gas in PDVSA operations (e.g., gas injection and cryogenic conversion into NGL), as well as to expand consumption in electricity generation, the steel industry and petrochemicals production and manufacturing. Greater consumption of gas in western Venezuela is also being considered. Table 4 provides a natural gas availability and utilization breakdown for 1992.

Table 3　　　　　Gas Profile, Venezuela, 1993 (mcm)

Production	42,365
Imports	0
Exports	0
Unused	4,932
TOTAL SUPPLY	**37,433**
Power Plants	6,317
Self Producers	1,473
Gas Treatment Plant	5,199
Own Consumption	6,074
Losses	5,330
TOTAL TRANSFORMATION	**24,393**
Industry	11,869
Residential/Commercial Sector, Service, Public	1,171
Non-Energy Consumption	0
TOTAL CONSUMPTION	**13,040**

Source: OLADE Energy-Economic Information System, December 1994.

Table 4　　　　　Availability and Use of Natural Gas by Company, 1992
(Millions of Cubic Feet/Day)

	CORPOVEN	LAGOVEN	MARAVEN	TOTAL
Availability[1]				
Associated	1,888	1,480	719	4,087
Non-Associated	0	0	11	11
Injected	667	522	123	1,312
Net available	1,221	958	607	2,786
Use				
Oil industry fuel	140	312	166	618
Sales	819	443	153	1,415
Flared/vented	60	101	176	337
Donations[2]	0	0	53	53
Shrinkage	202	102	59	363
Total Use	1,211	958	607	2,786
Artificial lift[3]	370	1,390	819	2,579

(1) Availability is equal to production, plus/minus intercompany transfers. The actual volumes are quite similar.
(2) Gas donated to municipalities.
(3) This volume is recirculated in artificial lift operations and is not counted in total use/supply.
Source: Venezuelan Ministry of Energy and Mines.

INFRASTRUCTURE

Consistent with maximizing the use of natural gas domestically, significant investments have been made in recent years in Venezuelan gas infrastructure, including new pipelines and connections for serving power plants.

GAS PRICES

As with gasoline prices, natural gas prices in Venezuela are heavily subsidized. As of late 1994, government regulated city-gate prices were around US $0.23 per Mbtu, less than half the production cost.

BRUNEI-DARUSSALAM[1]

BACKGROUND

Brunei has a long history of involvement in the petroleum sector. Exploration for petroleum began in the early 1900s and continued intermittently up to 1929 when the first onshore oil field was found. Production from this field had risen to 17 thousand barrels per day (kbd) by the start of the second world war in 1940. Production resumed in 1945 and production rose to 115 kbd by 1956, the year in which offshore drilling on the continental shelf first began. The hydrocarbons sector is very important to Brunei with some 60 per cent of Brunei s GDP coming from exports of oil and gas.

In 1963 the South West Ampa field was found to have large reserves of oil and gas. Additional reserves of gas have been found since then. At the time of South West Ampa's discovery only small deliveries of LNG had been attempted and pipelines were still regarded as the main means of getting gas to market. However, the development of new technology helped to change this view and the completion in 1972 of, what was at the time, the world's largest LNG plant at Lumut in Brunei provided a model for similar projects throughout the world.

Table 1   Overview of Brunei's Gas Sector

	1990	1991	1992
Total Primary Gas Supply (bcm)	**2.26**	**2.39**	**1.64**
Share of total primary energy supply (%)	(86)	(84)	(79)
Power sector	.51	.52	.56
Industry[1]	.76	.63	.63
Households	.03	.03	.04
Commercial[2]	-	-	-
Indigenous production (bcm)	**8.43**	**8.64**	**8.77**
Imports	-	-	-
Exports	6.17	6.25	7.13
Transit	-	-	-
Storage capacity (cubic metres LNG)	**120,000**	**120,000**	**120,000**
Storage capacity as % of exports	1.6	1.6	1.4

Notes: 1. For own use.
2. There are at present no commercial users of natural gas in Brunei. The remainder of production is accounted for by distribution losses.
Source: IEA and ASEAN statistics.

---

1.   Hereafter referred to as Brunei.

The gas sector in Brunei has since its inception been dominated by the production and export of LNG. The trade in LNG has in turn been dominated by the long term supply contract signed between Brunei and Japan. However, in the last few years Brunei has sold a number of spot cargoes of LNG and signed a short term contract with Korea for the supply of smaller quantities of LNG.

ORGANISATIONAL STRUCTURES

The Brunei Oil and Gas Authority (BOGA) was established in January 1993 to provide advise and make recommendations to the Sultan of Brunei on all policies (and their implementation) relating to oil and gas. The Authority is responsible for planning and controlling every phase of hydrocarbon activity, including exploration, development, processing, transportation and conservation. The Chairman of the Authority is the Minister for Finance. Figure 1 shows how the public energy sector in Brunei is organised.

Figure 1   Structure of the Public Energy Sector in Brunei

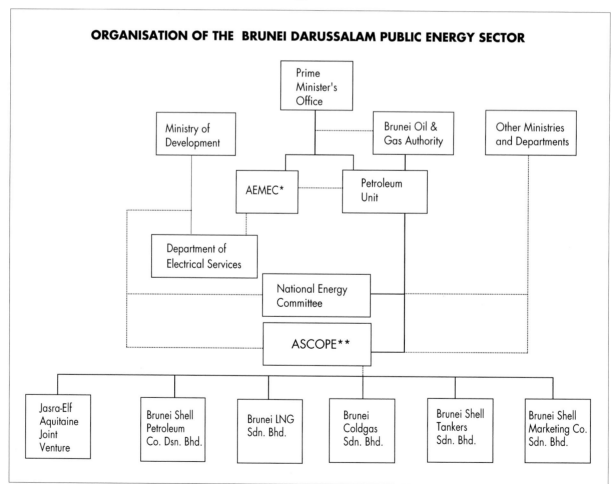

* AEMEC - ASEAN Economic Ministers on Energy Cooperation
** ASCOPE - ASEAN Council on Petroleum
Source: ASEAN - EC Energy Management, Training and Research Centre

The Director of the Petroleum Unit within the Office of the Prime Minister is the Secretary to the Authority and acts as its Chief Executive Officer and spokesman. The Petroleum Unit provides the Secretariat for BOGA.

There are at present four major companies involved in the gas sector in Brunei:

- Brunei Shell Petroleum (BSP) which explores for and produces oil and natural gas. It also owns the Brunei Refinery. The government of Brunei and Shell are equal shareholders in this company;

- Brunei LNG (BLNG), liquefies natural gas, which it buys for BSP, for sale to Brunei Coldgas. The government has a fifty per cent share holding in BLNG. The other Shareholders are Shell and Mitsubishi (with 25 per cent each);

- Brunei Shell Tankers (BST) owns seven LNG tankers which are chartered to Brunei Coldgas. The government and Shell are equal shareholders; and

- Brunei Coldgas (BC) buys LNG from BLNG and arranges its transport and sale to customers in Japan and elsewhere. The share holding is the same as for BLNG.

In addition to these companies, there is Brunei Shell Marketing (BSM), which is in charge of marketing of natural gas, petroleum products and chemicals in Brunei. The share holding of this company is similar to that of BSP.

GAS POLICY

Brunei's energy policy objectives are stated as being:

- economic optimization and reduced dependence on oil and gas reserves;
- energy diversification; and
- energy conservation.

Policy measures that Brunei has introduced in order to achieve these objectives include:

- expanding the use of alternative energy sources such as mini-hydro and solar energy;
- encouraging private sector participation in energy development in the form of build-operate-own (BOO) projects;
- considering only the most efficient types of power plants, such as combined cycle;
- revising energy prices to increase awareness of true energy costs and discourage energy wastage; and
- promoting energy efficiency in building design and materials choice.

In addition, as part of the Brunei government's economic diversification policy, the government has allocated 0.5 Tcf of its gas reserves for use in the industry sector. Internal studies by Brunei have shown this to be a less economic (on a micro scale) use of gas compared to processing it into LNG for export. However, the government believes that the multiplier effect of such an allocation will have significant benefits for the economy (on the macro level).

Exploitation of Natural Resources

In 1963 the government introduced the Petroleum Mining Act to cover all petroleum exploration and development activities. Under this Act exploration and development took place under concessionary agreements. In 1992 the Act was amended and its Schedules repealed. The reason for this change was the desire of the government to introduce other (non-concessionary) forms of agreements for future petroleum exploration and production.

Currently the government may invite persons to bid for a petroleum mining agreement and any bids must conform to such terms and conditions that the government imposes in its invitation to bid. The objective of this approach is to ensure that Brunei derives maximum benefit from any petroleum exploration by foreign companies and to increase competition between prospective concession holders.

The government did not pursue the approach adopted in many other Asian countries of setting up a state-controlled petroleum company principally because of a lack of human resources in the country to staff such an organisation.

Gas Pricing and Taxes

One of the Brunei government's key policies has been to improve the living standards of its people. Several of the subsidy schemes for important commodities and utilities put in place in the 60's and 70's are still in place today. The government has however stated that it wishes to revise energy prices to increase awareness of true energy costs and discourage energy wastage. It also recognises that low end-user prices are hampering upstream development.

Prices for all energy commodities are regulated by the government. The Ministry of Finance and the Petroleum Unit within the Office of the Prime Minister are responsible for price regulation. Residential gas customers are charged US$1.12 per thousand cubic feet (mcf) whereas the power sector pays US$0.28 per mcf[2]. There is no tax on natural gas sales.

Brunei levies both tax and royalty on the production of oil and gas. The rate of tax is currently 55 per cent. Royalty rates vary between 12.5 per cent onshore to 10 per cent close to the shore and 8 per cent in remote offshore areas. There are no limits on the recovery of costs. The government's share of oil production is between 85 and 75 per cent, depending upon the location of the field, with more remote locations attracting the concessional rate.

Gas Trade

Brunei was the first country in Asia to export gas as LNG. Gas is a significant export earner for Brunei. In 1989 it provided nearly 44 per cent of Brunei's total export earnings. In 1992 exports of LNG provided export revenue of around US$910 million, this grew to US$960 million in 1993. In the absence of any significant price rises or expansions of export capacity LNG export earnings should remain relatively constant, but nonetheless an important foreign exchange earner for the country. To the extent that Brunei's small surplus of LNG production capacity enables it to sell additional cargoes of LNG into the Asian market, LNG's share of total export earnings might increase.

---

2. This reduced cost of gas for power generation is reflected in the relatively low cost of electricity to customers (3.5 cents/kWh).

Foreign Participation and Private Investment

There is a considerable level of foreign participation in the gas sector in Brunei. All exploration, development and production of natural gas includes participation by foreign firms. The LNG export project also includes foreign participation.

GAS DEMAND

Domestic demand for gas in Brunei is dominated by the power sector which in 1992 took 94 per cent of all the gas consumed in the country. The remaining 6 per cent was used in the residential sector where it has been used since 1986, principally for cooking. In the eastern part of the country gas is distributed by bottle; in the western part there is a well developed gas distribution system. The distribution system is owned and operated by Brunei Shell Marketing.

The use of gas for power generation grew at around 6 per cent a year during the period 1990 to 1992. Brunei has a 100 per cent electrification rate. The demand for electricity is principally from the residential sector (62 per cent). Commercial users take another 15 per cent and the bulk of the remainder is used in the LNG plant and for marine construction. Electricity demand is forecast[3] to grow at between 7 and 10 per cent a year through to 2010 which suggests that gas demand for power generation could grow from 0.56 Mtoe in 1992 to as much as 3.1 Mtoe by 2010. This assumes that the efficiency of electricity generation and distribution and transmission losses remain unchanged over the forecast period.

Direct use of natural gas fell from 40 ktoe in 1989 to 28 ktoe in 1990. This drop was attributed to gas losing market share to the electricity sector. Direct gas demand was forecast to grow at the more modest rate of 2.5 per cent to the year 2010 which would have given a demand in 2010 of 70 ktoe. However gas demand since the drop in 1990 has grown at an average annual rate of over 13 per cent in the two years to 1992. Forecast demand growth in this sector has been revised upwards to 10 per cent a year.

One possible reason for this growth is the use of natural gas for air conditioning. Another is the competitiveness of using gas versus electricity. Most homes have a gas burner unit as well an electric stove and it is relatively simple to switch to using gas if the price relativities make it an economic option. There have also been reports of electricity failures which, if true, could encourage greater use of natural gas. If the higher growth rate is maintained over the forecast period then demand from the residential sector would increase to around .2 Mtoe by 2010.

GAS SUPPLY

As of 1 January 1994, Brunei's gas reserves totalled some 400 bcm[4]. This corresponds to about 0.3 per cent of the world's known gas reserves and nearly 6 per cent of South Asian reserves. All of Brunei's gas producing fields are located offshore. Ultimate reserves have been estimated[5] to be 640 bcm.

---

3. *"Natural Gas Utilisation in Brunei Darussalam"*, Hj Hamdillah Hj Abdul Wahab et. al, Gas Industry Summit, Jakarta, 5-6 June 1995.
4. *"Natural Gas in the World - 1994 Survey"*, Centre International d'Information sur le Gaz Naturel et tous Hydrocarbures Gazeux (CEDIGAZ), June 1994.
5. *"World Petroleum Assessment and Analysis"* by Charles D. Masters, Emil D. Attanasi, David H. Root, U.S. Geological Survey, National Center, Reston, Virginia, U.S.A.

Brunei's initial contract for the export of LNG was with Japan for 5.14 million tonnes (or 152 cargoes) a year. The contract was signed in 1972 and ran for twenty years. It was renewed in 1993 for a further term of twenty years. The confirmation of additional reserves of gas enabled the parties to increase contract volumes by some 8 per cent to 5.54 million tonnes (or 165 cargoes) a year. The contract includes an option to provide an additional 5 cargoes (or 0.17 million tonnes) a year. Figure 2 shows existing LNG exports and current LNG production capacity.

Following the recent overhaul of the LNG plant, its actual capacity is now closer to 7.2 million tonnes a year. If the additional deliveries to Japan are taken up then Brunei will have a surplus LNG supply capacity of nearly 1.5 million tonnes a year. It is expected that Brunei will seek to deliver additional cargoes of LNG into the Asian market. The operators of the plant have carried out studies of how this might best be done. By utilising existing facilities exports could be increased to 6.7 million tonnes a year. If the liquefaction trains were to be used to their full capacity additional debottlenecking work would need to be done. It would also be necessary to prove up additional gas reserves before long term contracts could be entered into.

In 1993 Brunei delivered a spot cargo (about 30,000 tonnes of LNG) to South Korea and additional sales of some 0.7 million tonnes are expected to be made in 1995 and 1996. Some reports suggest that these sales could translate into a long term contract for sales of up to 1 million tons a year to South Korea. If this did occur then this would fully utilise Brunei's LNG production capacity without additional debottlenecking and additional reserves being proven.

The rate of depletion of gas reserves will be strongly dependant on the level of LNG exports. Exports of LNG from Brunei could be about 6.3 million tonnes of LNG a year (including additional cargoes to Japan and possible sales to South Korea), or about 8.5 bcm a year. Taking into account own use and losses would require Brunei to produce some 9.3 bcm a year to meet its LNG supply arrangements. If we also include the approximately 0.7 bcm needed to meet existing domestic requirements then existing proven reserves should last for 40 years. Additional LNG sales will reduce this period. As domestic requirements increase this will also deplete reserves more rapidly. However even the relatively high forecast of domestic demand growth mentioned above would only add just over 1 bcm to annual gas production rates by 2010.

Shell believes there are adequate gas reserves in Brunei to justify an expansion of the existing LNG plant, however, the government is reluctant to approve additional facilities for LNG production and export, preferring to preserve those resources for future use.

INFRASTRUCTURE

Gas reserves are located offshore and natural gas is piped ashore through two main underwater gas trunklines to the LNG plant at Lumut. Gas is transported from the landfall to the only major domestic user of natural gas, namely the electricity generation sector. The pipeline is jointly owned by Brunei Shell Petroleum and Brunei Liquefied Natural Gas.

There are five gas fuelled power plants operated by the Department of Electrical Services (DES) in Brunei. These provided 98 per cent of Brunei's electricity requirements (the remaining 2 per cent is provided by diesel powered plant). In 1995 the total capacity of Brunei's gas fired plants

Figure 2   Brunei LNG Production Capacity and Contracted Sales

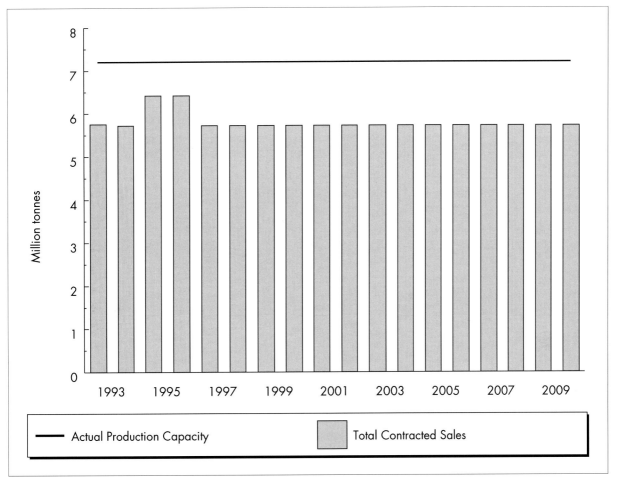

was about 470 MW. In addition there is a private power plant with a capacity of 180 MW. In the same year peak electricity load was 250 MW (not including private generation) which suggests a reserve margin[6] of some 47 per cent. DES is building a new power station, Gadong II, with a capacity of 133 MW. It is expected to be completed in 1995.

The Lumut LNG plant has 5 trains with a nameplate capacity of 5.3 million tonnes a year. A recent overhaul of the plant has increased its thermal efficiency and off take flexibility and actual capacity is now closer to 7.2 million tonnes a year. There are no new gas projects planned between now and 2010. The Lumut plant has three LNG storage tanks with a total capacity of 120,000 cubic metres[7].

LNG is transported in a fleet of 7 tankers each with a capacity of 75,000 cubic metres. It is possible that one or more of these tankers might be replaced after 1998. The jetty at Lumut was upgraded in 1992 and is now capable of taking larger tankers with a capacity of up to 130,000 cubic metres.

---

6. Here calculated as the spare generating capacity divided by the total generating capacity, expressed as a percentage.
7. *World LNG Trade,* Cedigaz, November 1991.

SECURITY OF SUPPLY

Very little information on gas security arrangements in Brunei is available. Domestic demand for gas is not great in terms of the absolute quantities used, however, it is nonetheless an important energy source in terms of the dominance that natural gas enjoys as a fuel for power generation.

Existing LNG storage capacity is sufficient to fill at least two of the existing 75,000 cubic metre tankers which are used to transport Brunei's LNG to Japan. These facilities could also, in theory, supply sufficient gas to keep Brunei's power stations running for about two months (if exports were suspended).

Approximately 12 per cent of Brunei's gas fired generating capacity is capable of fuel switching (the alternative fuel is distillate).

INDONESIA

BACKGROUND

As in many other countries, natural gas was first found in Indonesia by companies looking for oil. Initially gas was either flared or reinjected to help maintain oil reservoir pressure. In 1958 large nonassociated gas fields were discovered in South Sumatra. This discovery signalled the first significant use of gas domestically in Indonesia in the early 1960s, when fertilizer plants were built to use it as a feedstock.

Table 1   Overview of Indonesia's Gas Sector

	1990	1991	1992
Total primary gas supply (Mtoe)	**14.04**	**16.84**	**17.86**
Share of primary energy supply (%)			
Sectoral Shares (Mtoe) [1]	**(26.8)**	**(29)**	**(28.8)**
Power sector	.27	.28	.24
Industry [2]	4.09	4.34	4.58
Households [3]	.13	.20	.23
Commercial	.13	.20	.23
Indigenous production (Mtoe)	**38.19**	**43.18**	**45.49**
Imports	-	-	-
Exports	24.15	26.34	27.63
Transit	-	-	-
LNG storage (thousand cubic meters) [4]	**1,142**	**1,142**	**1,142**
Maximum daily sendout from storage	n.a.	n.a.	n.a.
Storage capacity as % of exports	2	2	2
Normal Production Capacity (gas) [5]	**250**	**750**	**750**

Notes: 1. The difference between total sectoral consumption and total primary gas supply is accounted for by oil refineries, own use, unspecified other uses and losses.

2. Does not include gas used in refineries, which in 1992 accounted for approximately .76 Mtoe.

3. Figures for gas consumption in the commercial and residential sectors are based on published data for manufactured city gas, less a 10 per cent loss. Consumption has been assumed to be evenly split between these two sectors.

4. This refers to the total gas storage capacity at the existing two LNG plants.

5. This refers to gas produced and consumed in Indonesia. In millions of cubic feet per day, net of any flaring or reinjection.

Source: IEA and ASEAN statistics.

A second phase in Indonesia's gas history began in 1977 when the first exports of LNG began. These have since increased to the point where Indonesia is now the world's largest exporter of LNG. A third phase in the development of Indonesia's gas industry is now under way. During this phase the Indonesian government plans to continue to expand its exports of LNG to the extent that sufficient gas reserves can be proven, as well as increase the domestic use of gas, particularly in the power sector.

ORGANISATIONAL STRUCTURE

Figure 1 shows the organisation of the Indonesian public energy sector. The government has the responsibility for policy decisions concerning oil and gas production, investment and domestic prices. The Ministry of Mines and Energy is responsible for energy matters. In that Ministry, the Director General of Oil and Gas (MIGAS) exercises control over the petroleum industry. The National Energy Coordinating Board (BAKOREN) was given the responsibility for formulating national energy policies for the development and utilisation of energy resources and to coordinate the implementation of these policies.

Figure 1   Organisation of the Indonesian Public Energy Sector

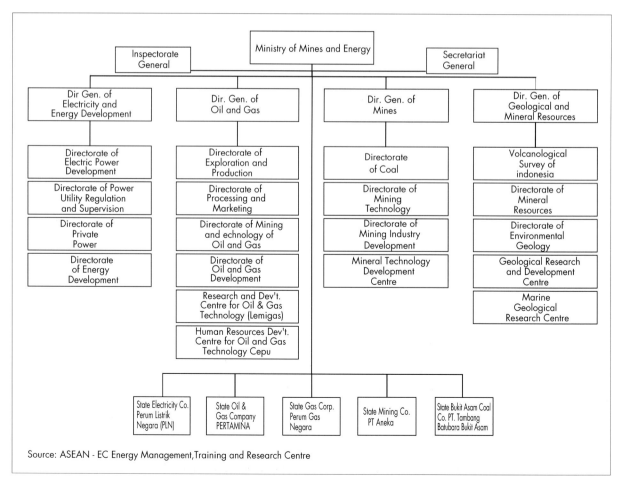

Source: ASEAN - EC Energy Management, Training and Research Centre

The state oil and gas company, Pertamina, was created in 1968 by the merger of two existing state-owned oil companies. It is charged with carrying out the functions of exploration, exploitation, processing, transportation and marketing of oil and gas. In doing so it is authorised to conclude cooperation agreements with other parties if this is considered necessary. Pertamina receives guidance from a Board of Commissioners which includes among its Members the Minister for Mines and Energy, the Head of the National Planning Agency, the State Secretary, the Minister for Research and Technology and the Minister for Finance.

The country's retailer of natural gas is Perum Gas Negara (PGN). Its role was expanded in 1992 by a Minister of Mines and Energy Decree which allows it to not only act as a gas distributor but also as a gas transmission company. It is planned that PGN will become a limited liability company in 1995, which will allow the company to have access to finance from commercial markets. Such access is needed to ensure that PGN is able to finance the significant expansion of the natural gas transmission network that is planned.

Distribution of natural gas to domestic customers is the responsability of five state-owned distribution companies which serve the metropolitain areas of Jakarta, Bogor, Medan, Surabaya and Cirebon. Each company has a monopoly over distribution in its region. At the beginning of 1995 these companies had a combined distribution network of nearly 1,500 km and a total of over 23,000 customers. Gas sales for petrochemical use are made directly to the customer by Pertamina.

The Minister of Mines and Energy has ruled out the privatisation of both Pertamina and PGN on the grounds that they are "social service companies". Nonetheless, given the scale and cost of the planned gas infrastructure construction, it is likely that private sector involvement in the gas sector will continue to expand. Pertamina has already acknowledged that it does not have the funds to pay for its 50 per cent share of the giant Natuna gas project and it is likely to farm out the majority of its stake. Private sector involvement in gas transmission projects is also well established and is likely to continue.

GAS POLICY

The Indonesian government has a policy of encouraging the domestic use of natural gas. In doing so it is able to meet a number of its energy policy objectives. These include:

■ diversifying domestic energy sources away from oil, thus making more oil available for export and bringing in valuable foreign exchange earnings;

■ expanding the country's infrastructure to support the government's industrialisation programs; and

■ protecting the environment and reducing greenhouse gas emissions.

The government is also seeking to extend existing LNG export contracts and enter into new contracts where the level of uncommitted gas reserves permits this.

Exploitation of Natural Resources

The ownership and the exclusive rights to explore for and produce all of the country's onshore and offshore hydrocarbon resources is vested in the State controlled oil and gas company, Pertamina. In order for foreign companies to gain access to Indonesian fields they enter into a Production Sharing Contract (PSC) with Pertamina. These contracts vary from company to company, but there are a number of common features, including:

■ Pertamina manages the operations of the contractor;

■ the contractor pays a bonus on signing the PSC, there is also a discovery and production bonus (these bonuses are not cost recoverable);

■ contractors provide the financial and technical capability to conduct petroleum operations and bear the exploration risks;

■ operating costs are recovered after commercial production begins;

■ contracts generally allow 6 to 10 years for exploration and 30 years total term if commercial production is established;

■ the contractor pays Indonesian income taxes (currently the rate is 48 per cent);

■ there is a domestic market obligation (DMO) under which the contractor supplies a portion of Indonesia's domestic crude oil requirements; and

■ costs are ring fenced, in other words, costs incurred in one contract area are not chargeable to the operations of a block under another contract.

Probably one of the more important terms of a PSC is the profit sharing split, namely the government's and the contractor's respective shares from lifted oil or gas. In most contracts the split is 70/30 for gas, however, the government has been seeking to stimulate oil and gas exploration and development and has introduced four separate incentive packages since 1988. The most recent of these introduced a production sharing split of 60/40 for gas[1]. This incentive package also increased the amount payable for the DMO from 15 per cent to 25 per cent of the export price after an initial five year period.

Gas Pricing and Taxes

Gas pricing has been identified by the government as a crucial issue to be resolved if the government's gas policy objectives are to be achieved. There is currently an internal debate within the government about price subsidies to consumers such as the fertilizer industry. This includes the size of any subsidy and its point of application.

The government participates in the process of determining the price of gas for domestic use. The main reasons for this are the interpretation of the constitutional responsibility of the government as the custodian of the national patrimony, coupled with the dominant role played by state enterprises in the energy sector.

---

1. The equity split for gas from a field developed in water deeper than 1500 metres is an even more favourable 55/45.

In the case of gas prices to fertilizer plants and steel works, Pertamina asks the Ministry of Mines and Energy for a price increase, they then consult with the Ministry of Finance which takes into account the potential inflationary impact of any price increase. In setting prices the government's objective is to ensure the availability of energy sources at a level and cost that efficiently promote economic growth and equity for all Indonesians.

In setting gas prices the government also considers the price of competing fuels, for domestic customers kerosene and for industry fuel oil. Pricing structures also reflect a policy of subsidising the fertiliser², paper and steel industries. To encourage the use of gas, natural gas prices in the transportation sector are set at half the price of petrol.

In the case of gas sales to large private sector users prices are determined by negotiation between the supplier and buyer. In such cases prices are based on the economics of individual projects. Similarly, private sector pipeline operators are allowed to set their transmission charges by negotiation with users. There are no rates of return specified by the government.

Prices to sectors where the government plays a role in the price setting vary considerably from one industry to another. In general, prices are lower than those prevailing on the international LNG market. For example, in 1991, fertilizer plants were able to purchase gas for both fuel and feedstock for between US$1 and US$1.50 per Mbtu, the Krakatau steel plant paid US$2 per Mbtu for gas for use as fuel (but only US$.65 per Mbtu for gas used as feedstock), the Kraft process paper mill at Aceh paid US$1.50 per Mbtu, whereas the state electricity company bought its gas for between US$2.45 and US$3 per Mbtu.

Gas sales to residential customers are at a single tariff across each distribution region, and each distribution region has a separate tariff. Commercial and small industrial users pay a range of tariffs depending upon their consumption, again these tariffs vary between regions. City gas prices vary between US$1.30 and US$1.70 per Mbtu. There are no taxes on domestic gas sales.

Gas Trade

Indonesia is the world's largest exporter of LNG. Gas is a significant export revenue earner for the country. In 1993 gas exports earned US$3.94 billion (average price of US$3.13 per Mbtu), slightly below the 1992 earnings of US$4.1 billion (average price of US$3.37 per Mbtu). Gas' share of total export earnings in 1992 was about 12 per cent, declining to 10.7 per cent in 1993.

This decline in the relative importance of gas (and oil) export revenues is due both to falling prices for LNG and the growth of other exports, such as manufactured goods. Nonetheless, gas' share of total petroleum export earnings is likely to increase in importance as LNG production capacity increases, particularly if Indonesia's oil production rate remains constant, or even declines, at the same time as an increasing amount of Indonesia's oil production is needed to meet domestic requirements.

---

2. The policy of subsidising the fertiliser industry is linked to the governments desire to ensure sufficient supplies of fertilisers to the nations rice growers to, in turn, ensure self sufficiency in rice production.

At present Indonesia does not export any gas by pipeline. However in the longer term such exports might be possible. For example, exports of pipeline gas to Singapore might be a logical extension of the proposed pipeline to Batam Island. Informal discussions have already taken place about the possibility of such sales as have similar discussions with Malaysia about possible sales of gas to penninsular Malaysia.

Foreign Ownership and Investment

There is a considerable level of foreign participation in the upstream gas sector in Indonesia. While Pertamina does carry out some exploration and development on its own, most exploration, development and production of natural gas includes participation by foreign firms under the terms of PSCs they have signed with Pertamina. Existing LNG export projects also include foreign participation. The Natuna project, if it proceeds, is also likely to have a high level of foreign participation (perhaps as high as 90 per cent).

There are already a number of existing private sector pipelines in Indonesia. For example, the pipelines supplying gas from offshore gas reserves to users in Jakarta and Gresik are both run by a consortium of private companies. The costs of transmission are charged to the users. In the case of the pipeline to Gresik, there is a throughput charge of US$0.90 per Mbtu. It has been estimated that the transmission charge for the Asamera to Duri pipeline might be around US$0.60 per Mbtu.

In the case of the domestic gas sector, the government is relying on both Indonesian private sector and foreign funding to finance the infrastructure needed to increase the domestic use of natural gas.

GAS DEMAND

With ample gas reserves and potentially high demand, the main restraining factor on domestic demand has been the lack of a gas transmission network in Indonesia and the large investment required to build such a network. Figure 2 shows the current and forecast consumption of gas in Indonesia by sector.

According to *Natural Gas in the World, 1995 Survey* (Cedigaz), total consumption of gas in 1994 was 28.26 bcm (22.25 Mtoe). If one excludes own use[3], then domestic direct consumption of gas is currently dominated by industry, and this sector is in turn dominated by the fertilizer industry. Fertilizer plants used some 97 per cent of the gas consumed in the industry sector in 1992. The bulk of the remainder was used for cement manufacture. Industry's gas consumption is forecast to increase by around 10 per cent to the turn of the century. This growth rate is asumed to continue to 2010.

City gas consumption grew rapidly between 1988 and 1992, increasing from 171 ktoe to 508 ktoe over the period, for an average annual growth of nearly 32 per cent. However, this growth slowed to only 4 per cent between 1992 and 1993. In January 1992 the state gas company,

---

3.   This is gas used for reinjection, gas lift, or as a fuel in the gas industry.

Figure 2   Forecast Sectoral Gas Consumption

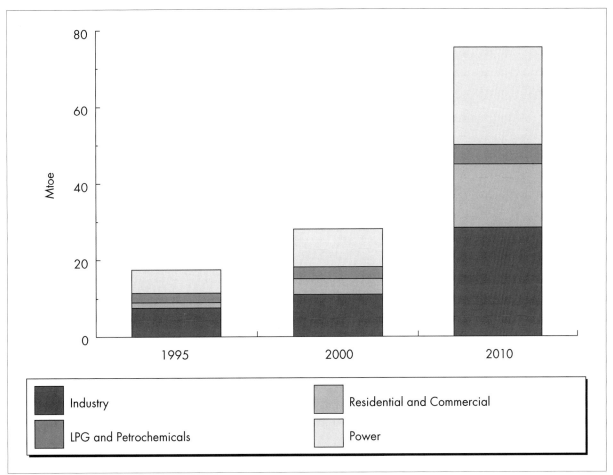

Perum Gas Negara (PGN), received authority to sell wholesale gas and to develop a series of major gas pipeline projects. In the light of this, and the emphasis placed by the government on expanding the use of natural gas throughout Indonesia, demand growth rates for gas in the residential and commercial sectors are likely to be relatively high. Indeed, PGN forecasts that combined natural gas consumption in these sectors will grow at around 30 per cent a year up to 2000. It is likely that the bulk of this consumption will be in the commercial sector since residential demand is primarily for cooking (rather than a higher demand requirement, such as for heating). The growth rate from 2000 to 2010 is assumed to be a more modest 15 per cent.

Gas consumption in the electricity generation sector started to increase modestly in 1987, yet consumption remained relatively constant at between 200 and 275 ktoe up to 1992. In 1991 nearly 12 per cent of the national power utility's, Perusahaan Umum Listrik Negara (PNL), installed capacity was gas fuelled. Most of this capacity was used to meet peak demand requirements and consequently gas fired plant only provided 7 per cent of the electricity generated by PNL.

In 1993 consumption in this sector more than tripled to almost 850 ktoe following the start up, in January 1993, of a combined cycle gas fired PNL plant at Gresik. The government wants to increase its reliance on gas for electricity generation (second only to coal). In 1994 two multi-unit gas fired plants in Jakarta were opened, Muara Karang and Tanjung Priok (520 MW). Also a 400 MW unit of a gas fired combined cycle plant Belawan in north Sumatra was commissioned in 1994 and a second 430 unit is due on-stream in 1995. Other combined cycle plants currently being built are the 1095 MW Muara Tawar plant near Jakarta, the 521 MW Tambak Lorok plant at Semarang in Central Java, the 800 MW Grati plant to be built near Surabaya, and the 855 MW Pusuruan plant in East Java. In addition, there are four Build-Own-Operate (BOO) gas fired plants which are currently being considered. These would have a total capacity of 1,165 MW.

If all the gas fired plants envisaged in the Sixth Five-Year Economic Plan are completed then Indonesia's gas fired generation capacity will increase from 2,112 MW in 1994 to about 7,500 MW in 1999. This will increase the share of capacity that is gas fuelled from below 6 per cent in 1993 to over 22 per cent. PGN forecasts that natural gas consumption in this sector will grow at around 14 per cent a year up to 2000. It is assumed that the growth rate to 2010 will be 10 per cent. This is in line with the expected growth in total generating capacity. In other words, it is assumed that gas will largely maintain its share of the fuel mix used for electricity generation.

The LPG production and the petrochemical sectors are other users of natural gas. Here consumption is forecast to grow at about 5 per cent a year up to 2000 and is assumed to maintain this growth rate to 2010.

Small quantities of natural gas are used as CNG by the taxi fleet in Jakarta, where some 1000 vehicles have been converted to run on natural gas. By the end of 1995 the government plans to have increased the number of CNG filling stations from the existing 6 in Jakarta in 1993 to a total of 53. The majority will be in Jakarta, but stations will also be constructed in 5 regional cities. Absolute consumption of natural gas in the transportation sector is likely to remain relatively insignificant over the forecast period. Indeed, PGN forecasts that natural gas consumption in the transport sector will remain constant to 2000. This view is shared by Pertamina.

GAS SUPPLY

According to the state oil company of Indonesia, Pertamina, as of 1 January, 1994, Indonesia's estimated gas resources are about 6000 bcm[4], of which 3200 bcm are proven and probable[5]. This corresponds to about 2.2 percent of the world's known gas reserves. Pertamina estimated that 43 per cent of its gas resources are onshore and 57 per cent offshore. Included in the offshore reserves is the big Natuna field situated in the Natuna sea 225 km northeast of Natuna Island. This field alone is estimated to hold more than 1000 bcm of recoverable natural gas.

According to *Natural Gas in the World, 1995 Survey* (Cedigaz), Indonesia's gross production of natural gas in 1994 was just over 82 bcm. Of this some 12 bcm was used for gas injection and

---

4. The publication *"World Petroleum Assessment and Analysis"* by Charles D. Masters, Emil D. Attanasi, David H. Root, U.S. Geological Survey, National Center, Reston, Virginia, U.S.A, estimates that ultimate recoverable reserves are 5346 bcm.

5. *1994 Petroleum Report*, US Embassy, Jakarta, 1994.

gas lift and could be available for subsequent production. At a net annual production rate of some 63 bcm, existing proven and probable reserves of gas are sufficient to last for around 50 years. If ultimate reserves are taken into account then production could continue at the current rate for 95 years.

Some 60 per cent of Indonesia's natural gas production is exported as LNG. Figure 3 shows existing contracts for LNG exports and current and planned LNG production capacity[6]. In 1994 Indonesia exported just over 25 million tons of LNG. This was some 3 million tons of LNG above the nameplate capacity for the plants at Arun and Badak, but close to the estimated actual production capacity.

Figure 3   LNG Capacity and Exports

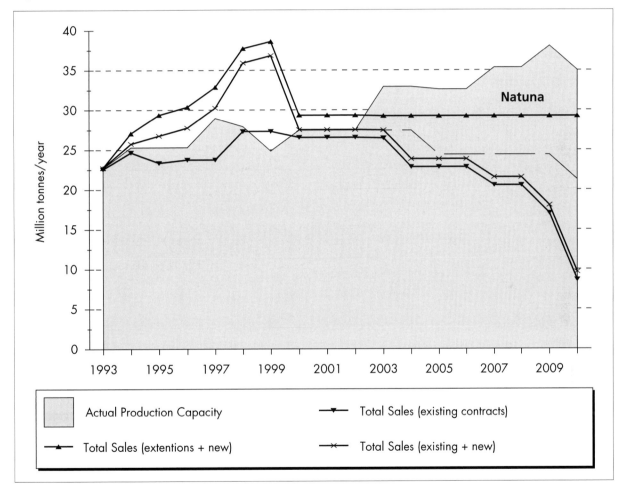

Existing contracts will ensure that exports will remain at around this level at least through to 1997, when a seventh train at Badak is scheduled to come on line. If the seventh and eighth trains at Badak both come on line as expected then they should help to ensure that Indonesia's LNG production will stay relatively constant out to 2002 despite the decline in production from the Arun field. Based on existing contracts, there may be a small surplus production capacity of LNG available for export up to 2002.

---

6.   Figure 3 shows estimated actual LNG production capacity. This is some 14 per cent higher than the nameplate capacity.

However, Indonesia is already negotiating additional contracts for LNG which, if they were all concluded, would mean that contracted sales would exceed existing and forecast actiual production capacity through to 2000 (see Figure 3). This deficit would be increased if existing contacts were extended past their current expiry dates. Figure 3 also clearly demonstrates the importance of Natuna if significant additional LNG exports are to be made from Indonesia after 2002.

INFRASTRUCTURE

Indonesia's gas industry has to date been largely focused on the export of LNG. There are two LNG plants in Indonesia, the Badak plant at Bontang[7], East Kalimantan and Arun[8] in Aceh province, North Sumatra. Both plants have six trains at present. The most recent train added was the F train at Badak. This train has a capacity of 2.3 million tons of LNG a year and cost just over US$500 million to build. Following recent gas discoveries, reserves have been reassessed and a seventh train is being built (the G train). The contract for the construction of the train has been offered to the Indonesian firm that built the F train, PT Inti Karya Persada Tehnik (IKPT). The plan calls for the G train to be completed by 1997 and also have a capacity of 2.3 million tons a year. The cost of the G train is expected to be closer to US$1 billion (however this cost includes the cost of building additional loading facilities. The possibility also exists for a eighth train, the H train, to be built by 2000. If this did go ahead then Badak's nameplate capacity would be 17.8 million tons a year in 2000.

Actual liquefaction capacity is significantly higher than the nameplate capacity. It has been estimated[9] that Indonesia's actual LNG production capacity is closer to 25.3 million tons a year, some 14 per cent above the nameplate capacity. This additional capacity has been obtained by debottlenecking and fine tuning the plant.

The Arun plant has a nameplate capacity of 9 million tons a year. While the production capacity of Badak is likely to continue to increase at least up to 2000, the opposite may happen at the LNG plant at Arun. Here existing reserves have been depleted to the extent that it is likely that two of the existing six production trains will have to be shut down by 2000. Indeed, unless additional reserves are proven and in production by 1998 the plant will be unable to meet existing contract commitments. The operators have identified two small fields that they are trying to see if they can develop. However, even if new these new fields are brought on stream this will only allow existing contracts to be met and by 2010 LNG production will cease unless significant new reserves are found.

The Bontang facility has 507,000 cubic meters of LNG storage capacity and the Arun plant has 635,000 cubic meters of LNG storage capacity[10]. This was equivalent to some 2.3 per cent of total exports in 1992.

---

7. The ownership of the plants at Botang and Arun are: Pertamina 55 per cent; Huffco 30 per cent; and Jilco 15 per cent.
8. The ownership of the plants at Botang and Arun are: Pertamina 55 per cent; Mobil 30 per cent; and Jilco 15 per cent.
9. "Natural Gas in the World - 1994 Survey", Sylvie Cornot-Gandolphe, Cedigaz, June 1994.
10. World LNG Trade, CEDIGAZ, November 1991

The possible decline in the production in LNG at Arun, coupled with the outlook for continued growth in LNG demand, reinforces the importance of the agreement reached in late 1994, between Exxon and Indonesia, to go ahead and develop the super-giant Natuna field. Development of this field will be important if Indonesia is to retain its preeminence in the LNG export arena.

The Natuna field is some 1,300 km north of Jakarta, 225 km north east of Natuna Island. The field is estimated to have recoverable hydrocarbon reserves of some 45 tcf. Agreement of the conditions governing the development of the Natuna field took a considerable time to reach. The principal reason for this was the high cost of developing the field due to its remoteness and the high level of carbon dioxide in the reservoir[11]. Negotiations between Exxon and the government centred on issues such as taxation rates and the production sharing split to be specified in the production sharing contract (PSC).

The project partners will now be seeking to sign up buyers for the LNG before construction can begin. Assuming the project does ultimately go ahead it is expected that it will involve the construction of 18 offshore platforms for extraction, initial processing of the gas and reinjection of the carbon dioxide. The gas would then be transported by pipeline to Natuna Island for processing into LNG prior to export[12]. It has been reported that the total lifetime cost of the project would be US$40 billion. Probably about half of this would be needed to for the construction of the platforms and the LNG plant.

The plant is expected to ultimately contain six liquefaction trains with a total capacity of 14.4 million tons a year. Contract negotiations for the sale of Natuna LNG have already begun and are expected to last between one and two years. The construction phase is expected to take at least six years. First shipments of LNG are not expected to occur before 2003[13]. Initially, the liquefaction facility will have a capacity of some 4.8 million tons a year. Capacity expansion will depend upon the availability of markets for the LNG, but will be in increments of 2.4 million tons a year.

Indonesian officials have estimated that some 60 per cent of the cost of the Natuna project is associated with very high carbon dioxide content. This will be reflected in the cost of the LNG from the project. The main difficulty that the Natuna project now faces will be to find buyers willing to pay this higher cost.

There are a number of pipelines already in Indonesia. In the past, many pipelines were "dedicated" ones, in other words, pipelines which were built to supply gas from a single field to one or a few individual customers. For example, pipelines built to supply fertilizer plants located close to LNG facilities.

More recently, following the government's decision to expand the domestic use of natural gas, there has been a move to build longer pipelines which in time may form the basis for a national pipeline network. In December 1993 a 420 km privately owned pipeline began transporting

---

11. It is estimated that some 71 per cent of the total gas in the reservoir is carbon dioxide. This gas will need to be separated out and reinjected into permanent underground storage.
12. Another possibility was to transport the Natuna gas 825 km by pipeline to Batam Island near Singapore then a further 1200 km to the LNG plant at Arun, however, this approach is now seen as unlikely.
13. A recent press report (Jakarta Post 8 February 1995) stated that construction of the first two trains could begin as early as 1997 and be completed by 1999. While such a time frame is possible the limiting factor is thetime which will be needed to construct the waste gas separation and reinection infrastructure.

425 MMSCFD of gas from the Pagerungan field to a power station at Gresik, near Surabaya. The pipeline has a maximum supply capacity of 600 MMSCFD. Another 62 km, 14 inch, pipeline from the Kodeco/Pertamina field offshore Surabaya supplies a further 40 MMSCFD of gas to Gresik. This pipeline is owned by the partners in the field.

Another project which is an advanced stage of planning is a 524 km, 28 inch, pipeline to transport 370 MMSCFD from the corridor block in southern Sumatra to the Duri field in Riau Province. The gas will be used to replace some 60,000 bpd of oil which is currently used to provide steam for the Duri steamflood enhanced oil recovery project. The cost of the pipeline is estimated at around US$1 billion. This project is likely to include a 280 km, 20 inch, spur pipeline to Batam Island.

Other possible pipeline projects include:

- a US$300 million, 30 inch, 500 km pipeline from Prabumulih, in the Palembang area, to Cilegon in northwest Java;
- a pipeline from Asamera corridor block to Palembang-Cilegon line;
- an interconnection of the east Java and west Java grids;
- a 277 km extension of the east Java grid at an estimated cost of US$110 million;
- a pipeline from Shell's offshore fields in central Java;
- a US$84 million, 24 inch, 270 km line to transport 51 MMSCFD from the BP fields in south Sulawesi to Ujung Pandang; and
- a US$115 million, 30 inch, 425 km interconnecting pipeline between Bandung and the Cilamaya-Jakarta pipeline.

Should all these projects proceed then Indonesia would have a 3,800 km pipeline system linking Batam Island, central and south Sumatra and Java. The total cost would be of the order of US$1 billion.

SECURITY OF SUPPLY

The Indonesian Government recognises that gas security is an important issue, and one that will increase in importance as Indonesia's use of gas increases. However, beyond relying on the linepack there are no measures in place to improve domestic gas security.

To date there has been no disruption to LNG export deliveries to any of Indonesia's customers. This is an achievement, particularly in view of the over 4,500 LNG cargoes that have left Indonesia since exports began in 1977.

The Bontang facility has 507,000 cubic meters of LNG storage capacity and the Arun plant has 635,000 cubic meters of LNG storage capacity. This was equivalent to some 2.3 per cent of total exports in 1992. In the event of a disruption to supply at one of the plants, existing storage facilities would be sufficient for between four and five shipments of LNG, assuming that the 125,000 cubic meters tankers normally used to transport the LNG were utilised.

MALAYSIA

BACKGROUND

Malaysia is well endowed with energy resources. Its principal energy sources are oil, natural gas and hydropower. Oil (including products) and gas dominate the Malaysian energy picture. In 1992, these two energy sources provided over 93 per cent of Malaysia's TPES.

Prior to 1983, Malaysia produced less than 1 Mtoe of natural gas and most of this was either flared or used in oil field operations. The rapid expansion of Malaysia's gas production since 1983 came initially as a result of the start up of the first LNG plant in Sarawak. However, the Malaysian government's decision to promote the domestic use of gas in all three regions of Malaysia as part of its "four fuel policy" (oil, gas, coal, hydro) has also contributed to the growth in demand. The bulk of domestic demand is for power generation. More recently industry, and in particular the petrochemical industry, has taken on a larger role.

Table 1   Overview of Malaysia's Gas Sector

	1990	**1991**	**1992**
Total gas consumption (Mtoe)	**6.79**	**10.11**	**11.39**
Share of primary energy supply (%)	31.8	38.9	40.6
Power sector	1.36	2.53	3.14
Industry	1.09	1.09	1.34
Households	.03	.03	.42
Commercial	-	-	.66
Indigenous production (Mtoe)	**15.48**	**18.39**	**19.64**
Imports	-	-	-
Exports	8.69	8.28	8.26
Transit	-	-	-
Normal Production Capacity (LNG)[1]	**8.1**	**8.1**	**8.1**
Surge capacity as % of production	27	27	27
Normal Production Capacity (gas)[2]	**250**	**750**	**750**

Notes: 1. This refers to gas produced offshore Sarawak, liquefied and then exported as LNG. In millions of tonnes per year., net of any flaring or reinjection.
   2. This refers to gas produced offshore Peninsular Malaysia and either consumed on the Peninsula (or exported to Singapore). In millions of cubic feet per day, net of any flaring or reinjection.
Source: IEA and ASEAN statistics.

ORGANISATIONAL STRUCTURE

In Malaysia responsibility for energy matters is split between a number of departments. Primary responsibility for gas matters rests with the Energy Division of the Economic Planning Unit of the Prime Minister's Department. However, the Ministry of Energy, Telecommunications and Posts is responsible for electricity policy, which, given that close to 70 per cent of power generation capacity is gas fuelled, has a bearing on gas use in Malaysia. The Department of Electricity and Gas Supply is responsible for the regulation of the gas sector.

Prior to 1974 various international oil firms dominated the oil and gas sector in Malaysia. This changed in 1974 when the Petroleum Development Act was enacted. This Act established the State controlled company of Petronas and vested in it the ownership and the exclusive rights to explore for and produce all of the country's onshore and offshore hydrocarbon resources. If a foreign company wants to gain access to Malaysian fields they must enter into a Production Sharing Contract (PSC) with Petronas. Petronas reports directly to the Prime Minister.

In 1984, a wholly owned subsidiary of Petronas, Petronas Gas Sdn. Berhad (PGSB), was created to handle gas operations in Peninsular Malaysia. It buys gas from the producers and processes it, transports and sells it to large consumers[1] such as power stations. The government plans to sell 25 per cent of Petronas Gas in mid 1995.

The 1993 Gas Supply Act was enacted to set the framework for the distribution and supply of natural gas to consumers in Malaysia. The Act makes provision for the appointment of a Director General of Gas Supply, the licensing of the supply of gas by pipeline to consumers, the supply of gas at reasonable prices, the control of pipelines, installations and appliances for reasons of public safety and other related purposes. The Gas Supply Act applies throughout Malaysia, however, the Minister responsible (the Prime Minister) may suspend the operation of the Act in whole or in part, in any State.

Under the Act all gas distributors and sellers are required to be licensed by the Director General of Electricity and Gas Supply, with the approval of the Minister. Once granted, a license cannot be transferred, assigned or otherwise disposed of without the approval of the Minister. There is no provision in the Act for the amendment of a license nor is the duration of a license set out in the Act. A license may be suspended or revoked by the Director General of Electricity and Gas Supply should any of its conditions be breached. In the event of a license being revoked, the Director General may also authorize another to take over a licensee's facilities provided payment of "adequate compensation" is made to the original holder of the license.

The licensee has a duty to supply gas to any consumer within the area of the supply of gas. If gas is supplied by the licensee, they have the power to recover expenses incurred and require

---

1. The Malaysian government allows Petronas gas to sell gas to customers with a demand greater than 2MMSCFD, whereas Gas Malaysia sells to customers with a demand below this.

Figure 1 Organisation of the Malaysian Public Energy Sector

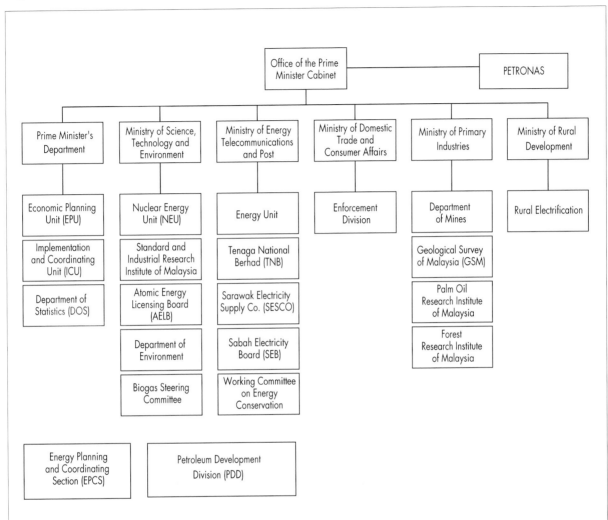

Source: ASEAN EC - Energy Managerment, Training and Research Centre.

security from the person to who gas is supplied. No distinction is made between a public gas supplier and any other supplier. Tariffs are set by the licensee, subject to the approval of the government. The licensee is not permitted to show undue preference or discrimination between consumers when setting tariffs. Disputes between a licensee and a consumer can be referred to the Director General of Electricity and Gas Supply.

Under the Gas Supply Act, Gas Malaysia Sdn. Bhd. has been licensed to distribute and market gas to industrial, commercial and residential customers. As noted above, Petronas Gas retains responsibility for sales to the power generation sector. The government does not envisage that any additional companies will be permitted to enter the distribution and retailing end of the market in the foreseeable future. However it is possible that the cap on sales by Gas Malaysia may increase and that on sales by Petronas Gas decrease thus allowing the two to compete directly for sales of gas.

GAS POLICY

The Malaysian government's energy policy objectives[2] are:

■ to ensure adequate energy supply by reducing dependence on oil and by developing and utilizing alternative sources of energy;

■ to promote and encourage the efficient use of energy and discourage wasteful and non-productive patterns of energy consumption; and

■ to minimize environmental degradation in realizing the above goals.

Gas is well placed to help the Malaysian government in achieving the above objectives. Indeed, one of the key Government policy objectives[3] in relation to natural gas are to seek to expand its use as a source of primary energy, particularly in areas where it can be used to substitute for oil, thus making more oil available for export. Another objective is to increase the export of LNG to boost foreign exchange earnings.

Natural gas is seen as being ideal for oil substitution in view of the size of Malaysia's proven reserves and the premium it commands in terms of its environmental benefits, greater efficiency and relatively lower economic costs. Consequently, gas and gas products are envisaged to substantially replace petroleum products in the power, commercial, industry and transport sectors.

In the transport sector the Government is seeking to encourage the use of CNG (Compressed Natural Gas) as an alternative to diesel and gasoline. To do this the Government has introduced a range of incentives to encourage drivers, particularly commercial fleets, to switch to CNG. These incentives include pricing natural gas for vehicles at half the price of petrol, and exemptions on sales tax and import duty on vehicle conversion kits.

Malaysia also has a policy of seeking to add value to its resource exports, including natural gas. Consequently, the government does not support additional sales of gas to Singapore or sales of gas to Thailand. However, the government is supporting a number of export oriented petrochemical projects designed to use natural gas as feedstock.

Exploitation of Natural Resources

The ownership and the exclusive rights to explore for and produce all of the country's onshore and offshore hydrocarbon resources is vested in the State controlled oil and gas company, Petronas. In order for foreign companies to gain access to Malaysian fields they have to enter into a Production Sharing Contract (PSC) with Petronas. PSCs normally have a duration of 25 years (5 years exploration and 20 years production). There is a signature fee payable by the foreign firm on the signing of a PSC, as well as a bonus on discovery and on production.

---

2. *"Energy in ASEAN - Country Profiles"*, ASEAN-EC Energy Management Training and Research Centre (AEEMTRC), August 1993.

3. Additional information on Malaysia's energy policies in general, and gas policies in particular, is found in Chapter 11 of the *Sixth Malaysia Plan 1991-1995*.

The PSC terms for gas are similar to those for oil except that the division of profits is made on gas sales rather than production. Under the basic terms of the PSCs the following production sharing formula is applied to profit gas[4]. Gas sales below 2.1 Tcf will be shared 50:50 with the contractor and if above 2.1 Tcf will be split 70:30 in Petronas' favour. Up to 60 per cent of gas sales can be assigned to cost recovery. The government also has the option of taking a 15 per cent equity share in any development project. It has exercised this option in all except one PSC to date.

Malaysia has a depletion policy which is aimed at extending the life of its oil and gas reserves. Under this policy, annual output from oil fields must be kept below 3 per cent of initial reserves. In the case of gas, production of gas from the fields offshore Peninsular Malaysia is at present limited to a maximum of 2000 MMSCFD (at present this is twice the actual production capacity). This cap will be reviewed as allowed by demand and reserve numbers.

In the last few years, faced with flagging crude production and reduced interest in exploration, Malaysia has sweetened the terms and conditions applying to oil exploration, development and production in order to attract a higher level of foreign interest in available exploration acreage, particularly in deep water tracts. Similar changes were made in 1985 to encourage gas exploration. Prior to this date the sales split was 70:30 in all cases and a maximum of 25 per cent of total sales could be attributed to cost recovery.

Gas Pricing and Taxes

The Sixth Malaysia Plan 1991-1995 states that pricing policies will be directed at ensuring that energy prices reflect the true or economic cost of supply and be able to raise sufficient revenues for the sector's development. In addition, this document states that the price of natural gas will be kept competitive to facilitate the penetration of gas into the industrial, commercial, residential and transport sectors. In the power sector, where fuel costs represent the single most important element in the operation of power utilities, gas will competitively priced to encourage switching away from oil as a fuel.

The landed price of gas in Peninsular Malaysia is set at 45 per cent of the price of MFO (medium fuel oil). This is of the order of US$2.50 per MMSCF. Prices paid for gas sold by Petronas Gas to large customers such as the power sector and industry are negotiated between the buyer and supplier. Gas Malaysia's gas prices for industry are set to be competitive with the alternative fuels of LPG and diesel[5]. Prices to the power sector are pegged to the price of fuel oil. Gas prices for commercial and residential customers are determined by Gas Malaysia, subject to the approval of the government.

Prices for natural gas in January 1994[6] were US$8.30, US$7.78, US$5.19, and US$4.15 per MMSCF for consumers in the residential, commercial, industrial and the power sectors respectively. These prices were some 5 per cent below the prices for gas in January 1993, however, most of this change was due to exchange rate movements. There are no taxes applied to gas sales.

---

4. This is the sales of gas after sufficient gas has been sold to cover the development and production costs incurred.
5. Some 40 per cent of industry s energy consumption is provided by LPG and diesel, most of the remainder is provided by fuel oil.
6. "A Survey of Domestic Energy Prices in the Asia Pacific Region", F. Fesharaki and J.P. Dorian, East-West Center, Hawaii, February 1995.

Prices for gas exported as LNG or pipeline gas are determined by negotiation between the seller and buyer. There are at present no taxes on exports of gas, however, as revenue from taxes on oil exports falls it is possible that the government may consider imposing taxes on gas exports.

Gas Trade

Malaysia is the only country in Asia that currently exports gas both as LNG and by pipeline. Gas is a significant export revenue earner for Malaysia. In 1993 it provided nearly 25 per cent of Malaysia's revenue from gross oil and gas exports. In 1992 exports of LNG provided export revenue of around US$915 million, this grew to just over US$1 billion in 1993. Gas' share of export earnings will increase in importance as LNG production capacity increases. Particularly, if Malaysia's oil production rate remains constant, or even declines, at the same time as an increasing amount of Malaysia's oil production is needed to meet domestic requirements.

Exports of pipeline gas to Singapore are unlikely to increase significantly unless additional reserves of gas can be found. There have been reports of possibly increasing the existing level of exports from 150 MMSCFD (1.55 bcm a year) by a further 10,000 to 20,000 MMSCFD for distribution as city gas in Singapore. Gas sales to Thailand are also unlikely to occur unless new reserves of gas are found, and even then the Malaysian government's policy of seeking to add value to its exports mean that it is more likely to be electricity rather than gas that is exported.

One possible exception might be if gas is found in the Joint Development Area (JDA). Such sales would depend upon the price that Thailand would be prepared to pay for gas from the JDA compared to the landed cost of the gas in Malaysia.

No license is required to export gas. However, approval has to be given by the government at the entry stage. An annual license to manufacture LNG must be obtained from the Customs Department for a fee of RM 2,400. Currently only Petronas exports gas from Malaysia.

Foreign Participation and Private Investment

There is a considerable level of foreign participation in the gas sector in Malaysia. Foreign firms participate in the exploration, development and production of natural gas under the terms of PSCs they have signed with Petronas. The LNG export project also includes foreign participation (35 per cent).

There is no mandatory restriction on the level of foreign participation in the gas sector. However the government wishes to see active participation by Malaysian companies in the petroleum sector and therefore encourages foreign companies to enter into joint ventures with local firms.

In the case of the domestic gas sector, the government is calling on both Malaysian private sector and foreign funding to fund the infrastructure needed to increase the domestic use of natural gas. The government recently awarded the Natural Gas Distribution System project to Gas Malaysia Sdn. Bhd., a joint venture between Malaysian companies and Tokyo Gas/Mitsui of Japan.

GAS DEMAND

When gas consumption in Malaysia first began to increase considerably, following the completion of PGU-I in 1984, consumption was split almost equally between industry and the power generation sectors. Both sectors were consuming of the order of 1 Mtoe a year. This situation persisted until 1991 when the completion of PGU-II in 1992 brought with it a dramatic increase in the use of gas for power generation. Demand from this sector doubled to around 2.5 Mtoe in 1991 and increased again to over 3.1 Mtoe in 1992, whereas demand from the industry sector rose to 1.3 Mtoe in 1992. Table 2 lists the power stations using natural gas as a fuel. Residential sector consumption is relatively small at around 30 to 40 ktoe a year.

The majority of domestic consumption occurs on Peninsular Malaysia, where the power sector dominates the market. In 1993, TNB consumed 3.25 Mtoe of natural gas. Malaysia's rapidly growing demand for power is expected to see total electricity generating capacity increase from 5660 MW in 1993 to around 10,000 MW in 2000 and close to 19,000 by 2010. The government's policy is to encourage the use of gas on Peninsular Malaysia for power generation. By 1995 gas' contribution to the power generation mix had climbed to 67 per cent. The government's aim is to have between 70 and 75 per cent of Malaysia's generating capacity fuelled by gas. This would be equivalent to some 7,500 MW of gas powered generating capacity in 2000 and 14,000 MW by 2010. These figures suggest that gas demand from this sector alone might increase to 9 bcm by 2000 and 16.8 bcm by 2010. This is in line with Petronas' forecast that the demand for gas in Peninsular Malaysia will be close to 20 bcm by 2010.

Table 2   Fuel-Switching Capability in Gas Fired Plants in Malaysia

Name & Location of Power Stations	Fuels	Existing Capacity (MW)	Order of Fuel Preference	Comments
Paka: TNB[5]	NG[4]/Distillate	900 MW[3] 174 MW[2]	1. NG 2. Distillate	Combined cycle GTS Conversion to combined cycle by November 1996 (+87 MW)
YLT - IPP[6]	NG	520 MW[2]	NG	Conversion to combined cycle in progress (+130 MW)
Pasir Gudang : TNB	NG/Distillate	174 MW[2]	1. NG	Conversion to combined cycle by July 1996 (+87 MW)
		240 MW[2]	2. Distillate	No plan for conversion to combined cycle
	NG/MFO	240 MW[1]	1. NG 2. MFO	Convention thermal (boiler/steam turbine) units
	NG	68 MW[2]	NG	Open cycle GTs
YTL - IPP	NG	260 MW[2]	NG	Conversion to combined cycle in progress (+130 MW)

Table 2 Fuel-Switching Capability in Gas Fired Plants in Malaysia (continued)

Name & Location of Power Stations	Fuels	Existing Capacity (MW)	Order of Fuel Preference	Comments
Tuanku Jaafar, P. Dickson : TNB	NG/MFO	360 MW[1]	1. NG 2. MFO	Conventional thermal units
	NG/Distillate	20 MW	1. NG 2. Distillate	Standby/Blackstart GTs
Port Dickson Power - IPP	NG/Distillate	440 MW[2]	1. NG 2. Distillate	Open cycle GTs
Connaught Bridge, Klang : TNB	NG/Distillate	300 MW[3]	1. NG 2. Distillate	Combined cycle GTs
	NG/Distillate	520 MW[2]	1. NG 2. Distillate	Open cycle GTs
	NG	68 MW[2]	NG	Open cycle GTs
Port Klang : TNB	NG/MFO	600 MW[1]	1. NG 2. MFO	Conventional thermal units
	Coal/NG/MFO	600 MW	1. Coal 2. NG 3. MFO	Conventional thermal units
	NG/Distillate	350 MW[2]	1. NG 2. Distillate	Open cycle GTs
	NG	108 MW[2]	NG	Open cycle GTs
	Coal/NG	1000 MW	1. Coal 2. NG	Future conventional thermal units, to be commissioned by 1998
Serdang : TNB	NG/Distillate	760 MW[2]	1. NG 2. Distillate	Open cycle GTs
Melaka : TNB	NG/Distillate	220 MW[2]	—	Conversion to combined cycle by October 1997 (+110MW)
Powertek - IPP	NG/Distillate	440 MW[2]	—	Open cycle GTs
Sepang: Genting Sanyen - IPP	NG/Distillate	429 MW[2]	—	Conversion to combined cycle by December 1995 (+251MW)
Lumut : IPP - Segari	NG/Distillate	1302MW[3]	—	Combined cycle, operational by 1996

Notes : (1) MFO - Medium fuel oil for boilers
(2) Open cycle GTs
(3) Combined cycle GTs
(4) NG - Natural Gas
(5) TNB - Tenaga Nasional Berhad
(6) IPP - Independent Power Producers

Consumption of natural gas in Sabah is forecast to increase from just under 1 bcm in 1995 to just over 1 bcm in 2010. Consumption in Sarawak will continue to be dominated by the production of LNG.

Malaysia also has ambitious plans to increase its (non power sector) domestic use of natural gas on the Peninsula. The government recently awarded the Natural Gas Distribution System project to Gas Malaysia Sendirian Berhad, a joint venture between private Malaysian companies (the Malaysia Mining Corporation and the Shapadu consortium) with 55 per cent, Tokyo Gas, and the Mitsui Corporation of Japan with 25 per cent and Petronas with 20 per cent. This company plans to invest RM 2 billion (USUS$780 million) in the period to 2010 to install 290 km of feeder lines and 6000 km of mains to provide gas to over 1,000 industrial, 5,000 commercial and 10,000-20,000 residential consumers[7].

Based on these forecasts, Gas Malaysia will be supplying about 100 million Mbtu a year (approximately 2.2 Mtoe) of gas to its customers by 2010. Over 98 per cent of this will be to industry. At present Gas Malaysia only supplies some 50 industrial customers and Petronas NGV, who in turn sells compressed natural gas (CNG) for use in the transportation sector.

GAS SUPPLY

According to Petronas, the national petroleum corporation of Malaysia, as of 1 January, 1994, Malaysia's gas reserves totalled some 2254 bcm. This corresponds to about 1.5 percent of the world's known gas reserves. All of Malaysia's gas producing fields are located offshore. They are found in three main areas: offshore Peninsular Malaysia (1000 bcm of reserves); offshore Sarawak (1185 bcm of reserves); and the remainder offshore Sabah. Ultimate reserves have been estimated[8] to be 5346 bcm.

Very little gas is lost in the production process in Malaysia and no gas is currently reinjected or flared. Thus, total production is basically equivalent to marketed production, which in 1994 was 26.13 bcm according to *Natural Gas in the World, 1995 Survey* (Cedigaz). Under the Peninsular Gas Utilization Project, the natural gas in fields offshore Peninsular Malaysia are reserved for use on the peninsula (and the existing export contact with Singapore). At the current maximum production rate of some 1000 MMSCF a day (10 bcm a year), existing reserves of gas are sufficient to last for around 100 years. When the third phase of the PGU project is completed existing reserves would last for about 50 years. At present the Malaysian government has set a cap of 2000 MMSCFD on the production of gas from offshore Peninsular Malaysia.

Actual rates of production from fields offshore Peninsular Malaysia will not only depend on domestic demand but also on the future level of gas exports to Singapore and possibly, in the longer term, whether exports of natural gas, or electricity produced by natural gas fuelled

---

7. These figures are Gas Malaysia estimates and may differ from official forecasts. However, the largest difference is in the number of residential customers, and since consumption from this class of customer is relatively low, total consumption figures do not differ significantly.

8. "World Petroleum Assessment and Analysis" by Charles D. Masters, Emil D. Attanasi, David H. Root, U.S. Geological Survey, National Center, Reston, Virginia, U.S.

plant(s), is exported to Thailand. Another possible source of gas for Thailand might be from any future discoveries in the Thailand-Malaysia Joint Development Area (JDA). Drilling in this area is scheduled to begin during 1995. Estimates of gas reserves in the JDA vary, but range between 3 and 8 Tcf. Any gas found will be split equally between Thailand and Malaysia.

If gas was found in the JDA then Malaysia could sell its share directly to Thailand. However, the Malaysian government's policy is to increase the added value component its exports, consequently Malaysia may decide to generate the electricity from gas themselves and then export the power to Thailand.

There have been reports of negotiations between Malaysia and Indonesia about the purchase of gas from Indonesian fields relatively close to Malaysian fields offshore Peninsular Malaysia. The gas could be imported via a new pipeline from the Indonesian fields to the existing Malaysian gathering system and then distributed through the Penisular Gas Utilisation pipeline network. Thailand and or Singapore could also buy gas from Indonesia and transport it to their country via Malaysia's PGU pipeline. This would require sufficient spare capacity in the Malaysian pipeline system and an agreement between Malaysia and the importing country on the transit fees to be charged.

Figure 2 shows existing LNG exports and current and planned LNG production capacity. The current level of exports of gas from offshore Sarawak is 8.1 million tonnes (Mt) of LNG a year, or about 30 million cubic meters a day, suggesting that existing proven reserves will last for 108 years. However, export capacity is expected to increase to 15.9 Mt a year by the start of 1997. At that rate of production, current reserves would last some 55 years. If the third expansion of the Bintulu facility proceeds, raising annual export capacity to 23.7 Mt, then existing reserves would be exhausted around 2035[9].

As can be seen from Figure 2, Malaysia's actual LNG production capacity exceeds the amount it has contracted to sell. Up to 1999, this opens the way for Malaysia to either sign additional long term supply contracts or sell the additional LNG on the spot market. Malaysia would prefer to sell any surpluses it has by means of long term contracts, but will sell any short term surplus on the spot market.

Should the LNG-Tiga project go ahead then the potential for additional exports increases by almost 10 Mt a year. Post 2003, "surplus" production capacity could be nearly 20 Mt. However, given that LNG-Tiga is unlikely to proceed unless there are firm commitments from buyers and that it is likely that existing long-term contracts will be extended past their current end dates, any real "surplus" is likely to be well below this figure.

GAS INFRASTRUCTURE

Nearly all of the gas produced offshore Sarawak is processed and exported as LNG from the LNG plant at Bintulu. The plant is a joint venture between Petroliam Nasional Berhad (PETRONAS) (with 60 percent), Shell and Mitsubishi (each with 17.5 per cent) and the State of Sarawak

---

9. As actual LNG production capacity is above the nameplate capacity reserves may be depleted somewhat quicker.

Figure 2   Malaysian Gas Production Capacity and Total Sales

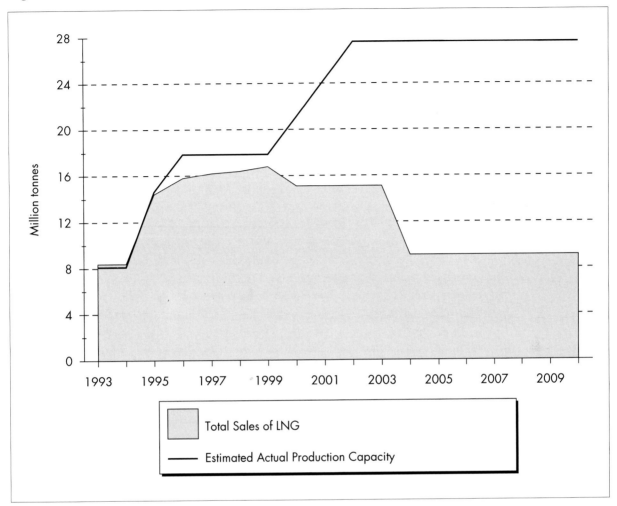

(5 per cent). The plant had an original design capacity of 6 Mt a year. Debottlenecking raised this to 8.1 Mt a year. Three additional trains (LNG Dua) are presently being added to the facilities at Bintulu. The first train came on line in early 1995, the second is expected to come on-line in November 1995, and the third in March 1996. LNG Dua will have a total nameplate capacity of 7.8 Mt a year. It is likely that the actual LNG production capacity of LNG Dua will exceed the nameplate capacity by some 25 per cent.

A third LNG facility at Bintulu (LNG Tiga) is being considered. If it proceeds, it would begin to come on stream in 2000 and would probably boost Malaysia's nameplate export capacity by a further 7.8 Mt of LNG a year. This would bring Malaysia's total actual LNG production capacity to 27.6 Mt a year.

LNG from the Bintulu plant is transported to its destination in a fleet of seven LNG carriers owned by Malaysia International Shipping Corporation, Bonny Gas Transport and Asia Gas transport. Five additional ships have been chartered from Chantiers de L'Atlantique to transport the LNG from LNG Dua.

On Sarawak, small quantities of natural gas are used in an export based fertilizer plant (50 MMSCFD) and for power generation. A middle distillate synthesis (MDS) plant has also recently been completed in Sarawak. This plant is designed to produce some 470,000 tonnes of kerosene, diesel, and naphtha and consumes some 100 MMSCFD of gas. There have however, been reports that this plant is only economic at oil prices above US$37 a barrel.

Gas produced from offshore Sabah is transported by pipeline to the Island of Labuan where it is used in two export oriented industries, a methanol plant and a hot briquetted iron plant. In addition, there is a small gas fired 47 MW power station on the island. Both offshore and onshore pipelines are owned by Petronas Gas Supply Labuan Sdn Bhd. The current capacity of the onshore pipeline is 115 MMSCFD. Present consumption is about 840 ktoe. There are plans to construct additional small gas fired power plants which would increase demand by about 280 ktoe by 1997.

The gas produced from offshore Peninsular Malaysia is principally for domestic consumption on the peninsula. However, a small quantity (150 MMSCFD) is exported to Singapore by pipeline. As part of its strategy to diversify its energy use pattern and substitute for the use of oil the Malaysian government implemented the Peninsular Gas Utilization Project (PGU). The first stage (PGU-I) was completed in 1984. This consisted of a 250 MMSCFD gas processing plant (GPP I) at Kerteh and some 50 km of transmission pipeline, to a 900 MW power plant at Paka (140 MMSCFD), the Perwaja steel mill (23 MMSCFD) and a pilot scale residential distribution network in Kerteh. Propane and butane are extracted from the gas stream and either bottled for household and industrial use or exported to Japan through the terminal facility at Kemaman, some 30 km to south of Kerteh.

The second stage of this project (PGU-II) was completed in 1991. This consisted of two new gas processing plants (GPP II and GPP III), both with a capacity of 250 MMSCFD, and a 730 km pipeline to Kuala Lumpur on the west coast and a spur line to Singapore. The initial design capacity of PGU-II is 700 MMSCFD, this can however, be increased to 1000 MMSCFD by installing additional gas compression. The cost of PGU-II was some US$2.4 billion. There are now four power stations on the west coast of Peninsular Malaysia using gas for fuel (see Table 2). The propane and butane extracted at GPP II and GPP III are used for petrochemical feedstock in three petrochemical projects.

The third phase of the Peninsular Gas Utilization Project (PGU-III) will extend the existing pipeline north from Kuala Lumpur up to the border with Thailand. As part of the third phase, GPP IV with a capacity of 250 MMSCFD has already been built and GPP V and VI (each with a capacity of 500 MMSCFD) will be completed in 1997 and 1998 respectively. This phase of the project is expected to be completed by 1998.

The Malaysian government is planning to loop sections of the existing pipeline network between Kerteh and Kuala Lumpur. The objective of the looping is not only to increase the capacity of the pipeline but also to improve gas security.

SECURITY OF SUPPLY

As domestic consumption of natural gas grows, Malaysia is increasingly focussing on gas security issues. It is argued that there will be sufficient system redundancy within the gas processing system to cope with the possible shut down of one of the processing plants. The government also plans to loop parts of the pipeline system in part to provide additional supply security (it is argued that the PGU pipeline can be used as a buffer storage in the event of a supply disruption).

The 1992 Malaysian Gas Supply Act has provisions for emergency requisition in the case of a event which gives rise to an emergency, or is in the interest of public safety. It also contains provisions allowing the supplier to cut off gas supplies in the event of a disruption to supply.

In view of the high degree of dependence on gas for power generation (currently some 70 per cent) the government is planning to require that future power plants be dual fired. Consideration is also being given to requiring combined cycle plants to hold two weeks supply of distillate to use as an alternative to gas in the event of a supply disruption.

The rapid growth in demand for natural gas in Malaysia (principally for power generation) has created some difficulties in meeting demand. This is due to infrastructure capacity constraints, in this case, in the offshore gas gathering system. Additional pipelines are being built to overcome this problem.

In the event of a disruption to LNG supplies, Force Majeure clauses in the Sales and Purchase Agreements allow for available LNG to be shared between buyers. There are five LNG storage tanks, each with a capacity of 65,000 cubic metres. Malaysia also is able to boost LNG production in the short term through use of a swing field. Surge production capacity is approximately 27 per cent of nameplate capacity.

ALGERIA

Brief discussions of Tunisia and Morocco which focus on their importance as transit countries for Algerian gas to Italy and Spain are included at the end of this annex.

GAS POLICY

The hydrocarbon sector is the backbone of the Algerian economy. Its extreme dependence on world markets is the major constraint influencing Algerian gas policy. The hydrocarbon sector accounts for 95% of the country's export earnings, 25% of its GDP and 57% of Government revenues. In 1994, gas export revenues were US$ 2.3 billion, 26% of total hydrocarbon export revenues. Algeria's public foreign debt is around US$ 26 billion ; the service of this debt absorbs about three quarters of all export revenues. US$ 3 billion per year (equivalent to 6% of GDP) have to be spent for basic food imports (meat, cereals, milk) to feed a rapidly growing population, and the same amount has to be invested every year just to maintain present industrial activity.

As a result of its financial constraints, Algeria is forced to pursue a very active export policy. The Government's objective is to increase total hydrocarbon exports from around 85 Mtoe in 1995 to 115 Mtoe in 2000. Gas will play a very important role in this: from one-third of exports in terms of energy content in the beginning of the 1990s, its share is now around 40% and will reach 50% by the end of this century. If condensates and LPG are included in the gas share, the total gas share will reach close to 75% in 2000. The Government reckons that investments of some US$ 14 billion will be needed to reach these export goals, even assuming that about three-quarters of the necessary investments in LNG facilities have already been made.

Since nationalisation of the petroleum sector in the 1970s, foreign companies have played a relatively modest role in Algeria. The need for foreign investment and technology and the increasing importance of boosting export revenues have led the Government to take steps to change this situation. A law adopted in 1991 (law no. 91-21 dated 4 December 1991) is the basis for this change in strategy. The major elements in this law are as follows:

■ authorization of Sonatrach the (Government-owned oil and gas company responsible for exploration, production, transportation and sales) to negotiate participation by foreign companies in oil and gas fields already in production;

■ introduction of international arbitration in case of dispute;

■ the introduction of more lenient taxation in some regions.

In the wake of this new legislation the Government's priorities have been to increase exploration, improve the recovery rate and the production profiles of fields in operation, to develop discovered fields that have not yet been exploited and to increase natural gas export capacity.

The recent changes in Algerian gas policy are also reflected in the strategy of Sonatrach which is the principal instrument available to the Government to realise its policy objectives. The company is now actively looking for partnerships in most parts of the gas chain and has changed its public relation strategy in the direction of more openness. It has stated that it wants to pursue downstream opportunities abroad in the gas sector.

Algeria has already reached a relatively high level of gasification, but there is still a potential for further increase. Sonelgaz (Societe Nationale d'Electricite et du Gaz), the company responsible for gas and electricity distribution on the domestic market, reckons that 450 000 new customers will be linked to the distribution system by 2000.

GAS DEMAND

Primary energy demand in Algeria in 1993 was about 28 Mtoe, of which two thirds were gas and most of the remainder petroleum products. The share of coal and hydropower in total primary energy demand is only 2.3%. The share of gas is increasing, partly as a consequence of the Government's policy of replacing the use of petroleum products by gas in order to free petroleum for exports. Table 1 shows the composition of total primary energy consumption in Algeria since 1980.

Table 1   Primary Energy Demand in Algeria (Mtoe)

	1980	1985	1986	1987	1988	1989	1990	1991	1992	1993
Solid Fuels	0.37	0.52	0.54	0.65	0.68	0.51	0.66	0.67	0.64	0.62
Petroleum and Petroleum Products	5.34	8.45	8.88	8.91	8.92	8.91	8.31	9.29	10.10	10.8
Natural Gas	6.61	10.66	11.53	11.49	11.73	15.84	14.66	15.50	15.90	16.4
Electricity (hydro)	0.06	0.15	0.06	0.11	0.01	0.02	0.02	0.02	0.02	0.02
TOTAL	**12.38**	**19.78**	**21.01**	**21.16**	**21.34**	**25.28**	**23.64**	**25.48**	**26.53**	**27.8**

Source: OME.

As explained below, only a relatively small share of the total Algerian gas production is commercialised (less than 40%). Table 2 shows how the commercialised volumes have been divided between exports and domestic consumption. Since the beginning of the 1980s, the export share has increased from around one third to around two thirds.

Table 3 shows how the distribution of commercialised production by sector has developed over time. The energy sector itself (disregarding electricity production) has always accounted for the largest offtake of gas, the explanation being the high energy consumption in liquefaction units and in pipeline operations. The liquefaction units consume 26 to 27% of total entry volumes.

Table 2   Commercialised production split by exports and domestic demand (bcm)

Year	Commercialised Production	Exports	Consumption
1980	18.04	6.67	11.37
1981	21.91	7.13	14.78
1982	26.69	9.92	16.77
1983	36.27	17.91	18.36
1984	35.04	18.91	16.13
1985	37.52	21.54	15.98
1986	37.94	20.44	17.50
1987	43.65	25.75	17.90
1988	46.29	26.12	20.17
1989	48.40	29.42	18.98
1990	51.60	31.33	20.27
1991	53.91	33.89	20.02
1992	55.80	35.17	20.63
1993	57.00	34.68	22.32

Source: Sonatrach.

Table 3   Production and Utilisation of Natural Gas in Algeria (bcm)

	1980	1981	1982	1983	1984	1985	1986
Commercialised production, of which:	14.11	16.37	21.18	30.63	30.93	34.32	34.58
Liquefaction units	9.54	11.28	15.39	22.19	17.37	17.64	17.64
(Auto consumption)	2.87	4.15	5.47	6.52	5.22	5.00	5.65
Natural gas exports	—	—	—	2.24	6.76	8.90	8.44
Fertiliser products	0.04	0.24	0.35	0.30	0.36	0.48	0.50
Petrochemical complexes	0.21	0.24	0.27	0.22	0.27	0.31	0.31
Refineries	0.15	0.12	0.20	0.14	0.19	0.36	0.51
LPG separation units	0.09	0.10	0.10	0.07	0.12	0.08	0.11
Oil and gas pipeline fuel	0.35	0.37	0.47	0.40	0.31	0.28	0.26
Other Sonatrach units	—	—	—	0.01	0.02	0.13	0.08
Deliveries to Sonelgaz*	3.73	4.02	4.40	5.02	5.41	6.02	6.59
Statistical differences	—	—	—	0.02	0.12	0.12	+0.14

	1987	1988	1989	1990	1991	1992	1993
Commercialised production, of which:	39.53	41.65	44.63	47.89	51.36	55.80	57.00
Liquefaction units	19.12	20.32	23.43	20.01	21.65	24.15	26.00
(Auto consumption)	5.10	5.49	6.41	5.43	5.35	5.80	6.95
Natural gas exports	11.73	11.29	12.40	12.28	14.76	15.60	14.43
Fertiliser products	0.30	0.23	0.30	0.32	0.41	0.29	0.30
Petrochemical complexes	0.34	0.35	0.30	0.31	0.37	0.34	0.29
Refineries	0.53	0.57	0.56	—	0.55	0.56	0.60
LPG separation units	0.11	0.12	0.12	0.12	0.11	0.12	0.14
Oil and gas pipeline fuel	0.28	0.31	0.38	0.39	0.41	0.38	0.38
Other Sonatrach units	0.24	0.06	0.07	—	0.05	0.07	0.08
Deliveries to Sonelgaz*	6.95	7.48	7.29	7.90	8.10	8.90	9.12
Statistical differences	-0.07	+0.92	-0.22	-0.13	-0.40	-0.41	+0.11

* Company responsible for internal distribution.
Source: Ministry of Mines, Sonatrach

Sonelgaz is generally responsible for gas distribution on the domestic market, the exception being refineries and petrochemical facilities in Arzew and Skikda which are fed directly by Sonatrach.

In 1993, Sonelgaz received 9.12 bcm of gas and Sonatrach 3.1 bcm. The volumes distributed by Sonelgaz can be broken down as follows:

- power stations   5.3 bcm
- industrial customers   2.0 bcm
- public distribution   1.82 bcm.

Gas consumption for electricity generation is increasing steadily and reached 5.3 bcm in 1993. The number of electricity customers has increased from 2.2 million in 1985 to around 3 million currently. Electricity production is now almost exclusively based on natural gas (93% in 1993).

The potential for increase in domestic gas consumption is large, especially in the substitution of oil products. National consumption of natural gas (the gas distributed by Sonelgaz) could reach about 20 bcm by 2000. To achieve this, it would be necessary to convert customers in the industrial and tertiary sector from oil products to gas, extend the distribution network in areas already reticulated and to expand the distribution network to new areas.

Because of major pipeline projects put in place to increase exports (see below), Sonelgaz will be able to distribute gas to customers in new areas. By the end of the century it will serve 2.2 million customers. Gas could then account for 66% of total national energy needs versus 53% in 1993. According to Sonelgaz, the growth in gas consumption in Algeria will necessitate the construction of 1650 km of pipeline and 131 new public distribution systems.

GAS EXPORTS

One of the most important objectives of the new hydrocarbon legislation is to increase gas export capacity in the form of both LNG and pipeline gas. Revamping the liquefaction units in Arzew and Skikda will give a total capacity of at least 32.35 bcm annually from 1995 and could reach 35.68 bcm. Present capacity utilisation is only 63% of nominal capacity.

The capacity of the Transmed pipeline serving Tunisia, Italy and Slovenia will be increased from 16 bcm to 26 bcm from 1995, with a potential for increasing this to 30 bcm by adding new compressor stations. The first phase of the Maghreb-Europe pipeline (capacity of 8 to 10 bcm a year) linking Hassi R'Mel to Spain and Portugal via Morocco and the Strait of Gibraltar is expected to come on stream in the second half of 1996. A second phase of this pipeline could increase capacity to 20 bcm with a view to deliveries to areas north of the Pyrenees. A third pipeline (capacity 3.6 bcm/year) is foreseen between Oued Saf-Saf and Zouara in Libya via Tunisia.

This increase in capacity is based on an export target of 60 to 65 bcm per year. Sonatrach considers that this goal has virtually been attained for the second half of this decade, when delivery commitments are 56 bcm of which 55% will be by pipeline.

Since 1981, Algeria has almost quintupled its gas exports, rising from 7.13 bcm to a preliminary peak of 35.17 bcm in 1992, an annual average growth rate of 16.8%.

Exports by pipeline started in 1983 when the Transmed pipeline came into operation. Since then pipeline exports have multiplied by seven, reaching a temporary peak of 15.6 bcm in 1992. The growth rate for LNG exports has been considerably lower, partly due to the temporary halt in or outright cancellations of some LNG contracts due to contractual disputes during the 1980s. Table 4 shows the development in export volumes for both pipeline gas and LNG since 1981. One factor contributing to the decline in Algerian exports over the last couple of years has been the revamping of the LNG facilities.

Table 4   Natural Gas Exports (bcm)

	LNG	Pipeline	TOTAL	LNG Share (%)
1981	7.13	—	7.13	100
1982	9.92	—	9.92	100
1983	15.67	2.24	17.91	87.5
1984	12.15	6.76	18.91	64.3
1985	12.64	8.90	21.54	58.7
1986	12.00	8.44	20.44	58.7
1987	14.02	11.73	25.75	54.4
1988	14.83	11.29	26.12	56.8
1989	17.02	12.40	29.42	57.9
1990	19.05	12.28	31.33	60.8
1991	19.14	14.75	33.89	56.5
1992	19.57	15.60	35.17	55.6
1993	20.25	15.06	35.31	57.3
1994	18.12	13.52	31.64	57.3

Source: Cedigaz.

France and Italy are by far the largest importers of Algerian gas, taking more than 60% of the total in 1994. Table 5 shows the development in exports by destination between 1981 and 1994. In addition to the countries shown in the table, Morocco and Portugal have made commitments to buy Algerian gas in the future.

According to the Government, the export volume could relatively easily be increased to 75 bcm a year. This could be done by increasing capacity at the LNG facilities to 35-37 bcm and putting in place the second phase of the Maghreb pipeline (adding 10 to 12 bcm) or a third phase of the Transmed (adding 6 bcm). In a longer term, the Ministry of Energy envisages an export volume of around 100 bcm a year. Table 6 gives an overview of the outlook for Algerian gas exports.

GAS SUPPLY

At the beginning of 1995, Algerian gas reserves were estimated at 3720 bcm. Gross gas production in 1994 was 129.4 bcm, implying a reserve/production ratio of 60 years. The rate of reserve replacement in 1994 was over 100%. Around 52% of total production, i.e. close to

Table 5   Gas Exports by Destination (bcm)

	1981	1982	1983	1984	1985	1986	1987	1988	1989	1990	1991	1992	1993	1994
Belgium	0.00	0.32	1.55	1.66	2.40	0.12	0.12	2.88	3.68	3.90	4.03	4.57	4.30	3.98
Spain	1.40	1.44	1.65	1.32	1.67	2.59	2.85	2.38	2.71	3.20	3.88	3.94	4.34	4.55
U.S.A.	1.04	1.56	3.71	1.03	0.71	1.62	1.69	0.57	1.19	2.47	1.93	1.26	2.32	1.42
France	4.28	6.58	8.76	8.14	7.86	7.67	9.36	8.95	9.04	9.31	9.16	9.21	9.00	7.65
Italy	0.00	0.00	2.13	6.58	8.22	8.12	10.84	10.53	11.19	11.11	14.24	15.34	13.94	11.78
Japan	0.00	0.00	0.00	0.00	0.00	0.00	0.00	0.00	0.30	0.09	0.00	0.00	0.00	0.00
U.K.	0.41	0.02	0.00	0.00	0.00	0.00	0.00	0.05	0.10	0.05	0.00	0.00	0.00	0.00
Slovenia	0.00	0.00	0.00	0.00	0.00	0.00	0.00	0.00	0.00	0.00	0.00	0.15	0.28	0.39
Tunisia	0.00	0.00	0.11	0.48	0.68	0.32	0.89	0.76	1.21	1.20	0.65	0.70	1.13	1.49
Turkey	0.00	0.00	0.00	0.00	0.00	0.00	0.00	0.00	0.00	0.00	0.00	0.00	0.00	0.38
TOTAL	**7.13**	**9.92**	**17.91**	**18.91**	**21.54**	**20.44**	**25.75**	**26.12**	**29.42**	**31.33**	**33.89**	**35.17**	**35.31**	**31.64**

Source: Cedigaz.

68 bcm was reinjected (in both oil and gas fields), 6.2 bcm was flared and 5.1 bcm was lost in other ways. Total commercialised production was 50.3 bcm, which made Sonatrach the fourth largest gas producer in the world. Production of associated gas in 1994 was about 18 bcm, about 14% of total gross production. Algeria has no offshore gas production.

To assure delivery of the gas committed in sales contracts, Sonatrach has reserved around 1500 bcm, amounting to about 40% of total reserves. Given that Algeria is a sizeable gas consumer herself, Sonatrach has, however indicated that sufficient gas reserves to satisfy the domestic market at least up to 2035-2040 will be set aside. For the period 1992-2005, 504 bcm have been reserved. If the present rate of reinjection is to be maintained (to increase the rate of oil and condensate/LPG recovery) and exports increase significantly, Algeria may be confronted with an availability problem in the somewhat longer term. The country is, however underexplored as far as gas is concerned (drilling density is only 1/15 of the OECD average per square kilometre of sedimentary surface), and the problem is probably one of attracting sufficient foreign interest.

To encourage exploration in difficult areas and application of enhanced recovery methods, the new legislation mentioned above provides for major reductions in taxes and royalties for foreign companies. Unlike the former legislation dating from 1986, the new legislation explicitly applies to gas and to fields already discovered or in operation.

To speed up development of discovered fields Sonatrach now offers production sharing contracts for all opened zones. This applies both to discovered fields that could be developed and to fields yet to be found. The legislation foresees two types of contracts:

■ production sharing contracts with a maximum of 49% of production going to the foreign company;

■ service contracts under which the contracting company is paid in cash or in hydrocarbons for the services rendered.

Table 6 Possible Future Algerian Exports (bcm/year)

	1992	**1995-96**	**2000**	**2005**	**2010**
1. Export Capacities					
LNG Facilities	21.14	32.5	32.5-35.9	32.5-35.9	32.5-35.9
Transmed pipeline	16	24	25.5	30	30
Maghreb-Europe pipeline	—	8	10.5	18.5	18.5
Sub-total	*37.14*	*64.5*	*68.5-71.9*	*81-84.4*	*81.4-84.4*
2. LNG - Contracted and Possible Volumes					
Gaz de France	9.21	10.15	10.15	8.65	8.65
Enagas (Spain)	3.94	3.25	3.75	3.85	3.85
Distrigaz (Belgium)	4.57	4.80	5.0	5.0	5.0
Enel (Italie)	0.59	—	2.0	2.0	2.0
Etats-Unis	1.26	3.0	5-7	7-8	8-10
DEPA (Greece)	—	0.2	0.6	0.6	0.6
BOTAS (Turkey)	—	1	2	2	2-3
Portugal	—	—	—	0-2	0-2
Sub-total	*19.57*	*22.40*	*28.5-30.5*	*29.1-32.1*	*30.1-35.1*
3. Pipelines - Contracted and Possible Volumes					
Italy: SNAM	14.75	19.25	19.25	19.25	19.25
Italy: ENEL	—	4	4	4	4
Spain: Enagas	—	0.6	6	6	6
Slovenia: Sozd Petrol	0.15	0.30	0.60	0.6	0.6
Portugal	—	0.5	2.5	2.5	2.5
Morocco	—	0.3	1.5	1.5	1.7
Tunisia	0.7	1.0	1.5	1.5	1.5
Other European Countries	—	—	—	6-8	6-8
Sub-total	*15.60*	*25.95*	*35.35*	*41.35-43.35*	*41.55-43.55*
4. Total Volumes - Contracted and Possible	**35.17**	**48.35**	**63.85-65.85**	**70.45-75.45**	**71.65-78.65**
5. Available Capacity:					
LNG	1.57	10.10	5.4-4.0	3.8-3.4	2.40-0.80
Pipeline	0.40	6.05	0.65	7.15-5.15	6.95-4.95
Total	*1.97*	*16.15*	*6.05-4.65*	*10.95-8.55*	*9.35-5.75*

Source: Sonatrach.

The new law abolishes Sonatrach's transportation monopoly in that it allows foreign companies to finance, build and operate pipelines and facilities linked to the transportation of hydrocarbons on behalf of Sonatrach. In addition, a third party access regime has been introduced which allows foreign companies producing gas in Algeria to transport gas on Sonatrach's pipelines. Explicit tariffs for this purpose have been published.

In spite of the difficulties in Algeria since 1991, the new legislation seems to have had some success, in particular as far as oil is concerned. Foreign companies doubled their drilling efforts between 1992 and 1993 and accounted for more than 40% of total drilling activity in 1994. That year the foreign companies shot almost three times more seismic than Sonatrach.

Historically, only three non-associated gas fields have been developed, Hassi R'Mel, Rhourde Nouss and Alrar. Production from those fields has been sufficient to meet needs both for exports and domestic markets. Since 1990, a development programme for eleven other wet gas fields located south of the Hassi R'Mel field has been put into place. The project, having a total cost of 6 billion US$, foresees recovery of 200 million tonnes of LPG and condensates and 300 bcm of natural gas. The development of a number of these fields is underway, and the first of them, the Hamra field, developed by Total, will come on stream in 1995. Negotiations concerning the In Salah field in Southern Algeria are underway with BP. The development of this field, which would necessitate a new transmission pipeline to the Hassi R'Mel area, could give 7 to 12 bcm of gas annually. These new fields are indispensable to compensate for the pressure fall in the Hassi R'Mel field where half of production is reinjected to maintain pressure and recover the condensates. Investments needed are estimated at US$ 2.5 billion.

Gas production costs in Algeria are generally well below 0.5 US$ per Mbtu and could probably be kept around that level for new developments in the south of the country. Transportation costs from Hassi R'Mel are 1 US$ per Mbtu to Spain and 0.9 US$ per Mbtu to Italy. This means that significant quantities of gas could be delivered to Europe from Algeria at a cost of less than 2 US$ per Mbtu. The cost of gas delivered from new LNG facilities would be higher.

The average gas export price in 1994 was 1.8 US$ per Mbtu. This low export price must reflect that a large share of exports is priced f.o.b. Table 7 shows how gas export revenues and prices have developed since 1986.

Table 7   Gas Export Revenues and Prices, 1986-1994

	1986	1987	1988	1989	1990	1991	1992	1993	1994
Value (US$ million)	2135	1979	2069	2251	2734	3477	3090	2837	2211
Volume (bcm)	20.6	25.3	25.8	29.1	30.5	33.3	34.8	35.1	31.9
Price (US$/Mbtu)	2.67	2.02	2.07	2.00	2.31	2.69	2.28	2.10	1.86

Source: Sonatrach.

MAIN INFRASTRUCTURE DEDICATED TO EXPORTS

The Algerian pipeline network has a capacity of close to 96 bcm/year (see Map). On average the capacity utilisation rate is between 75 and 80%. The pipeline from Hassi R'Mel to Arzew, the biggest LNG plant has a utilisation rate of 75%. The transmission pipeline system is 5300 km long, it feeds the domestic distribution system operated by Sonelgaz and transports export volumes through Transmed and the LNG facilities. It consists of two main axes:

Main oil and gas infrastructure in Algeria

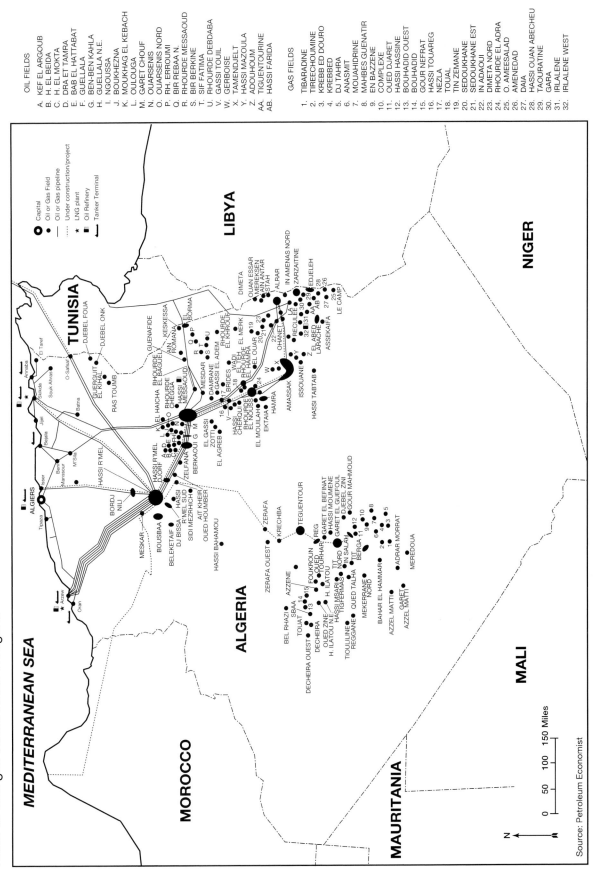

OIL FIELDS

A. KEF EL ARGOUB
B. H. EL BEIDA
C. H. EL MOKTA
D. DRA ET TAMRA
E. BAB EL HATTABAT
F. GUELLALA
G. BEN-BEN KAHLA
H. GUELLALA N.E.
I. NGOUSSA
J. BOUKHEZNA
K. MOUKHAG EL KEBACH
L. OULOUGA
M. GARET CHOUF
N. OUARSENIS
O. OUARSENIS NORD
P. RH. ERROUMI
Q. BIR REBAA N.
R. RHOURDE MESSAOUD
S. BIR BERKINE
T. SIF FATIMA
U. RHOURDE DEBDABA
V. GASSI TOUIL
W. GERBOISE
X. TAMENDJELT
Y. HASSI MAZOULA
Z. ADOUHOUM
AA. TIGUENTOURINE
AB. HASSI FARIDA

GAS FIELDS

1. TIBARADINE
2. TIREECHOUMINE
3. KREBB ED DOURO
4. KREBBED
5. DJ.TAHRA
6. ANASMIT
7. MOUAHIDRINE
8. MAHBES GUENATIR
9. EN BAZZENE
10. COMPLEXE
11. OUED DJARET
12. HASSI HASSINE
13. BOUHADID OUEST
14. BOUHADID
15. GOUR NEFRAT
16. HASSI TOUAREG
17. NEZLA
18. TOUAL
19. TIN ZEMANE
20. SEDOUKHANE
21. SEDOUKHANE EST
22. IN ADAOUI
23. DIMETA NORD
24. RHOURDE EL ADRA
25. O. AMEESALAD
26. AMENEDAD
27. DAIA
28. HASSI OUAN ABECHEU
29. TAOURATINE
30. GARA
31. IRLALENE
32. IRLALENE WEST

Source: Petroleum Economist

■ Hassi R'Mel-Northern Algeria: consists of eight lines with a total capacity of 84.1 bcm/year. It conveys gas from the Hassi R'Mel field to the liquefaction facilities in Arzew and Skikda and towards Oued Saf-Saf (Algerian-Tunisian border).

At present only one export pipeline is operational, Transmed, which transports gas to Tunisia, Italy and Slovenia. A second export pipeline linking Hassi R'Mel to Seville in Spain via Morocco is under construction.

■ South Hassi R'Mel-Hassi R'Mel: this network consists of three lines with a total capacity of 11.7 bcm allowing transportation of gas from the Gassi Toril, Rhourde Nousse and Alrar fields and the gathering of associated gas for reinjection.

■ The Transmed pipeline to Italy: this pipeline is 2500 km long and links the Hassi R'Mel field to Minerbio in the Po valley in Italy via Tunisia and Sicily. Its four main sections are as follows:

— the Algerian section from Hassi R'Mel to the Tunisian border (550 km). This is owned by Sonatrach and consists of two parallel, uncovered 48 inches lines with an initial capacity of 16 bcm;

— the crossing of Tunisia (370 km) by two 48 inches lines operated and owned by Snam and STEG (a Tunisian company);

— the Mediterranean section (155 km under the Sicily channel, 350 km in Sicily and 15 km under the Messina strait) belongs to the Transmediterranean Pipeline Company (TMPC), a joint venture between Sonatrach (50%) and Snam (50%). In addition to the original three lines, two additional lines have recently been laid, bringing total capacity to 26 bcm a year. The high pressure in the pipelines allows full contractual volumes to be transported even when one of the lines is not operational;

— the section in continental Italy (1070 km) to Minerbio where the biggest Italian storage facility is located.

While the gas is transported by means of natural pressure in the Hassi R'Mel field to the Tunisian border, 8 compressor stations (3 in Tunisia, 2 in Sicily and 3 in Italy) with a total rating of 450 MW are necessary to transport it to Minerbio. Construction of five additional compressor stations (three in Algeria and two in continental Italy) is foreseen to bring transportation capacity beyond 26 bcm.

■ The Maghreb-Europe pipeline: the construction of this pipeline, which is expected to become operational in the autumn of 1996, consists of two phases. The first phase, from Hassi R'Mel to Seville in Spain, was officially approved by the countries concerned in 1992. It consists of the following four sections:

■ Hassi R'Mel-Algerian/Moroccan border: Sonatrach will finance, build and operate this 48 inch 530 km long pipeline on its territory. A consortium between Sonatrach and an American company is responsible for the construction, expected to be finished by the end of 1995. Sonatrach will deliver the gas FOB at the Moroccan border.

■ Moroccan border to Tangier: this part is 525 km long, with a pressure of 80 bar maintained by two compressor stations, one of which will be located north of Tangier to compress the gas before the crossing of the Strait of Gibraltar.

■ Crossing of the Strait of Gibraltar: two 20 inch lines have been installed in a corridor of 45 km at a maximum depth of 400 metres between the Moroccan coast and the municipality of Tarifa in Spain.

■ The Spanish section from Tarifa to Cordoba: Enagas will finance, construct and operate this section. The new line will link up to a new pipeline to Portugal and to the existing pipeline network close to Cordoba.

In its first phase, the pipeline will transport 9 bcm a year of which 6 bcm will be delivered to Spain and 2.5 bcm to Portugal. The remainder will be delivered along the route in Algeria and Morocco. Morocco will receive a transit fee.

A second phase of the pipeline is foreseen in the longer term. The pipeline could be extended to the Spanish-French border and capacity increased to 18.5 bcm.

THE GAS LIQUEFACTION UNITS

Algerian liquefaction capacity consists of four complexes, three of which are located in Arzew (GL 1 Z, GL 2 Z and GL 4 Z) and one (GL 1 K) in Skikda:

■ GL 4 Z (Arzew): This unit came on stream in 1964. Its annual capacity is 1.2 million tonnes (3 trains with daily capacity of 2750 cum/day).

■ GL 1 Z (Arzew): Came onstream in 1978 and has an annual capacity of 8 million tonnes a year (6 trains with a daily capacity of 9000 cum each).

■ GL 2 Z (Arzew): Came on stream in 1972; its annual capacity is 8 million tonnes (6 trains with a capacity of 9600 cum/day each).

■ GL 1 K (Skikda): This unit came on stream in 1972 but was extended in 1981. Its annual capacity is 6 million tonnes (6 trains with an average capacity of 6000 cum/day each).

The installations are expected to run 330 days a year. The nominal capacity of all the units is 22.9 billion Ncum/year (gas equivalent) in Arzew and 7.9 billion Ncum in Skikda, i.e., a total of 30.8 billion Ncum/year or 51 million cum/year in liquid form.

Sonatrach initiated a refurbishment programme in 1990 to meet the projected increase in its LNG exports. Its objective is to reestablish initial production capacity, to modernise the equipment and do some de-bottlenecking to increase capacity. The expected result is additional production of 10.6 bcm of natural gas per year, bringing total LNG capacity to about 32.5 bcm in 1995.

SECURITY OF SUPPLY

In general, Algeria has a good security of supply record. Since the inauguration of the Transmed pipeline in 1983, no incidents necessitating interruptions in gas supplies have occurred. The only reasons for downtime on the pipeline has been technical controls, normally lasting for only a few hours. The regularity in deliveries from the LNG facilities has also been good, the few disturbances observed being due to technical problems or bad weather conditions in the Mediterranean.

The most important uncertainties relevant to security of supply are political. A study commissioned by the IEA and undertaken by the Observatoire Mediterranéen de l'Enérgie is summarised in Annex 2 of this book. Its main conclusions are that the likelihood that gas supplies would be permanently interrupted is low because the hydrocarbon sector accounts for almost all of Algeria's export earnings and no government, no matter what its colour, could afford to reduce export revenues if it wished to maintain a minimum economic and social equilibrium.

The main danger threatening European gas supplies from Algeria is rather due to the risk of upheavals in the political, economic and social environment: leading to the flight of technicians and managers, strikes, etc. which could paralyse the economy and thereby affect hydrocarbon exports.

Algeria has no storage facilities except for the storage tanks at the LNG facilities. These have a capacity of 979,000 cum of LNG (0.6 bcm in gaseous form) and represent 2% of Algeria's annual liquefaction capacity.

TUNISIA

Having little potential for becoming a major exporter of gas, Tunisia will be dealt with here primarily as a transit country for Algerian gas to Italy.

Tunisia is the smallest of the Maghreb countries but has many features in common with Algeria and Morocco, including high population growth, high indebtedness and the strong influence of Islam.

Tunisia produces both oil and gas and is a net exporter of crude and petroleum products. Oil production is declining, however, and, if new finds are not made, the country will become a net importer of energy by the end of the century. The Government is taking measures to encourage exploration and production. Other elements in its energy policy are to diversify the energy balance, free more oil for exports and to develop gas distribution.

The gas industry has a long history in Tunisia: manufactured gas produced from coal has been in use since the last century, long before the development of natural gas. From 1955, natural gas from a small field at Cap Bon was used to manufacture "city gas". Since 1984, city gas has been manufactured using natural gas from Algeria. A conversion project affecting the distribution network and household installations has been underway since then so that city gas can gradually be replaced by natural gas.

Gross natural gas production in Tunisia in 1994 was 0.77 bcm of which 0.35 bcm was marketed. Total consumption in 1994 was 1.84 bcm, the difference between domestic marketed production and total consumption being made up by gas from Algeria. Roughly two thirds was used for electricity production and the remainder for final consumption in the industry and residential/commercial sectors.

Natural gas imports from Algeria have been made possible by the fact that the Transmed pipeline linking Algeria and Italy crosses Tunisia. The Tunisian state owns the 370 km portion of the pipeline crossing Tunisian territory, but Snam of Italy holds the transportation rights. The Tunisian Government receives a fee from the shippers calculated as a percentage of gas volumes transited. The percentage increases slightly with new tranches of gas. This fee is payment for the rights of way and comes in addition to payment for transportation as such. The Government has the opportunity to take the transit fee in kind or in cash. In the initial stages, a high percentage of the gas was taken in cash, but most of the gas is now taken in kind since gas demand has increased.

The Transmed crossing of Tunisia is a good example of exporting, importing and transit country with common interests. The pipeline permits Tunisia as a transit country to benefit from the economies of scale in transportation and gives it access to an additional source of energy in addition to providing revenues. The country therefore has very strong incentives to keep the gas flowing.

MOROCCO

Except for a tiny amount of gas production fed into industrial use, natural gas does not play any role in the current Moroccan energy scene. It therefore the prospect of Morocco acting as a transit country for Algerian gas to Spain through the Maghreb-Europe pipeline that makes the country relevant to this study.

More than 80% of Morocco's TPES consists of oil. The country has a foreign debt almost equal to its annual GDP. It is therefore seeking both diversification of supply and new sources of revenue, which the new pipeline will to some extent provide. In addition to introducing gas for reasons of diversity, access to natural gas will also mean an opportunity to catch up with unsatisfied electricity demand. In recent years, the annual increase in electricity demand has been about 7%.

A World Bank study into potential demand for gas in Morocco has suggested that by 2000 the country will need 1.5 bcm, rising to 2.1 bcm in 2005 and 2.7 bcm in 2010. The study also concluded that the use of gas for power generation would justify the major part of the investment needed to set up internal transportation and distribution networks, with the proviso that gas would have to be competitive with coal and fuel oil.

Work is already under way on two of the main challenges involved in developing domestic gas utilisation: the preparation of a legal framework, or gas code, and clarification of pricing to ensure gas is properly used. Further evidence of the country's determination to maximise domestic gas utilisation is a proposal to spend US$ 160 million on a 270 km spur pipeline to supply gas to two new power stations, one at Mohammedia (650 MW) and the other at Kenitra (450 MW). Development of gas storage facilities in the salt domes of Mohammedia has been discussed.

The Moroccan section of the Maghreb-Europe pipeline (GME) will be a 545 km, 48 inches diameter pipeline with a maximum pressure of 80 bar. Two compressor stations are foreseen, one at Ain Benimathar close to the Algerian border and one near Tangier, close to the Strait of Gibraltar.

Three different companies have been set up to develop, finance and operate the various sections of the GME:

■ the Europe-Maghreb Pipeline limited (EMPL), a Jersey company with an operating branch in Morocco (owned largely by Gas Natural in Spain and Transgas in Portugal), will own and operate the major section of the pipeline running from the Algerian-Moroccan border to the Moroccan-Spanish border. It will be responsible for financing the Moroccan section and the underwater section crossing the Strait of Gibraltar to Spanish territorial waters. EMPL has exclusive right to use of the pipeline, and will retain this right for 25 years after the pipeline starts operating. EMPL will be exempted from taxes in Morocco in exchange for transit fees, and its financial liabilities will be guaranteed by the transport fee for which the future users of the line (Gas Natural through Enagas and Transgas and possibly other European companies later on) will be billed. Tariffs will be paid on a ship-or-pay basis. After completion of the project, bare ownership of the pipeline will be transferred to a company 100% owned by the Moroccan state;

■ Maghreb-Europe Transport de Gaz (METRAGAZ), a Moroccan company, will supervise and be responsible for the construction of the Moroccan section of the gas pipeline;

■ a company called SODUGAZ has been set up for gas distribution in Morocco.

Although no contract has yet been signed, Morocco intends to buy 1 bcm a year initially from Algeria. The quantity could increase to 2 bcm a year.

For the rights of way provided by the Moroccan government a royalty or transit fee is due to be paid, depending on gas prices. Royalty gas will be transported free of charge to the region of Fes/Meknes.

LIBYA

INTRODUCTION

Libya has considerable gas resources and a potential to become a much more important gas supplier than it is today. Compared with its oil sector, the gas sector is underdeveloped. The government has plans to develop the sector but limited UN sanctions against Libya and the unilateral US trade embargo remain obstacles to this, although they have not stopped Western and Asian companies from making long-term commitments in the Libyan hydrocarbon sector. The socialist oriented economy is highly dependent on revenues from the oil sector which account for practically all export earnings and about one third of GDP. Libya imports about 75% of its food requirements.

The Libyan National Oil Company (NOC) is the state-owned oil and gas company. Founded in 1968, it is involved in all phases of the oil industry, and in the gas industry through wholly-owned subsidiaries. NOC has participation agreements with foreign oil and gas companies operating in Libya.

GAS DEMAND

The energy market in Libya is small relative to the size of its exports (TPES of 13.5 Mtoe in 1993 versus total exports of 63.1 Mtoe). The share of gas in TPES was 29% in 1993. Gross gas production in 1994 was 12.51 bcm, but only 6.39 bcm were marketed, the remainder being reinjected, flared or lost. Oil is the dominant fuel in Libya, but a switch to natural gas has in recent years to some extent curbed the very rapid growth in demand for oil. The marketed production of gas is primarily used in power generation and as feedstock in the petrochemical industry.

Libya's power generating capacity of about 3000 MW is expected to reach 5300 MW by 2000. The expansion includes a 1260 MW gas fired complex, consisting of four 315 MW units to be completed in September 1997. Plans also exist for other new gas fired plants. In addition, conversion of old oil fired plants to natural gas will continue.

Reportedly there is some distribution of gas to the residential sector in Libya, but this is not reflected in official energy statistics.

Exports of natural gas take place exclusively in the form of LNG. Volumes have fluctuated significantly since the export activity started in 1971. The peak was reached in 1978 with 3.3 bcm. In 1994, it was 1.48 bcm, slightly lower than over the preceding three years. Libya has a contract with Enagas in Spain for deliveries of 1.5 bcm a year up to 2008. Snam in Italy no longer has a firm contract with Libya but occasionally buys spot cargoes.

GAS SUPPLY

At the beginning of 1995, Libyan natural gas reserves were estimated at 1310 bcm, which at present production levels gives a reserve/production ratio of more than 100 years. Most of the reserves are onshore and associated. Approximately 70 bcm of proved associated gas reserves lie in the offshore Bouri field. Unproved reserves in the "November 7 field", which is northwest of Bouri straddling the Libya-Tunisia border, are estimated at 250 bcm.

Libya's Petroleum Law No. 25 of April 1965 (amended several times) is the basis for all exploration and production (E&P) activity. Production-sharing is the basis for all exploration and production operations involving foreign companies. The positive response to Libyan E&P offerings since 1988 is reflected in an increase in the number of Western companies working in the country. The prospect of further gas finds in Libya is judged as good.

LNG supplies from Libya are exported from the Marsa El Brega plant built by Exxon in the late 1960s. Originally the plant was designed to produce high-calorific LNG, but has recently been modified to produce a normal, low-calorific grade of LNG, necessitating modifications of the reception terminals in Italy (La Spezia) and Spain (Barcelona). The capacity is 3.5 bcm a year. The owner and the operator of the plant now is Sirte Oil Company, a subsidiary of NOC. The Marmara Ereglisi terminal in Turkey has been mentioned as a possible receiver of Libyan LNG, but this has not been confirmed.

Libya's significance for Western European supply is related to the future export possibilities rather than present LNG exports. Reserves are probably sufficient to support an export programme of more than 20 bcm a year. A number of export proposals have been put forward, in particular by Italian companies: Agip and Snam have promoted the idea of Italy importing 8-10 bcm of Libyan gas through a pipeline to be built across the Mediterranean to Sicily, the length of which would be about 520 km; a second proposal is to link the reserves of both Egypt and Libya to Italy by pipeline and a third proposal is to build a pipeline from Egypt and Libya to Algeria where it would link up with the Maghreb pipeline to Morocco and Spain.

Some of these proposed pipelines could also become part of a proposed Mediterranean pipeline loop.

INFRASTRUCTURE

Libya has a limited gas pipeline network. Two of the most important pipelines are: a double 175 km, 36 inch link connecting the associated gas field at Zelten with the LNG plant at Marsa El Brega and a 4.1 mcm/day, 670 km, 34 inch pipeline running west along the coast from Marsa El Brega to Khoms.

The LNG plant at Marsa El Brega consists of four trains with a total design capacity of 3.6 bcm a year; actual capacity is about 10% higher. Intake capacity is about 5.8 bcm a year of unprocessed feed gas. The LNG site has two 48000 cubic metre storage tanks. In 1994, the capacity utilisation of the LNG was less than 30%.

In addition to Marsa El Brega, Libya has four plants processing associated gas. They were built in the 1970s with a nameplate capacity of 61.7 mcm/day, but actual capacity is now much lower, indicating a need for upgrading and modernisation.

New projects under construction, mostly promoted by NOC as part of efforts to increase the utilisation of natural gas, include the following two gas treatment and processing plants: the first in the Bu Attifel oil field in the Sirte Basin from which dry gas will be injected into another oil field and the second to be built on the coast for the associated gas of the El Bouri field.

SECURITY OF SUPPLY

Gas exports from Libya have run very regularly in the past. The few disturbances observed have been due to bad weather conditions in the Mediterranean. There is no doubt, however, that the economic sanctions hitting Libya might create difficulties for continued LNG supplies. The investment climate is affected by the international trade sanctions and perceived domestic political uncertainty.

NIGERIA

INTRODUCTION

In 1993, natural gas accounted for about 30% of TPES in Nigeria. Currently the country does not export gas. The role of gas is overshadowed by that of oil which is of paramount importance to the Nigerian economy in terms of GDP (about a third), export revenues (about 95%) and government revenues (more than 80%). However, the country has significant gas reserves (second largest in Africa after Algeria) and could become an LNG exporter through realisation of the Bonny LNG project. Development of the gas sector has been plagued by difficult environmental dilemmas and financial obstacles.

Gas reserves in Nigeria are about equally divided between associated and non-associated gas. About 85% of gas production (30.7 bcm in 1994) is associated gas, but most of this is reinjected or flared - in 1994, 77% was flared, 8% reinjected and only 15% marketed. The cost of bringing associated gas to the market is much higher than for non-associated gas and there is no incentive to do so. The Government has imposed penalties on flaring, but so far the operating companies have preferred paying these penalties to limiting the flaring. A fiscal incentives package was introduced in 1992 to encourage foreign companies to invest in gas utilisation projects, but so far this has had very limited effects.

The Government has taken steps to make investments in the gas sector attractive to both local and foreign entrepreneurs. 100% foreign equity is allowed, and generous tax holidays and attractive capital allowances have been provided. Companies wishing to establish plants in the gas downstream sector have the additional advantage that they are allowed 50% exemption on duty on imported construction materials.

GAS DEMAND

In 1993, flared gas volumes were bigger than total energy consumption in Nigeria. Of the total gas volumes brought to market (4.6 Mtoe in 1994), 40% went into power generation (five thermal power plants). Only 0.7 Mtoe went to final use, all of which went into industry. No gas is used in the residential sector.

GAS SUPPLY

Total gas reserves in Nigeria are estimated at 3450 bcm, giving a reserve/production ratio of 112 years at the present production rate. The volumes marketed in 1994 (4.6 bcm) came mainly from non-associated gas fields. That will also be the case for the gas to be fed into the Bonny LNG project.

THE BONNY LNG PROJECT

The Nigerian LNG project has a long history: as long ago as 1962 the first attempt was made to establish a project to export LNG from Nigeria. A second attempt was made under Nigeria's Fourth Development Plan (1975-80) and provided for the development of two LNG plants. The Shagari Government which came to power in 1979 decided that the project was too large and expensive and should be reviewed; it was subsequently abandoned. The third attempt started in March 1985 and led to the incorporation of the joint venture company "Nigeria LNG Limited" (NLNG) in May 1989. Equity participation of the shareholders was as follows:

Nigerian National Petroleum Corporation	60%
Shell Gas B. V.	20%
Cleag Bermuda (Elf)	10%
Agip International	10%

The project involved development of a two train liquefaction plant with associated feed gas transmission system and other facilities. In October 1991, tenders were invited from two approved contractor consortia.

Marketing negotiations were concluded with the signing of LNG sales agreements between NLNG and its buyers (Enel of Italy, Gaz de France, Enagas of Spain and Distrigas Corporation of the US) in May and June 1992.

Gas supply agreements for the supply of feedstock gas to the project over a period of 22.5 years were signed in June 1992 between NLNG and the following upstream joint venture partners:

NNPC/Shell/Elf/Agip	53.33%
NNPC/Agip/Phillips	23.33%
NNPC/Elf	23.33%

The gas is to be supplied from the companies' extensive reserves in the eastern Niger delta area, at transfer points close to the producing fields where 300 bcm from 7 non-associated gas fields were dedicated to the project. The gas is to be fed into the plant at Bonny through a 218 km pipeline gathering system.

Financing activities were pursued in parallel with engineering and sales with the assistance of the International Finance Corporation (IFC). Evaluation of the tenders led to the recommendation for the selection of the preferred contractor in October 1992. Various problems arose, however and the project effectively came to a halt in October 1992, only to be relaunched in December, 1993.

The status of the company changed from public sector to private sector by the agreed sale of 11% of NNPC's shares. The revised shareholding structure is as follows:

NNPC	49%
Shell Gas B. V.	24%
Cleag Bermuda (Elf)	15%
Agip International B.V.	10%
International Finance Corporation	2%

In November 1993, the Nigerian Government showed support for the project with Decree 113 which provided extensive tax exemptions.

The relaunch of the LNG project resulted in a change of process technology and an increase in expected LNG production. The average daily LNG production based on two LNG trains will now be approximately 17500 tonnes per stream day run down to the storage tanks, requiring some 26 million standard cubic metres of feed gas per stream day.

Annual LNG production, based on a plant availability of 329 stream days per annum, is to be about 5.78 million tonnes of LNG (equivalent to 7.6 bcm), an increase in capacity of 25% compared with the original plant design. The additional feed gas requirement has been accommodated.

The contracts between NLNG and its buyers for the purchase of the original plant output of 5.7 bcm are still in place. The yearly contractual allocations to the buyers are as follows:

Enel	3.5 bcm
Enagas	1.0 bcm
Gaz de France	0.5 bcm
Distrigas Corporation	0.7 bcm

The LNG sales to the European customers are on a C.I.F. basis while the sale to the US buyers is F.O.B.. As of July 1995, negotiations for the additional volumes of LNG which the plant will now produce, were close to being concluded.

In addition to the four ships which had already been acquired by NLNG's subsidiary, Bonny Gas Transport Limited, it is estimated that two additional ships will be required in view of the expected increase in LNG production.

Total project cost is estimated at US$ 3.6 billion, US$ 2.4 for the liquefaction plant and transmission pipeline, US$ 0.3 billion for ships (of which 0.2 billion has already been spent on acquisition of four LNG carriers) and US$ 1 billion for other development and financing costs.

The start-up of the first train is expected to take place during the first quarter of 1999, and exports of LNG are scheduled to start by mid 1999.

INFRASTRUCTURE

Existing gas infrastructure in Nigeria is linked to local utilisation of gas. Shell has played a central role from an early stage. In 1978 and 1981, it contracted to supply natural gas to the Sapele and Ughelli power plants of the National Electricity Power Authority (NEPA). Earlier, the Aba/Port Harcourt industrial area had started using gas for local power generation in manufacturing plants.

To further encourage natural gas utilisation, the NNPC established a subsidiary company, the Nigerian Gas Company (NGC), to put the necessary infrastructure in place for local gas transmission and marketing. To date, the NGC has constructed over 1000 km of pipeline for the transmission of natural gas to commercial and industrial users. The pipeline network includes a 24 inch diameter, 300 km pipeline from Escravos in the western Niger delta oil operational area to Lagos, Nigeria's main industrial centre (the Escravos Lagos Pipeline-ELP). The design capacity of the ELP is 600 MMSCF/D but this could be increased to 1 BCF/D by installation of more compression capacity. The largest single consumer of gas from the ELP is the National Electricity Company to whose plants a total of 4000 MMSCF/day per day is supplied at peak. Sales into electricity production account for about 72% of the domestic gas sales of NGC. A number of other spurlines have been built from the major trunk gas pipeline to deliver gas to cement factories, glass factories, steel plants, etc.

In the eastern area of the country, some factories, including the NAFCON fertilizer plant, the Eleme Petrochemicals plant and a power station, use natural gas supplied by the NGC. Construction of a major trunk gas pipeline to supply about 200 MMSCF/D to an export oriented aluminium smelting plant at Ikot Abasi will start soon.

In 1993, a preliminary feasibility study for the building of a Trans West African Gas Pipeline from Lagos in Nigeria to Ghana was undertaken with the involvement of the World Bank. The plans envisages the construction of a 400 km 24 inch diameter pipeline from the Nigeria/Benin border to Tema in Ghana with a possible 12 inch pipeline to Takoradi in Ghana.

SECURITY OF SUPPLY

Since Nigeria is not yet a gas exporter, there is no track record of supply reliability. Oil exports have flown fairly evenly in the past but have suffered periodically from political upheavals and strikes. The external problems of the LNG project seem to have been overcome, but financing remains to be settled. In recent years, the NNPC has not always kept up with its cash-call payments. Since its independence Nigeria has experienced ethnic and religious conflict. The present military regime has been criticised by some Western countries for human rights violation, leading the Government to threaten foreign companies operating in Nigeria. The present political climate is therefore not the most favourable for the realisation of major capital projects. On the other hand, Nigeria has a strong interest in the Bonny project, and it is to be carried out by partners who have long experience in tackling changing political circumstances.

IRAN

INTRODUCTION

Although Iran's proved gas reserves are estimated at 21,000 bcm, at present the country produces gas only for its own use. The petroleum industry needs to reinject increasing amounts of gas into its aging on-shore oil fields to keep production from declining so steeply as to overpower the envisaged growth in off-shore oil production. The power, industry and residential sectors account for roughly one-third each of total marketed gas production.

Iran's gas reserves could support a much higher production level than the country's 1993 output of 60 bcm (of which 22 bcm was reinjected), and Iranian authorities plan to increase gas penetration in all domestic consumption sectors and also to start exporting gas to Europe and Asia. However, Iran's battered economy and strained relations with Western governments and thus with international lending institutions make it difficult to see how the country's ambitious export targets and pipeline construction plans can be realised on the schedules put forth.

In the longer term, however, as Iranian-Western relations normalise, Iran could become an important gas supplier to Europe as well as to certain former Soviet republics, Pakistan, India and perhaps other Asian countries.

THE IRANIAN ECONOMY

Iran's gross domestic product peaked in 1976 at about 171 billion 1987 US$, but fell by a third in real terms in 1977-81. It took until 1992 before it was back at its 1976 level. Meanwhile the country's population had grown by some 75 per cent, implying a drop in GDP per capita between 1976 and 1992 of more than 40 per cent.

Being highly sensitive to domestic oil industry and global oil market developments, the Iranian economy recovered in 1982-85, in spite of the Iran-Iraq war, as oil production bounced back, but suffered another setback in 1986-88 as the oil price collapse necessitated cuts in foreign exchange. Following the ceasefire between Iran and Iraq in 1988, oil production and economic activity in general increased fairly rapidly. However, economic growth in 1993 was estimated at only 1.8 per cent, and preliminary data for 1994 indicated a slight decline in GDP.

Consumer price inflation between 1981 and 1992 averaged about 17 per cent a year. Prices rose by some 21 per cent in 1993 and apparently by more than 30 per cent in 1994.

With oil exports accounting for 57 per cent of total exports (1993/94), Iran's trade balance and current account also mirror oil production and price developments. The current account swung from a small surplus in 1990 to deficits of US$ 9.5 billion, US$ 6.5 billion and US$ 3.8 billion in 1991, 1992 and 1993 respectively. Due to cuts in imports the current account for 1994 will probably show a small surplus. Iran's total external debts are estimated at about US$ 20 billion.

The share of government revenues stemming from oil and gas sales increased from an average of 38 per cent in 1985-89 to 54 per cent in 1990-92, and was forecast to rise to 63 per cent in 1993-94. There are plans to increase tax revenues by phasing out tax relief currently available to about half of the population, and institute a broad based consumption tax. Government expenditures have exceeded revenues every year since 1976. In 1992 the budget deficit corresponded to about 2 per cent of GDP. The Government, in close co-ordination with the International Monetary Fund, is trying to curtail the deficit by reducing capital expenditures and discontinuing subsidy policies.

ENERGY BALANCE DEVELOPMENTS

Total primary energy supply increased by an average of 5.5 per cent a year between 1971 and 1981, by an average of 6.8 per cent from 1981 to 1991, by 10 per cent in 1992 and by an estimated 8.7 per cent in 1993. Energy use has increased every year since 1970 except between 1979 and 1982 when declines in GDP following the revolution caused a 21 per cent drop in TPES.

Table 1   Total Primary Energy Supply and Total Final Consumption, 1993
(million tonnes of oil equivalent)

	Coal	Crude oil	Oil products	Gas	Hydro/ other	Electricity	Total
Indigenous production	0.94	186.34	.	30.13	0.95	.	218.35
Import	.	.	8.93	.	.	.	8.93
Export	.	-131.57	-2.49	.	.	.	-134.06
Intn. marine bunkers	.	.	-1.69	.	.	.	-1.69
Stock changes	-0.04	.	.	.	.	.	-0.04
TPES	0.90	54.77	4.75	30.13	0.95	.	91.49
Electricity generation	.	.	-6.87	-10.44	-0.95	6.14	-11.50
Petroleum refineries	.	-54.77	50.25	.	.	.	-4.52
Other transformation	-0.03	.	-0.61	-1.13	.	-1.14	-3.51
TFC	0.87	.	47.52	18.57	.	5.00	71.96
Industry	0.87	.	6.99	10.58	.	1.34	19.78
Transport	.	.	15.91	.	.	.	15.91
Other sectors	.	.	21.02	7.99	.	3.66	32.67
Non-energy use	.	.	3.60	.	.	.	3.60

Source: IEA Secretariat.

Oil production has recently been running at 3.6-3.7 million barrels a day, i.e., at or slightly above Iran's OPEC quota. The National Iranian Oil Company (NIOC) has demonstrated that output can be increased to some 4.1 million barrels a day, but observers question the sustainability of such a level. A present, 85-90 per cent of Iran's oil production is onshore production; however, NIOC's plans to increase capacity to 4.5 million barrels a day centres on foreign investment in the country's offshore fields.

Iran's energy supply is heavily weighted towards petroleum. In 1993 TPES was composed of 1 per cent coal, 65 per cent oil, 33 per cent gas and 1 per cent hydro power.

The fuel structure of TPES has changed over the years mainly as a result of fluctuations in gas supply. Iran's domestic gas production increased rapidly in the early 1970s to 17.7 Mtoe in 1974, but declined slightly in 1975-79 and plummeted to 6.5 Mtoe in 1980 and less than 5 Mtoe in 1981. Since then it has recovered steadily to about 30 Mtoe in 1993. Gas exports fell from 7.5-8 Mtoe a year in the mid 1970s to zero in 1981-89 before starting to pick up in the early 1990s; the last couple of years, however, have seen exports drop to zero again. Consequently, the oil share of TPES increased from 58 per cent in 1971 to 83 per cent in 1981 before falling back to about two thirds in 1993 while the gas share declined from 39 per cent in 1971 to 14 per cent 10 years later before recovering to about one third in 1993. Coal and hydro power have each accounted for 1-2 per cent of TPES since the early 1970s.

Iranian authorities are deeply worried about the pace at which domestic energy demand in general, and oil product demand in particular, is increasing. The energy minister recently warned that oil exports could dwindle to zero by 2000 if consumption is not checked.

GAS RESERVES

Estimated at 21 trillion cubic metres, Iran's proved natural gas reserves make up almost half of the Middle East's total proved reserves, and are as big as North and South America's and OECD Europe's combined proved reserves. Only Russia has more gas. Most of Iran's gas is non-associated and the fields are located both onshore and offshore in the Arabian Gulf. Onshore, the main non-associated gas fields are Sarakhs, Tange Bijar, Sarajeh, Qeshm, Kangan, Nar, Dalan and the Aghar structures. Offshore fields include Pars, South Pars and a new, unnamed field discovered in 1993 some 50 km from South Pars.

GAS PIPELINES AND OTHER INFRASTRUCTURE

Iran's existing gas pipelines are concentrated in the western and northern parts of the country. The Government's gas development programme to 2010 includes expanding domestic transmission and distribution pipeline networks and, according to the Government, a total of 3,500 km of pipelines were constructed between 1989 and 1993.

Table 2   Iranian Natural Gas Pipelines

Pipelines	Length (km)	Diameter (mm)
Storage system	177	406-1,067
Branch lines	677	102-762
Gachsaran-Shiraz	255	254
Naftshahr-Kalantar	171	102
Kalantar-Pabetagh	63	152
Sarakhs-Neka	800	762-914
Transmission line: Gheshm-Bandar Abbas	69	305
Naftshahr-Patagh	62	102-152
Production platform-Sirri Island	32	254
Marun-Agha Jari-Astara (IGAT 1)	1126	1067-1016

Sources: Arab Oil & Gas Directory 1994, OPEC Annual Statistics Review 1992

Iran has one gas export pipeline: the 1126 km Iranian Gas Trunkline (IGAT 1) which was completed in 1970. It runs from Bid Boland at the centre of a gas gathering system serving the southern Iranian oilfields to the Iranian-Azeri border town of Astara. Construction of an IGAT 2 was started in 1978, but work stopped in 1985; part of that pipeline now serves the domestic gas system.

GAS EXPLORATION, PRODUCTION AND DISPOSAL

After the Iranian revolution in 1979, NIOC took control of all upstream oil and gas operations. Transport and marketing of gas was delegated to the National Iranian Gas Company (NIGC).

Table 3   Gas Production and Disposal, 1980-94 (billion cubic metres)

	1980	1985	1990	1993	1994
Gross production	20.08	31.60	54.53	60.00	66.15
Reinjection	2.34	11.00	18.13	21.80	22.70
Flared & vented	9.47	5.40	11.35	8.63	8.90
Other losses	0.27	0.60	1.90	2.50	2.75
Marketed	8.00	14.60	23.15	27.07	31.80
Exports	0.22	0.00	1.50	0.50	0.00
Domestic consumption	7.78	14.60	21.65	26.57	31.80

Source: Cedigaz, IEA Secretariat.

Iran's gross gas production increased by an average of 8 per cent a year between 1980 and 1993. The share of production that was flared or vented declined from 47 per cent in 1980 to 14 per cent in 1993, while the share that was reinjected increased from 12 per cent to 36 per cent. Marketed gas volumes increased by an average of 10 per cent per year, bringing the share of output that was used domestically or exported up from 40 per cent to 45 per cent.

In 1992 the Government presented a 20 year gas development programme forecasting domestic sales and reinjection at 260 bcm a year, and exports at 50 bcm a year, by 2010. In January 1995 Iran's oil minister presented a production target of 135 bcm a year by 2000. Reinjection which at present runs at about 28 bcm a year, must be increased by some 70 per cent, i.e., to almost 48 bcm a year, over the period 1995-2000 just to maintain onshore oil production at its present level. Increasing the share of gas in power generation is another important goal. In 1993, electric power generation capacity was 17,000 MW. Plans call for increasing capacity to 35,000 MW by the end of 1998, at costs estimated at US$ 20 billion, with most of the new plants being combined cycle gas power stations or dual fired stations.

Expanding gas usage in the bigger cities is the third leg of the programme. Iranian authorities are pushing ahead with their plans in this area — in August 1994 the Government announced that 1.1 million households had been connected to the distribution pipeline grids between 1989 and 1993. The rest of the incremental gas will be used in industry. Iran is now the second largest producer of petrochemicals in the Middle East after Saudi Arabia. Output increased by 83 per cent, to 5.5 million tonnes of plastics, fertilisers and chemicals between 1990/91 and 1993/94. Plans call for the expansion of capacity to 12 million tonnes a year by the end of the century. Iran sees itself as a future large scale exporter of MTBE and fertilisers produced from gas.

Peak gas exports to the Soviet Union via IGAT 1, 9.6 bcm, were attained in 1975/76. Deliveries were stopped in the early 1980s and, after a brief restart in 1990, again in 1991.

Iran's gas exports may increase considerably from the late 1990s if the Government's long term supply contract negotiations with various importing countries bear fruit, and its export pipeline plans are realised. The Government will, however, have to overcome serious problems in the form of negative attitudes towards Iran in international capital markets, recently strengthened by western Governments' steps to contain Iranian aspirations in the region and worldwide.

Iran has reportedly signed an agreement with a duration of 23 years and a value of US$ 20 billion to supply gas to Turkey. Deliveries will start at 2 bcm in 1998 and rise to 8 bcm in 2001 and 10 bcm a year from 2002. The deal may be seen as complementing an existing gas supply agreement between Turkmenistan and Turkey. The Iran-Turkey deal includes constructing a 1,600 km gas pipeline from Tabriz in Iran to Ankara in Turkey. This pipeline would be an extension to a Turkmenistan-Iran pipeline envisaged in the Turkmenistan-Turkey agreement.

Iran hopes to export gas to more European countries. In March 1993 NIGC and Gaz de France formed a joint venture, the French Iran Gas Co-operation Company, to study alternative projects and routes to European markets. In April the same year, a consortium, the Gas Europe Consortium, was set up to examine the feasibility of a specific project to export gas to Europe as LNG or by pipeline via Turkey. Consortium members are Gaz de France, Ruhrgas, OMV, Enagas, CCP (a Czech company) and SPP (a Slovak company).

Tehran has proposed to construct a gas pipeline from Iran via Pakistan to India with the intention of supplying both countries, and with longer term hopes of supplying the whole of south-east Asia. Earlier this year Iran and Pakistan signed a preliminary agreement on setting up a consortium to build a 1,600 km pipeline with a capacity of 16 bcm a year from the Iranian port of Assaluieh to Karachi. Costs are estimated at US$ 3.4-3.5 billion. Pakistan is reportedly willing to discuss an extension of this pipeline to India and joint Pakistani-Indian use of the system, but Indian authorities are concerned about being at the end of a pipeline transiting a country with which India has had several conflicts. Iran and India are therefore conducting separate negotiations on a sub-sea gas pipeline running from Iran along the continental shelf of Iran and Pakistan to India.

With respect to the former Soviet republics, Iran has agreed to deliver 1.83 bcm a year to Georgia, and plans to sell 3 bcm a year to Ukraine. Tehran sees the latter country as a potential large market for Iranian gas, and envisages the construction of a pipeline with a capacity of 25 bcm a year via Azerbaijan, Georgia and Russia to Ukraine.

Trying to capitalise on its location, Iran is striving to become transit country for Central Asian gas en route to Europe. Iranian authorities have signed a memorandum of understanding with the Turkmen Government on transiting gas from Turkmenistan across Iranian territory to Turkey. The memorandum stipulates exports of up to 31 bcm a year for a period of 25 years.

IRAQ

GAS SUPPLY AND PRODUCTION

Iraq's natural gas reserves are estimated at 3.1 tcm or about 2.1% of the world's natural gas reserves. The great bulk of Iraq's reserves are associated with crude oil reserves. Prior to 1990, Iraqi gas production consisted solely of associated gas in oil reservoirs and oil field gas caps. The main sources of production are the Ain Zalah, Butma, Kirkuk, Bai Hassan, Rumaila and Zubair fields. The al-Anfal field, with reserves of about 127 bcm, is located southeast of the Kirkuk oil field and provides the only non-associated gas production in Iraq. Gas production from this field began in 1990 with current production about 6 mcm/d. Gas is transported via a 30 km pipeline to a gas processing station and on to Jambur where it enters the northern gas network for use as feedstock for petrochemical facilities and fuel for power stations.

Iraqi gas development has focused on building a gas gathering system to capture and utilise the gas produced in association with crude oil. The northern area gas gathering system, or the Northern Gas Project, became operational in 1983 with initial handling capacity of 20 mcm/d. The processing plant was designed to produce 11 mcm/d dry gas in addition to natural gasoline, LPG and sulphur. The system includes about 250 km of pipelines for distribution purposes.

In southern Iraq, the Southern Gas Project was completed in 1985, but was shut-in until the end of the war with Iran. Inaugurated in 1990, the system consists of nine gathering systems with a handling capacity of 16 bcm/y from the Rumaila and Zubair oil fields. Gas is transported to a 3 mcm/d processing plant in Basra and a NGL fractionation plant in Zubair. Pipelines connect the processing facilities to an LPG storage facility and LPG loading terminal at Khor al-Zubair. The terminal began operation in July 1990.

Marketed gas production was equal to 3.17 in 1994, up from 2.55 in 1993. Lack of adequate processing capacity has historically limited the production of gas. The marketed share of natural gas produced in Iraq, however, increased to a high of 93% in 1993 from a low of 12% in 1983. Prior to 1985, the percentage of gas flared had been over 80% and the increase in marketed production between 1986 and 1989 was due to Iraq's gas exports to Kuwait. The higher percentages of marketed production between 1991 and 1993 are due to the reduction of associated gas output as crude oil production declined. Most of the marketed production in that period came from the al-Anfal gas field.

At the March, 1995 conference in Baghdad the government stated current gas processing capacity was 20.9 bcm/y of which 5.6 bcm/y was in the Northern Gas Project and 15.3 bcm/y was in the Southern Gas Project. This capacity is sufficient to handle crude oil production capacity of 3.5 million barrels per day (mbd). As Iraq increases its crude oil production capacity to 6 mbd, it plans to expand the gas processing capacity accordingly.

GAS CONSUMPTION

All of current gas production is consumed domestically. Iraq plans to maximise the use of its natural gas production for the production of LPG, for feedstock in its petrochemical industry and for electrical generation using gas-fired power plants. In the last three years, the focus has been on rehabilitation of generating capacity. Of the 17 power stations damaged in the Gulf War (out of 20 plants), 11 were totally destroyed with 5 being gas-fired facilities.

When the international sanctions end, most of Iraq's available resources will most likely be directed at capacity expansion of its oil sector in order to boost hard currency earnings. As a result, gas flaring can be expected to increase dramatically, as gas gathering systems will not be a priority.

Figure 1   Use of Natural Gas Produced in Iraq (bcm)

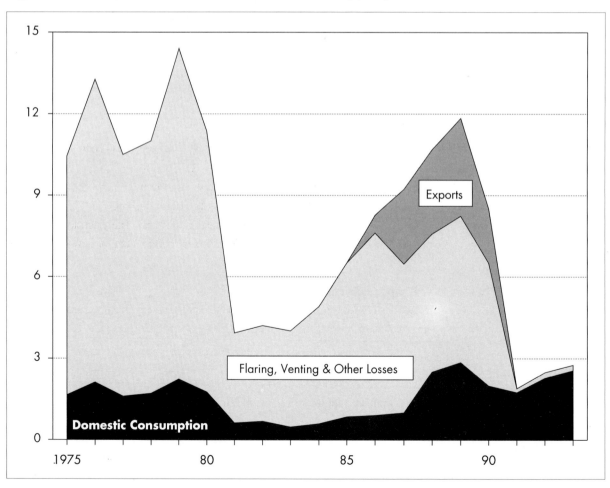

INFRASTRUCTURE

Iraq has a small network of gas pipelines, which are primarily situated in the southeast and central eastern parts of the country. The major pipelines are listed in Table 1.

Table 1   Iraqi Natural Gas Pipeline Network

Pipelines	Length (km)	Diameter (inches)
Rumaila/Kuwait	170	40
Basra/Baghdad	360	48
Northern Gas Project Network	250	—
Southern Gas Project Network	—	—
Al-Anfal/Jambur	30	20

At the March, 1995 conference in Baghdad the government stated its goals to use the natural gas which is produced from increasing crude oil production. Potential uses mentioned at the conference were power generation, export, petrochemicals and fertilizers. For these uses to be realised the government will have to expand the pipeline system to transport the natural gas from fields to various sites. Projects being examined are to expand the LPG pipeline, to construct a new NGL/LPG pipeline in southern Iraq and to complete the second stage of a regional gas pipeline.

FUTURE GAS PLANS

In March 1995, the Iraqi government outlined its gas sector goals and timetables. It stated its desires to minimise flaring of gas and to maximise the domestic use of natural gas in order to free more crude oil and more refined products for export. Most of this effort will go toward the utilization of gas produced in association with crude oil production. More extensive gas gathering systems will be required as crude oil production increases. The extension of existing gas networks will take precedence over the exploration and development of new gas reserves.

KUWAIT

Kuwait's proven natural gas reserves are estimated at 1.5 tcm, or about 1% of the world's total.[1] All of Kuwait's natural gas reserves are associated with oil, thus, all natural gas production is associated with oil production and produced by the Kuwaiti Petroleum Company (KPC). This association with oil is the main reason natural gas production declined between 1980 and 1985 as the production of crude oil declined over this period. To keep up with demand for natural gas KPC installed a gas gathering system and pipeline network in all of its oilfields. Exploration was unsuccessful in locating gas fields and by 1986 Kuwait was importing natural gas from Iraq. Since this source is no longer available, Kuwait is looking for alternatives.

Table 1   Kuwaiti Natural Gas Pipeline Network at Year End 1993

Pipelines	Owner/ Operator	Length (miles)	Diameter (inches)
Raudhatain/Ahmadi	KOC	57.0	30
Magwa/Ahmdi	KOC	9.7	20/40
Umm Gudair/Shuaiba	KOC	40.5	10/12
Burghan/Ahmadi	KOC	13.6	32/40

Source: OPEC, *Annual Statistical Bulletin*, 1993.
(KOC) Kuwaiti Oil Compagny.

Kuwait's gas industry suffered minor damage during the Gulf war; its LPG plant and bottling unit were unharmed but three of the country's five natural gas booster stations were damaged and one was destroyed.

The share of Kuwaiti produced natural gas that was marketed increased from 42% in 1975 to 74% in 1989. In 1994, the share had increased to 79%. The increase in marketed share was caused by a decrease in gas flaring and reinjection. In Figure 1, the large increase in losses and flaring in 1991 was due to the destruction of oil wells in Kuwait during the Gulf war. Since most gas production is associated with oil production, the large gas losses occurred because of uncontrolled oil flows. Total marketed production in 1994 was 5.97 bcm, all of which was consumed indigenously.

---

1. This total includes one half of the reserves located in the Neutral Zone between Saudi Arabia and Kuwait.

Figure 1   Natural Gas Use in Kuwait (bcm)

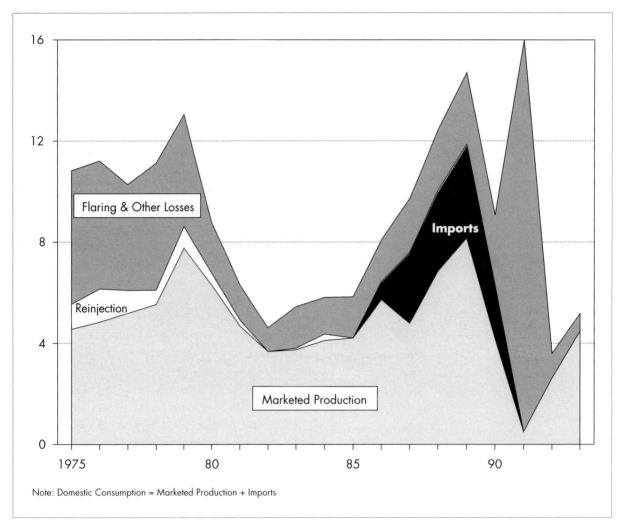

Note: Domestic Consumption = Marketed Production + Imports

OMAN

RESERVES AND PRODUCTION

The Government of Oman launched a long term gas exploration programme in 1986 aimed at diversifying the country's energy-based revenues. Large reserves of non-associated gas were discovered by Petroleum Development Oman (PDO), with the largest in the Saih Nihayda area (near Qarn al-Alam) where gas was discovered at a depth of 4000 metres. Expected reserves from the Saih Nihayda, Barik and Saih Rawl fields combined are estimated to be around 15 tcf. The Secretary of State for Petroleum in Oman (as quoted in *Natural Gas in the World, 1995 Survey*, Cedigaz) estimated that in January 1995 Oman had 750 bcm of proved natural gas reserves. According to Cedigaz, this figure most likely includes possible and probable reserves. The upward assessment of reserves (proven reserves were only 480 bcm in 1991) was based on recent discoveries and additional test wells on existing reservoirs.

Gross production in 1994 was 6.98 bcm, of which 4.34 bcm was marketed and consumed indigenously. Most of the dry gas is produced at Yibal; the Phase II development was completed in 1992. Other fields currently producing gas include Fahud, Natih and Saih Nihayda in the north and Birba in the south. Because of the recent discoveries in Oman, gas may soon overtake oil in its importance as an export fuel.

INFRASTRUCTURE

Oman has three main transmission pipelines. The first, 345 kilometres, 20 inch pipeline, links the processing plant in the Yibal field to the capital Muscat. It typically operates at 30 to 40 per cent per day, although nominal capacity is 3.5 million cubic metres per day. A second pipeline, 227 kilometres extending from Mureirat to Sohar, supplies gas to the copper complex at Sohar and gas customers along the coast. The third pipeline delivers gas from the processing plant at Saih Nihayada to southern Oman.

Oman aimed to have a pipeline to India, but the project has stalled due to financial and technical constraints. Potential equity partners in the project have rescinded their interest. In addition, the technical feasibility of constructing pipelines able to withstand the high pressures necessary for the deep-water route has been questioned. The Indian government has not committed to the long term purchase agreement, and the Omani government indicates that the project has limited chance of success (EIU, 1995 Report). Priority is instead given to the local Omani LNG project.

LNG PROJECT

PDO and Royal Dutch/Shell have identified the potential for a large scale LNG project in Oman. In 1992, a joint-venture agreement between Oman (51%) and Shell (34%) was set up with Total (4%), Oman Partex (2%), Mitsubishi Corporation (3%), Mitsui and Company (3%) and Itochu (1%). The project has provisions for both upstream and downstream facilities. The upstream facility will be owned by the Government of Oman and will consist of a gas dehydration and turbo-expander plant for condensate recovery and a 360 kilometre pipeline to the coast. Gas will be supplied from the Saih Nihayda, Saih Rawl and Barik fields. Seismic data estimated that proven reserves in these fields was equal to 9 Tcf in January 1995.

The downstream development includes liquefaction, shipping and marketing of the LNG. A two-train liquefaction complex with a nominal capacity of 6.2 million tonnes per year will be located on the northeast coast at Al Ghalihah, 15 kilometres north of Sur, and will be owned by Oman LNG LLC, the joint venture company. The engineering work for the downstream portion of the project was awarded to MW Kellogg and JGC in 1994 and is expected to be completed in October 1995.

GAS EXPORTS

Deliveries from the LNG project are expected to commence in 2000 with gas supplied to the Far East, primarily Japan, and perhaps to Western Europe. According to *Natural Gas in the World, 1995 Survey* (Cedigaz), the South Korean Company, Korea Gas Corporation, signed a letter of intent to buy 3 bcm of Omani LNG from the year 2000. China has also signed a preliminary agreement for 1.5 bcm per year. Japan is expected to be the largest importer of Omani LNG, with imports possibly reaching 7 bcm by the year 2010. There has been some discussion of delivering gas to Italy.

Oman is planning to export a small quantity of gas by pipeline to Ras al-Khaimah in the UAE in exchange for use of a separation and processing plant which belongs to the Ras al-Khaimah Commission.

QATAR

RESERVES

Qatar's proven natural gas reserves are estimated at 7.1 tcm or 4.8% of the world's total. These reserves are predominantly non-associated and concentrated in the offshore North gas field, the largest known, non-associated gas field in the world. Recoverable reserves for North field are estimated at 6431 bcm with Qatar's total natural gas reserves put at about 6714 bcm or approximately 40 billion barrels of oil equivalent.

Table 1   Qatari Natural Gas Reserves

Field	Production Start	Reserves (bcm)
Associated Gas		
Dukhan	1963	142.0
Edd El Shargi/Maydan	1979	127.0
Total Associated Gas		**269.0**
Non-Associated		
Dukhan Khuff	1978	14.2
Bul Hanine/N. Field	1991	6,431.0
Total Non-Associated		**6,445.2**
TOTAL		**6,714.2**

Source: *Arab Oil & Gas Directory,* 1994

Qatar's exploitation of its natural gas resources is focused on the offshore North field which is being developed in phases. An initial phase came onstream in 1991 and by 1993 output was about 9.1 bcm per year with 40 kbd of condensate. LPG is stripped from the gas stream and exported with the condensate. This phase comprised the design, construction and installation of a production complex in the North Field, offshore and onshore pipelines, an NGL plant and gas injection facilities at the onshore Dukhan field.

After the first phase of the North field came onstream, progress on further development appeared uncertain. That changed by the end of the 1992 when Mobil acquired a 10% share of the Qatar Liquified Gas Company (Qatargas), a joint venture set up to produce, transport and market LNG. Mobil also participates in a separate joint venture with QGPC, Ras Laffan LNG Company (Rasgas). The complete North gas field development slate includes LNG proposals, international export natural gas pipeline proposals and the domestic supply arrangement of Phase 1.

An important aspect of North field development is the increased production volumes of NGL (condensate) and LPG (propane and butane). NGLs have an API gravity in excess of 40° and are valuable in international oil markets. Because these NGLs are not produced in conjunction with oil, they are not included in Qatar's OPEC crude oil production quota. If just the Qatargas and Rasgas projects are completed, Qatar will have an additional 110 kbd of NGL exports and 1.330 million tonnes per year of LPG exports. The NGL alone is equivalent to a 27% increase in Qatar's 1994 crude oil production.

Table 2   North Field Development Projects

	Production Begins	Gas Output (bcm/y)	LNG Output (Mt/y)	Liquids Output (b/d)	LPG Output (Mt/y)	Status	Cost US$ billion
Phase 1	1991	9.1	—	35,000	.450	Onstream	1.3
Qatargas	1997	12.5	6	40,000	.500	Underway	6.0
Rasgas 1	1998	10.3	5	35,000	.415	Letters of Intent	4.5
Rasgas 2	2000?	10.3	5	35,000	.415	Letters of Intent	6.1
Enron	1998	10.3	5	35,000	.415	Uncertain	4.0
Elf/Sumit	2000?	8.3	4	30,000	.300	Uncertain	5.0
Eurogas	**?**	**12.5**	**6**	**44,000**	**.500**	**Uncertain**	**7.5**
LNG Total		**73.3**	**31**	**254,000**	**2.995**		**34.4**
ARCO	1996?	7.2	—	25,000	.250	Uncertain	0.8
GUSA	1999	20.7	—	75,000	.750	Design	4.0
Pipeline Total		**27.9**	**—**	**100,000**	**1.000**		**4.8**
TOTAL		**101.2**	**31**	**354,000**	**3.995**		**39.2**

The two main LNG projects (Qatargas and Rasgas — phases 1 and 2) have a combined cost of US $ 16.6 billion or about two times the size of annual Qatari GDP. During January 1995 Enron and QGPC signed a letter of intent to export additional LNG. If these three projects come to fruition, Qatar could be producing 48.3 bcm of gas per year and exporting 21 Mt/y of LNG, 2.025 Mt/y of LPG, and 170 kbd of NGL by the year 2000.

QATARGAS

Qatargas was originally organised in 1984 to develop and operate a liquefaction plant and market LNG overseas, but little progress was made and by January 1992 BP pulled out of the joint venture. At the end of 1992 Mobil, operator of the Arun LNG plant in Indonesia, acquired a 10% share of Qatargas in addition to its participation in a separate joint-venture with QGPC, Ras Laffan LNG Company.

Shareholders in the Qatargas venture differ in the upstream and downstream sectors. The upstream part, gas extraction, separation and marketing of liquids, is operated by Total. The downstream part, liquefaction, marketing and transportation of LNG, is operated by Mobil.

After extraction of the liquids, the dry gas will be wholly owned by the Qatari Government and sold to the downstream sector at a base price plus escalation clause. With regard to gas liquids, the government receives a royalty equivalent to 35% of production with the remaining 65% of production shared between the joint-venture partners. A government income tax of 35% is levied on the downstream sector of the project.

In May 1993, Qatargas (the lead North field development project) awarded more than US $1.6 billion worth of contracts for the North Field project. Awards included US $1.395 billion to Chiyoda Chemical Engineering and Construction Company for the engineering, procurement and construction of the two train LNG facility to be located at Ras Laffan.

In December 1993, a term sheet for a US $2 billion non-recourse loan for the downstream facilities was signed by the four lead underwriters, Bank of Tokyo, Industrial Bank of Japan, Fuji Bank and Sakura Bank. The loan is expected to be concluded in May or June 1994. About US $800 million in equity will be contributed in addition to the US $2 billion. The mandate to arrange a loan for the Qatargas upstream facilities of US $680 million out of a total upstream project cost of US $900 million has been awarded to Barclays, Credit Lyonnais, Gulf International Bank and Société Generale.

Chiyoda has begun construction of the liquefaction facilities at the Ras Laffan site and LNG exports are to begin in 1997. Chubu Electric Company of Japan signed a 25 year sales and purchase agreement for the delivery of 4 Mt/y to its plant in Nagoya. Chubu is committed to lift 2 Mt/y for the first year, 2.5 Mt/y for the second year, 3 Mt/y in the third year and 4 Mt/y by the fourth year. Chubu elected not to exercise an option to take another 2 Mt/y. During 1995 a consortium of seven Japanese electric utilities (Tokyo Electric Power Company, Tohoku Electric Power Company, Tokyo Gas Company, Osaka Gas Company, Toho Gas Company, Kansai Electric Power Company and Chugoku Electric Power Company) agreed to purchase an additional 2 Mt/y of LNG from Qatargas over a 25 year period. This raises the total amount of LNG sold under the Qatargas project to 6 Mt/y.

Shipping of the LNG has been arranged by a Japanese consortium under a 25 year time charter to Qatargas. The agreement calls for the ownership, construction, management and operation of seven LNG carriers each with a capacity of 135,000 cubic meters. The consortium members and their shares are the following: Mitsui O.S.K. Lines with 36.5%; Nippon Yusen Kaisha with 36.5%; Kawasaki Kishen Kaisha with 15%; Showa Line with 8%; and Iino Kauin Kaisha with 4%. The cost of construction for the seven LNG carriers is about US $1.6 billion, US $230 million for each carrier. The first carrier will be completed at the Mitsui Engineering and Shipbuilding Yard in November 1996.

Total cost for the Qatargas project is about US $6 billion composed of 17% for the upstream sector, 50% for the liquefaction trains and related facilities and 34% for the LNG carriers. Of that total, Qatargas is not financing the US $1.6 billion for the LNG carrier construction as the LNG transportation will be conducted under a time charter agreement.

RASGAS

The other major North field development project is the Rasgas project that is divided into two parts, Rasgas 1 and Rasgas 2. The Ras Laffan LNG Company or Rasgas was set up between QGPC (70%) and Mobil (30%) in 1993. The Rasgas project is independent of Qatargas but the infrastructure of both projects will be integrated to reduce costs and facilitate production, transportation and exports. As of March 1995 the joint venture had obtained five letters of intent for LNG sales volumes totalling 11 Mt/y, sufficient for the Rasgas 1 and 2 projects. The letters of intent come from Korea Gas Corporation (KGC) for 2.4 Mt/y, Taiwanese Chinese Petroleum Corporation for 2.1 Mt/y, China for 2 Mt/y, Turkey's Botas for 2 Mt/y and India's Essar for 2.5 Mt/y. In order to undertake financing and construction, Rasgas needs to convert these letters of intent to confirmed sales and purchase agreements. Negotiations continue regarding the conclusion of the final LNG purchase contracts.

The Rasgas project will be implemented in phases. On the purchase of LNG, for example, the letter from KGC stipulates that KGC would receive 600,000 tonnes in 1998, 1.2 million tonnes in 1999 and 2.4 million tonnes in the year 2000. On the supply side, initial Rasgas 1 plans call for a two train facility with a capacity of 5 Mt/y of LNG while Rasgas 2 would add 5 Mt/y capacity for a total of 10 Mt/y. Since actual production of LNG is typically greater than engineering specifications, Rasgas could probably supply the required volumes from this 10 Mt/y of "nameplate" capacity.

The offshore front-end engineering work for the proposed 10 Mt/y project was awarded to Hudson Engineering company and was completed by January 1995. Rasgas has already spudded its first delineation well to test the Khuff gas reservoir. The onshore front-end engineering design contract was awarded to Chiyoda Corporation and was completed by January 1995. Each LNG train will have a capacity of 2.5 Mt/y and the site of the trains will be in an industrial zone about 100 km north of Doha.

Approximate total cost for the Rasgas 1 project is about US $5.0 billion comprised of 24% for the upstream sector, 44% for the liquefaction trains and related facilities and 32% for the LNG carriers. A preliminary estimate for the Rasgas 2 phase is US $6.1 billion with a breakdown as follows: 25% for the upstream; 39% for the downstream; and 36% for the LNG carriers.

ENRON

During January 1995 Enron signed a non-binding letter of intent with QGPC to develop another LNG export project costing approximately US $4 billion and exporting 5 Mt/y of LNG over a 25 year period beginning in 1998 or 1999. The agreement has several important conditions: first, Enron will have to prove sales and purchase agreements, something that has not been completed. Second, Enron is required to arrange and provide all finance for the project. Reports indicate that Enron has a 40% share in the project and QGPC has a 60% share. These shares are planned to change over time as Enron's share will decline to 35% after the loan is repaid.

If the Enron project goes through, planned LNG exports would go to India (2.5 Mt/y) and Israel and Jordan (2.5 Mt/y). The LNG to India would go to a power plant at Dabhol that Enron is building in conjunction with General Electric and Bechtel. The power plant is scheduled to become operational in 1997, and Enron owns an 80% share of the project. At the same time, Enron is negotiating with the Israelis for the construction of a regasification plant.

Enron's project has progressed rapidly for three reasons. First, Enron was willing to provide all of the finance. Second, Enron uses a coordinated approach linking buyers with sellers in which it participates on both sides of the transaction. On the supply side Enron has 40% of the LNG project in Qatar, and on the purchase side Enron owns 80% of the power plant in India. Finally, the Enron project is not competing in markets already being addressed by Qatargas and Rasgas.

OTHER LNG PROJECTS

A fourth LNG venture is Qatar Europe Liquified Natural Gas Company (Eurogas) that was set up to produce and export LNG to Italy with the following members and shares: QGPC with 65%; Snam with 30%; and Nelson Bunker Hunt with 5%. Eurogas was unable to secure letters of intent for the purchase of its gas from European consumers. As a consequence, during February 1994 the foreign partner shares were transferred back to QGPC and the project will probably be dissolved. QGPC indicated that future demand for Qatari LNG would probably be met by existing ventures rather than new grassroots projects (although the Enron project was announced about one year after Eurogas was shelved).

In a fifth LNG venture, Elf and Sumitomo have initiated a feasibility study for a LNG production and export project after signing an agreement with QGPC in 1991. The Elf/Sumitomo project is contingent on finding buyers for the LNG and partners for the downstream portion of the proposed project. Approximate total cost for the project is US $5 billion.

GAS CONSUMPTION

Historically, marketed natural gas in Qatar was used exclusively for domestic consumption. The share of natural gas increased from 27% of gross production in 1970 to a high of 93% in 1988 (Figure 1). This will change in the future as the large export oriented gas projects become operational. During 1992, the marketed share declined to 74% as surplus gas from the North field was injected into the onshore Dukhan Khuff reservoir. The volume of gas used for reinjection purposes will most likely increase, but its share of total production will probably decline as it will be dwarfed by the large export oriented projects. The amount of gas flared has decreased from about 80% in 1972 to 0% after 1985. Some gas was vented in 1991 as the first production from the North field Phase 1 development programme got underway.

Figure 1   Use of Natural Gas in Qatar (bcm)

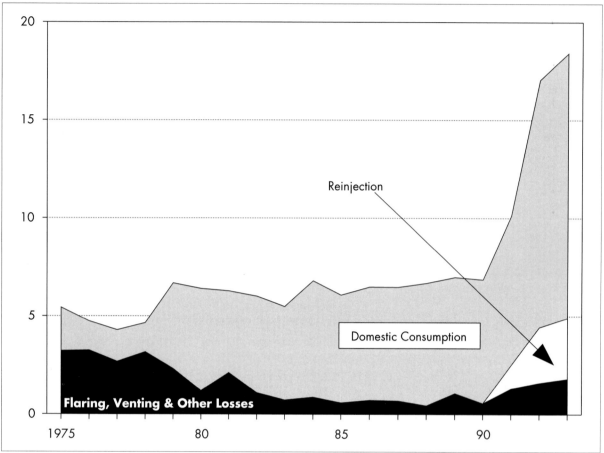

INFRASTRUCTURE

Qatar has a network of gas pipelines which connect the associated gas produced offshore with gas processing plants located at Umm Said, North field gas which supplies domestic consumption and reinjection into the Dukhan field, and power station and cement plants. An additional marine pipeline will be built from North field to Ras Laffan as construction of upstream facilities begins on the various LNG projects. If the Wintershall or Crescent development plans come to fruition, export gas pipelines will be built.

During 1994 ARCO Qatar Incorporated (a subsidiary of Atlantic Richfield Company) and British Gas Exploration and Production acquired equity stakes in a project that used to be called the Wintershall project. After equity participation ARCO became the group operator with a 27.5% share. Gulfstream Cyprus has a 27.5% share, British Gas a 25% share, Wintershall a 15% share and Deilmann Erdol Erdgas a 5% share. Under the previous exploration and production sharing arrangement Wintershall had a 50% interest in an offshore block containing an undeveloped gas/condensate structure directly adjacent to the North field together with partners, Gulfstream 33.85% and Deilmann 16.15%. The new project partners have not released details on their planned development of this acreage.

Table 3 Qatari Natural Gas Pipeline Network at Year End 1993

Pipelines	Owner/Operator	Length (miles)	Diameter (inches)
North Field/Umm Said NGL Plant	QGPC	129	34
Umm Said/Fahahil Reinject Comp.	QGPC	56	20
Umm Said/Point "B"/Power Station	QGPC	28,29,29	30,24,24
Idd El Shargi/Umm Said	QGPC	75	24
Fahahil/Point "B" Plant	QGPC	28	24
Point "B"/Umm Said	QGPC	28	24
Point "B"/Power Station	QGPC	29	18

Source: OPEC, *Annual Statistical Bulletin,* 1993

Prior to the acquisition by ARCO and British Gas, the Wintershall group was granted an 8 year extension (until 1996) on its exploration agreement from a ruling at the Hague in 1988. The ruling also included a provision that the agreement could be extended another 15 years until 2011 if the field came onstream by 1996. In 1992, the group submitted a proposal for development to QGPC that envisioned production of 7.2 bcm/y gas and 25 kbd condensate. The development plan was based on estimated reserves of 906 bcm gas, 576 million barrels of condensate and 538 million barrels of LPG. Marketing plans under the old project involved export by pipeline to Kuwait, Bahrain or UAE, probably for industrial use. Preliminary cost estimates were US $0.75 billion for the project.

The Gulf South Asia Gas Project (GUSA) is being proposed to transport natural gas from Qatar to Pakistan. The project is sponsored by UAE based Crescent Petroleum, Transcanada Pipeline, and Brown and Root. The project would transport up to 20.7 bcm/y through a 1000 mile, 44 inch pipeline that extends from Qatar to Pakistan via the UAE mainland and then offshore Iran. The proposed pipeline would have "T joints" at predetermined locations so other nations could utilise the pipeline, either to withdraw gas or to inject gas into the system.

Under the proposed plan, QGPC would sell the gas to GUSA and then GUSA would be responsible for transporting and selling the gas. The original plan calls for financing arrangements to be in place by 1995 with construction work taking three years. The technical feasibility study was completed during 1994 and preliminary cost estimates are US $4 billion.

Another pipeline project foresees gas trade between Qatar and Israel. Qatar and Israel began exploratory talks in 1993 concerning gas supplies in conjunction with Israeli plans to gradually convert its power stations and petrochemical facilities to dual fuel use. First discussions envisioned a gas pipeline, however latest plans centre on an LNG export project (the Enron project). Initial amounts would be about 3 Mt/y, potentially rising to 8 to 10 Mt/y. However, the future of a Qatar-Israel LNG supply project is uncertain. An announcement by the Qatari Foreign Minister in March 1994 served to delay future talks pending further progress on the Israeli and Palestinian peace accord. If the Enron LNG project goes forward and includes sales to Israel, a natural gas pipeline to Israel would probably be delayed.

Another proposed pipeline project would construct a natural gas pipeline network that would link GCC member nations. The Gulf Organization for Industrial Cooperation began conducting a feasibility study of the project during 1994. The proposed network would link Qatar with Kuwait through Bahrain and Saudi Arabia while another pipeline would travel through Oman to Dubai of the UAE. This project will enable GCC member nations to substitute natural gas for oil in electricity generation thereby freeing oil for export.

FUTURE GAS PLANS

The focus of Qatar's gas strategy is to optimise the production and use of its natural gas resources in an effort to maximise revenues. QGPC's primary aim is on developing the offshore North field gas reserves, increasing LNG exports and significantly expanding petrochemical exports to Qatar's export trade of crude oil, refined petroleum products, LPG and petrochemicals. The bulk of the development focus is directed at LNG projects with designated exports to the Far East. Increased gas production from the North field is also planned for domestic consumption, including power generation and desalination plants as well as export-oriented petrochemical facilities. QGPC is also evaluating plans for export gas pipelines. One project consists of a system that would connect Qatar with Kuwait, Saudi Arabia, Bahrain and Dubai. A second project envisions a gas pipeline to Pakistan with marine and overland sections. A third project involving gas supply to Israel has also been discussed with two variations: pipeline and LNG. If the Qatargas, Rasgas and Enron projects are implemented, Qatar could be exporting 21 Mt/y of LNG by the year 2002. The total cost of those LNG projects is approximately US $20.6 billion or three times the value of Qatar's GDP.

SAUDI ARABIA

GAS SUPPLY AND PRODUCTION

Proved natural gas reserves in Saudi Arabia were estimated to be 5.1 trillion cubic metres in January 1995. Gross production in 1994 was equal to 70.2 bcm but only 37.7 bcm was marketed. Processing capacity is the current constraint on marketing gas in Saudi Arabia. All of the marketed gas is consumed indigenously.

Saudi Aramco is the sole producer of natural gas in the Kingdom and natural gas is only sold domestically while LPG is exported. Most extracted gas is associated with oil and thus the Ghawar field is the largest source of gas. Most gas was flared until 1982 when the Master Gas System (MGS) began operation. The system is composed of 60 gas separation plants at Ghawar, Zuluf, Safaniyah and Khurais; three gas processing plants at Berri, Shedqum and Uthmanniyah; two gas fractionation plants at Yanbu and Juaymah; and the NGL pipeline. The MGS has a gathering capacity of 61 bcm/y and a processing capacity of 41 bcm/y. Thus, processing capacity is the current constraint.

On a worldwide basis, Saudi Arabia flares and vents the second largest volume of gas. Flaring represented 77% of gross production during the 1970s but has declined dramatically. In part this occurred because of decreased natural gas production associated with the decline in crude oil production between 1982 and 1985. To supplement associated gas production and maintain adequate supplies to SABIC, the state owned petrochemical company, Saudi Aramco began an exploration program to produce non-associated gas. By 1991 non-associated gas production was at 20 bcm/y. When associated gas production was low this posed no problem, however, as associated gas production increased, the total gas produced became larger than the processing capacity of the MGS. In addition, gas gathering facilities have not been expanded to transport all associated gas to the MGS. As a result, Saudi Aramco flares about 15 bcm/y of natural gas.

GAS CONSUMPTION

Domestic consumption of natural gas in Saudi Arabia increased about 13% per year between 1975 and 1993 due primarily to the rapid expansion of the Saudi petrochemical industry. SABIC was founded in 1976 to develop and produce fertilizer and petrochemicals. Between 1984 and 1990 SABIC's nominal productive capacity increased 396% while production increased 470% as plants performed above rated capacity. SABIC's rapid growth is the major factor in the large increase in domestic gas consumption between 1984 and 1990. Today, SABIC is a major supplier of base petrochemicals to the world market demanding large volumes of natural gas from Saudi Aramco.

Figure 1   Use of Natural Gas in Saudi Arabia (bcm)

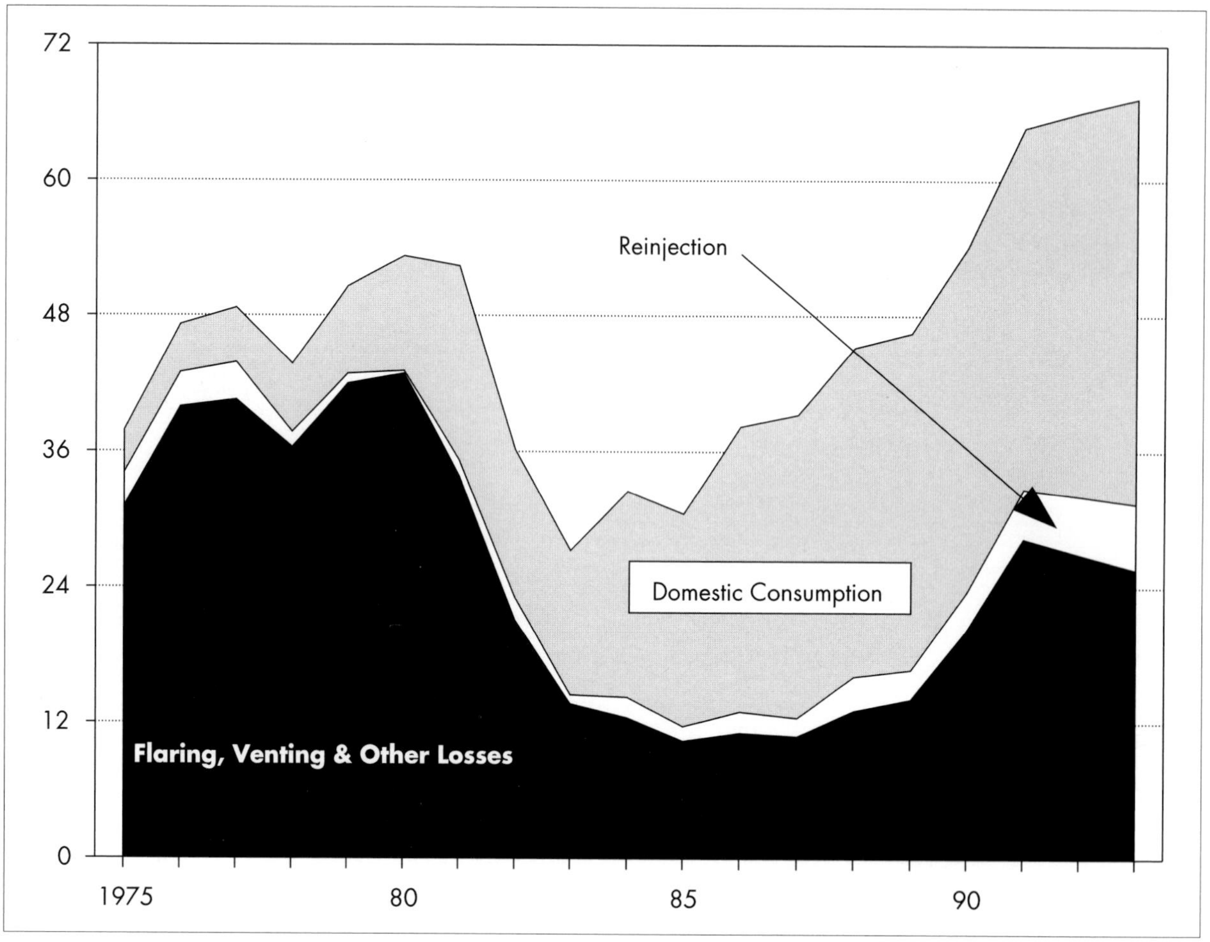

DOMESTIC GAS PRICES AND PRODUCTION COSTS

The price of natural gas to domestic customers is set by the government. For the Saudi petrochemical industry the price has been US $0.50 Mbtu for the last few years, low compared with prices petrochemical companies pay in IEA member countries.

Saudi Aramco is unwilling to increase the processing capacity of the MGS because Aramco claims the cost of increasing processing capacity (US $0.75 Mbtu) is greater than the sales price of the natural gas; and because the cost of expanding the MGS is greater than the cost of flaring. For some consumers the government raised the price of natural gas to US $2.00 Mbtu, however, there is no general policy change and the official price is still US $0.50 Mbtu for most customers.

UNITED ARAB EMIRATES

RESERVES AND PRODUCTION

The federation of the United Arab Emirates (UAE) is composed of seven emirates: Abu Dhabi, Ajman, Dubai, Fujairah, Ras al-Khaimah, Sharjah and Umm al-Qaiwain. The federation is united under a provisional constitution that is in force for five years and the current constitution was approved in 1991.

The UAE's proven reserves are estimated to be 5.8 tcm of natural gas or about 4% of the world's total. In Abu Dhabi, which accounts for over 92% of the nations' oil and gas reserves, decisions on oil affairs are under the jurisdiction of the Supreme Petroleum Council (SPC) which is chaired by the crown prince of Abu Dhabi.

Figure 1   Natural Gas Production by Emirate (bcm)

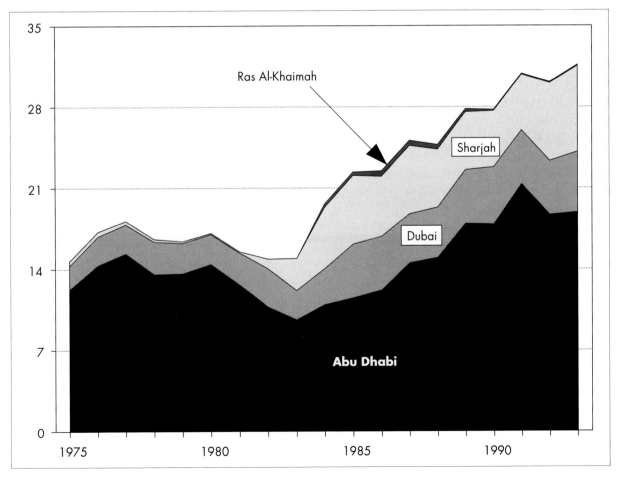

UAE gross production of natural gas increased about 4% per year between 1975 and 1993 reaching 34.4 bcm in 1994. Marketed natural gas (composed of domestic consumption and exports) increased steadily from about 11% of gross production in 1975 to about 74% of gross production in 1994. Of the marketed gas, domestic consumption accounted for around 21 bcm and net exports accounted for 4.3 bcm. About 5 bcm of gross production was reinjected, 0.3 bcm was flared or vented and 3.6 bcm was classified as other losses.

Abu Dhabi is the largest producer of natural gas with gross production of 20.8 bcm in 1994 or just over 60% of UAE production. Ranked second is Sharjah with 8.2 bcm or 24% and ranked third is Dubai with 5.3 bcm or 15% of UAE production.

Abu Dhabi's natural gas exploration programme focuses on non-associated gas. The programme has been more successful offshore than onshore and in 1994 13 gas wells were completed in the UAE.

Abu Dhabi, Dubai and Sharjah manage their gas industries differently. In Abu Dhabi there is the Abu Dhabi Gas Liquefaction Company (ADGAS), which exports LNG from Das Island, and Abu Dhabi Gas Industries Company (GASCO), which treats gas at Ruwais. In Dubai, gas output is

Figure 2   Use of Natural Gas Produced in the UAE (bcm)

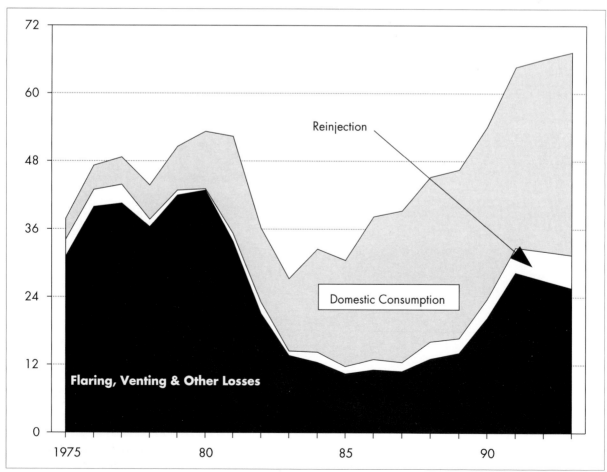

treated by Dubai Natural Gas (DUGAS) at Jebel Ali and is obtained from Arco's onshore gas condensate field. In Sharjah, Crescent Petroleum consortium developed the offshore Mubarak field while an Amoco led consortium developed the Sajaa gas field.

Most of the gas reserves in the UAE are associated with oil and historically natural gas production has grown with oil production. Abu Dhabi's production goal is to increase daily gas production by 100% between 1998 and 2003 and in 1990 Abu Dhabi approved plans for large scale onshore and offshore gas development. Abu Dhabi plans to increase associated gas production by increasing oil production and is developing non-associated gas reserves from onshore and offshore fields. Onshore, the output of associated and non-associated gas is set to rise from the Bab and Bu Hasa fields. At the Bab field under Project 545, associated natural gas production will increase to 20.8 bcm/y in 1995 from 5.7 bcm/y in 1992 and non-associated gas production will increase an additional 3.1 bcm/y. As part of the project, condensate recovery will increase to 131 kbd from a current level of 5 kbd. Offshore, gas production will increase from the Khuff gas structure (located under the Abu Al-Bukhoosh oil field) and from the Umm Shaif field. Umm Shaif is one of the largest non-associated gas fields in the world and gas from this field will be piped to Das Island where it will be used in the new LNG train. When this project is complete, gas production will be 11.4 bcm/y compared with a current level of 6.0 bcm/y.

Dubai's natural gas is produced from the Margham non-associated gas field and the gas fields associated with Fateh, Galah, Southwest Fateh and Rashid oil fields. Dubai consumes more gas than it produces and has been importing natural gas from Sharjah. Domestic demand has been increasing rapidly and Dubai is examining options to import additional gas from a new supplier—possibly Qatar or Iran.

Within the UAE, Sharjah has the second largest volume of natural gas reserves and the majority of its reserves are located in the onshore field of Mubarak.

LNG PROJECTS

The LNG plant on Das Island is operated by ADGAS and is the only facility exporting LNG in the Middle East. The project was conceived to minimise pollution from flaring and to provide gas to a growing Japanese market. Negotiations between Tokyo Electric Power Company (TEPCO) and ADGAS were concluded in 1972 with an agreement that ADGAS would provide TEPCO with 2.0 Mt/y of LNG and 0.5 Mt/y of LPG for 20 years beginning in 1977. Ground was broken in 1973 for the new liquefaction plant and production commenced in 1977.

The Das Island LNG plant consists of two liquefaction trains using cryogenic technology. These trains are designed to process 4.3 bcm/y of associated gas from 11 gas streams from Umm Shaif and Zakum oil fields. Output from the plants has been above design capacity and includes 2.5 Mt/y of LNG, 1.2 Mt/year of LPG and 0.3 Mt/y of pentane plus. All of the plant's LNG and most of its LPG are exported to Japan under the long term contract.

To transport the LNG from Das Island to Tokyo, Liquified Gas Shipping Company (LGSC, a subsidiary of ADGAS) charters 5 LNG carriers: one has a capacity of 87,600 cubic meters (cm) and four have capacities of 125,000 cm. There are also three LPG carriers that have capacities of 79,600 cm. The distance to Tokyo from Das Island is 10,500 km and round trip takes about 34 days.

In 1990 TEPCO and ADGAS agreed to extend the period of the contract for an additional 25 years with LNG volumes increasing to 4.3 Mt/y and LPG volumes increasing to 0.7 Mt/y. The new agreement took effect in 1994.

To meet the contract volumes ADGAS began construction of a third LNG train at Das Island in 1991. The third LNG train was completed during 1994 with a capacity of 2.5 Mt/y of LNG and 0.25 Mt/y of LPG. Smaller volumes of LPG will be produced since most of the natural gas for the new LNG train will from come non-associated gas fields. The expansion utilises storage capacity and the terminal capacity that was in place on Das Island. The frequency of tanker loadings will increase to one tanker every three days, thus, scheduling will be "tighter".

During 1995 production of LNG from the new plant was averaging 20% more than design capacity and ADGAS was considering methods to further increase output by debottlenecking the plant. With LNG production greater than TEPCO requirements, ADGAS began selling LNG shipments to the European market.

In December 1993 the National Gas Shipping Company Limited (NGSCO) was established to provide shipping services to ADGAS and to manage the LNG and LPG fleet of LGSC. NGSCO became fully operational in 1994 and will operate the eight carriers ordered by ADGAS. The eight tankers have capacities of 137,500 cm: four are replacements for the old fleet and four are designed to provide additional transportation capability for the increase in LNG exports. Three of the carriers have already been delivered with the remaining five scheduled for delivery between 1995 and 1997.

The cost of the third LNG train was US $1.3 billion and the cost of each tanker was US $250 million. All eight tankers thus cost US $2.0 billion. The cost of the expansion (new LNG train plus 4 LNG tankers) is US $2.3 billion. All of the project cost is funded by the ADGAS partners (no financing) with ADNOC providing 70% of the funds.

INFRASTRUCTURE

The UAE has a vast network of pipelines linking gas fields to processing plants, terminals and domestic customers. Table 1 illustrates the existing network in 1993.

In addition to the pipelines listed in Table 1 there is a 76 kilometre (km), 24 inch pipeline built to transport gas from Sharjah to Dubai. In Abu Dhabi, a new 46 inch pipeline is being built from Umm Shaif to Das Island. Another new project is an 87 km submarine gas line that is being built between the offshore Mubarak field in Sharjah and Dubai's Jebel Ali industrial zone. In Sharjah, a 24 inch, 40 km pipeline is being built between the onshore Sajaa gas field and a power station.

Table 1   UAE Natural Gas Pipeline Network at Year End 1993

Pipelines	Owner/ Operator	Length (inches)	Diameter (miles)
Asab/Bab	GASCO	55	20
Bu Hasa/Bab	GASCO	28	20
Bab/Maqta	HPD-ADNOC	2X81	30/24
Maqta/Baniyas	HPD-ADNCO	11	16
Bab/Ruwais	HPD-ADNOC	63	30
Bab/MP21	GASCO	21	20
Bu Hasa/MP 21	GASCO	21	16
MP 21/Ruwais	GASCO	41	24
Asab/Bab	GASCO	55	20
Umm Shaif/Das Island	ADMA-OPCO	19	30
Zakum/Umm Shaif	ADNOC	37	18
Murgam/Jabel Ali	Dubai Govt.	47	24
Junction 2/Ajman	EGPC	8	10
Sajaa/Junction 6	EGPC	26	20
Junction 6/New Qidfa	EGPC	49	14
Junction 6-10-7/Rak	EGPC	59	16/10/6
Sajaa/Sharjah	EGPC	27	18/6/4

Source: OPEC, *Annual Statistical Bulletin*, 1993.

In Abu Dhabi the associated natural gas produced at the onshore oil fields is piped to gathering stations, then to processing plants at Bu Hasa (4 bcm/y processing capacity), Bab (1.5 bcm/y) and Asab (3.1 bcm/y) and then to a fractionation plant at Ruwais. All of these facilities are operated by GASCO. ADNOC operates two natural gas processing plants at Thamama F (2.6 bcm/y) and Thamama C (4.9 bcm/y). Processing of natural gas at Thamama C is being expanded with the construction of a second processing plant that will have a capacity of 3.3 bcm/y when completed in 1995. ADGAS operates the LNG plant at Das Island and recently doubled output capacity.

Output from the fractionation plant at Ruwais is 4.75 Mt/y. This output is composed of 1.22 Mt/y of propane, 1.41 Mt/y of butane and 2.12 Mt/y of pentane plus. GASCO operates the plant, exports plant output and is debottlenecking this plant to handle the planned increase in gas recovery. When the expansion is complete, the capacity of the fractionation plant at Ruwais will be 6 Mt/y. Output from the Thamama C processing plants include 4.5 kbd of NGL, 26 kbd of condensates and 800 tonnes of sulphur.

In Dubai, associated gas from the various fields is piped through an undersea pipeline to the DUGAS NGL plant at Jebel Ali, which has a capacity of 1.35 bcm/y. Output from the plant is composed of 1000 tonnes of butane, 700 tonnes of propane and 9 kbd of condensates.

In Sharjah, there is a gas processing plant at the Sajaa field that has a capacity of 5.7 bcm/y and output from the plant includes 60 kbd of condensates.

FUTURE GAS PLANS

The Emirates are undertaking a significant expansion in the production and marketing of natural gas. In particular, Abu Dhabi seeks to increase daily natural gas production by 100% between 1998 and 2003. Export volumes of LNG from Abu Dhabi to Japan are set to double in 1995 with additional spot sales to other markets. Future natural gas production and recovery will increase substantially, as will the domestic utilisation of natural gas. Much of the gas will be reinjected into oil reservoirs, thus helping to maintain crude oil output.

REFERENCES

CHAPTER II   European Commission (1990) "Security of Supply" *Energy in Europe* No. 16, reprinted in "Energy Policy - An Agenda for the 1990s" Science Policy Research Unit, University of Sussex, May 1993.

International Energy Agency (IEA) (1994) *Natural Gas Transportation: Organisation and Regulation*, OECD Paris.

International Energy Agency (IEA) (1985) *Energy Technology Policy*, OECD Paris, reprinted in "Energy Policy - An Agenda for the 1990s" Science Policy Research Unit, University of Sussex, May 1993.

Natural Petroleum Council (NPC) (1993) "Natural Gas Study", Washington.

CHAPTER III   Cedigaz (1995) *Natural Gas in the World*, 1995 Survey, Rueil-Malmaison.

Cedigaz (1994) *Natural Gas in the World*, 1994 Survey, Rueil-Malmaison.

Cedigaz (1993) *European Natural Gas Trade by Pipelines*, Rueil-Malmaison.

Dahl, Carol and Eystein Gjelsvik, "European Natural Gas Cost Survey", *Resources Policy*, September 1993.

Hafner, Manfred (1994) "Gaz Naturel, et Production d'Électricité - Analyse Technologique et Économique de la Génération d'Électricité et du Transport de Gaz pour les Pays du Bassin Méditerranéen", Thèse de Doctorat à l'École des Mines de Paris et à l'Institut Français du Pétrol, Editions Technip.

Hawkshaw, John, "Where Will Europe's Future Supplies Come From?", Paper presented at the GASTECH conference in Kuala Lumpur, October 1994.

International Energy Agency (IEA) (1995a) *Oil, Gas and Coal Supply Outlook*, OECD, Paris.

International Energy Agency (IEA) (1995b) *World Energy Outlook*, OECD, Paris.

International Energy Agency (IEA) (1994) *Natural Gas Transportation: Organisation and Regulation*, OECD, Paris.

Masters, Charles D., Emil D. Attanasi and David H. Root (1994), "World Petroleum Assessment and Analysis," USGS, Reston, mimeo.

National Energy Board (NEB) (1994a) *Canadian Energy Supply and Demand 1993-2010*, Calgary, July 1994.

National Energy Board (NEB) (1994b) *Supply and Demand - Technical Report*, Calgary, 1994.

OME (1995) "Future Natural Gas Supplies for Europe, the Role of Transit Countries and Security of Supply", study conducted for the IEA by the l'Observatoire Méditerranéen de l'Energie.

Pauwels, Jean-Pierre (1994) *Géopolitique De L'Approvisionnement Énergétique De L'Union Européenne Au XXIe Siècle*, Bruylant, Bruxelles.

CHAPTER IV   American Gas Association (1994) *Gas Facts 1994*, Washington.

Canadian Gas Association (1994) *Canadian Gas Facts 1994*, Ontario.

Chabrelie, Marie-Francoise, *European Natural Gas Trade by Pipelines*, Cedigaz, Paris, 1993.

Cornot, Sylvie, *Underground Gas Storage in the World, 1990 Survey*, Cedigaz, Paris, 1990.

De Vany, Arthur and W. David Walls (1994) "Natural Gas Industry Transformation, Competitive Institutions and the Role of Regulation" *Energy Policy*, Vol.22, No. 9.

Department of Energy/Energy Information Agency DOE/EIA (1995) *Annual Energy Outlook 1994*, Washington.

Energy Information Agency (EIA) (1994) *Natural Gas 1994 - Issues and Trends*, Washington.

International Energy Agency (IEA) (1994) *Natural Gas Transportation: Organisation and Regulation*, OECD, Paris.

Natural Gas Supply Association (1994) *1994 Natural Gas Deliverability Survey*, Washington.

Stern, Jonathan, "Britain Dithers as Canadian Reform Pushes Ahead", *Gas Matters*, April 1994.

Sutherland, Ronald F. "Natural Gas Products in the Emerging Competitive Market" *Energy Policy*, December 1993.

CHAPTER V   Warwick, Stephen R. "Marketing Natural Gas after Order 636", *Utilities Policy*, January 1994.

Barret, C. (1994) "Outlook for Regional Gas Markets: Asia/Pacific" Presentation to the DRI Energy Outlook Conference: Natural Gas Market Prospects, Essen, 16-17 June 1994.

Department of Energy (DOE) (1995) *Weathering the Cold of 1994: A Review of the January 1994 Energy Supply Disruption in the Eastern United States*, Washington, May.

Department of Energy/Energy Information Agency DOE/EIA (1995) *Annual Energy Outlook 1994*, Washington.

Department of Energy/Energy Information Agency DOE/EIA (1994) *Annual Energy Outlook 1993*, Washington.

Dutch Electricity Generation Board (SEP) *Electricity Plan 1995-2004 and Notes to Electricity Plan 1995-2004,* Arnhem, August 1994.

Energy, Mines and Resources Canada, International Natural Gas Division, *The Role of Canadian Natural Gas in US Non-Utility Power Generation,* April 1993.

Enseling, Gerhard (1994) "Perspectives for Natural Gas in Western Europe" 17th Annual International Energy Conference of the IAEE, Stavanger, 27 May 1994.

Federation of Electric Power Companies (FEPC) (1994) *FEPC Report 1993/94,* Tokyo.

Gainey, Brian W. (1991) *Natural Gas for Power Generation,* Shell Selected Papers, November 1991, based on a presentation at the World Gas Conference, Berlin, July 1991.

International Energy Agency (IEA) (1995a) *Energy Prices and Taxes,* OECD, Paris.

International Energy Agency (IEA) (1995b) *World Energy Outlook,* OECD, Paris.

International Energy Agency (IEA) (1994a) *Electricity Supply Industry: Structure, Ownership and Regulation in OECD Countries,* OECD, Paris.

International Energy Agency (IEA) (1994b) *Energy Policies of IEA Countries, 1993 Review,* Paris, OECD, 1994.

International Energy Agency (IEA) (1994c) *Natural Gas Transportation: Organisation and Regulation,* OECD, Paris.

International Energy Agency (IEA) *Combined Heat and Power Generation in IEA Member Countries,* OECD, Paris, October 1994, unpublished.

IEA/CIAB (1994) *Industry Attitudes to Combined Cycle Clean Coal Technologies - Survey of Current Status,* Paris.

IEA/OECD (1993) *Electric Power Technologies: Environmental Challenges and Opportunities,* Paris.

The INGAA Foundation (ed.) *Natural Gas for Electric Generation: Realising the Potential,* Washington, May 1994.

International Panel on Climate Change (IPCC) (1995) *IPCC Guidelines for National Greenhouse Gas Inventories,* Volumes 1, 2 and 3, Greenhouse Gas Inventory Workbook.

Jonchère, J.-P. (1993) "Fuel Sources and the Utilities in a Changing Environment: Gas in the Power Market to the Year 2000", Presentation to the World Electricity conference, 16-17 November 1993.

Makovich, L. and Smalley, G. (1993) *Survey of Electric Utility Fuel Switching and Implications of Electric Utility Fuel Switching.* Report prepared for the Gas Research Institute, Chicago and Washington, December 1993.

Ministère de l'industrie, des postes et télécommunications et du commerce extérieur/DGEMP-DIGEC: *Les coûts de référence - production électric d'origine thermique.* Paris, 1993.

North American Electric Reliability Council (NERC), *Reliability Assessment 1992-2001*, Princeton, 1992.

OECD/NEA (1993) *Nuclear Energy Agency/International Energy Agency: Projected Costs of Generating Electricity.* Update 1992, Paris.

Prior, M. (1994) "The Supply of Gas to Europe", *Energy Policy* 22 (1), pp. 447-54.

Slaughter, A. (1994) "The Outlook for Oil and Gas Prices" Presentation at the DRI Energy Outlook Conference: Natural Gas Market Prospects, Essen, 16-17 June 1994.

Toichi, Tsutomu (1994) "LNG Development at a Turning Point and Policy Issues for Japan", *Energy in Japan*, March 1994, bimonthly report no. 126.

Union pour la Co-ordination de la Production et du Transport de l'Électricité (UCPTE) *Annual Report 1992*, Madrid.

CHAPTER VI American Gas Association (1994) *Fact Sheet on Natural Gas Industry Actions, January 1994*, Washington, February 4.

Cedigaz (1994) *Natural Gas in the World, 1995 Edition*, Rueil-Malmaison.

Department of Energy (DOE) (1995) *Weathering the Cold of '94: A Review of the January 1994 Energy Supply Disruptions in the Eastern United States*, Washington, May.

Gas Research Institute (GRI) *Maintaining Reliability in the Natural Gas Delivery System*, August 1994, United States.

International Energy Agency (IEA) (1994) *Natural Gas Transportation: Organisation and Regulation*, Paris.

National Energy Board (1993) *Natural Gas Market Assessment: Canadian Natural Gas Market Mechanisms - Recent Experiences and Developments*, Calgary, November.

Natural Resources Canada (NCR) (1994) *Natural Gas Storage: A Canadian Perspective*, Ottawa.

CHAPTER VII Department of Energy (DOE) (1995) *Weathering the Cold of '94: A Review of the January 1994 Energy Supply Disruptions in the Eastern United States*, Washington, May.

DOE/EIA (1994) *Annual Energy Review 1993*, Washington.

DOE/EIA (1991) *Manufacturing Fuel Switching Capability 1988*, Washington.

F. Ledger and H. Sallis (1994) *Managing the Power Supply*, Routledge, London.

International Energy Agency (IEA) (1994) *Energy Prices and Taxes*, OECD, Paris.

Petroleum Industry Research Associates (PIRA) (1993) *Gas-to-Oil Fuel Switching*, Washington.

MAIN SALES OUTLETS OF OECD PUBLICATIONS
PRINCIPAUX POINTS DE VENTE DES PUBLICATIONS DE L'OCDE

ARGENTINA – ARGENTINE
Carlos Hirsch S.R.L.
Galería Güemes, Florida 165, 4° Piso
1333 Buenos Aires   Tel. (1) 331.1787 y 331.2391
Telefax: (1) 331.1787

AUSTRALIA – AUSTRALIE
D.A. Information Services
648 Whitehorse Road, P.O.B 163
Mitcham, Victoria 3132   Tel. (03) 873.4411
Telefax: (03) 873.5679

AUSTRIA – AUTRICHE
Gerold & Co.
Graben 31
Wien I   Tel. (0222) 533.50.14
Telefax: (0222) 512.47.31.29

BELGIUM – BELGIQUE
Jean De Lannoy
Avenue du Roi 202
B-1060 Bruxelles   Tel. (02) 538.51.69/538.08.41
Telefax: (02) 538.08.41

CANADA
Renouf Publishing Company Ltd.
1294 Algoma Road
Ottawa, ON K1B 3W8   Tel. (613) 741.4333
Telefax: (613) 741.5439
Stores:
61 Sparks Street
Ottawa, ON K1P 5R1   Tel. (613) 238.8985
211 Yonge Street
Toronto, ON M5B 1M4   Tel. (416) 363.3171
Telefax: (416)363.59.63

Les Éditions La Liberté Inc.
3020 Chemin Sainte-Foy
Sainte-Foy, PQ G1X 3V6   Tel. (418) 658.3763
Telefax: (418) 658.3763

Federal Publications Inc.
165 University Avenue, Suite 701
Toronto, ON M5H 3B8   Tel. (416) 860.1611
Telefax: (416) 860.1608

Les Publications Fédérales
1185 Université
Montréal, QC H3B 3A7   Tel. (514) 954.1633
Telefax: (514) 954.1635

CHINA – CHINE
China National Publications Import
Export Corporation (CNPIEC)
16 Gongti E. Road, Chaoyang District
P.O. Box 88 or 50
Beijing 100704 PR   Tel. (01) 506.6688
Telefax: (01) 506.3101

CHINESE TAIPEI – TAIPEI CHINOIS
Good Faith Worldwide Int'l. Co. Ltd.
9th Floor, No. 118, Sec. 2
Chung Hsiao E. Road
Taipei   Tel. (02) 391.7396/391.7397
Telefax: (02) 394.9176

**CZECH REPUBLIC – RÉPUBLIQUE
TCHÈQUE**
Artia Pegas Press Ltd.
Narodni Trida 25
POB 825
111 21 Praha 1   Tel. 26.65.68
Telefax: 26.20.81

DENMARK – DANEMARK
Munksgaard Book and Subscription Service
35, Nørre Søgade, P.O. Box 2148
DK-1016 København K   Tel. (33) 12.85.70
Telefax: (33) 12.93.87

EGYPT – ÉGYPTE
Middle East Observer
41 Sherif Street
Cairo   Tel. 392.6919
Telefax: 360-6804

FINLAND – FINLANDE
Akateeminen Kirjakauppa
Keskuskatu 1, P.O. Box 128
00100 Helsinki

Subscription Services/Agence d'abonnements :
P.O. Box 23
00371 Helsinki   Tel. (358 0) 12141
Telefax: (358 0) 121.4450

FRANCE
OECD/OCDE
Mail Orders/Commandes par correspondance:
2, rue André-Pascal
75775 Paris Cedex 16   Tel. (33-1) 45.24.82.00
Telefax: (33-1) 49.10.42.76
Telex: 640048 OCDE

Orders via Minitel, France only/
Commandes par Minitel, France exclusivement :
36 15 OCDE

OECD Bookshop/Librairie de l'OCDE :
33, rue Octave-Feuillet
75016 Paris   Tel. (33-1) 45.24.81.81
(33-1) 45.24.81.67

Documentation Française
29, quai Voltaire
75007 Paris   Tel. 40.15.70.00
Gibert Jeune (Droit-Économie)
6, place Saint-Michel
75006 Paris   Tel. 43.25.91.19
Librairie du Commerce International
10, avenue d'Iéna
75016 Paris   Tel. 40.73.34.60
Librairie Dunod
Université Paris-Dauphine
Place du Maréchal de Lattre de Tassigny
75016 Paris   Tel. (1) 44.05.40.13
Librairie Lavoisier
11, rue Lavoisier
75008 Paris   Tel. 42.65.39.95
Librairie L.G.D.J. - Montchrestien
20, rue Soufflot
75005 Paris   Tel. 46.33.89.85
Librairie des Sciences Politiques
30, rue Saint-Guillaume
75007 Paris   Tel. 45.48.36.02
P.U.F.
49, boulevard Saint-Michel
75005 Paris   Tel. 43.25.83.40
Librairie de l'Université
12a, rue Nazareth
13100 Aix-en-Provence   Tel. (16) 42.26.18.08
Documentation Française
165, rue Garibaldi
69003 Lyon   Tel. (16) 78.63.32.23
Librairie Decitre
29, place Bellecour
69002 Lyon   Tel. (16) 72.40.54.54
Librairie Sauramps
Le Triangle
34967 Montpellier Cedex 2   Tel. (16) 67.58.85.15
Telefax: (16) 67.58.27.36

GERMANY – ALLEMAGNE
OECD Publications and Information Centre
August-Bebel-Allee 6
D-53175 Bonn   Tel. (0228) 959.120
Telefax: (0228) 959.12.17

GREECE – GRÈCE
Librairie Kauffmann
Mavrokordatou 9
106 78 Athens   Tel. (01) 32.55.321
Telefax: (01) 32.30.320

HONG-KONG
Swindon Book Co. Ltd.
Astoria Bldg. 3F
34 Ashley Road, Tsimshatsui
Kowloon, Hong Kong   Tel. 2376.2062
Telefax: 2376.0685

HUNGARY – HONGRIE
Euro Info Service
Margitsziget, Európa Ház
1138 Budapest   Tel. (1) 111.62.16
Telefax: (1) 111.60.61

ICELAND – ISLANDE
Mál Mog Menning
Laugavegi 18, Pósthólf 392
121 Reykjavik   Tel. (1) 552.4240
Telefax: (1) 562.3523

INDIA – INDE
Oxford Book and Stationery Co.
Scindia House
New Delhi 110001   Tel. (11) 331.5896/5308
Telefax: (11) 332.5993
17 Park Street
Calcutta 700016   Tel. 240832

INDONESIA – INDONÉSIE
Pdii-Lipi
P.O. Box 4298
Jakarta 12042   Tel. (21) 573.34.67
Telefax: (21) 573.34.67

IRELAND – IRLANDE
Government Supplies Agency
Publications Section
4/5 Harcourt Road
Dublin 2   Tel. 661.31.11
Telefax: 475.27.60

ISRAEL
Praedicta
5 Shatner Street
P.O. Box 34030
Jerusalem 91430   Tel. (2) 52.84.90/1/2
Telefax: (2) 52.84.93

R.O.Y. International
P.O. Box 13056
Tel Aviv 61130   Tel. (3) 49.61.08
Telefax: (3) 544.60.39

Palestinian Authority/Middle East:
INDEX Information Services
P.O.B. 19502
Jerusalem   Tel. (2) 27.12.19
Telefax: (2) 27.16.34

ITALY – ITALIE
Libreria Commissionaria Sansoni
Via Duca di Calabria 1/1
50125 Firenze   Tel. (055) 64.54.15
Telefax: (055) 64.12.57
Via Bartolini 29
20155 Milano   Tel. (02) 36.50.83
Editrice e Libreria Herder
Piazza Montecitorio 120
00186 Roma   Tel. 679.46.28
Telefax: 678.47.51

Libreria Hoepli
Via Hoepli 5
20121 Milano   Tel. (02) 86.54.46
Telefax: (02) 805.28.86

Libreria Scientifica
Dott. Lucio de Biasio 'Aeiou'
Via Coronelli, 6
20146 Milano   Tel. (02) 48.95.45.52
Telefax: (02) 48.95.45.48

JAPAN – JAPON
OECD Publications and Information Centre
Landic Akasaka Building
2-3-4 Akasaka, Minato-ku
Tokyo 107   Tel. (81.3) 3586.2016
Telefax: (81.3) 3584.7929

KOREA – CORÉE
Kyobo Book Centre Co. Ltd.
P.O. Box 1658, Kwang Hwa Moon
Seoul   Tel. 730.78.91
Telefax: 735.00.30

OECD PUBLICATIONS, 2 rue André-Pascal, 75775 PARIS CEDEX 16
PRINTED IN FRANCE
(61 95 24 1) ISBN 92-64-14658-X - No. 48354 1995